❧ THE PLANT WORLD

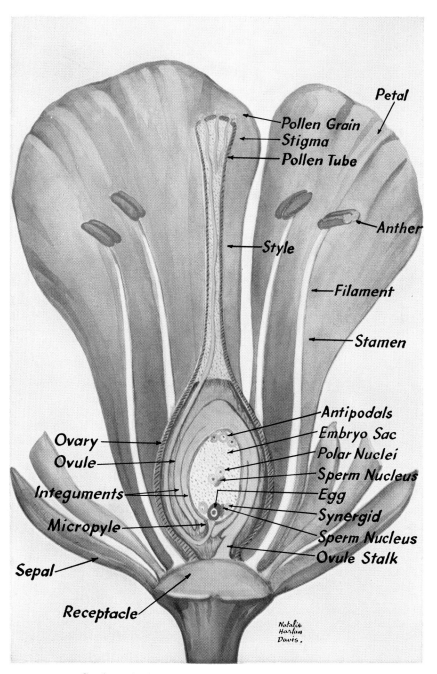

Petal

Pollen Grain
Stigma
Pollen Tube

Anther

Style

Filament

Stamen

Antipodals
Embryo Sac
Polar Nuclei
Sperm Nucleus
Egg
Synergid
Sperm Nucleus
Ovule Stalk

Ovary
Ovule

Integuments

Micropyle

Sepal

Receptacle

Natalie
Harlan
Davis.

Section of a flower showing the reproductive parts.

THE
PLANT
WORLD

A TEXT IN COLLEGE BOTANY ‹‹‹‹‹‹‹‹‹‹‹‹-

FOURTH EDITION

Harry J. Fuller
Zane B. Carothers
UNIVERSITY OF ILLINOIS

HOLT, RINEHART AND WINSTON, INC.
NEW YORK · CHICAGO · SAN FRANCISCO · TORONTO · LONDON

To DON MARION BENEDICT
botanist, teacher, and friend

Cover photograph, Schistostega,
courtesy Monkmeyer Press Photo Service.

Preface to the Fourth Edition

THIS FOURTH EDITION has been written principally for college students in one-semester introductory botany courses, and, like the earlier editions, it represents a broad approach to the study of plants. We have again placed special emphasis upon the biological principles of the plant kingdom and upon the relationships between plants and man. Although intended primarily for those undergraduates who are not majors in plant science, this text contains sufficient material to prepare students for further work in that area.

The present edition has been updated throughout. Recent discoveries and concepts reflecting current biological thought have been added insofar as they are appropriate for an introductory text. Included among the new or revised physiological topics are photosynthesis, respiration, translocation, nucleic acids, proteins, and growth-regulating substances. Information on cell ultrastructure has been added to Chapter 4, and discussions of the chemical basis of inheritance and of multiple genes to Chapter 17. The system of classification has been modified in accordance with more recent data on plant phylogeny. A modern interpretation of evolutionary processes has also been included, and the chapter on ecology has been extensively revised. Finally, there have been added many new reading references for interested students.

The usefulness of this edition has been further enhanced by the inclusion of over 50 new or improved illustrations. Among these are the fine photographs generously contributed by Dr. Constantine J. Alexopoulos of the University of Texas, Dr. Theodore Delevoryas of Yale University, Dr. Donald A. Eggert of Southern Illinois University, Dr. T. Johnson of the Canadian Department of Agriculture Research Station at Winnipeg, and Dr. C. L. Porter of the University of Wyoming, to each of whom we express our gratitude. For other excellent illustrations, for constructive criticism, and for helpful suggestions, we acknowledge the valuable assistance of our colleagues at the University of Illinois, especially Drs. Lawrence C. Bliss, Dominick J. Paolillo, Jr., Donald P. Rogers, Dale M. Smith, and Wilson N. Stewart. The authors, of course, claim full responsibility for errors of any kind. Finally, we wish to express our sincere appreciation to Diane F. Carothers who typed the manuscript and helped greatly with proofreading and the many other onerous chores associated with preparing a book for press.

Z. B. C.
H. J. F.

Urbana, Illinois
January, 1963

Preface to the Third Edition

IN THIS EDITION of this book, I have tried to steer a mid-channel course between the Scylla of pedantic minutiae and the Charybdis of superficiality. In writing primarily for those students in one-semester introductory botany courses who will escape the pleasure of further courses in botany, I have attempted to emphasize the general biological principles of the plant kingdom and the involvements of plants in human life. At the same time I have tried to include sufficient detailed material to give an adequate foundation to those students who will pursue further study of the plant sciences. Knowing the many difficulties which college freshmen encounter in their introductory study of science, I have made use of the technique of repetition in many places and have employed chapter summaries, review questions, and other devices to facilitate their study of plants.

Since I have studied plants for only twenty-five years and "since to look at things in bloom fifty springs are little room," my ignorance of plants exceeds my knowledge of them. Errors in this book must accordingly be attributed to the brevity of human life and to this ignorance.

In this third edition, I have brought up to date the material on the physiological activities of plants (insofar as this new material is suitable for study by college undergraduates); in addition, I have prepared, as a study guide to the morphology, physiology, and evolution of the major plant groups, a tabular scheme of representing the salient characteristics of these groups; I have also included a number of new drawings and photographs to present more vividly the basic features of plant structures and processes; and I have greatly expanded the material on the significance of plants in human life, with its overtones in human history and in the origins of cultivated plants.

This edition could not have come into existence without the valuable aid of many persons and agencies. I am especially grateful to Elizabeth Derrough Kirk, Natalie H. Davis, Dr. Wilson N. Stewart, and Dr. Cheng Lee Lee for their fine drawings. I acknowledge with sincere thanks the generosity of many botanists and agencies in furnishing both photographs and permission to use them; among those to whom I am especially grateful are Prof. F. W. Went, Dr. Charles F. Hottes, Dr. George T. Moore, director-emeritus of the Missouri Botanical Garden, the General Biological Supply House of Chicago, Triarch Botanical Products of Ripon, Wisconsin, the Boyce Thompson Institute for Plant Research, U. S. Forest Products Laboratory, Monsanto Chemical Co., E. I. du Pont de Nemours & Co., Weyerhaeuser Lumber Co., Eli Lilly & Co., Chicago Natural History Museum, and Doctors Oswald Tippo, Leland Shanor,

O. T. Bonnett, M. M. Rhoades, Richard Benjamin, R. V. Drexler, A. L. Whiting, V. E. Shelford, William C. Steere, J. M. Schopf, A. G. Vestal, C. J. Alexopoulos, E. J. Kohl, Benjamin Koehler, H. M. Buley, G. W. Martin, and Albert Vatter. My thanks go also to Eileen Mayer, Doris Poiriez, Carol Englehardt, and Mary L. Fuller for typing my manuscript and to Dr. Amy Skallerup for reading proof and preparing the index.

H. J. F.

April, 1955

Contents

The Nature of Plant Science

HISTORICAL BACKGROUND

The study of plants arose probably in the effort of prehistoric man to utilize more effectively his vegetational environment as a source of food, clothing, shelter, and fuel. Various primitive peoples of antiquity gathered much information about the growth and uses of plants, especially those of agricultural and medicinal value. Ancient manuscripts, pictures painted on the walls of tombs, plant remains in caves and burial sites, and carvings in stone preserved through the ages have given modern scientists at least fragmentary insight into early man's knowledge and uses of plants. Studies of such remains indicate, for example, that the Assyrians, ancient Chinese, Egyptians, Greeks, and Romans, as well as ancient American aboriginal races, possessed extensive knowledge of plant cultivation, of edible crops, of the medicinal properties of plants, of irrigation of agricultural lands, and of fibers, beverages, and other useful plant products. The interests of these ancient peoples were centered primarily upon the practical aspects of plant life, and relatively few of their intellectual leaders attempted to study plants for their intrinsic scientific value. Most present-day botanists would be unwilling to regard these early plant students as botanists, since their interests in plants were so limited and since they achieved little progress in the discovery of fundamental natural laws. In the Golden Age of Greece, a few scientists, such as Theophrastus and Aristotle, made several discoveries of a scientific nature about plants, and a few scholars, chiefly in monasteries and universities, of the Middle Ages contributed further to our knowledge of the structure, functions, and reproduction of plants. Medieval botanical books, called Herbals (Figures 1–1 and 1–2), contain some accurate information about plants, together with many superstitions about the magical properties of plants, the influences of the planets upon plant growth, and the close relationships between plants and animals; some of these old manuscripts, for example, picture the transformation of flowers into butterflies and the development of fish and birds from plant buds.

The foundations of modern botany

1

Portraict de l'Arbre qui porte des fueilles, lesquelles tombées sur ter-re se tournent en oyseaux volants, & celles qui tombent dans les eaux se muent en poissons.

(*Courtesy of Missouri Botanical Garden.*)

FIG. 1–1. An illustration from an herbal of a tree, the leaves of which, falling upon the soil, turn into birds; falling into the water, become fish.

were laid principally during the seventeenth and eighteenth centuries. Scientists purged their studies of the superstitions and inaccuracies of the Middle Ages and expanded the objective, experimental study of plants to satisfy their curiosity about plant structure and plant physiology and thus to discover the natural

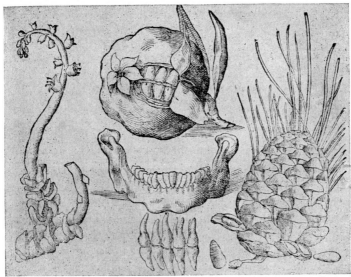

(Courtesy of Missouri Botanical Garden.)

FIG. 1–2. Herbal illustration of Doctrine of Signatures, a medieval belief that certain plant parts resembled human structures and constituted a remedy for diseases of the latter. Note resemblance of human teeth to pomegranate seeds and pine cone scales.

laws that underlie the plant world. The first branches of botany to expand under this newer approach were the largely descriptive sciences: **taxonomy,** the study of plant classification and relationships, and **morphology,** the study of plant structure. These branches of botany were the first to expand because they required little technical apparatus; the chief prerequisites for the investigator were patient observation and the ability to describe plants accurately. The finer details of internal structure of plants awaited the discovery and perfection of magnifying lenses, as a result of which **plant anatomy** began its career. **Plant physiology,** the study of plant functions and processes, grew rapidly after the basic principles of physics and chemistry were established. Along with these other fields there developed **plant pathology,** the science of plant diseases, **ecology,** the study of the relations of plants to their environments,

and more recently, **genetics,** the study of inheritance, and **cytology,** the microscopic study of cell structure and cell behavior. The greatest advances in these fields of botany have occurred during the nineteenth and twentieth centuries, and research at the present time is steadily adding to our knowledge of the lives of plants.

Numerous other fields of plant science are based directly or indirectly upon the above-mentioned branches of botany. Among these are **bacteriology,** the study of minute, one-celled plants responsible for many diseases of plants and animals, for processes of decay and decomposition in nature, and for the industrial production of valuable chemicals; **agronomy,** the science of field crop production; and **horticulture,** the study of orchard, garden, and greenhouse crops, with its subsidiary sciences of **floriculture,** the science of ornamental plants, **olericulture,** the study of vegetable crops, and **pomology**, the science of fruit crops. These fields have become so highly specialized and have developed such an abundance of their own literature that they are usually not included in the science of botany. Rather, we usually define botany as the study of the classification, structure, identification, physiology, inheritance, distribution, and evolution of plants. The objectives of such study center upon man's curiosity about the world he inhabits and do not necessarily involve the consideration of practical aspects of plant life. There is no sharp line of separation, however, between botany as a pure science and such applied sciences as agronomy and horticulture, for the practical, economically valuable discoveries made in these applied sciences may commonly be traced back to the pure-science discoveries made by botanists, as will be indicated in various chapters of this book.

WHY STUDY BOTANY?

There are several cogent arguments for devoting a part, small though it may be, of one's life to the study of plants. In the first place, we are indebted to plants for our very existence. Green plants are the mechanisms by which raw, inorganic materials of the air and soil are converted into those complex, organic compounds called foods, which are essential for the existence of all animal life. All the food we eat comes from plants directly, or indirectly in the form of meat, fish, eggs, and other animal products, which were formed at the expense of plant tissues eaten by animals. Green plants are essential to the existence of animals in another way: green plants are the only major source of oxygen in the world, the oxygen that animals must inhale if they are to

live. Further, we are indebted to plants for the other necessities of our modern lives: fibers for clothing, lumber for homes, drugs for our ills, as well as for the many luxuries that add comfort and delight to life, such as spices, perfumes, beverages, dyes, paper and other cellulose products, rubber for our tires, paints, lacquers, and dozens of other plant products. The tremendous indebtedness of mankind to plants is sufficient reason in itself to justify the study of plants.

In the second place, a liberal education is enriched by a study of plants. Education is frequently defined on the basis of its desired result: the most satisfying and most advantageous adjustment to one's environment. The study of plants, then, is an essential feature of liberal education, for in man's environment there are two dominant, omnipresent entities: the sky and the green vegetational cover of the earth.

In the third place, the study of plants offers philosophical rewards. The appreciation of the beauties of flowers, of forests, and of all other aspects of plant life is sharpened and amplified by a knowledge of the myriad activities that occur on the stage of nature but are apparent only to those who seek them out. Further, the discovery of the unifying principles of plant and animal development and behavior, the awareness of the order underlying the growth and structure of plants, and the appreciation of the sensitive balances regulating the lives of all organisms contribute to the unfolding of a sane and appreciative philosophy of life and an awareness of man's place in nature's economy.

Finally, students planning to enter professional careers in applied plant sciences —horticulture, agronomy, forestry, plant disease control, soil conservation, and pharmacology—require botanical knowledge as a fundamental tool in their work. Even in fields less directly related to botany, such as bacteriology, the practice of medicine, and public health services, a knowledge of botanical principles is often desirable.

VOCATIONAL OPPORTUNITIES IN PLANT SCIENCES

Students who have a deep interest in plants and who wish to embark upon careers in plant science have many opportunities before them, chiefly in the applied fields of agronomy, horticulture, and forestry. The positions available in these areas may be classified into three types: teaching agronomy, horticulture, or forestry in agricultural colleges and forestry schools; working in state and federal governmental agencies involved with soil conservation, grassland ecology, national parks, forestry, plant breeding, plant disease control, and plant nutrition; and working in private industries, such as seed companies, nurseries, companies that manufacture fertilizers, chemical weed killers, and other agricultural chemicals, large timber-cutting companies, and companies operating orchards, vegetable fields, rubber and tropical fruit plantations, and sugar estates.

Many job opportunities are available also in bacteriology: in hospitals, medical research institutes, and public health agencies; in food-processing companies; in sewage disposal plants; in plant disease control; and in drug and chemical companies.

Professional opportunities in the field of pure botany are less numerous than those in the applied plant sciences, but they nevertheless offer many careers to well-trained, industrious, and intelligent students. These careers include teaching or research, or both, in secondary schools, colleges, and universities; research and lecturing in museums; fundamental botanical research in commercial companies that produce antibiotic drugs, agricultural and other chemicals, and crop seeds, and in governmental agencies in the fields of soil conservation, timber crops, plant diseases, plant breeding, etc.

Students who plan to enter careers in these plant sciences should complete a college major in the field of their special interest, with minors in other plant sciences and, if possible, chemistry, and should make provision for the completion of at least two years of graduate study. While advancement in these careers depends largely upon individual ability and initiative, the possession of an advanced degree usually brings more rapid promotion. Students who look forward to work in the plant sciences in industry or in governmental agencies will find that some background in chemistry will be valuable to them, for jobs in these categories increasingly involve chemical approaches to plant science investigations.

PLANTS AS LIVING ORGANISMS

Plants and animals constitute the living world about us. Before we proceed to a detailed study of plants, we should have some conception of what is meant by the words "plant," "life," and "animal." The more obvious indicators of life—movement, growth, reproduction—are valid criteria of life only if more specific definition is made, since they also characterize nonliving entities in some degree; rivers grow, stalactites grow, a bit of camphor on the surface of water moves swiftly to and fro, but they are not living.

If we examine more carefully the phenomena of life processes, we can qualify these obvious indicators and specify at least five characteristics that seem peculiar to living things:

1. Living organisms possess a characteristic type of structure that distinguishes them fron nonliving things. The bodies of plants and animals consist of structural units called **cells,** each of which consists of a tiny mass of living substance, or **protoplasm,** and an enclosing wall or membrane.

2. Living organisms possess the power of **reproduction** of similar kind, that is, offspring of the same kind as themselves. This is one of the most obvious characteristics of living things, yet we do not often consider it, for it is commonplace that bean seeds always grow into bean plants and that cats always give birth to more cats.

3. Living organisms have the property of **irritability,** that is, the ability to react to factors or changes in their environment. Irritability is a twofold phenomenon, for it involves first the ability to receive external stimuli, then the ability to react, through movement of the whole organism or of its parts, to these external factors. Living protoplasm of both plants and animals is sensitive to such external stimuli as light, moisture, temperature, chemicals, and pressure and is able to respond in various ways to these stimuli.

4. Living organisms carry on **metabolism,** an intricate group of chemical processes that are necessary for the formation, maintenance, and repair of protoplasm and thus for the continuation of life. Among the principal metabolic processes of living organisms are: **respiration,** the chemical breakdown of foods, with the release of energy that is stored in foods and that is essential for the opera-

tions of living protoplasm, such as movement, growth, and reproduction; **photosynthesis,** the fundamental process of food manufacture in nature, which is carried on by green plants and which utilizes the energy of sunlight in the synthesis of carbohydrate foods from carbon dioxide and water; **digestion,** the transformation of water-insoluble or complex foods into water-soluble or simpler foods; **assimilation,** the conversion of nonliving chemical compounds, chiefly proteins, into living protoplasm.

5. Living organisms are capable of **growth.** Growth is a complex of phenomena that result from processes of food manufacture, respiration, assimilation, and other metabolic activities. Growth not only involves an increase in the size of living organisms, but includes processes of division of labor among body parts, of coordination of activities, and of development according to a definite plan for every kind of organism. The basic plan of growth for each kind of organism is determined by the hereditary characteristics received from its parents. Although the fundamental architecture of growth is determined by heredity, it is susceptible to modification by factors of the environment.

Thus we see that life is a flexible, plastic phenomenon. It involves numerous processes of chemical and physical change, of growth, of movement and reactions to stimuli, of food getting and assimilation. It is apparent that these characteristic activities of living things are explainable largely in terms of less complex chemical and physical processes that are constantly ebbing and flowing in protoplasm. It is a fact that all chemical elements found in living protoplasm occur likewise in the nonliving materials of soil, rocks, air, and water. Thus, there is no single chemical element that is peculiar to living matter or that is responsible for the phenomena of life. The secret of life lies not in the nature of the ultimate substances of which protoplasm is composed, but rather in the organization of these chemical elements into a living system. The example of a watch, broken, then repaired may be used to illustrate this point. The watch, in its broken, useless state, contains exactly the same kinds and quantities of constituent materials as it does when it is repaired, but the repaired watch possesses an organization that makes it a functional instrument.

The time and method of the origin of living protoplasm on the earth are lost in antiquity and possibly will never be known. Some persons believe that an accidental combination of chemical elements in the presence of water and favorable temperature may have given rise to living protoplasm; others believe that living matter is a product of Divine Creation. In the absence of direct evidence, we may consider the problem of life's origin as outside the scope of our scientific study of plants, and we may begin our study of plants from the accomplished fact of their existence on the earth. Some biologists believe that the first living organisms possessed a mixture of plant and animal characteristics and that, with the passage of time, a differentiation of these first living creatures into plants and animals occurred.

It is not a simple matter to express in words the differences between plants and animals. Although we have no difficulty in distinguishing between a rosebush in our garden and our pet dog, the task of definition becomes increasingly difficult when we examine certain primitive organisms that seem to have a mixture of plant and animal characteristics and that are classified by zoologists as animals and by botanists as plants. If we disregard these "plantimals," as one biologist has called them, we may list a few criteria that serve to distinguish *most* kinds of plants from *most* kinds of animals:

1. Animals are unable to manufacture their own food. They are completely dependent upon plants, either directly (herbivorous animals) or indirectly (carnivorous animals) for their nourishment. In contrast, most plants are able to manufacture foods from simple chemicals of the air and soil; these **autotrophic** (self-nourishing) plants possess a green pigment, **chlorophyll,** which is essential in photosynthesis, the basic process of food manufacture. There are numerous plants, however, such as molds, mushrooms, and puffballs, that lack chlorophyll and are unable to manufacture their own food. Such organisms resemble animals in their nutrition.

2. Most plants possess a structural framework of cell walls, the most abundant chemical constituent of which is **cellulose,** a carbohydrate. Animals generally, with the exception of a small, apparently degenerate group called tunicates, lack cellulose.

3. Most animals possess the power of **locomotion,** that is, the ability to move from place to place, whereas most plants are firmly anchored in one place and are therefore unable to move. There are some exceptions to this generalization; there are some rather primitive plants that are able to swim about from place to place in water, and there are some lower animals that pass their lives in an immobile condition.

4. Animals generally possess a **closed system** of growth, in which a mature individual attains a characteristic form and maximum size that undergo relatively little

size change after maturity is reached. In this limited type of growth, virtually all growth tissue is used up in the process of maturation, except for small masses of growth tissue available for regeneration. Plants, however, have an **open system** of growth, a condition in which the maximum size attainable by members of a given species is exceedingly variable and depends in large degree upon external conditions. In the bodies of most plants, growth tissues persist in considerable masses in many parts, and, as a consequence, growth continues in these parts, often over a period of many years. As older tissues mature and die, they usually remain in place and serve only for added strength and support; the young, active, growing tissues continue to grow away from the older parts, producing new lengths of stems, of roots, and of other organs.

A study of these differences emphasizes the fact that there is no single difference that separates all plants from all animals. It is relatively easy to distinguish, on the basis of these four criteria, the higher types of plants from higher animals, but such distinction is difficult, often impossible, in lower organisms. The inevitable conclusion is that plants and animals are very similar in many ways and that they have probably arisen in their development from common ancestors.

THE KINDS OF PLANTS

One of the most conspicuous features of the plant world is the infinite variety of size, form, and behavior of plants. Plants vary in size from structurally simple, microscopic organisms, such as bacteria, some of which are only $\frac{1}{2}$ micron long by $\frac{1}{5}$ micron wide (about $\frac{1}{50,000}$ inch by

$\frac{1}{125,000}$ inch), to large, structurally complex plants such as California redwood trees, which may attain heights of over 350 feet and diameters of 30 feet. Such plants as bacteria and redwoods represent the extremes of size in the plant kingdom; between these limits are all other kinds of plants, such as mosses, ferns, mushrooms, oak trees, corn plants, and thousands of others. Size is in itself no indication of relationships among plants; thus, the seaweeds, which are very primitive plants, may attain lengths of over 100 feet, while the duckweeds are seed plants of high position in the plant kingdom, yet are only a fraction of an inch in length.

The forms of plants are also extremely variable, and it is chiefly on the basis of variations in form and structure of parts that we learn to distinguish among different species of plants. There are known at present almost 350,000 species or kinds of plants, each with its own characteristic habit of growth, structure, method of reproduction, and other peculiarities that give it an identity of its own. Some plants lack true roots, stems, and leaves, others possess these parts. Some have flowers and seeds, some do not. Some species are trees, others are shrubs, some are vines, and still others are herbs of low stature.

Plant species differ in many of their physiological qualities, as well as in size and structure. Thus, some species store foods chiefly as sugars or starch, others as fatty substances. Some species require abundant supplies of water for their survival and growth, others thrive in desert regions. Many plant species inhabit only the hot, humid forests of equatorial regions, others are found growing in regions of hot summers and cold winters, still others thrive where temperatures are never

FIG. 1–3. Thallophyta: an alga, *Polysiphonia*.

FIG. 1–4. Thallophyta: an alga, *Agardhiella*.

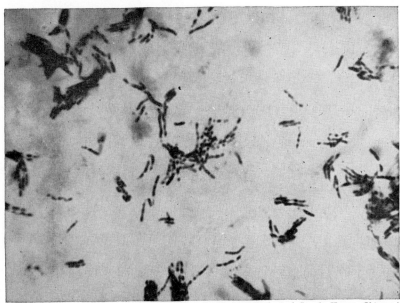

FIG. 1–5. Thallophyta: bacteria (*Mycobacterium*) that cause tuberculosis in man. Greatly magnified.

(Photo by Missouri Botanical Garden.)

FIG. 1–6 (*above, left*). Thallo-phyta: a mushroom fungus, *Co-prinus.*

FIG. 1–7 (*above, right*). Thallo-phyta: a fungus, earthstar, or *Geaster.*

FIG. 1–8 (*right*). Thallophyta: white-rust fungus (*Albugo*) on horseradish leaves.

(Copyright, General Biological Supply House, Chicago.)

(Photo by H. W. Anderson.)

FIG. 1–9 (*above*). Embryophyta: a liverwort, *Marchantia*.

FIG. 1–10 (*below*). Embryophyta: a moss, *Polytrichum*.

11

FIG. 1–11. Embryophyta: a horsetail, *Equisetum.*

FIG. 1–12. Embryophyta: a clubmoss, *Lycopodium.*

FIG. 1–13. Embryophyta: a fern, *Polypodium.*

FIG. 1–14 (*above*). Embryophyta: Coniferae—young western yellow pines, *Pinus*.

FIG. 1–15 (*below*). Embryophyta: Cycadae—a cycad, *Cycas*.

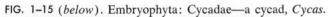

FIG. 1–16. Embryophyta: Angiospermae—columbine, *Aquilegia*, a flowering plant.

hot. Some plant species live submerged in water, others inhabit the land. Yellow pigments accumulate in the petals of some species, red ones in others, blue pigments in still others. Most higher plants have in common the possession of chlorophyll, the characteristic green pigment of leaves and often of stems and other parts.

Plants differ also in their longevity. Thus, some species such as oak trees, irises, and rose bushes are **perennials,** that is, plants that live through several to many years. Other plants, such as corn, soybeans, and sweet peas, are **annuals,** living for one year or a portion of a year. Carrots and beets are **biennials;** these have a life span of two years, during the second of which they reproduce.

One of the most striking differences among plants is found in their diverse methods of reproduction and in the varying structure of their reproductive parts. These reproductive differences, together with differences in structure, are the major criteria used by botanists in classifying plants into various groups. One of the major aims of scientists is to classify the phenomena that they study, in order to achieve regularity and uniformity in their work. In their pursuit of this aim, botanists have classified plants into groups of varying size in an effort to facilitate the identification of plants and also to indicate something of plant relationships. These tasks lie in the field of **plant taxonomy,** referred to briefly in an earlier section of this chapter. Chiefly on the basis of their studies of plant structure and reproduction, botanists divide the plant kingdom into two subkingdoms: **Thallophyta** and **Embryophyta.** The **Thallophyta** comprise such primitive, structur-

ally rather simple plants as pond scums, seaweeds, bacteria, molds, mushrooms, puffballs, and many others. The **Embryophyta** include mosses, ferns, club mosses, pines and other cone-bearing trees, and the thousands of species of flowering plants. Members of the Embryophyta produce many-celled, young plants, or **embryos,** which for at least a brief period are enclosed by some many-celled protective structure; Thallophyta do not form embryos.

Each of these two subkingdoms consists of a number of smaller groups, or **divisions.** Thus the Thallophyta comprise ten divisions, the Embryophyta two divisions. Each division is further subdivided into smaller classificational units, which will be considered in detail in a subsequent section of this book. The most advanced plant group in the subkingdom Embryophyta is the class **Angiospermae,** or true flowering plants; this is the largest single group of plants, numbering about 200,000 known species, which are the most highly developed of all plants. Less specialized than the angiosperms but similar to them in that they produce seeds are the two gymnospermous classes: **Coniferae,** including pine, spruce, fir, ginkgo, etc., and the **Cycadae,** including the less familiar cycads. Because they constitute the largest of all plant groups, because they are the most conspicuous and most numerous plants inhabiting the land areas of the earth, and because they are the most important of all plants in human life, the flowering plants will be studied in greater detail than any other group. The next sixteen chapters of this book will treat chiefly of the Angiospermae. Figures 1–3 through 1–16 illustrate representatives of various plant divisions.

⫷⫷← SUMMARY

1. Botany is the science of plant life.
2. Various ancient peoples had a wide knowledge of plants, chiefly from the practical standpoint.
3. During the Greek and Roman periods and the Middle Ages, some progress was made in the study of the purely scientific aspects of plant structure and classification, but the modern science of botany did not begin to develop rapidly until the seventeenth and eighteenth centuries.
4. The major fields of modern botany are: plant taxonomy—the study of plant classification and identification; plant morphology—the study of plant structure; plant anatomy—a phase of morphology, emphasizing internal, microscopic structure; plant physiology—the study of the functions and activities of plants; plant pathology—the study of plant diseases; plant genetics—the study of inheritance and breeding; plant ecology—the study of the relations between plants and their environments; plant cytology—the study of cell structure and processes.
5. Closely related to botany are these fields of plant science: bacteriology—the study of bacteria; agronomy—the science of field crops; forestry—the science of trees; horticulture—the science of orchard, garden, and greenhouse crops.
6. The study of botany is valuable for these reasons: it enables man to appreciate his dependence upon his relationship to plants; it enriches the cultural life of man and increases his appreciation of the beauties of nature; it forms an important informational background for students seeking careers in agronomy, horticulture, forestry, and other practical plant sciences.
7. The characteristic properties of living organisms are: cellular structure; reproduction of like offspring; irritability; metabolism; growth.
8. The properties of life depend upon the intricate organization of chemical elements and compounds into living protoplasm.
9. The time and method of origin of living protoplasm on the earth are unknown.
10. Some primitive organisms have mixtures of plant and animal characteristics.
11. The principal differences between plants and animals are:
    a. Animals are unable to manufacture their own food, most plants possess this ability.
    b. Most plant bodies contain cellulose, most animals do not.
    c. Animals usually possess a closed system of growth, plants an open system of growth.
    d. Most animals are able to move from place to place, most plants lack this ability.
12. There is no single difference that distinguishes all plants from all animals.
13. The plant kingdom comprises about 350,000 known species or kinds of plants.
14. These plant species differ in many ways: in their size, structure, physiological qualities, life span, etc.
15. The classification of plants is based chiefly upon structural and reproductive characteristics.

16. The plant kingdom is divided into two subkingdoms: Thallophyta and Embryophyta.

17. Thallophyta include many species of pond scums, seaweeds, molds, mushrooms, etc. Embryophyta include mosses, ferns, club mosses, pines, flowering plants, etc.

18. Members of the Embryophyta form embryos; members of the Thallophyta do not form embryos.

19. The largest and most important group of Embryophyta is the class Angiospermae, or flowering plants.

⋘ SUGGESTED READINGS FOR INTERESTED STUDENTS

1. Arber, Agnes, *Herbals*. Cambridge University Press, Cambridge, England, 1938.
2. "Careers in Botany," Botanical Society of America, Department of Botany, University of Texas, Austin 12, Texas, 1961.
3. "Educational Requirements for Employment of Biological Scientists," VA Pamphlet 7–8.2, Veterans Administration, Washington 25, D. C., 1955.
4. Peattie, D. C., *Flowering Earth*. Putnam, New York, 1939.
5. Reed, H. S. *A Short History of the Plant Sciences*. Ronald Press, New York, 1942.

⋘ TOPICS AND QUESTIONS FOR STUDY

1. How do you think primitive man may have discovered the medicinal properties of certain plants?

2. Why have primitive and civilized men frequently used plants as designs in their paintings, architecture, and sculpture?

3. Which may be regarded as the oldest branch of pure botany? Why?

4. List as many ways as you can in which plants are beneficial in human life. List the ways in which plants may be harmful or disadvantageous in human life.

5. How does a knowledge of other sciences aid the study of botany?

6. Name and define the modern branches of botany.

7. Name and define three applied fields of plant study.

8. List and describe the characteristic properties of living organisms.

9. Why did plant physiology and plant anatomy develop much later than plant taxonomy?

10. Define: metabolism, respiration, photosynthesis, digestion, assimilation.

11. List and describe the major differences which separate the plant kingdom from the animal kingdom. Which of these differences applies to all plants and all animals?

12. List as many ways as you can in which plants differ from each other.

13. Distinguish among annuals, biennials, and perennials.

14. Distinguish between Thallophyta and Embryophyta.

15. What are Angiospermae? How many species of Angiospermae are known?

Seed Structure and Germination

The study of the flowering plants (Angiospermae) may logically begin with a study of seeds, for seeds are familiar objects, they constitute an early stage in the development of an angiosperm plant, and their production is a distinct phase in the life cycle of flowering plants. Seeds of angiosperms are formed within structures called **fruits** (the word "angiosperm" means "covered seed," in reference to the development of seeds within the tissues of a fruit); a fruit is produced by a flower. Thus, flowers produce fruits and fruits contain seeds. When a fruit is mature, it splits open or disintegrates, releasing the mature seeds. The reproductive processes that lead to the production of seeds will be described in detail in the chapter on flowers.

SEED STRUCTURE

A seed consists essentially of an immature, undeveloped plant **(embryo)**, accompanied by a quantity of stored food available for its early nourishment, and protective seed coat. All mature seeds ca-

pable of **germination** (sprouting) have embryos and seed coats (Figure 2–1). In every young developing seed there is, in addition to an embryo and a seed coat, **endosperm,** or food storage tissue, which either before or during seed germination is digested and absorbed by the embryo. In the seeds of beans, peas, peanuts, pumpkins, and other species of plants, the food in the endosperm tissue is absorbed by the embryo before these seeds leave their parent plants. Thus, when such seeds are mature, they consist only of embryos and seed coats. In many other species, such as corn, castor bean, and wheat, the digestion and absorption of the endosperm foods by the embryos do not occur until after the seeds are planted and begin to absorb water. In each of such seeds, then, there are present at maturity an embryo, a seed coat, and endosperm. Seeds of this type generally germinate slowly, for their embryos must remove food from the endosperm before they can begin vigorous growth. Beans, peas, and other seeds, the embryos of which absorb the foods stored in the endosperm tissues

18

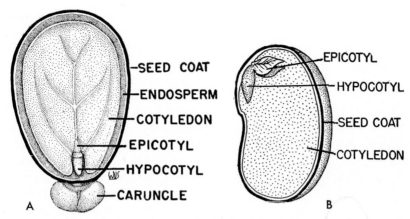

FIG. 2–1. Seed structure. A: Longitudinal section of a castor bean seed.
B: Longitudinal section of a garden bean seed.

before the seeds are mature, generally germinate more quickly, for the preliminary step of food transfer from endosperm to embryos is completed before the seeds are planted.

In some seeds a tough, outer seed coat and a thin, inner coat are present; in others only a single coat is present. Seed coats in most species of plants are rather tough and often partially waterproofed. Seed coats reduce the amount of water evaporation from the internal tissues and also afford protection against the entry of parasites, against mechanical injury, and, in some species with thick seed coats, possibly against unfavorably high and low temperatures. In some species of plants (peas, orchids, peanut), the seed coats are thin and papery, in others (Indian lotus, cotton, clover), the seed coats are tough and hard. There usually appears on a seed coat a small scar, called the **hilum,** that marks the place of attachment of the seed to the seed stalk, which connects the seed with the inside of the fruit. Also apparent on the coats of many kinds of seeds is the **micropyle,** the pore through which the fertilizing pollen tube (to be described later) entered the undeveloped

seed or **ovule** prior to fertilization. In some species, such as garden beans, the micropyle is distinctly visible at maturity, whereas in other species, the micropyle is obscured by post-fertilization growth of the coat. Seed coats of some plants (for example, castor bean) bear a ridge **(raphe),** formed by the fusion of the seed stalk with the seed coat. Castor bean seeds also bear a spongy structure, the **caruncle,** that aids in water absorption when the seeds are planted.

An angiosperm embryo consists of one or two **cotyledons,** or **seed leaves,** and a somewhat elongated axis from which the cotyledons grow out as lateral appendages. The portion of the axis above the point of attachment of the cotyledons is called the **epicotyl** (sometimes called the **plumule**), that below the attachment of the cotyledons, the **hypocotyl,** the lower end of which is the **root primordium,** or **radicle.** The cotyledons are structurally leaves that function primarily in the digestion, absorption, and storage of food from the endosperm that surrounds, or lies adjacent to, the embryo. Because of their specialized functions, cotyledons rarely resemble the mature leaves of the

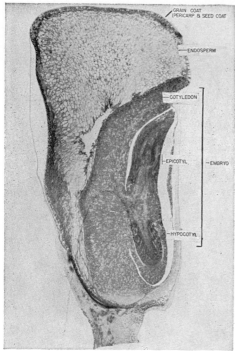

GRAIN COAT
(PERICARP & SEED COAT)
ENDOSPERM
COTYLEDON
EPICOTYL   EMBRYO
HYPOCOTYL

(Photo by Dr. J. P. McCollum.)

FIG. 2–2. Photograph of a longitudinal section of a corn grain.

plants of whose seeds they are parts. In some species, such as castor bean, the flat, broad cotyledons persist for several weeks after germination, become green, and carry on food manufacture. In garden beans, on the other hand, the fleshy cotyledons wither and fall off within a few days after germination, following the exhaustion of the stored food they contain.

The hypocotyl, the portion of the embryo axis below the cotyledons, is a very short cylindrical mass of tissue; at the lower end of the hypocotyl is the radicle, which develops into the first or **primary** root of the seedling. The epicotyl, the part of the embryo axis above the cotyledons, grows into the young stem of the new plant. Both hypocotyl and epicotyl are composed chiefly or in part of growth tissue that makes possible the development of roots and shoots respectively from these parts of the embryo axis.

The endosperm tissue contains in its cells large amounts of usually insoluble stored food, which is withdrawn by the embryo before or during seed germination, as described earlier. Carbohydrates are stored in large quantities in the seeds of many plants, chiefly as starches (corn, wheat, rice, beans), less frequently as sugars, and occasionally as more complex foods called hemicelluloses (date seeds, nasturtium seeds). Carbohydrates serve chiefly as sources of energy for growth, in part for the structural material (**cellulose**) of cell walls. Proteins are stored in all seeds; they are used chiefly in the formation of new protoplasm as germination begins and continues. In some seeds, such as those of peas, beans, and soybeans, large quantities of proteins are stored. Fats and oils are reserve foods, used primarily for energy, in the seeds of many species of plants. Seeds exceptionally rich in fats and oils are castor beans, peanuts, flax, coconut, and sunflower. In the endosperm of the seeds of some plants, such as lilies and tulips, no starch whatsoever is present; the chief energy foods in the seeds of these species are fats and oils. In most kinds of seeds, all three major groups of foods—carbohydrates, fats, and proteins—are represented in the storage tissues. In all seeds, digestion (the conversion of water-insoluble foods to water-soluble foods) is a preliminary phase of germination, for only those foods that dissolve in water can be readily utilized by growing embryos.

Examples of common types of seeds in angiosperms are the seeds of garden beans, castor beans, and corn. The seeds of garden beans and of castor beans contain embryos with two cotyledons, those of corn have embryos with one cotyledon. The angiosperms are divided into two subgroups on the basis of this cotyledon difference: **monocotyledons,** which have one cotyledon in their embryos and which include grasses, lilies, irises, sedges, palms, and orchids, and **dicotyledons,** which have embryos with two cotyledons and which include beans, peas, geraniums, oaks, sunflowers, and thousands of other species.

SEED GERMINATION

Dormancy. In many species of plants, seeds require a period of relative rest or **dormancy** before they are able to germinate or sprout. This dormant period is advantageous to seeds, particularly in temperate zones, for dormant seeds remain in a condition of low physiological activity during the winter when low temperatures might kill seeds in an active state of germination or postgermination growth. Seeds may thus be regarded, in some degree at least, as structures that are able to carry a species safely through a period of unfavorable environmental conditions that might be fatal to actively growing plant tissues.

The causes of seed dormancy in different species of plants are varied, frequently complex, and by no means well understood. Some seed coats are thick and impermeable to water or oxygen. In such seeds, germination cannot occur until the seed coats have been cracked or rendered permeable by natural forces such as bacterial action or freezing and thawing or by artificial scratching of the seed coats **(seed scarification).** Many agriculturally important seeds (for example, sweet clovers and other members of the legume family) must be scarified prior

to planting. In some species of plants, the seeds contain water-soluble inhibitory compounds that prevent germination. Only after these inhibitors have been leached out can germination take place. In other species, the embryos are not fully developed at the time when the seeds are shed from the fruits; in such seeds a period of dormancy occurs during which the maturation of these embryos is completed. In many seeds, complex chemical changes must be completed before germination is possible. These reactions are initiated in some seeds by such factors as exposure to light or low temperatures. Hawthorn seeds must experience a slowly increasing acidity of internal tissues before they can sprout. Not uncommonly, a seed will require more than one external stimulus in order to remove the block or blocks that prevent germination; for example, seeds of garden cress must receive light and temperature stimuli before they can sprout.

A distinction must be made between dormancy, which is the result of one or more internal conditions of a seed, and **quiescence,** which is a rest period caused by external conditions unfavorable to germination. A seed may pass through its dormant period and may be capable of sprouting, yet fail to germinate because of insufficient available soil moisture, of subfreezing temperatures, or of some other external factor that retards or prevents germination.

Seed Viability. Different kinds of seeds retain their **viability,** or ability to germinate, for varying periods of time. The seeds of certain orchids and willows remain viable for only a few days or weeks, while those of the Indian lotus have been reliably reported to retain their ability to germinate for approximately 400 years. In most species of plants, the periods of

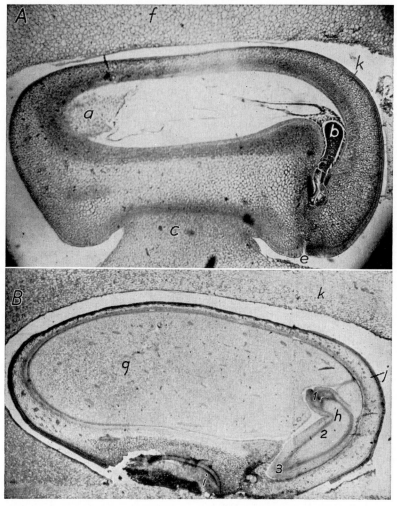

FIG. 2–3. Development of seeds of garden bean.

A. Seed with young embryo
    a. endosperm
    b. embryo
    c. seed stalk
    e. micropyle
    f. ovary tissue
    k. seed coat

B. Later stage in bean seed de-
    velopment
    g. cotyledon
    h. embryo: 1. epicotyl, 2. hypo-
        cotyl, 3. radicle
    i. seed stalk
    j. seed coat
    k. ovary tissue

seed viability do not exceed four to ten years. Sensational newspaper accounts of the growth of seeds from the tombs of ancient Egyptian kings are merely one more example of the falsehoods of some mod-ern journalists; no reputable botanist has ever found seeds of such great age to be viable. Although each species of plant has a characteristic viable period, the length of this period is affected in part by storage conditions. Seeds stored in cool, dry places generally retain their viability longer than those exposed to warm, humid air. Also, if the seeds are stored in a poorly ventilated bin, the heat generated by respiration during incipient germination may become sufficiently great to damage the embryos and even to cause fire in the stored seeds. Poor ventilation in a warm, moist seed bin also encourages the growth of fungi that rob seeds of food and injure or kill their embryos.

The causes of loss of seed viability are not fully known. As seeds grow old, a slow coagulation of proteins in the protoplasm occurs, there is often a loss of activity of regulatory substances involved in respiration, and cells lose their ability to divide. Exhaustion of food reserves is not a cause of loss of viability in most seeds, for seeds, long after they have lost their ability to sprout, usually still contain appreciable quantities of starch, fats, and other storage foods.

Physiology of Seed Germination. The completion of the dormant period, the age of a seed, the amount of growth-regulating substances present, and the amount of stored food available are important internal factors influencing both rate and percentage of seed germination. There are also many factors of the external environment that exert marked effects upon the sprouting and early growth of seeds. Most important of these external influences are **moisture, temperature,** and **oxygen.** Also important but less well understood are the roles played by carbon dioxide and light in seed germination. Abundant water must be available for seed germination; the early stages of germination result in a tremendous increase (from approximately 25 to 200 percent) in the volumes of seeds, an increase attributable largely to water intake. Water is important in the germination of seeds in that it softens seed coats and thus enables the radicle and epicotyl to break through them more easily; it promotes the entrance of oxygen into seeds, for gases pass more readily through moist cell walls than through dry walls. The uptake of water enables enzymes to activate physiological processes—digestion of foods, movement of foods from endosperm into cotyledons, respiration, and growth—in the protoplasm, which in dry seeds contains so little water (5 to 10 percent in most seeds) that physiological activities are able to proceed at only very slow rates; and it provides internal pressure that is necessary for growth and that results in the emergence of the growing embryo.

An adequate supply of atmospheric oxygen is ordinarily required to support the high respiration rate at the time of germination. Since oxygen content decreases with increasing soil depth, many kinds of seeds will die from lack of oxygen if planted too deeply. If water is present in such large quantities in the soil that oxygen is reduced or excluded, seeds frequently rot, for they are usually unable to germinate without some atmospheric oxygen and they are often attacked by bacteria that thrive in low concentrations of oxygen. Thus, seeds often die in water-logged soils, particularly those of the clay type, which holds water very tenaciously. However, seeds of such plants as water lilies and cattails, which live in water or swampy soils, germinate more rapidly under water or in water-soaked soils than they do under conditions of moderate moisture in the substratum.

It is known that high carbon dioxide levels within the seed will retard certain enzymatically controlled reactions and

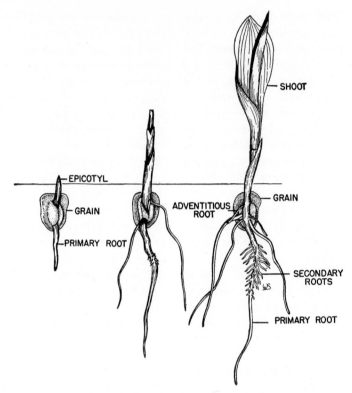

FIG. 2–4. Germination of corn grain.

thus adversely affect germination. The respiration rate of seeds stored under cool, dry conditions is typically very low; hence, little carbon dioxide is liberated by the respiratory process. Conversely, excessive amounts of carbon dioxide are commonly encountered in seeds that have been improperly dried and stored. Poor storage conditions—for example, warm, moist atmosphere and inadequate ventilation—often facilitate the rapid growth of fungi and other heterotrophic organisms and thereby permit the rapid accumulation of carbon dioxide and a concomitant increase in temperature.

The temperature requirements for the germination of seeds usually coincide with the temperature requirements for the growth of active plant organs. Seeds of different species vary widely in their minimum, maximum, and optimum (most favorable) temperature requirements for germination. Seeds of tropical plants ordinarily germinate at higher minimum temperatures than do seeds of temperate-zone and subarctic plants. Thus, barley grains are able to germinate at a soil temperature near the freezing point of water, while corn grains and pumpkin seeds ordinarily germinate well only if soil temperatures exceed 50°F. It is a reasonable generalization to state that few seeds are able to germinate at soil temperatures lower than 40°F, that seeds of most species germinate best at temperatures of 65°F to 85°F, and that temperatures above 100°F often are harmful to germinating seeds.

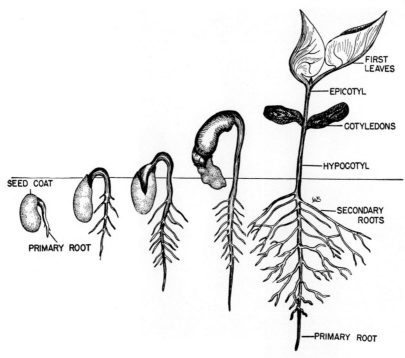

FIG. 2–5. Germination and seedling growth of garden bean.

That some seeds will not germinate un-til they have been exposed to light has been known for at least a century. Only in recent years have botanists made significant progress toward understanding the physiological basis of this fact. These investigators have shown that such seeds contain minute amounts of a light-sensitive, protein pigment, **phytochrome,** that permits germination after brief exposure to red light but that inhibits germination after exposure to light in the far-red portion of the spectrum. This physiological mechanism may explain why some seeds will germinate in a forest clearing exposed to full sunlight but will not germinate on the forest floor where the sunlight has been filtered by the foliage overhead.

Seeds of most species of plants are able to germinate readily if these three external requirements are present: available soil moisture, favorable temperature, and adequate supplies of free oxygen. Most seeds contain sufficient quantities of stored food within their tissues to promote germination and to support the growth of seedlings until they produce their own food-synthesizing organs, the leaves. Thus, most seeds do not need soil nutrients for germination, although if seedlings are to continue their growth and develop into normal, mature plants, they must begin to absorb soil nutrients at an early stage in their lives; however, soil nutrients are not necessary for germination itself, as shown by the fact that most seeds can be germinated in pure water.

When seeds absorb water, enzymes are activated, the digestion of stored foods begins, the rate of respiration increases rapidly, and the assimilation of foods into protoplasm begins. The

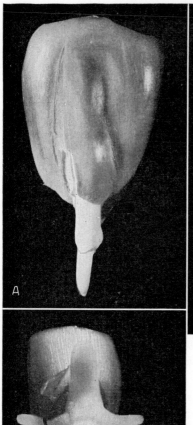

FIG. 2–6. Germinating grains.

A. Corn grain in early stage of germination. The primary root has penetrated the sheath and is emerging from the grain.

B. A later stage in the germination of a corn grain. The primary root has numerous root hairs, and the plump epicotyl has emerged. Adventitious roots are seen behind the epicotyl.

C. A germinating wheat grain, showing the primary root with root hairs, the short, blunt epicotyl, and several young adventitious roots.

stored foods in respiration. The energy released by respiration is used chiefly in assimilation, cell division, and other phases of growth; some of this energy is radiated as heat from germinating seeds and can be measured by suitable thermometers. With the absorption of water, the release of energy, and the inception of growth processes, the embryo becomes too large for the seed coat. Splits appear in the coat and the root-forming tip of the hypocotyl emerges (Figure 2–4). The emergence of the young root before other parts of the embryo is distinctly advantageous, for a root system that anchors the seedling and absorbs water and nutrients is thus established before the epicotyl begins its rapid development into the shoot system. When the epicotyl commences its activities, the primary root and a few secondary roots are supplying to the embryo the large amounts of water needed for subsequent embryo growth.

amount of stored food decreases as digestion and respiration continue; sprouted seeds usually have smaller dry weights than ungerminated seeds largely because of the utilization of some of the

In some species of plants, such as garden peas and corn, the hypocotyl and cotyledons remain in the soil; only the shoot, formed by the growth of the epicotyl, appears above the surface of the soil. In other species, such as garden beans and castor beans, the root primordium of the embryo forms the primary root, as in peas and corn; but the upper part of the hypocotyl, instead of remaining below the soil as it does in pea and corn seedlings grows above ground for several inches, carrying the cotyledons above the soil. The upper part of the hypocotyl is frequently arched during its growth upward through the soil and straightens out after it has emerged into the air. The arch of the hypocotyl forces a path through the soil, as a result of which the epicotyl and cotyledons are protected against injury by soil particles, for they are literally pulled up by the growing crook-shaped hypocotyl. They do not push their own way upward through the soil. In beans and castor beans, the lowermost part of the stem is hypocotyl, whereas the stems of peas and corn develop entirely from epicotyls, the hypocotyls remaining in the soil.

When the shoots have appeared above the soil, their growth and development continue, producing the mature organs of the plants. These organs will be studied in the following chapters.

Seeds are able to sprout and grow, often for several weeks, in darkness. This growth continues only so long as there is stored food available within the seedling for further growth and respiration. When all the food reserves are exhausted, seedlings in darkness die. Continued growth beyond this point can occur only when the seedlings are illuminated, since light is essential for food manufacture in leaves.

FIG. 2–7. Stages in the germination of pea. Note that the cotyledons remain in the substratum.

FRUIT AND SEED DISPERSAL

Many kinds of plants have fruits or seeds that are equipped with special structures or peculiarities of behavior that increase the effectiveness of their spread, or **dispersal,** over wide areas. Among the common dispersal mechanisms of seeds and fruits are:

1. *Wings*—such as those of elm, maple, and ash fruits, and catalpa seeds. These structures facilitate dispersal by wind.

2. *Plumes*—such as those of dandelion fruits and milkweed seeds, which are likewise dispersed by wind.

3. *Spines* and *barbs*—such as those of the fruits of needle-grass, beggar's tick, and wild carrot. These fruits are fastened

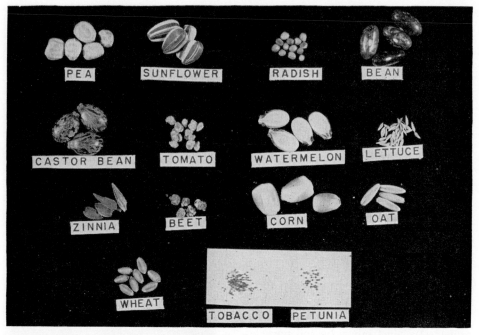

FIG. 2–8. Seeds of some familiar plants. (Some of these structures are really one-seeded fruits—for example, sunflower and zinnia.)

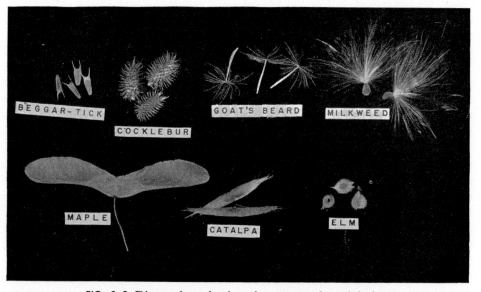

FIG. 2–9. Dispersal mechanisms in some seeds and fruits.

by their spines to the fur of animals and to the clothes of human beings and are thus carried in this manner as "hitch-hikers."

Many other methods of seed dispersal occur in plants. Brightly colored, sweet, pulpy fruits, such as raspberries, cherries, and currants, are eaten by birds and other animals; the seeds in these fruits may pass through these animals without suffering damage, are dropped in the feces of the animal, and are thus dispersed. Some kinds of fruits and seeds are buoyant and can float in water for long periods of time; such structures often travel great distances in the currents of rivers and oceans and are thus dispersed. One of the most interesting examples of the effectiveness of water dispersal is the frequent appearance of seeds and fruits from the Orinoco river valley of South America upon the beaches of the Scandinavian peninsula. Some species of plants have fruits that explode as they mature, scattering their seeds widely. Such explosion sometimes occurs as the result of unequal drying of fruit tissues, as, for example, in wood sorrel, the fruits of which suddenly split as they mature, shedding their seeds in the process. In other types of explosive fruits (for example, those of the squirting cucumber), the cause of the explosion is the development of water pressure within the fruits; when this pressure reaches sufficient magnitude, a segment of the fruit bursts forth, followed by a stream of internal tissues and seeds, which may be shot out for a distance of several feet. Some kinds of seeds are readily dispersed by virtue of their small size and light weight; thus the minute seeds of orchids, several dozen of which just cover the head of a small pin, are carried considerable distances by winds.

Man is one of the most important agents of seed dispersal. In his migrations he has carried with him to all parts of the world valuable crop plants and likewise, inadvertently, some of his most obnoxious weeds. Thus, rice, a native of southeastern Asia, is now grown in tropical and subtropical regions of both hemispheres; corn, a native of tropical America, is extensively grown in both the old world and the new world; and some of our most troublesome weeds, such as thistles and dandelions, are truly cosmopolitan in their distribution.

ECONOMIC IMPORTANCE OF SEEDS

Seeds are of fundamental importance to man because they constitute the chief method of propagation of the seed plants. Many seeds provide man's most important foods—for example, corn, wheat, rice, barley, rye, oats, beans, peas, soybeans, peanuts, walnuts, pecans, almonds, and coconuts. Some furnish oils; the oils from coconuts, soybeans, flax seeds, tung, cotton, and corn are used as foods and in the manufacture of paints, varnishes, linoleum, lubricants, soaps, and other products. Many seeds are used for the flavors they impart to foods: anise, dill, caraway, nutmeg, mustard, and others. Some seeds furnish medicines—for example, castor beans, chaulmoogra (used in the treatment of leprosy), and psyllium. Seeds of coffee and cacao (or cocoa) furnish important beverages. Hard hemicellulose material of the seeds of the ivory-nut palm furnishes "vegetable ivory," used in the manufacture of buttons and as a substitute for ivory in inlays, chessmen, toilet articles, etc.

⋘   SUMMARY

1. Seeds are the reproductive structures of seed plants (gymnosperms and angiosperms).

2. A seed consists of a seed coat, a miniature plant or embryo, and food-storage tissue. In many angiosperm seeds, the endosperm tissue is absorbed by the embryo before the seeds leave their parent plants; such seeds contain no endosperm at the time of their maturity.

3. Seed coats are protective structures that reduce evaporation of water from seed tissues, protect the inner structures of seeds from attacks of certain insects and fungi, and often render seeds resistant to unfavorable external temperatures and mechanical forces.

4. An embryo consists of one or two (sometimes more) cotyledons, an epicotyl, and a hypocotyl. Cotyledons digest and absorb foods stored in endosperm tissues; the epicotyl grows into the young stem of a seedling; and the hypocotyl (or the greater portion of it) produces the primary root of a seedling.

5. Starch, fats and oils, and proteins are stored in the endosperm and cotyledons of seeds.

6. Dormancy is a resting condition of seeds that results from certain internal conditions. Dormancy may be the result of immature embryos, impermeability of seed coats to oxygen or water, or the incompleteness of certain chemical changes. Dormancy is ended under natural conditions by such factors as freezing and thawing, the action of certain bacteria upon seed coats, and aging. Dormancy may be terminated also by seed scarification.

7. Quiescence is a resting condition of seeds resulting from environmental conditions, such as low temperatures and insufficient supply of moisture, which retard or prevent seed germination.

8. Viability is the ability of seeds to germinate. The seeds of different species of plants retain their viability for differing periods. Cool, dry storage conditions are more favorable for the retention of viability than warm, moist conditions. The loss of seed viability appears to involve chiefly coagulation of protoplasmic proteins and failure of cell division.

9. Seed germination is affected by various internal factors: completion of the dormant period, seed age, amount of growth-regulating substances present, amount of stored food, condition of protoplasmic proteins, and presence of inhibitory compounds.

10. The principal external factors influencing seed germination are: temperature, water supply, and free oxygen availability. Seeds of different species vary greatly in their requirements of these three conditions. Most seeds do not require soil nutrients for germination.

11. Seed germination begins with water absorption, which is followed by food digestion, energy release in respiration, cell division, and other growth processes.

12. In germination, the embryo swells, rupturing the seed coat. The hypocotyl tip, or radicle, is the first part of the embryo to emerge from the seed coat, forming

the primary root. As this root becomes established in the soil, the epicotyl emerges and begins its development into the young stem of the plant. The cotyledons may remain in the soil, or may be carried into the air by the upward growth of the upper part of the hypocotyl.

13. Cotyledons may persist on the seedling for several weeks and sometimes become green, leaflike food-making organs, or they may wither and fall shortly after germination when their food reserves are depleted.

14. Seeds are able to germinate in darkness and seedlings similarly are able to develop in the absence of light, until all their food reserves are exhausted. Unless they receive the light necessary for food manufacture, they die.

15. Seed and fruit dispersal are brought about by various mechanisms and modes of behavior. Wind, water, animals, and man are the most important agents of seed dispersal.

16. Seeds furnish man with foods, drugs, oils, and many other economically valuable products.

⫷ SUGGESTED READINGS FOR INTERESTED STUDENTS

1. Crocker, William, "Life-span of seeds." *The Botanical Review,* Vol. 4, pp. 235–274, 1938.
2. Koller, Dov, "Germination." *Scientific American,* Vol. 200, No. 4, pp. 75–84, April 1959.
3. *Seeds.* The Yearbook of Agriculture, U. S. Government Printing Office, 1961.

⫷ TOPICS AND QUESTIONS FOR STUDY

1. Describe the structure of a typical embryo, and list the functions of its parts.
2. What is endosperm? Its function?
3. What are the functions of seed coats? What are some of the visible structures or marks of seed coats?
4. What is a micropyle? What is its significance in seed germination?
5. Distinguish between epicotyl and hypocotyl. What do these words mean?
6. Name some seeds whose cotyledons furnish food to man.
7. Name some seeds whose endosperm furnishes food to man.
8. Distinguish between monocotyledons and dicotyledons, and name some plants that belong to each group.
9. List the major structural differences among corn, castor bean, and garden bean seeds.
10. Define dormancy, and state when it may be advantageous in some species of plants.
11. Name the major causes of dormancy.
12. Distinguish between dormancy and quiescence. What environmental factors are responsible for quiescence?
13. What factors in nature are responsible for ending the dormancy of seeds?
14. What artificial treatments may be used to shorten or "break" the dormancy of seeds?

15. What is meant by seed viability? What environmental factors favor a prolonged period of viability? What factors tend to decrease the viable period?

16. State two reasons why large masses of seeds, stored in poorly ventilated bins, may lose their ability to sprout.

17. Name and describe briefly the principal external factors that are necessary for the germination of most kinds of seeds.

18. To what extent do seeds depend upon soil nutrients for their germination? Suggest an experiment that would give the answer to this question.

19. Describe the principal physiological processes that occur during the germination of seeds.

20. What are the advantages of the early emergence of the hypocotyl during germination?

21. Is light necessary for seed germination? For postgermination growth? Explain.

22. Name the principal structural devices and modes of behavior that promote seed and fruit dispersal. Name the environmental condition or factor in each case that facilitates dispersal.

23. What advantages do seeds have over vegetables and fruits as sources of food for man?

24. Name some economically important products, other than foods, that are derived from seeds.

3

The Gross Structure and Activities of Flowering Plants

In the last chapter we considered the salient features of seed structure, seed dispersal, and seed germination. We learned that a seed contains a tiny, only slightly developed plant, the embryo, that upon germination grows into a young active plant, a seedling. A seedling, as a result of complex processes of growth and development, ultimately becomes a mature plant. In this chapter, we shall consider the generalized structure of a typical flowering plant, and in subsequent chapters, we shall study the details of structure and physiology of flowering plant bodies.

The bodies of most flowering plants are composed of four kinds of structures: **roots, stems, leaves,** and **flowers,** the last of which are **reproductive** structures. The roots, stems, and leaves are called **organs.** Flowers are not properly termed organs, since they are really specialized stems bearing structures comparable with leaves and branches and concerned with reproductive processes; thus, flowers are really clusters of organs. An organ may be defined as a major part of an organism, a part that performs a single main

function or a group of closely related functions. Roots, stems, and leaves are termed the **vegetative** parts of a seed plant's body, because their functions center upon the intake of raw materials, the manufacture of food, and the utilization of food for growth and development. The vegetative organs have no direct role in the fundamental process of reproduction through the formation of seeds, although they may bring about the production of new plants by the growth and development of runners, underground stems, and root "suckers." Such multiplication of plants is termed **vegetative** reproduction. The **reproductive** parts of a flower are concerned with the formation of seeds. In the angiosperms, flowers produce structures called **fruits,** within which the seeds are formed, as has already been stated.

An intimate relationship exists between the vegetative and reproductive activities of plants. Every plant in its life span, which extends from its inception as an embryo of a seed to its death, passes through a series of physiological stages. Vegetative activities—the absorption of

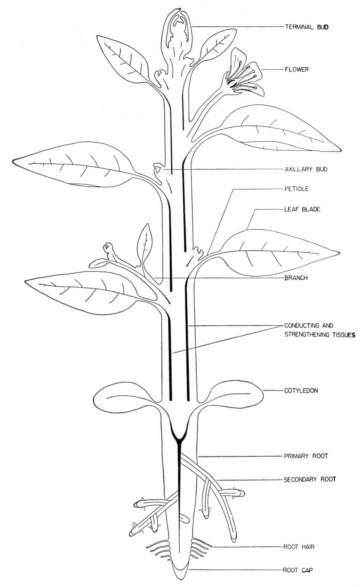

FIG. 3–1. Diagram of the body of a typical flowering plant, showing the major parts.

raw materials, the manufacture of food, and the utilization of foods as souces of energy and building materials for growth —predominate during the greater portion of the life cycle in most plants. After these vegetative activities have proceeded for some time, flowers are formed and seeds are produced. One of the requisites for the development of flowers is a suitable food reserve, which is built up by vegetative processes. When reproductive functions begin, there is often an accompanying decrease in vegetative activity, in part as a result of the movement of food reserves from vegetative organs into developing fruits and seeds. In **annual** plants (for example, sweet peas, marigolds), most of the life span of a few weeks or months is spent in vegetative activities; these are followed by the usually rapid formation of flowers and the production therefrom of fruits and seeds, which draw so heavily upon the food reserves of the vegetative parts of the plant that death of the plant results. The individual is sacrificed during the production of seeds, which maintain the species from generation to generation. In **biennial** plants (for example, beets, carrots), a similar situation obtains, with this difference: the vegetative period extends through two growth seasons, during the second of which reproduction occurs, followed by the death of the plant. In **perennial** species (for example, tulips, roses, apple trees), the individual has a life span of several to many years; during a brief period of one to several years immediately following the sprouting of the seed, activity is exclusively vegetative; when a food reserve has been built up, reproduction occurs. Thereafter during each year of its life the perennial plant carries on both vegetative and reproductive activities, ordinarily forming seeds during each year of its existence.

The **roots** of most plants are nongreen in color and usually grow beneath the surface of the soil. The principal functions of roots are the absorption of water and nutrients from the soil, the anchorage of the plant body in the soil, and the conduction of materials upward into the stem and downward from the stem and leaves. In some plants, in addition to performing these functions, the roots store considerable quantities of food. There are other,

more specialized functions of roots, which will be considered in detail in a later chapter.

Stems arise usually as branched continuations of the root system above the surface of the ground. Their structure varies greatly with different species of plants. The primary functions of stems are the conduction of materials upward, downward, and transversely, and the production and support of leaves and flowers. In addition, most stems store food, and in some plants, if chlorophyll is present in the stems, these organs manufacture food. Other, more highly specialized functions of stems will be described later.

Leaves are outgrowths of stems and in their most common form are broad, flat, and thin, less frequently needlelike or scalelike. The chief work of leaves is the manufacture of food by the process of **photosynthesis,** though specialized types of leaves in some plants perform other functions. The term **shoot** is often applied to a stem with its attached leaves.

The bodies of seed plants, as described in the preceding chapter, are anchored in the soil or other material in which their roots grow. The fixity of the positions in which most plants grow places certain restrictions upon their activities and influences markedly their entire development and character, and, in some degree, their distribution upon the earth's surface. The limitations imposed by immobility influence significantly the operation of physiological processes in plants; plants can absorb water and various nutrients only from those portions of the soil penetrated by their roots. Exhaustion or diminution of these essential materials within the range of root systems results in the development of physiological abnormalities that may lead to death. Fixity of position, moreover, limits the nature and extent of the responses that plants may make to changing environmental conditions. Thus, plants as individuals are less efficient than animals in making certain adjustments to surrounding conditions, particularly those involving the acquisition of nutrient substances.

SUMMARY

1. The bodies of flowering plants consist of:
   a. Vegetative organs: roots, stems, and leaves
   b. Reproductive structures: flowers
2. Vegetative organs are concerned primarily in the absorption of raw materials, the manufacture and utilization of foods, and growth. Flowers produce seeds.
3. Reproduction of new plants is sometimes brought about by growth from vegetative organs and is called "vegetative reproduction."
4. In angiosperms, seeds are produced within structures called fruits.
5. In seed plants, vegetative activities precede the formation of seeds. Vegetative processes result in the accumulation of food stores that are necessary for the production of fruits and seeds.
6. Annual plants complete their life span in a single year or portion thereof. Biennial plants require two years (or two growing seasons) for the completion of their lives. Annuals and biennials ordinarily flower and produce seeds only once. Perennial plants live for several to many years, producing flowers and seeds a number of times, commonly once a year.
7. The principal functions of roots are:
   a. Anchorage.
   b. Absorption of water and mineral salts from the soil.
   c. Conduction of substances.
   d. Food storage.
8. The principal functions of stems are:
   a. Conduction of substances.
   b. Production and support of leaves and flowers.
   c. Food storage.
9. The principal function of leaves is food manufacture. A stem with its leaves is termed a shoot.
10. The fixed position of plants places restrictions upon their acquisition of nutrients.

SUGGESTED READINGS FOR INTERESTED STUDENTS

1. Bold, H. C., *The Plant Kingdom*. Prentice-Hall, Englewood Cliffs, N. J., 1960.
2. Galston, A. W., *The Life of the Green Plant*. Prentice-Hall, Englewood Cliffs, N. J., 1961.

TOPICS AND QUESTIONS FOR STUDY

1. What are the vegetative organs of seed plants? What are vegetative processes?
2. What is vegetative reproduction? Name some familiar plants that are propagated by vegetative means, and state how each is propagated.

3. Distinguish among biennial, annual, and perennial plants, and name specific plants as examples of each.
4. Describe the functions of roots, stems, and leaves.
5. What is the function of flowers? What is the relationship between flowers and fruits?
6. What problems must higher plants solve as a result of their fixed position in the soil? How do these problems differ from those that face animals?

The Microscopic Structure
of Plants: Cells and Tissues

THE CELLULAR ORGANIZATION OF PLANTS

Botanists have been familiar for many centuries with the external forms of seed plants and the gross features of internal structure, but their knowledge of the details of the microscopic structure of plants is scarcely more than one hundred years old. The study of the microscopic features of plant bodies was made possible only after the invention and improvement of the magnifying lenses of microscopes. If one examines with the aid of a microscope a thin slice of tissue cut from a root or leaf or any other portion of a plant body, he observes immediately that the section is composed of very small compartments or **cells,** each of which consists of a **cell wall** surrounding a tiny droplet of living substance, or **protoplasm.** Similar microscopic study of thin portions of the bodies of all species of plants reveals fundamentally the same architectural plan— namely, cells as the basic units of structure in plants. All growth of a plant is the result of the formation of new cells from pre-existing cells. Further, in the production of offspring, certain cells become specialized in or on the body of a parent and

subsequently separate from the parent plant. The newly formed offspring then begin a process of growth to maturity, the result of the formation and development of cells.

Even a cursory microscopic examination of plant sections shows that not all cells are alike, but that there is considerable variation in size and form among them. These size and structural differences are reflections of different functions that various cells perform. In the development of young, newly formed cells into mature cells there occurs a phenomenon termed **differentiation** or **maturation,** during which cells assume the different functions and structures that they usually retain during the life of the organ they comprise. The processes taking place in cell differentiation involve a **division of labor** among cells; some cells become food-making cells, others function in the conduction of materials in plants, still others serve for strength, support, food storage, absorption, etc.

When botanists and zoologists first became aware that the bodies of plants and animals were composed of cells, they regarded these individual cells as of prime

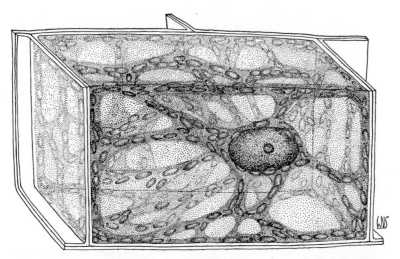

FIG. 4–1. Three-dimensional view of a living, green plant cell, with a portion of the cell cut away. A nucleus (with its nucleolus), chloroplasts, cytoplasm, and vacuoles are visible.

importance. They believed that the activities of the whole plant or animal might be considered as a summation of the activities of the individual, constituent cells. This idea was embodied in a statement known as the **cell theory.** Subsequently, another interpretation known as the **organismal theory** replaced in part the ideas of the cell theory. According to the organismal theory, the entire organism, and not the individual cells, constitutes the entity of prime importance; the whole organism is considered the primary agent of organization. More specifically, the theory holds that a many-celled plant or animal is not merely a group of individualistic cells, but is rather an individual itself, a more or less continuous quantity of protoplasm, which, in the course of evolution, has become subdivided into cells. Cells are formed by differentiation within this mass of protoplasm; the individual is not the result of the aggregation of individual cells.

The organismal theory emphasizes a biological concept that has developed partly as a result of physiological research upon correlation or the coordination of the various tissues and organs of living beings, upon the mutual interaction between different tissues and organs. In other words, these investigations have shown that the mere summation of the activities of individual cells does not explain sufficiently the behavior of organisms, but that there is a coordination among cells that results in the entire organism's function as a unit.

The bodies of seed plants are **multicellular** in nature; moreover, there is a considerable degree of differentiation in structure and function among their many cells. Among certain of the Thallophyta there are organisms that consist of only a single cell (for example, the bacteria). Such organisms are called **unicellular.** Frequently these unicellular organisms remain grouped together in aggregations termed **colonies.** In most colonies, there is little or no differentiation of labor among the cells, and the individual members of the colony can continue their life proc-

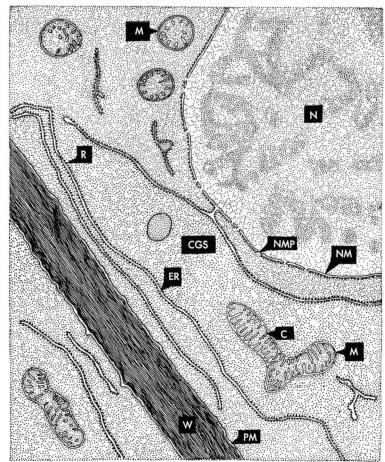

(Based on Whaley, et al.)

FIG. 4–2. Composite representation showing portions of two adjacent meristematic cells as they appear in electronmicrographs. Nucleus (N) at upper right is limited by nuclear membrane (NM), in which are seen small perforations (NMP). A portion of the endoplasmic reticulum (ER) is continuous with the nuclear membrane. Numerous, minute ribosomes (R) contact the endoplasmic reticulum. Dispersed in the cytoplasmic ground substance (CGS) are mitochondria (M), the inner membranes of which are infolded to form cristae (C). The plasma membrane (PM) limits the protoplast to the outside. Wall material (W) separates adjacent cells.

esses if they become separated from the other cells of the colony. In a few types of colonies, the constituent cells are differentiated into two types: vegetative and reproductive cells.

THE SIZES OF CELLS

Plant cells are minute objects, most of them invisible to the naked eye, some of them so small that they appear merely as tiny spheres or rods under the highest magnifying power of the light microscope. Most cells of higher plants vary between 0.1 and 0.01 millimeter ($\frac{1}{250}$ to $\frac{1}{2500}$ inch) in diameter. Between 4 and 40 such cells would just span the period at the end of this sentence. Not all cells, however, are so small. The cells of a green alga, *Valonia*, may exceed an inch in length. The fruit cells of various members of the melon family often approximate 1 millimeter (about $\frac{1}{25}$ inch) in diameter. In the stems of woody plants, fiber cells may be 6 to 8 millimeters in length. In the nettle family (Urticaceae), some cells may reach a length of 200 millimeters—about 8 inches. The smallest plant cells are those of bacteria, some of which are only 0.0002 millimeter, about $\frac{1}{125,000}$ inch, in length. Such sizes, however, are extremes among plant cells. The great majority of them fall within the 0.1 to 0.01 millimeter range.

THE STRUCTURE OF CELLS

Plant cells are extremely varied not only in size but also with respect to their form, the functions they perform, and the structures they contain. If we examine with the microscope a living cell, such as that of a leaf, we find structures that can be classified into three groups:

A. The **cell wall,** which encloses the living substance.

B. The **protoplast,** or living component of a single cell.

C. The **ergastic substances,** nonliving materials present within the protoplasm.

The Cell Wall

The cell wall is a comparatively strong and semirigid structure arranged in the form of a box usually with six or more

FIG. 4–3. Two plant cells with the form of tetrakaidekahedra (14 sides each). (From a research paper by Dr. R. L. Hulbary.)

faces, or possessing a more or less spherical, ovoid, cylindrical, much elongated, or occasionally very irregular form. In spite of their great strength, plant cell walls possess a considerable degree of resilience, which enables the walls to be stretched, compressed, or twisted without their being fractured. It is because cell walls are so pliable and at the same time so strong that stems, leaf stalks, and other plant organs may be bent and buffeted by winds and yet return to their original form and position when the winds diminish. In multicellular plants, the cell walls form interconnecting systems that have the important function of giving strength and support to the plant body.

Plant cell walls have a layered structure and are generally considered to be nonliving. The formation of new walls begins with the deposition of a **cell plate** between daughter nuclei in a dividing cell (Figure 5–6). The cell plate appears to consist of **pectic substances** and forms a filmlike partition across the dividing cell. In this manner the protoplast of the mother cell is subdivided into two daughter protoplasts, each of which participates in the formation of the **middle lamella** by the addition of more pectic substances to the cell plate. The middle lamella consists largely of calcium and magnesium pectates and functions as an intercellular cementing substance that binds together the completed walls of adjacent cells. Pectic compounds are also incorporated into the walls of many cells as incrustations and as depositions between component wall layers. The fruits of many plants contain pectic substances in considerable concentrations. Commercial pectin used in the manufacture of jellies and jams is usually obtained from apples and from citrus fruits.

As cells grow, other materials are deposited by the protoplast in successive layers upon the middle lamella. The layer that is added directly to the middle lamella is called the **primary wall** and consists chiefly of cellulose, hemicelluloses, and pectic materials. This layer is very elastic and pliable and is capable of growth, extension, and changes in thickness. The primary wall is formed while the cell is still growing and, like the middle lamella, is usually quite thin. Under an ordinary light microscope the middle lamella and the primary walls of two adjacent cells commonly appear as a single structure, the **compound middle lamella.** Many plant cells produce only primary walls. In many other plant cells, however, a **secondary wall** is deposited by the protoplast upon the primary wall. Secondary walls are usually formed after the cell has attained its final size. Cellulose is the chief constituent of secondary walls; noncellulosic materials are commonly present, although pectic compounds are usually absent. The secondary wall is frequently formed in three layers and is considerably less pliable and less elastic than the primary wall.

The physical properties of cell walls are attributable largely to cellulose, which is their most abundant constituent and which forms their structural framework. Some of the factors that determine the resilience and toughness of cell walls are:

the great length of cellulose molecules (estimates range as high as 50,000 Ångstrom units, that is, about 0.005 mm or $\frac{1}{5000}$ inch); the aggregation of these molecules into partially crystalline, submicroscopic **microfibrils;** the orientation of microfibrils in the various wall layers; and wall thickness. Cellulose will not dissolve in water, though it absorbs water in large quantities. As a result, most of the cell walls of living plants are in a highly hydrated or saturated condition. The physiological significance of this fact will be discussed in later chapters. Special properties are often imparted by depositions of noncellulosic substances in the walls of certain cells. For example, **suberin,** the fatty material found in cork cells, and **cutin,** the waxy compound in epidermal cells, may render their walls nearly impermeable to water. **Lignin,** an abundant constituent in the middle lamellae and walls of wood cells, imparts great resistance to decay in addition to certain structural properties.

The thickness of cell walls varies greatly. In many cells, such as the green cells of leaves and the storage cells of roots, cell walls remain very thin, rarely more than a few thousandths of a millimeter in thickness. In other cells, such as the outer cells of date seeds and the stone cells of peach fruits, the walls become enormously thickened, so that at maturity the cavity within the cell wall is almost completely replaced by the thick cell wall.

The walls of most cells are not uniformly continuous. In many kinds of cells, especially in wood, the secondary wall layers do not develop at certain points. Thus, minute, thin areas are left in the cell wall. These thin areas, called **pits,** facilitate the passage of water and dissolved materials from cell to cell. In many types of cells exceedingly small canals pass through the wall layers and, through these pores, delicate strands of protoplasm called **plasmodesmata** extend from the protoplasm of one cell to that of another. These protoplasmic connections are thought to be important in the interchange of foods and other materials from cell to cell. Plasmodesmata are so very fine and delicate that they usually cannot be seen without the aid of special techniques. Evidence indicates that plasmodesmata occur in all living tissues of a plant.

The Protoplast

Protoplast is a term denoting all the living parts of a cell as they are organized into a single unit. *Protoplasm,* a general term coined more than a century ago, is the name given to all the living substance of which the protoplast is composed. Rather gross examinations showed protoplasm to be viscous, ranging in consistency from watery to that of semisolidified gelatin. It was also found to be elastic, somewhat mucilaginous, and usually transparent and colorless. Although the light microscope showed protoplasm to be of heterogeneous composition, it was not until studies could be made with the electron microscope that we learned how complex and extensively structured the protoplasm is. Thus, our concept of the general term protoplasm changes as we increase our knowledge of structure and function of both the formerly unknown, "invisible" components and the larger, more conspicuous parts of the protoplast.

Nucleus. Perhaps the most conspicuous of the living protoplasmic components is the **nucleus,** which, in the nondividing condition, appears as a rather large spherical, ovoid, or sometimes elongated structure. The number of nuclei per cell varies according to the organism and the type of tissue; most frequently, each cell contains a single nucleus. The living nu-

FIG. 4–4.   Plasmodesmata extending through thickened cell walls of persimmon endosperm (food-storage tissue of seed).

cleus is colorless, transparent, and generally more viscous than other parts of the protoplast. It may move about within the protoplast and change its shape as it does so. If the cell is treated with suitable fixatives and dyes, it becomes apparent that the nucleus, like the whole protoplast, is not structurally uniform but is made up of several distinct parts.

A very thin, tenuous **nuclear membrane** delimits the nuclear contents from other portions of the protoplasm. Pictures made with the electron microscope show this nuclear envelope to be a double membrane that is perforated by minute pores (Figure 4–2). It is composed of proteins and lipids (fatty compounds) and is thought to exercise control over the passage of materials into and out of the nucleus. Within the nucleus is the protein-rich **nuclear sap** and the **chromatin.** Chromatin, as it appears in stained preparations, has a finely granular texture and is organized into a diffuse, irregular network. It consists chiefly of **deoxyribonucleic acid** (DNA), the material that bears the genetic information of each cell. In addition, chromatin contains relatively small amounts of proteins and another nucleic acid, **ribonucleic acid** (RNA). During nuclear duplication, it is the chromatin that becomes organized into **chromosomes.** Also present within the nucleus are the small, spherical **nucleoli.** These structures are produced in association with specific chromosomes, each nucleus commonly having one nucleolus per set of chromosomes. Typically, nucleoli are rich in RNA and proteins but are devoid of DNA; moreover, they lack membranes and usually disappear altogether during nuclear duplication. To date there is considerable uncertainty regarding nucleolar function. There is no doubt, however, that the organized nucleus functions as a primary directive center of the major physiological activities of the cell. Cells from which the nuclei have been removed soon exhibit abnormalities, resulting after a time in the death of the cells. Among the chief activities controlled by the nucleus is the transmission of hereditary characteristics from one cell generation to the next. The structural changes that the nucleus undergoes during its duplication will be discussed in the next chapter.

Cytoplasm. The protoplasm in which the nucleus and other protoplasmic bodies are embedded is called **cytoplasm.** In very young cells, nucleus and cytoplasm together occupy nearly all the volume of the cell. As plant cells become older and grow markedly in size, the cytoplasm fails to increase in quantity proportionately and forms a thin layer lining the wall. The central region of the cell, that inside the cytoplasmic layer, is a cavity, or **vacuole,** filled with **cell sap.** This watery solution contains various kinds of substances such as sugars and salts, and often pigments, tannins, and organic acids. The vacuole functions as a repository of various non-protoplasmic materials; it also plays an important part in the maintenance of cell turgidity, as will be described in the next chapter.

An inner surface film, the **tonoplast** or **vacuolar membrane,** separates cytoplasm and vacuole. The **ectoplast** or **plasma membrane** is the surface film that delimits cytoplasm to the outside, that is, next to the wall. Both of these membranes are of cytoplasmic origin and both are exceedingly important in cellular physiology in that they control in a large degree the passage of materials into and out of the living protoplasm. Unlike the nuclear membrane, the plasma membrane appears to be imperforate and to consist of a single layer. Electron microscopic examination of immature plant cells also reveals the presence of an extensive system of membranes *within* the protoplast. This system, the **endoplasmic reticulum,** forms a network of mostly flattened vescicles that occasionally contact the plasma membrane. The membranes of the endoplasmic reticulum have a double structure similar to that of the nuclear envelope with which they are continuous. This system of membranes provides large areas over which chemical reactions occur; it may also facilitate the transfer of materials between nucleus and cytoplasm. Whether the endoplasmic reticulum persists in mature, differentiated cells is still in doubt.

In young, actively growing cells there are large numbers of minute particles

(ribosomes) distributed on parts of the outer surfaces of the endoplasmic reticulum and suspended freely in the cytoplasmic ground substance. These nearly spherical structures consist of approximately equal amounts of RNA and protein. It appears that ribosomes are unable to reproduce themselves. Experimental evidence indicates that they originate in the nucleus and then migrate to the cytoplasm, possibly through the pores in the nuclear envelope. Ribosomes function as centers of synthesis of cytoplasmic proteins. Apparently each ribosome is able to direct the formation, at its surface, of one or at most a few kinds of protein. The necessary "instructions" that the ribosome follows in the stepwise construction of specific proteins resides in the RNA component. This "information" was previously imparted by nuclear DNA at the time of ribosome formation. The nature and significance of nucleic acids will be discussed in Chapter 17.

Nearly all living cells contain subcellular organelles called **mitochondria.** These small, rod-shaped or spherical bodies are dispersed in the cytoplasmic ground substance and may occasionally contact the endoplasmic reticulum. Mitochondria are quite numerous, some investigators estimating as many as 1000 or more per cell. Unlike ribosomes, these cytoplasmic organelles reproduce themselves. Each mitochondrion is bounded externally by a double membrane, the inner layer of which is deeply infolded, forming internal membrane extensions called **cristae** (Figure 4–2). The mitochondria play an important part in cellular physiology for they are the principal centers of respiratory activity. In the process of respiration, energy is released by oxidative chemical reactions within the mitochondria where it is immediately *transferred* to molecules of an energy-transporting compound. These molecules in their high-energy state are then moved out of the mitochondria to other parts of the cell where that energy is used to sustain the various life processes.

The most conspicuous cytoplasmic bodies found in mature plant cells are **plastids.** They occur in a great variety of shapes but in higher plants are most frequently ovoid or spherical. These organelles are larger than mitochondria and much less abundant, ranging from one to several dozen per cell. Plastids are classified as **chromoplasts** and **leucoplasts,** according to pigmentation. One type of chromoplast, the **chloroplast,** contains the photosynthetic pigments **chlorophyll** *a* and **chlorophyll** *b,* which impart the green color to many plant cells. **Carotene** and **xanthophylls,** respectively deep and pale yellow pigments, are also present in chloroplasts but their color is masked by that of the more abundant chlorophylls. The structure and function of chloroplasts as related to photosynthesis will be discussed in Chapter 12. Nonchlorophyllous chromoplasts contain carotenoid pigments, including carotene and xanthophylls, which impart yellow, orange, or red coloration to some flower petals, fruits, and other plant parts. The exact physiological significance of these plastids is not known; however, bright coloration often plays a part in pollination and fruit dispersal. Leucoplasts are colorless plastids, occurring most commonly in storage cells of roots and underground stems. They are centers of starch-grain formation in these storage cells.

It is interesting that plastids of one type are transformed under certain conditions into other types. In tomatoes, for example, leucoplasts are present in the tiny, undeveloped fruits. As the fruits enlarge, the leucoplasts slowly develop into chloroplasts, and in the last phases of ripening the chloroplasts are changed into chromoplasts, which are responsible for the color of the fully ripened fruits.

Ergastic Substances

Ergastic substances, which are nonliving bodies in cells, are not actually part of the living protoplasm, but they may be necessary for its normal physiological activities. Some of them may thus be compared with the oil and gasoline necessary for the proper functioning of an automobile. The lubricant and fuel are not actually a part of the automobile's mechanism, but they are necessary for its operation. Among the most frequent kinds of ergastic substances in plant cells are the cell sap contained in vacuoles; crystals, and stored

parently waste materials of physiological activity of the protoplasm.

The relationships among the various structures described above may be summarized in the form given below.

TISSUES

As has been emphasized, the cells of plants show great variations in size and structure, differences that reflect the diverse functions of these cells in the life of a plant. A group of cells performing essentially the same function and commonly of similar structure is called a **tissue.** An organ, such as a leaf or root, is composed of **tissues;** usually in an organ the various tissues perform interrelated functions. Tissues are classified on different bases: on their origin, their structure, or their physiology. A common classifica-

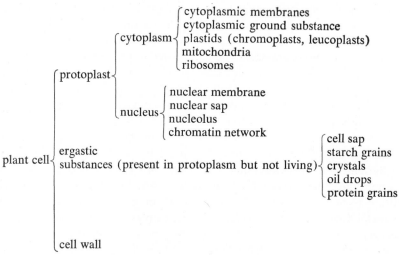

Relationships of cell parts.

foods in solid form, such as starch grains, protein bodies; and oil drops. Crystals are found usually within vacuoles, rather than in cytoplasm. Crystals and certain other types of nonliving inclusions are ap-

tion, based on morphological and physiological features, is the following:

1. **Meristematic tissue (growth tissue)**
2. **Permanent tissues (matured tissues)**

A. **Simple permanent tissues (consisting chiefly of one kind of cell)**
   a. **Epidermis**
   b. **Parenchyma**
   c. **Sclerenchyma**
   d. **Collenchyma**
   e. **Cork**
B. **Complex permanent tissues (consisting of several kinds of cells)**
   a. **Xylem**
   b. **Phloem**

Meristematic Tissue

Meristematic tissue is located near the tips of roots and in the buds of stems, between the bark and wood of trees and shrubs, in bark, and elsewhere in the bodies of plants wherever extensive growth occurs. These tissues at the tips of stems and roots are called **apical meristems.** The meristematic tissue between wood and bark is called **vascular cambium** and causes growth in diameter of stems and roots. The meristematic tissue in the outer bark is the **cork cambium,** which produces the cork tissue of trees and shrubs. These meristematic tissues are composed of actively growing cells that form new cells by a process called **cell division.** Some meristematic cells are small, thin walled, and commonly cubical or nearly so in form; cambial cells, on the other hand, are often much elongated and sometimes have moderately thick walls. Meristematic cells are usually tightly packed and lack extensive intercellular spaces. All other types of plant tissues develop from meristematic cells as a result of processes of growth.

Epidermal Tissue

Epidermal tissue is usually only one cell thick and forms the surface layer of leaves, flower parts, many types of fruits, and the younger portions of stems and roots. The epidermis of the aerial parts of plants functions chiefly in conserving the moisture supply of the inner tissues and in offering a certain amount of protection against parasites. The outer walls of these cells are sometimes rather thick and are often covered by a layer of **cutin,** a waxy, waterproof substance secreted by the protoplasts of epidermal cells. Epidermal cells, except the **guard cells,** which control the opening of epidermal pores **(stomata),** are generally colorless; however, in some plants, red, blue, or purple pigments may be present in the vacuoles of epidermal cells and may thus give the leaves in which they occur a like color, as in purple-leafed cabbage. The epidermis of roots functions chiefly in absorption of water and nutrients from soils.

Parenchyma Tissue

Parenchyma tissue is one of the most common and most abundant plant tissues, occurring in all organs of higher plants. Parenchyma cells are usually spherical, ovoid, or sometimes cylindrical, with large vacuoles and relatively thin walls. Parenchyma cells often form homogeneous masses of considerable volume, with many intercellular spaces, although they are also found intermingled with other types of cells, such as conducting cells. The parenchyma tissue of roots and much of that in stems is usually colorless and functions chiefly in storage of food and water. In leaves and in some of the younger portions of stems, the parenchyma cells contain chloroplasts and function chiefly in food synthesis.

Collenchyma Tissue

Cells of collenchyma tissue are often long lived and have unevenly thickened

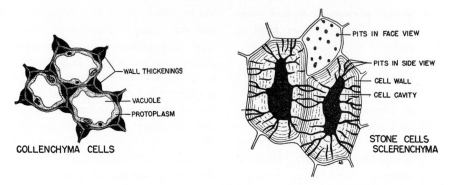

FIG. 4–5. Collenchyma and sclerenchyma cells in sectional view.

primary walls that are rich in pectic substances. They are usually elongated and function in providing strength and support in relatively young, growing plant parts such as stems, leaf stalks, and leaf blades.

Sclerenchyma Tissue

Sclerenchyma tissue consists of cells with thickened walls, which contain lignin in addition to the cellulose and other compounds ordinarily occurring in cell walls. There are two types of sclerenchyma cells: **fibers** and **sclereids.** Fibers are elongated cells that have tapering ends and that possess both great strength and flexibility. Because of these qualities and also because they are aggregated into strands, fibers are important in the manufacture of twine, rope, and textiles. Sclereids resemble fibers in their great strength, but are not elongated; they form the greater portion of seed coats and nut shells; they form gritty masses in the pulp of pears; and they occur in the bark of trees. Sclerenchyma tissue functions chiefly in providing strength and support in plant organs.

Xylem Tissue

Xylem has two principal functions: conduction and support. Xylem conducts water and dissolved substances, chiefly nutrients, absorbed from the soil, upward through roots and stems and into leaves, flowers, and fruits. This conduction is carried on by **tracheids** and **vessels.** Tracheids are elongated, tapering cells, the protoplasm of which dies when the cells reach maturity. The walls of many tracheids are thickened by spirals or rings of lignified cellulose and often possess thin areas or **pits,** which facilitate the passage of water and dissolved materials from tracheid to tracheid. In addition to their function of conduction, tracheids contribute to the strength and support of the organs in which they occur. Vessels are not single cells, but are vertically arranged tubes composed of cylindrical **vessel members** that are arranged end to end and from which the end walls have wholly or partly disappeared. Vessel members have pits in their lateral walls and frequently contain various types of thickenings similar to those of tracheids. Like tracheids, vessels function both in conduction and support, and lack protoplasm at maturity. Other types of cells in xylem are **ray parenchyma cells,** which conduct substances radially in stems and which sometimes store food; strengthening **fibers;** and **xylem parenchyma,** which stores foods.

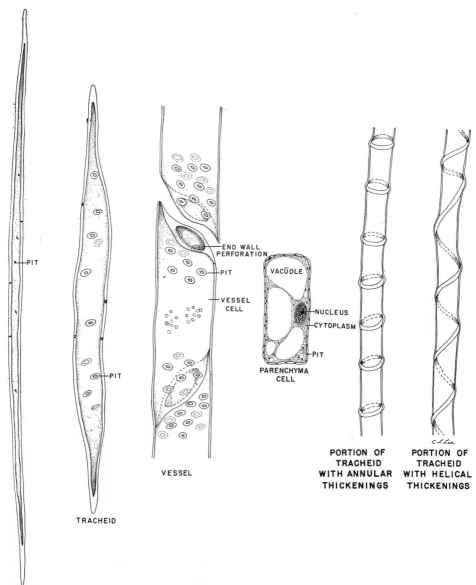

FIG. 4–6. Types of xylem cells.

Phloem Tissue

Phloem, like xylem, is primarily a conducting and supporting tissue; it conducts principally foods, manufactured in leaves, downward through the aerial parts of plants into roots. Phloem always contains two types of cells: **sieve cells** or **sieve tube members** and **phloem parenchyma;** in addition, **companion cells, ray parenchyma cells,** and **phloem fibers** are commonly present. Sieve tubes, like xylem vessels, are vertically elongated rows of cylindrical cells. The end walls of the

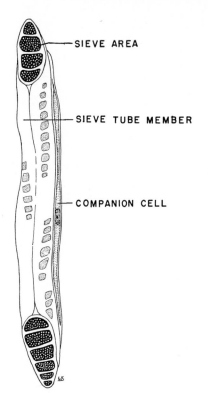

FIG. 4–7. Phloem cells.

aid the sieve tubes in conduction. Phloem fibers contribute to the strength of the parts in which they occur, ray cells conduct foods and other substances transversely and store food, while phloem parenchyma functions chiefly in food storage.

Cork Tissue

Cork tissue is composed of cells that lack protoplasm at maturity and that have walls impregnated with fatty, waterproof suberin. Cork cells, together with remnants of dead phloem, comprise the rough outer bark of woody stems and roots, and they occur also in some fruits, in bud scales, and in certain other plant parts. Their principal function is the reduction of water evaporation from underlying tis-

component sieve tube members contain numerous, usually circular perforations like those in a sieve. Sieve tubes contain living protoplasm, but nuclei are absent at maturity. The cytoplasm is continuous from cell to cell through the sieve plates of the end walls. In some plants, individual sieve cells rather than sieve tubes conduct foods. In flowering plants, companion cells, which are likewise vertically elongated but usually somewhat shorter and smaller in diameter than sieve tube members, are found bordering upon the latter. Like sieve tube members, they are living, but they retain their nuclei throughout their lives. Since there are cytoplasmic connections between sieve tube members and adjacent companion cells, it is thought by some that the latter may

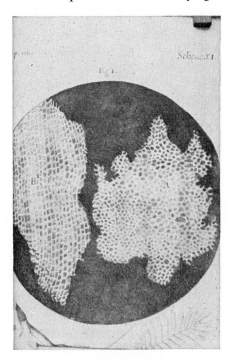

FIG. 4–8. The first illustration of cells: cork tissue, from Robert Hooke's *Micrographia,* published in 1665.

sues. Cork tissue may also protect inner tissues from extremes of temperature, from mechanical injury, and from fire. Commercial cork is obtained from the thick, outer bark of the cork oak tree, a species native in the Mediterranean area.

Once the permanent tissues are formed from the meristematic tissues, they ordinarily do not undergo pronounced changes in their structure and functions. Some of these mature tissues, however, retain the capacity for further growth and change, and, under certain conditions, may resume growth and may even produce tissues of some other type. Thus, parenchyma cells may undergo development into sclerenchyma, collenchyma, and other tissues.

A study of the structure of these various tissues illustrates strikingly the inseparable connection between form and function. Cells that furnish strength and support are thick walled, elongated, tough, and flexible. Conducting cells have in their walls thin areas and perforations that facilitate the transportation of materials from cell to cell. Protective cells, such as cork, are dead at maturity, are frequently formed in considerable thicknesses, and are waterproofed so that they reduce or eliminate evaporation of moisture from the underlying tissues. The study of morphology alone, without consideration of physiological activities, is as meaningless as the study of functional processes without reference to the structure of the cells and tissues that perform them.

⫷⫷⫷ SUMMARY

1. The bodies of plants are composed of cells.
2. The cell theory regards a plant or animal as an aggregation of cells. The organismal theory regards the whole organism as a unit, which is subdivided into functional units, the cells.
3. Some lower plants consist of one cell; these are called unicellular plants. Frequently unicellular plants remain grouped together in colonies; there is little or no division of labor among the cells of a colony. A plant that consists of many cells among which there is usually structural and functional differentiation is called a multicellular plant.
4. Cells differ greatly in their structure and functions; these differences develop as a result of processes of differentiation or maturation.
5. All growth and reproduction of living organisms result from the formation of new cells from pre-existing cells.
6. Most plant cells vary in diameter from $\frac{1}{250}$ to $\frac{1}{2500}$ of an inch. Some cells are larger or smaller than these dimensions.
7. A living plant cell typically consists of a cell wall and, within the wall, a mass of living substance, protoplasm, plus nonliving inclusions (ergastic substances).
8. Plant cell walls have a layered structure and are generally considered to be nonliving. A primary wall consisting chiefly of cellulose and pectic substances is formed while the cell is enlarging. Primary walls of adjacent cells are held together by the middle lamella, a layer of intercellular cementing material that is formed directly from the cell plate. In many cells, a layered secondary wall consisting largely of cellulose is deposited against the primary wall.

9. Long cellulose molecules aggregated into crystalline microfibrils form the structural framework of cell walls. Materials such as lignin, suberin, and cutin may impregnate the cellulose framework and impart special characteristics.

10. Cell walls are tough and strong, yet somewhat elastic, and give strength and support to plant bodies.

11. Both pits (thin wall areas) and plasmodesmata (fine cytoplasmic strands passing through cell walls) are believed to facilitate passage of substances from one cell to another.

12. Protoplast is a term denoting all the living parts of a cell as they are organized into a single unit. Protoplasm is a general term given to all the living substance of which the protoplast is composed. Structurally complex, the protoplast contains various organelles, some of which may be seen only with an electron microscope.

13. The nucleus is a conspicuous protoplasmic body that serves as a directive center of most cellular activities. A nucleus is separated from the remainder of the protoplasm by a nuclear membrane and contains nuclear sap, one or more nucleoli, and chromatin. Chromatin bears the genetic information of the cell and becomes organized into chromosomes during nuclear duplication.

14. Cytoplasm is the protoplasmic material outside the nucleus. Cytoplasm contains a number of structures among which are:
    a. Plastids: commonly spherical or ovoid in shape. Chloroplasts: contain green chlorophyll pigments; centers of food manufacture. Leucoplasts: colorless; centers of starch formation. Chromoplasts: yellow, red, or orange, often needle shaped or irregular in form.
    b. Cytoplasmic membranes, including plasma and vacuolar membranes and the extensive endoplasmic reticulum, a membranous system within the cytoplasm.
    c. Ergastic substances: nonliving materials such as starch grains, crystals, oil droplets, and the cell sap contained in vacuoles.
    d. Mitochondria: the centers of respiratory activity.
    e. Ribosomes: minute, spherical bodies that function in the synthesis of cytoplasmic proteins.

15. A group of cells of similar structure and closely related functions is called a tissue.

16. The principal plant tissues are:
    a. Meristematic tissue.
    b. Epidermal tissue.
    c. Parenchyma tissue.
    d. Collenchyma tissue.
    e. Sclerenchyma tissue.
    f. Xylem tissue.
    g. Phloem tissue.
    h. Cork tissue.

17. Cell structure and cell functions are intimately related. Cell structure usually indicates the nature of the functions which cells perform.

⫷⫷ SUGGESTED READINGS FOR INTERESTED STUDENTS

1. Brachet, Jean, "The living cell." *Scientific American,* Vol. 205, No. 3, pp. 51–61, September 1961.
2. Esau, Katherine, *Anatomy of Seed Plants.* Wiley, New York, 1960.
3. Galston, Arthur W., *The Life of the Green Plant.* Prentice-Hall, Englewood Cliffs, N. J., 1961.
4. Preston, R. D., "Cellulose." *Scientific American,* Vol. 197, No. 3, pp. 156–168, September 1957.
5. Swanson, Carl P., *The Cell.* Prentice-Hall, Englewood Cliffs, N. J., 1960.
6. Whaley, W. Gordon, H. H. Mollenhauer, and J. H. Leech, "The ultrastructure of the meristematic cell." *American Journal of Botany,* Vol. 47, No. 6, pp. 401–449, June 1960.

⫷⫷ TOPICS AND QUESTIONS FOR STUDY

1. Define cell differentiation.
2. Distinguish between the cell theory and the organismal theory. Are these theories completely contradictory?
3. Distinguish among unicellular, colonial, and multicellular organisms. What different kinds of problems of existence must be solved by these types of organisms?
4. Describe the structure and function of the middle lamella. Distinguish between middle lamella and compound middle lamella.
5. Describe the physical properties of plant cell walls.
6. Describe briefly the structure and chemical nature of plant cell walls. How are plant cell walls important in human life?
7. What are the functions of plant cell walls?
8. Describe the structure of pits and comment upon their significance in the life of a plant.
9. What are plasmodesmata? What is their importance?
10. What are ergastic substances? Give examples.
11. Describe the structure and biological importance of nuclei. How may the indispensable nature of nuclei be demonstrated?
12. Define these terms: protoplast, protoplasm, cytoplasm, and nucleus. Describe their relationship to each other.
13. Name and describe the cytoplasmic membranes.
14. Name and describe the kinds of plastids found in plant cells. State their known or supposed functions.
15. What are chlorophyll, xanthophyll, and carotene? Distinguish among them.
16. Where in cells is DNA located? RNA?
17. Describe the structure and function of mitochondria and of ribosomes.
18. Name and describe the principal types of plant tissues and state their functions.
19. Describe the relationship between tissue structure and functions.

5 ‹‹‹‹‹‹‹‹‹‹‹‹‹‹‹‹

Some Physiological
Activities of Plant Cells

PHYSICOCHEMICAL NATURE OF PROTO-
PLASM

Physical Structure of Protoplasm. It was
mentioned in the preceding chapter that
protoplasm is a viscous, transparent liquid, the consistency of which varies from
time to time. Protoplasm from the physical standpoint is a **colloidal** system of
solid and liquid particles in water. In a
typical colloidal system, the solid particles
(micelles) present are not individual
molecules, separated from each other, as
in a sugar solution, but are aggregations
of molecules. The approximate size range
of these particles is 0.001 to 0.1 micron
in diameter. They are sometimes large
enough to be detected under a light microscope, but are usually too small to be
seen even under high-power magnifying
lenses. In such cases, the presence of
such particles is inferred by the turbidity
they give to the liquids in which they are
present, or by the reflection of light rays
from their surfaces. Colloidal particles
may be suspended in gases, in solids, or
in liquids. These particles may remain
suspended indefinitely in the medium in
which they are present without settling

out. In other colloidal systems, the particles are exceedingly unstable and may be
caused to precipitate by slight changes in
the chemical or physical nature of the
medium. Colloidal systems may be in liquid condition, as in the protein-in-water
colloidal system of egg-white, or they may
be semisolid, as in gelatin desserts. The
former colloidal state is termed a **sol,** the
latter a **gel.** Protoplasm is for the most
part a sol, though under certain conditions it loses its liquid quality and becomes a gel. Such changes in the colloidal
state of protoplasm are often reversible
and are induced in large part by changes
in external factors, such as temperature,
acidity, and certain types of light rays,
and in part by internal changes. Sometimes the gelation of a colloidal sol is not
reversible, as for example, when egg-
white is coagulated by boiling water. Coagulation is thus an irreversible colloidal
gelation and results in the death of protoplasm.

The physiological activities of living
protoplasm are in large degree dependent
upon its colloidal organization. Varied
chemical and physical reactions can proceed simultaneously in different parts of

the same protoplast. This is attributable to such protoplasmic properties as heterogeneity of composition, the great surface attraction of certain colloidal particles for various molecules and ions, the development of electric charges upon colloidal particles, and the frequent instability of these particles. These colloidal systems of the protoplasm and cell walls are capable of absorbing large quantities of water and of holding them tenaciously against drying forces, just as a gelatin dessert remains moist after several days' exposure to dry air. In living protoplasm the liquid in which the colloidal particles are dispersed is, of course, water; the particles themselves are principally proteinaceous in nature.

Careful studies of the physical structure of protoplasm indicate that not all the substances in living protoplasm occur in a colloidal state, but that many of them are present in true solutions, emulsions, and suspensions. A true solution is a system in which the dispersed or solute particles are molecules of less than colloidal size (less than 0.001 micron in diameter), or ions.* These solute particles are stable and tend to remain dispersed without settling out. True solutions generally appear clear and without turbidity, as, for example, a solution of sugar or salt in water. An emulsion is a dispersion of tiny droplets of one liquid in another. The dispersed droplets, which are larger than col-

* Molecules of substances called electrolytes when in solution break up into electrically charged portions called ions, some of which bear positive electric charges, others negative charges. Ions of the former type are called cations, of the latter type anions. An ion may be a single atom (for example, potassium chloride, or KCl, molecules dissociate into K and Cl ions), or an ion may consist of groups of atoms (for example, potassium nitrate, or KNO_3, molecules dissociate into K and NO_3 ions).

loidal particles (larger than 0.1 micron in diameter), do not dissolve or thoroughly mix with the dispersing liquid and tend to separate from it; for example, an emulsion of oil in water, in which the dispersed oil droplets slowly rise to the top of the water. A suspension is similar to an emulsion in that it is unstable; that is, its suspended particles tend to separate from the dispersing liquid, usually by settling to the bottom of the liquid. The dispersed particles of a suspension are solids rather than liquids and are larger than colloidal particles. The dispersed particles of a suspension, such as fine grains of sand, are often visible to the naked eye, or with the aid of a lens of low magnifying power. The microscope shows many minute suspended particles in living protoplasm. Scientists who have specialized in the study of protoplasmic structure generally agree that the basic structure of protoplasm is colloidal. The substances in colloidal condition are visualized by some as a framework of elongated colloidal masses, enmeshing and intertwining, with emulsions, suspensions, and true solutions filling the submicroscopic spaces among the colloidal strands. This interpretation of protoplasmic physical structure is sometimes called the "brush-pile" theory. The colloidal constituents may be compared with a pile of tree branches and twigs tightly compressed, and the encompassed watery protoplasmic suspensions, emulsions, and solutions with the spaces among them.

Some of the dynamic aspects of protoplasm can be seen by examining living cells with a microscope. Living protoplasm frequently exhibits streaming movements, which are often very rapid. Protoplasmic viscosity and elasticity continually undergo alteration. At times, the viscosity is very great and protoplasmic streaming slow or apparently suspended; again, the viscosity is very low, the protoplasm is thin and watery, and movement is rapid and extensive.

Chemical Nature of Protoplasm. The most careful chemical analyses of protoplasm have never presented a completely accurate account of all the kinds of chemical compounds present and the exact proportions in which they occur. Because living protoplasm is so unstable and sensitive, it is often greatly altered or killed by many analytical procedures. Such methods can indicate the kinds of chemical *elements* present in protoplasm, the relative proportions in which they occur, and also the nature and amounts of the more stable chemical *compounds* present. A few methods have been used successfully in assaying certain compounds in *living* cells or cell parts. For example, some chemical constituents can be identified by their ability to absorb radiant energy such as ultraviolet light. Others may be detected through the use of special dyes (vital stains) that can be applied to living protoplasm. Organelles such as nuclei, mitochondria, and ribosomes can be isolated from living cells by various fractionation techniques. Isolation greatly facilitates the chemical and physiological characterization of such cellular components. Although much information has been obtained through the use of these and other techniques, much more remains to be learned.

Certain chemical elements are present in all living protoplasm, both plant and animal. Most abundant of these are oxygen, carbon, hydrogen, and nitrogen, listed in the descending order of their abundance. These four elements ordinarily constitute 95 to 98 percent of active, living protoplasm. In addition, other chemical elements, probably always present (in green plants, at least), in smaller quantities, are sulfur, zinc, boron, manganese, phosphorus, calcium, magnesium, potassium, iron, molybdenum, copper, and chlorine. All the above elements are physiologically significant and perform definite functions, at least in green plants. Frequently chemical analyses show the presence in plant tissues of other elements such as nickel, gold, tin, and mercury. These elements are apparently not required in the physiology of plants; in fact, they may even be toxic. Such elements are found in plants because they happened to be present in the soil in which the plants grew and because the plants were unable to prevent their absorption. In recent years plants have been used to help locate deposits of valuable minerals such as uranium and selenium. One method involves the use of indicator plants; that is, location and analysis of plants known to tolerate the accumulation of abnormally large quantities of certain minerals. Another technique involves chemical analysis of many or all the species growing in a test area. These methods have been employed with some success and their continued use seems likely. Botanical prospecting is an interesting variation upon Shakespeare's theme of "sermons in stones and tongues in trees."

Chemical elements for the most part do not occur in elemental form in protoplasm but are combined in the form of chemical compounds. Water is the most abundant chemical compound in active protoplasm, varying in percentage from 70 to 97. In dormant structures, such as seeds, however, the water content may be as low as 4 or 5 percent. Proteins, which include the largest and most complex molecules in protoplasm, are second in abundance. In addition to water and proteins, many other kinds of chemical compounds are present in living cells. Common among these are sugars, starch, fats, organic acids, mineral salts, pigments, alkaloids, and numerous others. Many of these substances, however, are not actually constituents of living protoplasm. Some of them, such as alkaloids and certain organic acids, are apparently waste products of physiological processes, others are raw materials that the protoplasm builds up into foods, still others, such as sugars, are foods used as sources of energy or assimilated into living protoplasm. Such compounds are the fuel and exhaust of the protoplasmic machine.

A notable fact concerning the chemical constitution of living protoplasm is the impossibility of classifying the individual constituent compounds as living or nonliving. Every single chemical compound, isolated from all others in protoplasm, is nonliving. Only when certain of these, chiefly the proteins, nucleic acids, and certain fatty materials, are present together in the proper organization does the living condition exist.

Of the many physiological activities that go on in plant cells, only two groups of processes will be described in this chapter: the absorption of water and of substances dissolved in water, and the formation of new cells. An understanding of these activities is essential to an understanding of the functions and growth of roots, which will be described in the next chapter. Detailed accounts of other important physiological processes, such as photosynthesis, digestion, and respiration, will be deferred until subsequent chapters.

THE ABSORPTION OF WATER BY CELLS

In the performance of their physiological activities, plant cells are continually tak-

ing in certain materials and allowing others to pass out. The ability of cells to act in this manner is prerequisite to all other processes of plants. Of the substances that enter plant cells, water is fundamentally important. It is the liquid in which the protoplasmic colloids are dispersed; it is a raw material of photosynthesis; it is the liquid in which solid materials must ordinarily be dissolved before they can enter or leave a cell or move from one portion of a plant to another; it is the medium in which most of the chemical reactions of protoplasm occur; and it provides the internal pressure necessary for the maintenance of form and for growth of cells. Thus, knowledge of how living cells absorb water is necessary to an understanding of the basic processes of plants.

The absorption of water by living plant cells is not thoroughly understood, but appears to involve at least two processes: 1. **Imbibition;** 2. **Osmosis.** Both of these are purely physical processes; that is, they occur in nonliving systems as well as in living cells and thus are not peculiar to living matter.

Imbibition

When a cell is in contact with water, the cell wall and the protoplasm absorb water by the process of imbibition, which may be defined as the soaking up of a liquid by solid materials, especially substances in colloidal condition. Imbibition is the phenomenon observed when a dry sponge or a piece of gelatin soaks up water. Cellulose, pectic substances, protoplasmic proteins, and other organic compounds in plant cells have great powers of imbibition. Both cell walls and living protoplasm absorb water by imbibition and increase in size as they do so, as may be readily observed in the swelling of seeds placed in water. Imbibing materials, if they are confined, exert considerable pressure as they absorb the liquid and swell. If a glass jar with a tight-fitting lid is partly filled with dry seeds, if the lid is punctured with two or three small holes that admit water, and if the jar is then inverted in a pan of water so that the seeds may imbibe water, the seeds may burst the jar within 24 hours as a result of the **imbibitional pressure** they exert. The bursting of the seed coats of germinating seeds is the result of imbibitional pressures developed within the seeds as they soak up water. The engineers of ancient Egypt, in building the pyramids, split rock masses by hammering thoroughly dried wooden wedges into cracks in the rock and pouring water slowly over the wedges; the wooden wedges slowly imbibed water and swelled as they did so, exerting sufficient pressure to fracture the rocks.

Osmosis

The phenomenon of imbibition is sufficient to explain the uptake of water by cell walls, and to some extent by protoplasm, but in living protoplasm, additional forces are involved in the process of water absorption. One of these additional forces is the physical phenomenon of osmosis, which is basically a process of **diffusion.** Diffusion is the spreading out of the molecules or ions of a substance, because of their continual motion, through all the space they can reach, from the place where they are more abundant to places where they are less abundant. Diffusion may be regarded as a tendency toward reaching an equilibrium, for it results in the equal distribution within the given space of the diffusing particles. For

example, if a bottle of ether is opened in a closed room, there will be a net movement of ether molecules out from the bottle (the place of greater abundance or concentration of ether). Eventually the molecules become equally distributed throughout the space inside the bottle and that of the room. If the doors of the room are opened, there is no longer an equal distribution of ether in the available spaces, for the ether-less space outside the room contains zero concentration of ether molecules, while that inside the room possesses numerous equally scattered particles. Because of their ceaseless vibration and movement, ether molecules will diffuse out through the opened doors, as a result of the difference in their concentration (relative numbers), in accordance with the tendency to reach equilibrium or equalized concentrations. A similar phenomenon occurs when a lump of sugar is dropped into a beaker of water. The sugar slowly dissolves and there is a net movement of its molecules, without being carried by currents, from the surface of the lump (region of greater concentration) to more remote parts of the water in the cup (regions of lesser concentration of sugar) as shown in Figure 5–1. After a time, the lump of sugar disappears and the sugar particles, having overcome the resistance of the solvent by means of their motion, become equally distributed throughout the surrounding liquid.

As particles diffuse, they exert pressure, known as **diffusion pressure.** This pressure is proportional to the concentration, or numbers of the diffusing particles; that is, the greater the concentration of diffusing particles in a system (in other words, the higher the number of diffusing molecules or ions), the greater is their diffusion pressure. Thus, in the sugar experiment just described, the diffusion pressure of the sugar molecules is initially greatest near the dissolving lump, since the concentration of sugar molecules is greatest in that place; the diffusion pressure is least in the more remote portions of the water, since the concentration of sugar molecules is lower at the greater distances from the lump. We may express the behavior of the diffusing sugar molecules by stating that they diffuse from the region of their greater concentration to the region of their lesser concentration, or we may describe their behavior in terms of diffusion pressures by stating that they diffuse from the region of their greater diffiusion pressure to that of their lesser diffusion pressure.

Not only does the *direction* of diffusion of a substance depend upon the relative concentrations of that substance in different places, but the *speed* of diffusion also depends upon relative concentrations. The greater the difference in the relative amounts of a substance in different places, the more rapid is the rate of diffusion from the region of higher concentration to that of lower. Another significant feature of diffusion is that a diffusing molecule moves independently of other molecules in the available space. If both sugar and salt are added to a beaker of water, the molecules of each of these substances diffuse until they are equally distributed in the liquid. The rate and direction of diffusion of the molecules of one substance in a mixture of molecules of other substances are ordinarily determined by the concentrations of each substance, considered by itself.

If over the mouth of the bottle of ether mentioned above we were to tie a membrane that would allow ether molecules to penetrate it, the ether would still continue to diffuse from the bottle into the room, although at a somewhat slower

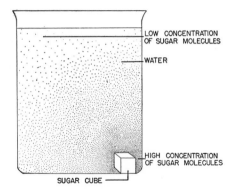

LOW CONCENTRATION OF SUGAR MOLECULES

WATER

HIGH CONCENTRATION OF SUGAR MOLECULES

SUGAR CUBE

FIG. 5–1. Illustration of diffusion of a solid in a liquid.

rate. Such diffusion of a substance through a membrane may be termed **osmosis.** There exists considerable dispute among scientists as to the exact definition of this term. Physical scientists frequently define it in the broad sense employed above—namely, the diffusion of any substance through a membrane. Others define it as the diffusion of a liquid through a membrane, and still others, principally biologists, interpret the process as the diffusion of water through a membrane. It seems desirable in considering osmosis in relation to living cells, to limit the definition of this process to the diffusion of water through a differentially permeable membrane from a region of higher water concentration (higher water diffusion pressure) to a region of lower water concentration (lower water diffusion pressure). To understand the essential features of osmosis, the student should bear in mind that the principal force involved is diffusion, which is the result of motion of molecules or ions.

A **differentially permeable** or **semipermeable** membrane is one that allows certain substances to pass through and that prohibits or restricts the passage of others. A pig bladder is a membrane of this type and permits, for example, the

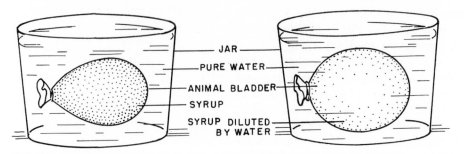

FIG. 5–2. Osmosis experiment with animal bladder filled with syrup. *Left:* At beginning of the experiment. *Right:* After several hours.

passage of water but prevents the movement through it of sugar dissolved in water. When a membrane prevents such passage, it is said to be **impermeable** to the particular substance that is held back, and **permeable** to the substance that passes through. The cytoplasmic membranes of all living cells are membranes of the differentially permeable type. They allow water and certain nutrient particles to pass through readily, but restrict or prevent the movement through them of certain sugars, pigments, and other materials, especially those of organic nature. The differentially permeable nature of cell membranes is continually changing. Physiological reactions in a cell alter the concentrations of materials within the protoplasm, thus disturbing the equilibrium between materials inside and outside the cell. Changes occur in the acidity or alkalinity of protoplasm, foods are digested or stored, waste materials are formed; these and other processes influence the differentially permeable condition of the plasma membranes. The state of membrane permeability likewise varies with age, the health and vigor of the protoplasm, and also with various factors in the external environment. The fluctuating permeability of the membranes of living protoplasm is attributable to the sensitivity of living matter and to its power

ers of adjustment to rapidly changing internal and external conditions. In nonliving membranes there are no such frequent and continuous alterations of permeability. The effects of a change in the permeability of cell membranes upon protoplasmic contents may be demonstrated by placing a sliced red beet in cold water. The membranes of the beet cells are impermeable to the red pigment and thus prevent its diffusion into the water. The water remains colorless, except for traces of the pigment freed by the cutting of certain cells by the knife. If, however, the beet slices in the water are heated to the death point of protoplasm, the high temperature kills the protoplasm and alters the state of the membranes, which become permeable to most of the red pigment, allowing it to diffuse out of the cells and thus to color the water red.

The phenomenon of osmosis may be demonstrated by the experiments pictured in Figures 5–2 and 5–3. If a thoroughly cleaned animal bladder is filled with a very concentrated sugar solution, such as syrup, if its apertures are tightly bound to prevent leakage, and if it is then immersed in a vessel of water, osmosis into the bladder occurs. The volume of liquid within the bladder increases, and the bladder becomes distended by the pressure of the accumulating liquid; this

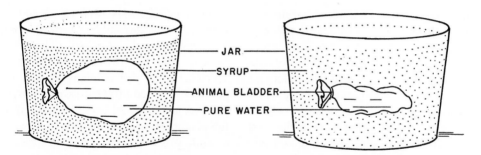

FIG. 5–3. Osmosis experiment with animal bladder filled with water and immersed in syrup. *Left:* At beginning of the experiment. *Right:* After several hours.

pressure may become sufficiently great to burst the bladder. In this experiment, the bladder membrane is impermeable to sugar molecules, which remain within it, but is permeable to water. Because of the presence of sugar molecules, the liquid within the bladder contains a lower concentration of water molecules than the liquid (pure water) outside the bladder. The net movement of water molecules is from the region of high concentration of water (outside the bladder) toward the region of lower water concentration inside the bladder. If conditions of the experiment are reversed by filling the bladder with water and submerging it in syrup, the net diffusion of water molecules is from the inside of the bladder to the surrounding syrup, and the bladder shrinks as a result of the loss of the enclosed water; in this experiment, water molecules behave exactly as they did in the first experiment with the bladder—their net movement is from the region of high water concentration (in the second experiment, inside the bladder) toward the region of lower water concentration (outside the bladder).

There is an analogy between a plant cell and the simple physical experiment described above. In a plant cell, the plasma and vacuolar membranes, with the thin layer of cytoplasm between them,

behave as a differentially permeable membrane, comparable with the bladder. The cell sap is a droplet of water, with various materials, especially sugars and salts, dissolved in it. The cell sap is comparable with the sugar solution inside the bladder, for the cell membranes are impermeable to many of the materials dissolved in the cell sap, just as the bladder is impermeable to sugar. Such a cell is in contact with other cells or, if it is an epidermal cell of a root, it is in contact with the water and dissolved materials **(soil solution)** in the soil. The soil solution normally contains a much smaller concentration of dissolved materials than does the cell sap; or, stated conversely, the soil solution contains proportionately more water than does cell sap. The equalization tendency of diffusion prevails, and there is a net movement of water from the place of its greater concentration (or of greater water diffusion pressure)— namely, the soil—into the cell, which is the place of lesser water concentration (or of lower water diffusion pressure). Thus, the soil solution is roughly comparable with the pure water in the dish surrounding the bladder in our simple physical experiment. In similar manner, water inside a plant may move from a cell with a relatively high concentration of water (low concentration of solutes) into a cell with a lower concentration of water (higher concentration of solutes). The net movement of water from cell to cell or from the soil solution into root cells continues as long as there is a difference in the relative concentrations (or diffusion pressures) of water between cells or between the soil solution and the root cells. The rate at which water moves into a cell depends chiefly on the difference between its concentration inside the cell and outside the cell; the greater the difference, the more rapid the movement. The term "osmotic concentration" is frequently used to indicate the relative amount of dissolved materials within the cell sap. A cell with a high osmotic concentration has a large number of such dissolved particles, one with a low osmotic concentration has a smaller number of solute particles in the same volume of solution.

It should be emphasized that the comparison between the bladder experiment and a plant cell is a crude one. The same fundamental principle of diffusion is operative in both cases, but the bladder membrane is a nonliving membrane with unchanging properties, whereas the membranes of a cell are living and are continually altering in their permeability. The concentration of materials in the cell sap varies from one moment to the next and likewise the concentration of soil solution or that of adjacent cells continually fluctuates, so that in the absorption of water by living cells, although the basic physical forces of diffusion are at work, their actual operation is conditioned by the temper of the living protoplasm itself.

Plant cells, except when wilting occurs, contain water in such quantity that the protoplasm is forced outward against the cell walls by the pressure of the water in the cell sap. The extent to which the protoplasm can be expanded is, of course, limited by the surrounding wall of cellulose, which can be stretched only so far by this internal pressure. The pressure exerted by the cell contents against the cell wall is called **turgor pressure.** Turgor pressure is the actual pressure exerted by the protoplast against the cell wall, while **osmotic pressure,** often used erroneously as a synonym of turgor pressure, is really the maximum pressure that can be developed in the cell sap solution separated from pure water by a rigid membrane that is permeable only to water. The turgor pressure of a cell is usually less than the actual osmotic pressure that the cell sap might develop under the conditions described in the preceding sentence. The relationship between osmotic pressure and turgor pressure may be compared with the relation between the potential and actual speeds of a motor car. Although a modern automobile is capable of speeds in excess of 100 miles per hour, a car is almost never driven at this potential velocity. Osmotic pressure may be likened to the potential speed and turgor pressure to the actual speed, which is almost always lower than the potential speed. The osmotic pressure of the cell sap of some species of plants may exceed 100 atmospheres (1 atmosphere is 15 pounds per square inch). In most species of plants, however, the osmotic pressure of the cell sap is less than 25 atmospheres. A cell, the protoplasm of which exhibits turgor pressure, is said to be **turgid** or to possess **turgidity.** Turgidity is responsible for the crisp, rigid condition of lettuce leaves or of celery that is immersed in water. When such vegetables wilt, the protoplasts in their cells lose so much of their water that they no longer exert an outward pressure against the cell walls and the tissues become limp; that is, they

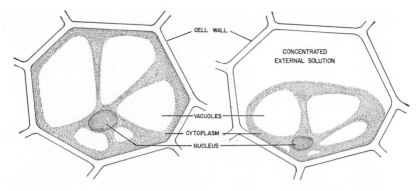

FIG. 5–4. Plasmolysis. *Left:* Normal, turgid cell. *Right:* Plasmolyzed cell.

lose their turgidity. Turgidity is important in plants in that it aids in the maintenance of form and provides in young cells the pressure that makes possible the growth in size of such cells. All plant tissues that are well supplied with water and that do not lose water more rapidly than they absorb it are normally turgid.

PLASMOLYSIS

In accordance with the laws of diffusion, there is a net movement of water out of a plant cell when the relative concentration of water outside the cell becomes less than that inside the cell sap. This is a common phenomenon in the transfer of water from one cell to another. In plant tissues, normally, when water moves from cell to cell, the cell that is losing water is in most cases simultaneously receiving water from some other cell. As a result of this give-and-take, the water supply of a cell is replenished on one side as it is decreased on another side and thus the cell retains its turgidity. If, however, water passes out of a cell toward a region of lesser water concentration and if this outwardly moving water is not replenished, the inevitable result is a loss of volume of the protoplast and its consequent shrinkage (Figure 5–4). The shrinkage of

protoplasm away from the cell wall, due to reduced internal pressure as a result of excessive water loss, is termed **plasmolysis.** Plasmolysis may be demonstrated by placing a strip of carrot root or potato tuber in a concentrated salt solution. The relative concentration of water, volume for volume, is less in the concentrated salt solution than it is in the cell sap. Because there is a greater diffusion pressure within the cells, there is a net movement of water from the cell of the potato or carrot into the salt solution, causing a loss of turgidity, and the plasmolyzed tissues become very limp. Plasmolysis, if it continues too long, causes the death of the plasmolyzed cells. If, after a short time, however, the plasmolyzed tissues are transferred from the salt solution to pure water, the direction of net water movement is reversed, for there is now relatively more water outside the cells than there is inside. Water thus passes inward, the protoplasm increases in volume as the turgor pressure of the cell sap increases, and the tissue regains its turgidity.

The principle of plasmolysis is employed in a number of practical ways. In the making of fruit jellies, usually more sugar is added to the juice than the amount needed to achieve the desired de-

FIG. 5–5. Effects of plasmolysis on cuttings of *Coleus*. *Left:* Cutting in water. *Right:* Cutting after 1 hour in 15-percent salt solution.

gree of sweetness. This raises the solute content of the jelly (decreases the relative proportion of water) to such an extent that decay and fermentation bacteria and the reproductive cells of molds falling into the jelly are quickly plasmolyzed, because the water in them diffuses outward toward the region of lesser water concentration, namely into the jelly. Thus, the jelly will not spoil even when exposed to the open air. Through the addition of quantities of salt to meat and fish the same object is fulfilled. The organisms of decay that come into contact with the salted foods are plasmolyzed and killed, and thus the meat or fish does not spoil. Another application of the plasmolysis principle is found in the spreading of salt on clay tennis courts or in the cracks of brick walks to kill undesired plants. The seedlings of these plants coming into con-

tact with salt are plasmolyzed and are thus killed. Pasture weeds, such as the obnoxious Canada thistle, which are difficult to uproot, may be destroyed by placing a small quantity of salt about their roots. Plants killed in this manner wilt and turn brown as they die. Because of the wilting and browning of plasmolyzed plants, their manner of death is frequently termed "burning" by farmers and gardeners. "Burning" of leaves is sometimes caused by residues of insecticidal and fungicidal sprays.

If, in the application of fertilizers to soils, excessive amounts are added, the relative concentration of water in the soil solution may become less than that in the cell sap of plants growing in the soil. As a result, the cells of the plants are plasmolyzed and the plants wilt and die unless the excessive quantity of salts is washed away by rain. Thus, directions given for the spreading of fertilizers should be followed implicitly if the disastrous effects of plasmolysis are to be avoided.

THE ABSORPTION OF SOLUTES

The absorption of dissolved particles by root cells from the soil solution, as well as the absorption of such particles by one cell from an adjacent cell, is a complex phenomenon, not all the forces of which are known by physiologists. Only two of the several processes known to be involved in the absorption of solutes will be discussed here. One of these, **simple diffusion,** is described as a *passive* process since it requires no energy expenditure by the cell; the other, **active transport,** is an *active* process because it utilizes energy liberated by metabolism.

Simple Diffusion

In this process, dissolved materials follow the basic law of diffusion; that is, they diffuse from a region in which there is a high concentration of their solute particles toward a region of lower concentration of their particles. This type of absorption involves principally sugars and other compounds the molecules of which do not ionize (do not form ions) or which ionize only to a slight extent. In this type of solute absorption, molecules move into a plant cell, for example, a surface cell of a root, only when the concentration of those molecules is greater outside the root cell than it is inside the cell. The continuation of such absorption depends upon the maintenance of a concentration difference of the particles of the diffusing substance; entry of these particles into a cell by simple diffusion continues only so long as the particles are present in greater concentration outside the cell than inside. As these particles enter a cell, they may undergo transformation into other chemical compounds or they move on to other cells; thus, these particles do not often accumulate to a high concentration within a cell.

Active Transport

In this process, ions, formed by the dissociation of molecules (for example, NH_4^+ ions and NO_3^- ions formed by the dissociation of ammonium nitrate, or NH_4NO_3 molecules) enter a cell in violation of the basic law of diffusion; that is, they move into a cell even though their concentration may be higher in that cell than in the soil or in adjoining cells. In other words, such movement is in a direction opposite to that which would be maintained in the case of simple diffusion. The result of such behavior is the accumulation of some ions to a concentration many times greater in plant cells than outside the cells. It appears that this process accounts for a much greater part of solute absorption by cells than does simple diffusion. The process is thus an exceedingly important one. This absorption of solute particles against a concentration gradient requires the expenditure of energy by living protoplasm and thus is directly related to the energy-releasing process of respiration. Experimental evidence indicates that oxygen supply and presence of respirable foods, such as sugars, are closely connected with ion accumulation, for oxygen and foods are essential to respiration. When the oxygen supply is reduced, when food supplies are scanty, or when chemicals that reduce respiration are added to plant tissues, ion accumulation diminishes or ceases. Relatively little is known about the actual mechanism of active transport. A current theory suggests the existence of a "carrier" that facilitates transport across the membrane. According to this explanation, the ion at the outer membrane surface enters into a temporary chemical union with the carrier; then, after passing through the membrane, the ion and the carrier dissociate. There is considerable controversy regarding the nature of the carrier, and a variety of compounds including the protoplasm itself have been suggested.

The molecules of the important mineral salts of the soil, for example, magnesium sulfate, potassium nitrate, and calcium phosphate, dissociate freely in the soil solution. Ordinarily such substances must be dissolved in soil water before they enter a cell, but investigations have indicated that root cells may absorb molecules and ions directly from soil particles without dissolution in soil water.

THE FORMATION OF NEW CELLS

Development of the tissues and organs of a plant begins with the formation of new cells by a process called **cell division.** This process occurs most commonly in the meristematic tissues of root and shoot tips, in vascular cambium, and in cork cambium. The newly formed cells subsequently undergo enlargement and differentiation, processes to be discussed in later chapters. Cell division consists of two major steps: first, the division of the parent cell nucleus into two nuclei, and second, the division of the cytoplasm and the concomitant formation of the cell plate. The process of nuclear division is called **mitosis,** that of cytoplasmic division, **cytokinesis.** In the cells of some

plants, several divisions of the nucleus occur without the formation of new walls; this results in cells with more than one nucleus, a condition found chiefly in some lower plants. In higher plants, however, each cell usually has one nucleus, and when cell division occurs, two cells, each with a single nucleus, are formed.

Mitosis

The net result of mitosis is the production of two daughter nuclei that are qualitatively and quantitatively identical; each daughter nucleus possesses the same hereditary materials and potentialities as the parent nucleus prior to its division. Such an exact distribution is achieved by the duplication and subsequent separation of the hereditary material in the nucleus. Duplication involves principally the molecular replication of deoxyribonucleic acid (DNA), the chief constituent of chromatin. This synthesis of hereditary material occurs in the so-called **interphase nucleus,** that is, the nucleus as it exists between successive divisions. The nuclear structure described in Chapter 4 is that of an interphase nucleus. The chromatin network, which is revealed when an interphase nucleus is treated with a suitable stain, is composed of a group of elongated, slender, twisted chromosomes. During interphase, the individual chromosomes are in their thinnest and most extended condition and are extremely difficult to demonstrate. The numbers of chromosomes per nucleus vary in different species of plants. In flowering plants, the numbers range from 4 to about 200; most species have fewer than 100. The chromosomes usually occur in pairs in most cells (for example, those of embryos, roots, stems, leaves,

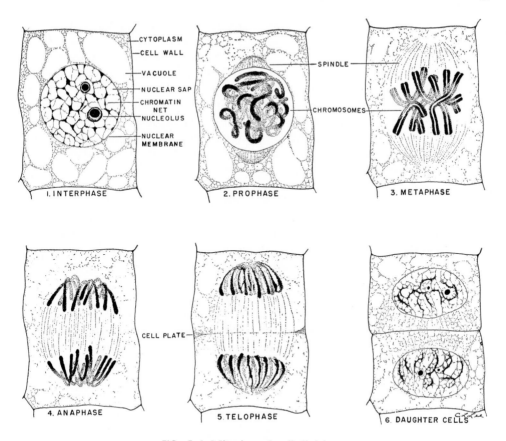

1. INTERPHASE

— CYTOPLASM
— CELL WALL
— VACUOLE
— NUCLEAR SAP
— CHROMATIN NET
— NUCLEOLUS
— NUCLEAR MEMBRANE

2. PROPHASE

— SPINDLE
— CHROMOSOMES

3. METAPHASE

4. ANAPHASE

CELL PLATE —

5. TELOPHASE

6. DAUGHTER CELLS

FIG. 5–6. Mitosis and cell division.

petals) of flowering plants (except in some reproductive cells to be described later) and thus their numbers are usually even, for example, 20 in corn, 14 in red clover, 28 in durum wheat. The members of a chromosome pair are called **homologous chromosomes.** Structural and size differences among the various chromosome pairs in a plant are often readily visible under a microscope (Figure 5–8). The individuals of any given plant species are generally considered to have the same number of chromosomes in all their nonreproductive, or body, cells.

For the sake of convenience, biologists usually divide the process of mitosis into a number of **phases** (Figure 5–6), each of which bears a technical name. Actually the process of mitosis is a continuous one with no distinctly marked stages. These "phases" are thus comparable with the moon's "phases," which gradually merge into each other. A description of the events that take place during the various phases of mitosis follows:

Prophase. In this first phase of mitosis, the chromosomes undergo a marked shortening and thickening, developing into rod-shaped structures that are distinctly visible as separate entities and may be only $\frac{1}{20}$ the length of the interphase chromosomes. With these processes of shortening and thickening, the netlike structure in the interphase nucleus disappears. Under the light microscope, each chromosome appears to consist of two longitudinally arranged threads, called **chromatids,** which are often coiled around each other. As mitosis proceeds the longitudinal split between chromatids becomes more pronounced. A structure called the **spindle** begins to develop at opposite ends **(poles)** of the nucleus; from the poles, a cluster of fiberlike structures begins to grow inward toward the nucleus. The nuclear membrane then disappears and the fiberlike components of the spindle extend through the nucleus from one pole of the spindle to the other. Prior to, or simultaneous with, the beginning of spindle development, the nucleolus typically disappears. The process of spindle formation is poorly understood. The spindle apparatus is known to contain proteins, fatty substances, and ribonucleic acid (RNA); it appears that in plant cells it develops largely from nuclear material and, to a much lesser extent, from cytoplasm. The spindle "fibers" are not fibers in the usual sense of this term, but are probably strands of specialized colloidal materials in a gel or semigel condition. When a cell is stained, these structures assume a fiberlike appearance.

Metaphase. In this phase of mitosis, the chromosomes, now with pronounced longitudinal splits, become arranged in the central, wide portion **(equator)** of the spindle midway between the poles. At this time, the constricted region **(centromere)** of each chromosome becomes attached to the poles of the spindle apparatus by minute **chromosomal fibers.** These fibrous connections are established in such a way that daughter chromatids are *never attached to the same pole;* instead,

the two chromatids of the same chromosome are always linked to opposite poles of the mitotic apparatus. Usually by the end of metaphase, daughter chromatids are united only at the centromere. The position of the centromere on a chromosome divides that chromosome transversely into two portions (arms) of equal or unequal length. In metaphase, it is the centromeres that are aligned in the equatorial plane; the chromosome arms may extend in almost any direction. In dividing cells of higher plants, the metaphase chromatids are commonly split longitudinally and thus appear as double structures. Each of these "half-chromatids" will become a chromatid when the next mitotic cycle begins.

Anaphase. This stage begins with the simultaneous, longitudinal splitting of the centromeres, following which the daughter chromatids (now chromosomes) begin to separate. One new chromosome of each pair moves toward one pole of the spindle, the other chromosome of the same pair migrates toward the opposite pole. Moreover, the spindle itself elongates; that is, there is a further separation of its poles. Little is known about the mechanism of these movements. At the termination of anaphase, two groups of chromosomes are present, one group at each pole of the spindle. The number of chromosomes present in *each* of these groups is the same as the number present in the prophase of mitosis, since each of the prophase chromosomes splits longitudinally by separation of its chromatids and since each of the two chromatids of a prophase chromosome becomes a fully developed chromosome after their separation in the anaphase.

Telophase. In this phase the two groups of daughter chromosomes are at the spindle poles. The nuclear membranes and

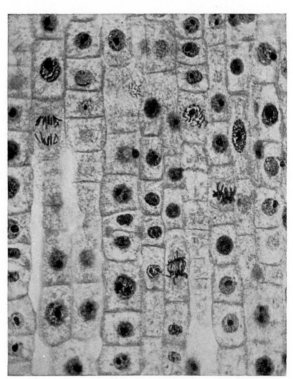

FIG. 5–7. Photomicrograph of a portion of the meristematic tissue of a root tip, showing various stages in mitosis.

(*Photo by Triarch Botanical Products, Ripon, Wis.*)

nucleoli become reconstituted, and the chromosomes become transformed into those long, slender threads characteristic of the interphase nucleus. Thus, in the telophase, two daughter nuclei are formed, one at each end of the spindle. Telophase concludes the process of mitosis.

Cytokinesis

As the reorganization of interphase nuclei proceeds in the telophase, the spindle begins to disappear near the nuclei and widens greatly at the equator until it extends almost completely across the cytoplasm. Electron microscopic studies have shown that as the spindle of the plant cell widens, there is a migration of certain organelles from the poles to the equatorial plane. These organelles include portions of the endoplasmic reticulum and small, nearly spherical bodies that are thought to play a role in subsequent wall formation. Minute droplets of what may be pectic substances are also deposited in the equatorial plane. In some little known manner, this material is then organized into a thin, continuous **cell plate** that extends across the cell, separating the cytoplasm into two portions, each with its new nucleus. The cell plate becomes the middle lamella or intercellular layer upon which the primary walls are subsequently deposited by adjacent daughter protoplasts. The formation of the cell plate marks the end of cytokinesis; wall formation continues through cell enlargement and differentiation.

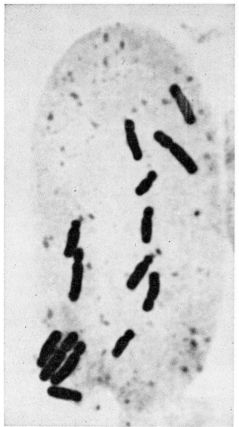

(Photo by D. M. Smith.)

FIG. 5–8. Chromosomes of root tip cell of *Phlox pilosa L.*

Rate of Mitosis

The time required for the completion of mitosis and cytokinesis varies in different cells and in different species of plants. Its speed is also influenced by varying en-vironmental conditions. In most dividing plant cells at temperatures of 70°F to 80°F, the processes of mitosis and cytokinesis are usually completed within 60 to 90 minutes. Thus it is apparent that the complex processes of chromosome condensation, spindle formation, chromosome splitting, etc., take place rather rapidly.

Significance of Mitosis

The complex phases of mitosis achieve the quantitatively and qualitatively equal distribution of the hereditary units, or **genes,** from a parent nucleus to the daughter nuclei developed from it. The genes, which will be discussed in detail in the chapter on heredity, are arranged in linear fashion in chromosomes like beads on a string. When a chromatid divides to form two "half-chromatids," the genes are similarly duplicated, so that the two "half-chromatids" bear identical genes. Thus, the daughter nuclei, as a result of mitosis, receive chromosome sets and genes that are identical with each other and that are identical with the chromosome set and genes of the parent nucleus from which the daughter nuclei are formed. As a result of this carefully controlled passage of hereditary material from one cell to another, the body cells of an individual organism are generally considered to possess the same hereditary potentialities.

SUMMARY

1. Protoplasm is a complex organization of colloidal systems, solutions, emulsions, and suspensions.
2. The physiological processes of protoplasm are in large part associated with and dependent upon the physicochemical activities of colloidal particles.
3. The most abundant chemical elements in living protoplasm are carbon, hydrogen, oxygen, and nitrogen, which constitute between 95 and 98 percent of protoplasm.

4. The remaining 2 to 5 percent of protoplasm is made up of or contains sulfur, calcium, phosphorus, potassium, iron, magnesium, manganese, zinc, boron, copper, molybdenum, chlorine, and probably other chemical elements.

5. Plant cells often absorb from the soil elements that have no apparent role in the physiology of plants.

6. The chemical elements in protoplasm occur chiefly in chemical compounds. Most abundant of these compounds are water and proteins. Less abundant are fats, sugars, pigments, and other compounds.

7. Some of these compounds are constituents of the living machine, others are energy-supplying materials, regulators, and waste products of physiological processes.

8. It is impossible to classify the compounds in protoplasm as living or nonliving. The complex organization of these compounds is living; the individual, component substances are not.

9. Plant cells absorb water and dissolved substances from the soil and from each other.

10. Plant cells absorb water by imbibition and osmosis. Imbibition is the soaking up of a liquid by solid materials, especially those in a colloidal condition. Cell walls and protoplasm absorb water by imbibition.

11. Osmosis is the diffusion of water through a differentially permeable membrane from a region of higher water concentration (higher water diffusion pressure) to a region of lower water concentration (lower water diffusion pressure).

12. Cytoplasmic membranes are differentially permeable. Vacuoles are droplets of water with high concentrations of dissolved materials, especially sugars. Cytoplasmic membranes and vacuoles play important roles in osmosis.

13. Protoplasm normally contains such quantities of water that it exerts pressure against the enclosing cell wall. Such a cell is turgid; its internal pressure is called turgor pressure.

14. Plasmolysis is the shrinkage of protoplasm away from the cell wall due to outward diffusion of water from protoplasm.

15. Two of the processes involved in solute absorption by protoplasm are: simple diffusion of solute particles (chiefly molecules) into a cell when the concentration of those molecules is greater outside the cell than inside; active transport, in which ions move from a region of lower ion concentration outside a cell to a region of higher ion concentration inside a cell, as a result of expenditure of energy by living protoplasm.

16. The formation of new cells results from the division of pre-existing cells. Two processes are involved in cell division: division of the nucleus, or mitosis; and cytoplasmic division, or cytokinesis. In mitosis, chromosomes are split longitudinally each into two chromosomes. One chromosome, resulting from the splitting of a parent chromosome, moves to one new nucleus, the other chromosome formed from the same parent chromosome passes into the other nucleus. After mitosis, a cell plate is formed between the two daughter nuclei, and thus cytokinesis is completed. Mitosis results in the qualitatively and quantitatively equal division of chromatin between the newly formed cells.

17. The number of chromosomes is generally considered to be the same in all the body cells of plants of the same kind. Chromosomes are also individualistic in their form and structure. Chromosomes bear the hereditary determiners, or genes.

⋘ SUGGESTED READINGS FOR INTERESTED STUDENTS

1. Holter, Heinz, "How things get into cells." *Scientific American,* Vol. 205, No. 3, pp. 167–180, September 1961.
2. Mazia, Daniel, "How cells divide." *Scientific American,* Vol. 205, No. 3, pp. 100–120, September 1961.
3. Meyer, B. S., D. B. Anderson, and R. H. Böhning, *Introduction to Plant Physiology.* D. Van Nostrand, Princeton, N. J., 1960.
4. Swanson, Carl P., *The Cell.* Prentice-Hall, Englewood Cliffs, N. J., 1960.

⋘ TOPICS AND QUESTIONS FOR STUDY

1. Describe the principal characteristics of colloidal systems.
2. What is an electrolyte? An ion? Name some electrolytes.
3. Distinguish among a true solution, a suspension, an emulsion, and a colloidal system, and describe some examples of each.
4. Which of these systems occur in living protoplasm?
5. Describe briefly the "brush-pile" theory of protoplasmic structure.
6. Define viscosity and elasticity.
7. What physical changes indicate that protoplasm is a dynamic organization?
8. Name the chemical elements that occur most commonly in living plant protoplasm. Which of these occur in greatest abundance?
9. Does the presence of a particular element in protoplasm signify that that element has a physiological function? Explain.
10. Distinguish between a chemical element and a chemical compound, and name some examples of each.
11. Name the most abundant chemical compound in active, living protoplasm.
12. Name other compounds that occur in living plant protoplasm.
13. Define imbibition, and mention some examples of this process. Describe how imbibition is important in plant cells.
14. What is imbibition pressure? Describe an experiment to illustrate it.
15. Define diffusion and describe several examples of this process. Is diffusion peculiar to living cells? Explain.
16. Define diffusion pressure and explain its cause. What factors influence the magnitude and speed of diffusion pressure?
17. Give a specific definition of osmosis as applied to living cells.
18. What is the relation of diffusion pressure to osmosis?
19. Describe a physical experiment to illustrate osmosis.
20. Describe an experiment to illustrate osmosis in living cells or tissues.
21. What conditions must be present in order that osmosis may occur in any system?
22. What is the importance of cytoplasmic membranes in osmosis in living cells? Of vacuoles?

23. Comment upon the permeability characteristics of cytoplasmic membranes.
24. Purple cabbage leaves do not lose their color in cold water, but do in boiling water. Explain.
25. Define turgidity, and describe its importance in plant cells.
26. Where, on the luncheon table, does turgidity contribute to your enjoyment of your food?
27. Is the turgor pressure of a plant cell constant, or does it vary? Explain, and describe how you would demonstrate your answer experimentally.
28. Define plasmolysis, and criticize this statement: "Plasmolysis is the opposite of osmosis."
29. Describe an experiment to illustrate plasmolysis.
30. Could you preserve meat by adding sufficient sugar to it? Could you preserve jellies by adding salt to them? Explain your answers.
31. Why must the directions for applying fertilizers to soils be carefully followed?
32. Would you use salt to kill weeds in a garden? In a pasture or on a clay tennis court? Explain.
33. Explain briefly the process of active transport.
34. Explain this statement: "Sugars are the most important osmotically active substances in plant cells."
35. Distinguish between mitosis and cell division.
36. Describe, in the order of their occurrence, the principal events in the process of mitosis.
37. What is a chromatid?
38. What are homologous chromosomes?
39. What is the biological significance of the complex process of mitosis?

Roots and the Relation of Roots to Soils

It is through their roots that higher plants are in contact with soils, the source of most of their essential nutrients. The functions of roots are: the absorption of water and solutes (chiefly nutrient ions) from soils; the firm anchorage of the plant body in the soil; the conduction of substances upward into stems and downward from stems; and, often, the storage of foods and other substances.

THE ORIGIN AND STRUCTURE OF ROOTS

Root Systems. The root system of a flowering plant begins its development from the hypocotyl of the embryo of a seed. The basal end of the hypocotyl grows out of the seed after the seed has absorbed water and its physiological processes have become accelerated, and produces the first or **primary root** of the new plant. The primary root begins to produce branches before it is many days old; these branches in turn give rise to branches of their own. The branches of the primary root are called **secondary roots.** The primary root usually grows

straight downward, whereas the secondary roots and their branches grow out at first in somewhat horizontal position and may later turn diagonally downward near their tips. Sometimes roots are produced on stems or on various types of leaves; roots of this type, which arise from some structure other than the primary root or one of its branches, are termed **adventitious roots** (Figure 6–4). The aerial roots of poison ivy, which attach the stems of this vine to a solid support, the roots that grow from bulbs and other kinds of underground stems, and the roots that develop from stem cuttings of roses, geraniums, and many other plants are adventitious roots. The vegetative propagation of plants from stem cuttings or from leaves is possible because of the ability of such parts of the plant body to form adventitious roots. The prop roots of corn, which arise from the stem joints at or above the surface of the soil and grow downward into the soil, sometimes form the principal portions of the root systems of such plants.

The entire mass of subterranean roots

produced by a plant is called its **root system.** The degree of branching, the depth of penetration into the soil, the extent of horizontal spreading of branches, and other features of root systems vary in different species of plants. Botanists distinguish between two common types of root systems: **diffuse (fibrous) root systems** and **taproot systems** (Figures 6–1 and 6–2).

Diffuse root systems are composed of numerous rather slender roots the main ones of which are nearly equal in size. Diffuse root systems are often entirely adventitious in origin, as in corn and other grasses, in which the primary root fails to continue its growth and is replaced by a number of adventitious roots. In other plants with diffuse root systems, the primary root may develop a number of secondary roots that grow more rapidly than it does and ultimately constitute the main part of the root system. Roots of this type are, of course, not adventitious, since they arise as branches of the primary roots. Diffuse roots often remain slender, as in corn and other grasses, in which case they are termed **fibrous roots** (Figure 6–3). In such plants as the sweet potato and dahlia, the larger diffuse roots become enlarged with stored food; such roots are called **fleshy diffuse roots.** In many trees the diffuse roots become woody after years of growth. A taproot system is one in which the primary root grows most rapidly and remains the largest root, with a number of smaller secondary roots. Root systems of this kind are found in carrots, dandelions, and radishes. Some taproots may be slender, some may be fleshy, and others woody.

The form of root systems and the depth of their penetration into the soil vary with different species and with different factors in the soil. Each species of plant has, as

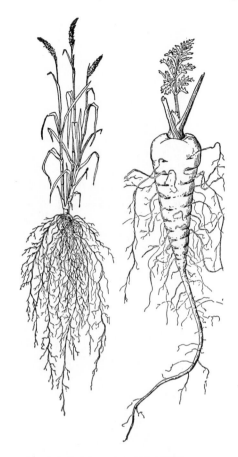

FIG. 6–1. Root systems. A: Fibrous root system of a grass. B: Taproot system of a carrot.

a rule, a certain characteristic form of root system, often a preferred depth of growth. Both of these features, particularly the latter, however, are susceptible to the formative effects of the soil. In many types of plants, particularly herbs, the depth of the mature roots is often greater than the height of the stem above ground. In wheat plants, for example, the stem usually reaches a maximum height of 3 to 4 feet, whereas their roots have been found to penetrate 9 feet or more into the soil. Other plants with deep root systems are alfalfa, roots of which have

FIG. 6–2 (*left*). Taproot of hickory tree, partly exposed by soil erosion.

FIG. 6–3 (*below*). Undersurface of a mat of blue-grass sod, showing fibrous roots and slender creeping stems (rhizomes). Sods are very effective soil binders.

(*Photo by Missouri Botanical Garden.*)

(*Photo by R. B. Musgrave.*)

been reported to reach depths of 12 feet, sugar beets with roots frequently more than 4 feet long, and bur oak trees with roots known to penetrate 15 feet into the soil. Many other species of plants such as corn, bluegrass, and some other members of the grass family have roots that are confined to the uppermost layers of the soil, chiefly within 10 or 20 inches of the surface. Plants with shallow root systems commonly grow in regions of scanty rainfall, which usually reaches only the few upper inches of soil. Plants with deep root systems, on the other hand, can reach sources of water located deeper in the soil, water that is not ordinarily available to the shallower root systems. In some plants there are abundant roots in the surface layers of soil and likewise roots that penetrate deeply into the lower layers. Plants of this type, of course, have a great advantage over those species that have more restricted root systems. Because of their location out of sight and because of the difficulty in removing entire root systems from the soil for study, root systems have received little notice. A research publication on the root system of a rye

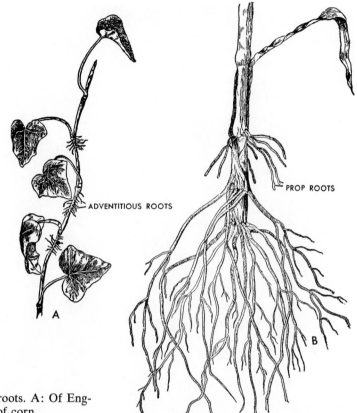

ADVENTITIOUS ROOTS

PROP ROOTS

FIG. 6–4. Adventitious roots. A: English ivy. B: Prop roots of corn.

plant presents some astounding figures: total number of roots 13,815,762, combined length of roots 387 miles, total surface area of roots 2554 square feet.

Root Anatomy and Growth. An examination of their external structure shows that roots are typically cylindrical. The tip of a root is usually bare of outgrowths for a length of one to several millimeters; above this bare tip are numerous root hairs (Figure 6–6), the principal absorptive structures of roots. Functional root hairs are commonly limited to a region a fraction of an inch long above the root tip. These hairs are delicate, tubular outgrowths of epidermal cells. They vary in length from sizes imperceptible to the naked eye to more than half an inch. Their special significance lies in the fact

that they increase enormously the absorbing surface of root systems. The tip of a root is sometimes slightly enlarged. This swelling is the **rootcap,** a thimble-shaped mass of cells that fits over the meristematic tissue situated just above the tip. Rootcaps are present in roots of most plants, but usually are too small to be visible to the naked eye. The rootcap acts as a buffer that protects the delicate meristematic cells located above and partly within it against mechanical injury from contact with rock particles and other hard objects in soils.

If a longitudinally cut, thin section of the terminal portion of a young root (Figure 6–7) is examined microscopically, four cell regions of rather different aspect are apparent. At the very tip of the root

FIG. 6–5. Adventitious roots of *Pandanus*.

is the rootcap, already mentioned, a protective cover that fits over the **meristematic region.** The outer portion of the rootcap is rather rough and uneven because the surface cells are worn away by contact with rock particles as the root tip pushes its way through the soil. The meristematic region just above the rootcap produces new cells more or less continually, some of which are added to the inner portion of the rootcap. Thus, the rootcap is built up by new cells on its inner surface as the older cells of the outer surface are worn away. The cells of the meristematic region are small, thin walled, and usually more or less cubical in form. They contain very dense protoplasm, in which the vacuoles are small and usually inconspicuous. When this region of the root is examined with the microscope, numerous cells with their nuclei in various stages of mitosis can be seen. This meristematic region, or growing point, is the cell-form-

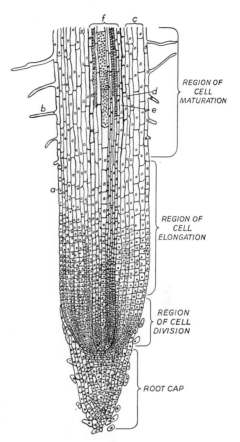

FIG. 6–7. Longitudinal section of a young root of barley.

a. epidermis
b. root hair (a protuberance from an epidermal cell)
c. cortex
d. endodermis
e. pericycle
f. differentiating conducting tissues of stele

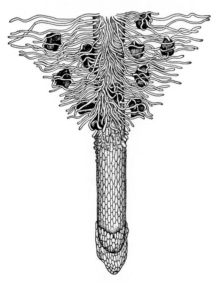

FIG. 6–6. Terminal portion of young roots, showing rootcap and root hairs, some of which are attached to soil particles.

ing region, which contributes largely to the growth of the root in length. Above the meristematic region is the **cell-elongation (cell-enlargement) region.** Here the cells newly formed as a result of mitosis and cell division in the meristematic region undergo rapid enlargement chiefly in the longitudinal direction. The cell

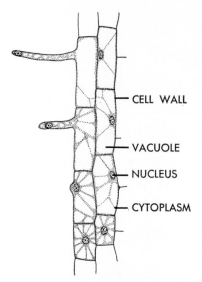

— CELL WALL

— VACUOLE

— NUCLEUS

— CYTOPLASM

FIG. 6–8. Root epidermal cells (at left), showing stages in root hair development.

walls increase in length and consequently the total volume of the cells becomes larger. The protoplasm also increases in volume, but at a slower rate than the increase in the size of the cell cavity. The small vacuoles of the meristematic cells fuse usually into a single large, central vacuole in each cell of the elongation region. The large vacuole fills the major portion of the cell cavity, with the protoplasm in the form of a thin layer outside the vacuole and pressed against the cell wall. The meristematic and elongation regions together are seldom more than a millimeter or two in length. Above these regions is the **region of maturation** or **differentiation.** Here the growing cells of the elongation region are undergoing division of labor and an accompanying differentiation of structure. Some of them are transformed into parenchyma cells, some into xylem cells, others into phloem cells, and so on. All the portions of the root above the maturation zone may be termed the **matured region,** for all these

portions are composed of the matured, differentiated tissues of the root system.

In the younger part of the maturation region are produced the root hairs. These structures should not be confused with branch roots that often appear almost as small as hairs. A branch root is a many-celled structure with a rootcap, meristematic region, xylem, phloem, etc., whereas a root hair is an extended portion of a single cell. A root hair begins as a small outgrowth of an epidermal cell near the lower limits of the maturation zone (Figure 6–8). The rate of growth of root hairs is usually fairly rapid and their life spans are rather short, usually not more than a few days or, rarely, a few weeks. Root hairs grow in great profusion (Figure 6–9); in some species of plants more than 200 root hairs grow from each square millimeter of root surface in the root hair zone. The production of new root hairs continues just above the region of elongation of the root tip as the tip grows downward into the soil, the youngest root hairs developing always at about the same distance above the root tip. The oldest root hairs at the upper end of the root hair zone may die off at about the same rate that the new root hairs are produced at the lower end of the zone; thus the total length of the root covered with root hairs may remain fairly constant.

Root hairs are thin walled and delicate. They will wither and die after a few minutes' exposure to dry air, and their extreme fragility enables them to be easily torn from the roots of a plant being moved to another location. The loss of great numbers of root hairs drastically reduces the water-absorbing surface of the roots. Most water loss from the plant occurs through the leaf surface; therefore, the common horticultural practice of "cutting back" after transplanting com-

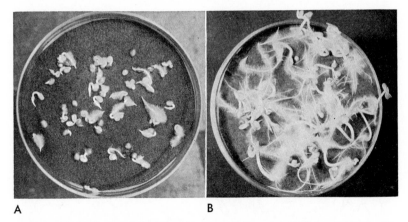

A   B

FIG. 6–9. Radish seedlings, showing root hairs. A: 48 hours old. B: 96 hours old.

pensates for the reduced absorbing surface in the roots by removing a fairly large percentage of the foliage. Root hairs are present in most higher types of plants, with the exception of certain aquatic species.

Examination of a transverse or cross section (Figure 6–10) of a root in the root hair zone of the maturation region shows several highly differentiated tissues. The surface layer of cells, the **epidermis,** produces the root hairs and thus is an absorptive tissue, as well as a tissue that furnishes some protection to the underlying cells. The **cortex,** inside the epidermis, is composed of parenchyma cells that are rather large, thin walled, and roughly spherical or ovoid in form. Numerous intercellular spaces occur in the cortex; these are important as avenues for the diffusion of water and of gases among the cortical cells. The cortex stores much of the reserve food that accumulates in the roots and it also transports the water and salts absorbed by the root hairs to the conducting cells in the center of the root. Water moves inward from the root hair cells to the outermost cells of the cortex and from one cortical cell to

another toward the conducting tissues as a result of differences in the osmotic relationships of these cells and of transpiration from the aerial parts of the plant. The inward movement of nutrient ions is also attributable in part to differences in the concentrations of those ions in the root hairs and cortical cells, and in part to ion accumulation phenomena.

The innermost layer of cortical cells comprises the **endodermis.** A distinguishing feature of an endodermal cell is the presence, on the radial and transverse walls, of a continuous zone or band within which the wall material is impregnated with suberin. The function of the endodermis is not known with certainty but it is believed that the fatty material deposited in these bands blocks the passage of water through the walls. Consequently, all water and solutes moving from cortex to xylem must pass through the living endodermal protoplasts, where some selectivity or other control may occur. In later stages of development the radial, transverse, and inner tangential walls commonly become thickened and lignified. Occasional thin-walled cells may be found in the older endodermis; these are

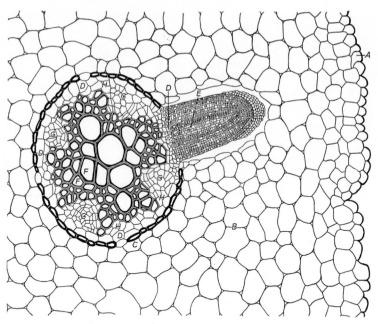

FIG. 6–10. Portion of root cross section.

A. epidermis   E. branch root originating from pericycle
B. cortex   F. xylem
C. endodermis   G. phloem
D. pericycle   H. parenchyma of stele

thought to facilitate the passage of water and other materials.

Enclosed by the endodermis is the **stele** or **vascular cylinder,** the principal conducting and strengthening portion of the root. The outermost tissue of the stele is the **pericycle,** a layer of small parenchyma cells, capable of producing new cells that grow outward from the stele and form branch roots. The origin of branch roots is thus internal with respect to the cortex and epidermis. Such root branches must force their way out through these latter tissues before they reach the soil. The branch roots are similar in structure, growth, and function to the main roots from which they arise.

Within the pericycle are found the xylem and phloem tissues. As seen in cross section the xylem is usually arranged in the form of a star or in the form of separated groups of cells situated radially, like the spokes of a wheel. The tracheary or conducting cells of the xylem of flowering plants are thick-walled vessel elements that, when joined in vertical files, constitute the vessels. The vessel elements are also responsible for much of the strength of the root. Xylem tissue conducts water and nutrient ions upward into the stem and at certain times may also transport upward foods previously stored in root tissues. Located between adjacent points of the xylem star or situated in shorter bands alternating with the radially arranged xylem groups are small clusters of phloem cells. These clusters are usually smaller than the xylem masses, and the cells comprising them are typically smaller and thinner walled than

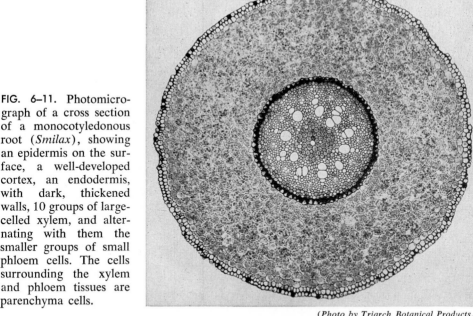

FIG. 6–11. Photomicrograph of a cross section of a monocotyledonous root (*Smilax*), showing an epidermis on the surface, a well-developed cortex, an endodermis, with dark, thickened walls, 10 groups of large-celled xylem, and alternating with them the smaller groups of small phloem cells. The cells surrounding the xylem and phloem tissues are parenchyma cells.

(Photo by Triarch Botanical Products.)

those of the xylem. The phloem consists chiefly of sieve tube members and their associated companion cells. The sieve tubes carry down into the root foods that have been manufactured in the leaves and transported downward through the phloem tissue of the stem. The alternate arrangement of xylem and phloem tissues in young roots is an advantageous one, for such arrangement makes possible ready access of these tissues to the root cortex, through which water and minerals move into the stele and in which water and food are commonly stored. In most vacular plants the xylem "star" constitutes the central core of the stele. In a smaller number of species, however, the center of the stele consists of pith parenchyma.

The tissues thus far described in roots are **primary tissues.** They develop from a terminal growing point, namely the meristematic region at the tip of the young root; primary tissues are produced during growth in length. The roots of most trees, shrubs, and other types of perennial plants have **secondary tissues** in addition to primary tissues. Secondary tissues are those produced by a **cambium;** they are formed in a transverse direction in stems and roots, as contrasted with primary tissues, which are formed chiefly in a longitudinal direction. Thus, secondary tissues are involved chiefly in increase in diameter of roots and stems. In perennial roots of many plants, a growth layer, termed the **cork cambium,** frequently develops in the pericycle tissue. The cells produced by the cork cambium on its outer surface become suberized and thus waterproofed and are termed **cork cells.** The epidermis, cortex, and endodermis disintegrate as cork cells develop, and their protective function is assumed by the cork cells. The older roots of perennials are thus frequently covered

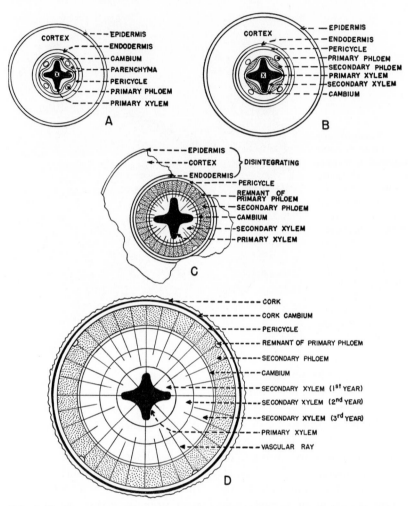

FIG. 6–12. Diagrammatic representation of secondary growth in a dicotyle-donous root. A: Primary tissues only. B: Beginning of secondary growth. C: Secondary growth continuing, with outer tissues sloughing off. D: Three-year-old root, with three xylem rings.

with a corky layer much like that of the outer bark of the stem. In many plants (for example, in most annuals), roots never become thickened beyond the extent of their primary tissues, but in perennials, roots usually grow considerably in diameter as a result of the formation of secondary vascular tissues (Figure 6–12). These tissues are produced by the growth activity of a **vascular cambium** that de-

velops from procambial cells lying *between* the xylem and phloem groups and from some of the pericycle cells. By cell division the cambium layer, which is only one cell thick, forms secondary xylem cells toward the axis of the organ and secondary phloem cells toward the outside. These are added to their respective primary tissues, and their continued formation brings about the greater part of

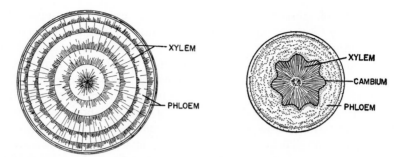

FIG. 6–13. Cross section of storage roots of beet, *left,* and of carrot, *right,* showing rings of vascular tissue in beet and the extensive phloem development in carrot.

the transverse growth of the roots of woody plants. The cambium forms xylem cells more rapidly than it does phloem cells, so that ultimately the xylem, or wood, constitutes the greater part of the total volume of such roots. Older roots with secondary tissues are much like woody stems in structure, with a surface layer of bark, a large woody cylinder inside the bark, and a cambium layer between the two.

ROOTS AND SOILS

Soil is the medium in which roots of most flowering plants live and perform their functions. There are many types of soils in which plants grow. These soils differ in their chemical and physical properties, their depth, and in many other qualities. Although soils differ widely, there are certain characteristics common to all soils in which plants grow. Such soils are complex organizations of particles of varying kinds and sizes, they possess substances soluble in water, they contain air, they are the habitats of soil organisms, and, if they support plant growth, they contain moisture.

Mineral particles, which form the largest proportions of most soils, vary from microscopic particles of clay to coarse particles of sand and gravel. They develop chiefly from the disintegration of rocks by the action of water, winds, glaciers, freezing and thawing, and carbon dioxide given off by roots. The character of rock particles is important in determining the volume of air space in the soil, the amount of water held by the soil, and the nature of soil solutes. Rock particles are the sources of many of the nutrients essential to plant growth: calcium, iron, phosphorus, magnesium, zinc, and others. Especially important in soils are clay particles, which occur chiefly in a colloidal state, forming a kind of structural framework of the soil. Clay particles hold on their surfaces various nutrient ions, such as calcium, magnesium, and potassium, which root hairs remove from these clay particles. Clay particles absorb water readily and swell as they do so, often forcing air out of the soil; for this reason, soils with large clay fractions are not suitable for the growth of many plants that require abundant air for their roots, for clayey soils become easily waterlogged and thus often contain inadequate supplies of air.

Soil air contains oxygen, which is essential to root respiration and which is thus directly related to processes of active water absorption and of ion accumulation. Inadequate soil aeration thus retards absorption by roots and may cause physiological derangements that lead to the stunting and death of roots. Oxygen in the soil air is necessary also for the activities of bacteria, worms, fungi, and other soil organisms that decompose dead leaves, bark, wood, dead animals, and animal excreta and that thereby contribute to the supply of nutrient solutes required by higher plants. Soil air also contains carbon dioxide, a respiration product of roots, bacteria, fungi, and soil animals. Carbon dioxide aids in the absorption of ions from clay particles by roots, but, if its concentration becomes excessive, it may lead to inhibition of root growth. Also in soil air is nitrogen gas, which is used by certain bacteria in the soil and in the roots of legumes (such as soybeans, clovers, and alfalfa); these bacteria convert gaseous nitrogen into nitrogen compounds in the soil and in roots and thus increase soil fertility.

Water in soils is derived chiefly from rain and snow. A portion of this water may run off the soil surface, another portion **(gravitational water)** trickles down through the soil into underground streams and springs, and still another portion **(capillary water)** remains loosely held within and upon the soil particles and in the air spaces of soil. Roots absorb chiefly the water loosely held by soil particles, although they may also absorb some gravitational water as it moves downward over root surfaces. Run-off and gravitational water may carry away soil nutrients (a process called **leaching**) and thus may decrease soil fertility; leaching must be compensated for by the addition of fertilizers to soils. There is relatively little movement of capillary moisture from one soil particle to another; thus, as roots absorb water, they dry out the soil particles near

them and, unless fresh supplies of water reach the soil, may cease to absorb moisture, with the resultant wilting and often death of plants. Soil moisture, with its solutes, is the soil solution.

Soil moisture may be conserved by the use of **mulches** spread over the soil surface; mulches of straw, grass clippings, leaves, manure, and paper are effective in shading the soil and thus in lowering its temperature, and in offering protection against drying winds. Mulches are valuable in other ways: they reduce the growth of weeds, which compete with crop plants for water and nutrients; they protect roots from frost and low temperatures; and some of them, especially manure and grass clippings, add nutrients to the soils on which they are spread. Glass wool and paper strips have come into recent use as mulches; in Hawaii, paper strips are used as a mulch around pineapple plants, and elsewhere are used to mulch tobacco fields. Straw and paper are valuable mulches for strawberry plants, for, in addition to the other beneficial qualities of mulches, they prevent contact of the strawberries with the soil, thus diminishing their rotting.

Organic matter consists of decomposing plant remains, such as leaves, stems, roots, and fruits, of dead animal bodies and animal excreta, and of dead microorganisms. All soils in which plants grow, and on or in which animals live, contain organic matter. The proteins, fats, cellulose, and other compounds of plant and animal tissues are decomposed by bacteria, fungi, and other soil organisms and are broken down into simpler substances, such as water, ammonia, nitrates, and phosphates. This disintegration of organic matter thus produces a continuing supply of nutrients that are essential to the fertility of soils and the growth of green plants. Organic matter is important also because it holds large supplies of water that can be absorbed by roots and because it loosens soils, prevents their caking, and increases their porosity and aeration. Some organic particles hold nutrient ions loosely on the surfaces from which roots absorb them. Organic matter of soils may be increased by the addition of manure, dead leaves, and peat and by plowing under certain crops such as alfalfa and cowpeas. Such treatment increases soil nutrients, improves drainage and aeration, loosens the soil, and generally renders the soil more favorable for plant development.

Soil solutes occur, as has been mentioned, in the soil water and on the surfaces of soil particles, and are derived in part from rock disintegration and from decomposing organic matter. These solutes ordinarily occur in low concentrations in soils, although in some soils, as in Utah's Great Salt Desert, the concentration of soil solutes may be so high as to result in plasmolysis of root cells and thus prevent plant growth. Soil solutes consist in part of organic compounds and in part of inorganic compounds, such as bicarbonates, sulfates, nitrates, and phosphates of calcium, magnesium, potassium, and other elements. Molecules of these inorganic substances undergo dissociation in the soil solution, forming positively charged ions such as calcium, potassium, iron, and magnesium, and negatively charged ions such as phosphate, nitrate, and sulfate. Positively charged ions are usually held on the surfaces of soil colloids, from which they are absorbed by roots, while negatively charged ions for the most part occur in the soil solution, from which roots absorb them. The nature of soil solutes influences the reactions of soils, that is, their acidity

or alkalinity. Soil reaction is an important factor in influencing plant distribution, for different kinds of plants are adjusted to certain specific ranges of reaction. Most agricultural crops thrive in neutral or slightly acid soils. Some plants, such as cranberries and rhododendrons, are able to grow only in acid soils, while others, such as cliff ferns, thrive only in alkaline soils. Continued plant growth often causes soils to become more acid; under such circumstances, limestone and other alkaline chemicals are often added to soils to counteract acidity.

Soil organisms affect the chemical and physical features of soils and thus influence the growth of higher plants. Soil organisms include many types of animals (worms, insects, spiders, rodents, reptiles, and others) and many kinds of plants (algae, mushrooms, molds, bacteria) together with roots. Of soil animals, earthworms are especially significant in their influences upon soils; they mix and move large quantities of soils, passing them through their bodies and thereby bringing about chemical changes in the soils. Charles Darwin found that earthworms in one acre of soil may pass 15 tons of soil through their bodies in one year. In addition to their chemical effects on soils, earthworms transport soils from deeper layers to the surface, thus bringing fresh supplies of soil to roots, and they form channels that promote drainage and aeration. All soil animals cause movement of soils, thus keeping them open and loose, and all contribute to the organic matter of soils through decay of their dead bodies and feces. Soil algae are green plants that manufacture foods, thus increasing soil organic matter as they grow, multiply, die, and decompose; algae are important also in that they serve as food for bacteria, fungi, and animals. Bacteria influence soils in many ways: they attack dead bodies and excreta, breaking their complex constituents down into simpler substances that roots absorb and that are utilized by higher plants in food manufacture, and they are especially important in soil nitrogen transformations that benefit higher plants. Mushrooms, molds, and other fungi, like bacteria, bring about decay of dead bodies and animal wastes and thus increase the soil's supply of nutrients essential to the growth of higher plants.

Flowering plants influence the soils in which they grow in three major ways: they absorb water and nutrient ions from soils by processes described in the last chapter; they add substances to soils as a result of the decomposition of their cast-off parts and their dead bodies; and they influence the physical nature of the soils by means of their roots. If plants live on the same soil year after year, their fallen leaves and branches, dying older roots, old fruits, and seed coats return to the soil, through disintegrative action of soil organisms, substances of which these parts are composed, so that a continuing supply of soil nutrients is ensured. A different situation obtains, however, in soils that are intensively cultivated, for the harvesting of fruits, grains, and other crops results in the removal of many nutrients from the soil. If these soil nutrients are not replaced, these soils become less productive; that is, they lose their fertility. The frequent addition of fertilizers to cultivated soils is essential to replenish the nutrients removed in crops, and it ensures continued productive fertility. The plowing under of stubble and other residues compensates in part for the nutrients that crops take from the soil. The absorption of water by roots has marked effects upon soils,

for plant growth results in the depletion of soil moisture; thus, if large numbers of plants grow on a given soil area, they may withdraw so much water that the soil moisture is reduced to a level inadequate to support growth of productive crops. Roots affect soils also in a purely physical manner; root branches growing through the soil tend to keep it open and loose, not only because of the organic matter left by dead roots, but also because of the mechanical effects of roots in penetrating soil lumps and hard soil layers. The roots of many plants, especially grasses, which form dense sods, hold soils in place and thus reduce or prevent soil erosion by water and wind. When sods are plowed up or forests are burned or cut off, their roots are destroyed, their binding effect upon soils is lost, and widespread erosion is the result.

THE ABSORPTION OF MATERIALS BY ROOTS

As described in the last chapter, the absorption of water and solutes by living cells involves a group of complex processes that are still not completely understood. The absorption of water results chiefly from imbibition and osmotic action; the intake of nutrient solutes involves both simple diffusion and active transport. These processes operate not only in the absorption of these substances by root hairs but also in their transfer from epidermal cells across cells of the root cortex into the stele.

In addition to these generalizations, several other conclusions can be drawn from numerous investigations of absorption. Among these are the facts that solutes may be absorbed by root hair cells independently of the direction of movement of water; that the entrance of any particular solute into root hairs is in the main independent of the entrance of other kinds of solutes; and that both water and solutes, as they are absorbed by root hairs, do not remain in these cells but move into other cells of roots and then ultimately into the xylem cells that carry them upward into stem and leaf cells.

As already stated, root cells absorb solute ions, not only from the soil solution, but also directly from the surfaces of soil particles. The cell walls of root hairs, because of their high content of pectic substances, possess strong adhesive power, as a result of which root hairs become tightly glued to soil particles. Ionic exchanges occur between the root hairs and the particles to which they adhere, so that many of the ions absorbed by root hairs are absorbed from these particles without entering the soil solution.

Botanists have shown that plants take in water by two principal means, called **passive water absorption** and **active water absorption.** Passive absorption is the mechanism that accounts for most of the water uptake in a plant. In this process, the forces that cause absorption are initiated in the upper parts of the plant. Rapid evaporation of water from the internal leaf cells produces a water deficit that in turn creates a pull on the water column extending downward through the stem into the roots. The tension on the water column is attributed to the strong tendency for water molecules to cohere or stay together. The role of the living root cells is thought to be passive in this type of water uptake; in fact, dead roots will absorb water for a few days provided there is rapid evaporation from the leaf cells. It appears, therefore, that the movement of water from its absorption into

the roots to its evaporation in the leaves is a mass flow in which imbibitional forces are more important than osmotic forces. However, since dead roots absorb water only for relatively short periods and since water uptake may continue over very long periods in living roots, it may be concluded that the presence of living cells in the root is essential to normal water uptake.

A second mechanism, active water absorption, accounts for certain phenomena that cannot be explained by passive absorption. For example, under conditions of abundant soil moisture and very low rate of water loss from the leaves, some plants continue to absorb water until a definite pressure (**root pressure)** has been developed. Root pressure causes the exudation of water in liquid form from the leaves, a process called **guttation.** It also causes the "bleeding" or exudation of water and solutes from a cut stump following the removal of a shoot from its root. This bleeding may continue for days in certain plants, for example, from the stumps of pruned grape vines. Evidence indicates that root pressure is caused by osmotic forces that develop when living root cells accumulate certain solutes against a concentration gradient (active transport). Such accumulation raises the osmotic concentration of the cell sap, causing water to move in. The above-mentioned absorptive processes are, of course, affected by numerous external and internal factors. Of these, the rate of water loss from the plant appears to be the most important.

Morphology and Growth of Roots in Relation to Absorption. The rate of absorption of water and solutes from soils by roots is determined not only by such factors as the rate of evaporation of water from leaves, respiration of root cells, osmotic concentration of the soil solution, availability of soil moisture, and osmotic properties of root cells; it is influenced also by the structure and growth of root systems. The form of a root system, the depth of its penetration into the soil, the number of its branches, and the direction of their growth markedly affect the absorption of materials from the soil, since these features determine the amount of root surface and the extent to which roots grow into new soil regions with higher water content. As stated in an earlier section of this chapter, the root systems of many plants are of enormous extent. A single rye plant with its total 387 miles of roots possesses a root surface of over 2500 square feet—about 130 times the surface of the stems and leaves—in contact with the soil; in such a root system, the average daily linear growth of roots is 3.1 miles. A squash plant has been shown to have about 16 miles of roots, with a total surface area of 84,000 square feet. The extent of root growth is vitally important in absorption, since ordinarily there is limited movement of water in soils toward roots; roots obtain additional supplies of water by growing into new regions of soils with greater stores of available water.

The root hair system of plants is another root factor that is directly related to the absorption of water and solutes from soils. The number of root hairs, their distribution on root surfaces, their longevity, and their rates of growth affect absorption processes. The zone of maximum absorption corresponds with the root hair zone of roots in most species of plants. Root hairs may increase the absorbing surface of most roots from 5 to 20 times. These structures frequently occur in huge numbers on a single root system; in a rye plant, for example, more

than 14,000,000,000 root hairs with a total length of about 6600 feet and a surface of 4321 square feet are present. Caution is necessary in interpreting the significance of these figures, since the amount of water absorbed by roots is not absolutely proportional to the root hair surface. All water and solutes taken in by a root hair must pass into the internal root tissues through the base of the root hair; thus, the area of the base of the cylindrical root hair at the point of juncture between the root hair and its parent epidermal cell limits the movement of water into roots.

SPECIALIZED ROOTS

Specialized or modified roots perform functions other than the usual root functions of anchorage, absorption, conduction, and food storage. In some plants, roots perform **reproductive** functions. The roots of cherry and apple, for example, produce "suckers" that develop into new plants, and sweet potatoes and dahlias are commonly propagated by man by means of roots. Some plants, such as corn, screwpine, and banyan trees, produce adventitious prop roots that arise from aerial portions of the stem and grow downward until they reach the soil. The chief function of such roots is to give added support to the stem system. In some plants adventitious roots act as climbing roots, which anchor stems to the walls, fences, and trees along which they grow. Roots of this type are found in poison ivy, English ivy, and other species of vines. The spongy **aerial** roots of **epiphytic** orchids (epiphytes are plants that grow nonparasitically upon other plants, wires, poles, etc.) take water from falling rain and atmospheric humidity, absorb raw materials from the debris that

(Photo by C. F. Hottes.)

FIG. 6–14. "Knees" of bald cypress.

collects about them, and help to anchor the whole plant to the object upon which it grows. Sometimes these aerial roots contain chlorophyll, as in the vanilla plant, which is an orchid, and are thus able to manufacture food. Bald cypress trees in swamps develop peculiar root projections that grow upward above the surface of the water or swamp soil in which the trees grow (Figure 6–14). The function of these so-called knees is not understood. Earlier it was believed that they provide aeration for the submerged roots, but more recent evidence tends to discount this idea. Certain parasitic seed plants, such as dodders and mistletoe, absorb their food directly from other plants and do not have contact with the soil during most of their lives. These roots are modified into suckers **(haustoria)** that penetrate the tissues of their host plants and absorb food directly from them.

ECONOMIC SIGNIFICANCE OF ROOTS

The fundamental importance of roots in the scheme of nature and in man's existence needs no further discussion, except to reiterate that the growth of all higher plants, upon which man depends, would be impossible without roots. It is of interest to mention some specific plants, the roots of which are directly useful to man. Among these are a number of medicinal plants: aconite, asafetida, gentian, goldenseal, licorice, and valerian, all of which are used in pharmaceutical preparations. The principal root crops used as food by man are: beets, carrots, salsify, parsnips, radishes, turnips, rutabagas, sweet potatoes, yams, and cassava (tapio-

(*Photo by Monsanto Chemical Co.*)

FIG. 6–15. Soil conditioners, such as Krilium, promote a loose, open structure of soils, prevent soil caking, and promote seed germination and plant growth. *Left:* Seed germination in caked, untreated soil. *Right:* Seed germination in soil treated with soil conditioner.

ca). Some of these (for example, turnips, beets, carrots) are biennial species; during the first year of their growth, they manufacture abundant food, much of which is stored in the taproot and which is used mainly in the production of flowers and seeds during the second year of their life. Man robs these plants of their food during the first year of their growth. A beet root develops several cambium layers, which form rings of tissues visible to the naked eye in a beet root cross section (Figure 6–13). Spices and other aromatic substances are furnished by the roots of several species of plants: angelica, horse-radish, sarsaparilla, turmeric, and sassafras. The roots of madder and alkanna furnish important dyes, the former being the source of the widely used "turkey-red." As already stated, root systems are effective in checking soil erosion.

⧁ SUMMARY

1. The functions of roots are: absorption of water and solutes from soil, anchorage, conduction, and food storage.
2. A root system is the total mass of roots of a plant. Two common types of root systems are taproot and diffuse (fibrous) root systems.
3. A primary root is the root that develops directly from the hypocotyl of an embryo. Secondary roots are branches of primary roots. Adventitious roots arise from some structure other than a primary root or its branches.
4. Root systems differ in their degree of branching, depth of penetration into the soil, lengths, and other features.
5. Roots are typically cylindrical in form.
6. The tip of a root is covered by a protective rootcap.

7. Immediately above the rootcap is the meristematic region (region of cell division) in which new cells are formed. Above this is the region of cell elongation, in which the newly formed cells undergo enlargement, chiefly in length. Above the region of elongation is the region of cell maturation in which the tissues of the root undergo differentiation. Root hairs cover part of the region of maturation.

8. A root hair is a protuberance from a root epidermal cell.

9. Root hairs are very delicate and usually short lived, and easily damaged.

10. In transverse section the maturation region of a young root shows the following regions and tissues, from outside in:
    a. Epidermis.
    b. Cortex.
    c. Endodermis (the innermost layer of the cortex).
    d. Stele, consisting of pericycle, xylem, phloem, and parenchyma tissue. The primary xylem and phloem tissues are radially arranged.

11. Older roots may develop a cambium tissue from parenchyma cells between the xylem and phloem tissues. The cambium forms secondary xylem and phloem cells and is in large part responsible for the growth of roots in diameter.

12. Both cork cambium and branch roots originate in the pericycle.

13. Soils in which plants grow contain complex particles of different kinds, water, solutes, air, and living organisms.

14. Mineral particles include clay, sand, and gravel, and furnish many nutrient solutes. Clay particles form the structural framework of soils.

15. Soil air contains oxygen, essential to root respiration and root growth and functions. Soil air also contains carbon dioxide and nitrogen.

16. Soil moisture, derived from rain and snow, may run off the surface, trickle downward, or be held by soil particles and in the spaces among soil particles. Roots absorb chiefly the moisture held by soil particles and in soil spaces.

17. Soil moisture may be conserved by mulches.

18. Organic matter consists of plant and animal residues and wastes. Organic matter is decomposed by bacteria, fungi, and other soil organisms and is the source of various nutrient solutes. Organic matter promotes water retention and keeps soils loose and open.

19. Sol solutes arise in part from mineral particles and in part from organic matter, and are absorbed by roots chiefly in ionic form. Some ions are held on soil particles from which roots absorb them; others occur in the soil solution.

20. Soil organisms include bacteria, fungi, algae, worms, insects, rodents, and others. Activities of these organisms improve soil properties in relation to plant functions and plant growth.

21. Roots influence soils in several ways: they absorb materials from soils, they loosen soils, they bind soils against erosive action of wind and water.

22. Crops remove nutrients from soils; the addition of fertilizers to soils maintains a continuing supply of essential nutrients for plant growth.

23. Roots absorb water by imbibition and osmosis, ions by simple diffusion and active transport.

24. Root pressure is attributed to active water absorption, that is, the osmotic uptake of water associated with ion accumulation by living root cells under conditions of abundant soil moisture and low evaporation rate in leaves.

25. Most water uptake is accounted for by passive water absorption, in which the deficit produced by evaporation in the leaves creates an imbibitional pull on the water column, causing a mass flow of water into the roots and up through the plant.

26. Root hairs are the principal absorbing structures of roots. Root hairs increase the absorptive area of roots, make intimate contacts with soil particles, and constantly enter new regions of the soil.

27. Specialized roots perform specialized functions other than, or in addition to, the usual functions of roots. Examples of morphologically specialized roots with rather specialized functions are:
    a. Prop roots of corn and other plants.
    b. Climbing roots of ivies.
    c. Spongy, aerial, water-absorbing roots of epiphytes.
    d. Suckers (haustoria) of dodder and mistletoe.

28. Some roots function in vegetative reproduction through their formation of "suckers."

29. Roots furnish many economically important products, such as foods for man and other animals, drugs, dyes, and spices.

⫷ SUGGESTED READINGS FOR INTERESTED STUDENTS

1. Bonner, James, and Arthur Galston, *Principles of Plant Physiology*. Freeman, San Francisco, 1952.
2. Esau, Katherine, *Anatomy of Seed Plants*. Wiley, New York, 1961.
3. Kramer, Paul J., and Theodore T. Kozlowski, *Physiology of Trees*. McGraw-Hill, New York, 1960.
4. *Soil*. The Yearbook of Agriculture, U.S. Government Printing Office, 1957.

⫷ TOPICS AND QUESTIONS FOR STUDY

1. List the functions of roots.
2. What is a primary root? A secondary root? An adventitious root?
3. Distinguish between diffuse and taproot systems.
4. Name six plants that store large amounts of food in their roots.
5. Why is our knowledge concerning the structure and growth of root systems less extensive than our knowledge of structure and growth of stems?
6. Describe the structure, origin, and importance of rootcaps.
7. Describe the structure of a young root as seen in longitudinal section, and describe the functions of the tissues seen in such a section.
8. Describe the growth of roots in length.
9. Describe the structure and origin of root hairs. What is the importance of root hairs?
10. When plants are transplanted, a ball of soil should be kept around the root system. State three reasons for this practice.

11. Describe the arrangement and structure of the tissues seen in a cross section through the maturation region of a young root. State the functions of these tissues.
12. Distinguish between primary and secondary tissues, and name the primary and secondary tissues of roots. Explain how these secondary tissues develop in a root.
13. What is cork cambium? Its function?
14. Name the principal constituents of soils.
15. In what ways is the clay fraction of soils important in plant growth?
16. Name some of the chemical compounds in the mineral particles of soils.
17. What are the sources of organic matter in soils? What is the importance of organic matter for the growth and functioning of roots?
18. What are mulches? How do they benefit plant growth? Name some common mulches.
19. What is the source of soil water? What type of soil water is most commonly absorbed by roots?
20. Describe the importance of soil air for plant growth.
21. Name some common soil solutes and comment upon their importance for green plants.
22. What are ions? By what processes do roots absorb ions?
23. Name some common soil organisms, and describe their importance for plant growth.
24. Describe the processes involved in the absorption of water by roots.
25. What is transpiration? What is its relation to the absorption of water by roots?
26. Describe root structure and root growth in relation to the absorption of water and solutes.
27. Name four types of specialized roots, and list their functions.
28. Describe the importance of roots in human life.

7

The Origin and Gross Structure of Stems

THE ORIGIN AND NATURE OF STEMS

The first stem of a seed plant has its origin from a portion of the embryo axis in the seed known as the **epicotyl,** which is a continuation of the **hypocotyl,** the structure from which the primary root develops. The epicotyl is a cylindrical structure with a small mass of meristematic tissue and frequently a pair of tiny leaves at its apex. When a seed germinates, the radicle is usually first to emerge. This behavior is important, for since the radicle or a portion of it develops into the first root of the seedling, its early entrance into the soil makes it possible for the embryo to begin absorbing the water and minerals necessary for its future development before the reserves of the seed are exhausted. Soon after the emergence of the radicle, the epicotyl leaves the seed coat and begins its upward growth through the soil, and the entire stem develops from the epicotyl, as in the garden pea plant. In other plants, the garden bean, for example, the upper portion of the hypocotyl rises above the surface of

the soil for several inches, the basal portion of the stem developing from the hypocotyl, the remainder from the epicotyl.

There are two chief functions of stems in flowering plants: the conduction of materials and the production and support of leaves and flowers. Other functions of the stems of certain plants to be described in greater detail later are food storage, food manufacture, and reproduction.

A stem with its leaves is called a **shoot,** an entire stem with all its branches and leaves, a **shoot system.** Stems that grow above the soil are termed **aerial stems** to distinguish them from the underground, or **subterranean stems.** The stems of flowering plants are chiefly aerial. The aerial stems of most plants are **erect,** as in elm trees, petunias, and corn, but in some species, such as morning-glories and grapes, the stems have a **climbing** habit of growth. In still other species, such as watermelon and cucumbers, the aerial stems are **prostrate** or creeping; that is, they are not strong enough to be-

(Photo by Missouri Botanical Garden.)

FIG. 7–1. False dragon's head (*Physostegia virginiana*), with herbaceous stems.

come erect, but grow in a horizontal direction over the surface of the soil.

THE EXTERNAL STRUCTURE OF STEMS

Stem Types. Stems vary a great deal in different species of plants in their external form, size, internal structure, longevity, and other aspects. From the standpoint of their external structure and their growth habits, aerial stems may be divided into two types: **herbaceous** and **woody.** Herbaceous stems are rather soft and green, with virtually no development of tough, woody tissue, and with relatively little growth in diameter. The tissues of herbaceous stems are largely, sometimes entirely, primary tissues. Herbaceous stems are covered with an epidermis, and as a rule are annual; that is, their life span is only one growing season. Some plants may have annual stems, with perennial roots, in which case the stems are usually herbaceous, the roots often woody. In certain types of hibiscus, this situation obtains. Likewise, in columbines and peonies, the stems are annual but the roots are perennial. In such plants as peas and squash, both roots and stems are annual and the plants thus live only one season, not for a number of years as do peonies and columbines. Some annual stems, such as those of sunflowers, develop moderate amounts of wood, but annual stems in most plants are distinctly herbaceous. Most woody stems are perennial, remaining alive and active for more than two years. Stems of this type are composed chiefly of secondary tissues, largely xylem or wood. Woody stems are thicker, harder, and tougher than herbaceous stems, and since their surfaces are covered with cork cells, which replace the epidermis of very young twigs, they are usually rough in surface texture and lack the green color

FIG. 7–2. American elm tree (*Ulmus americana*).

of herbaceous stems. Also, since they grow for a number of years, woody stems are usually much taller, as well as thicker, than herbaceous stems. A **tree** is a woody stemmed plant that possesses a main stem, or **trunk,** that rises some distance above the ground before it branches (Figure 7–2). A **shrub** is a woody plant in which usually several stems of approximately equal size appear above the soil line (Figure 7–3).

Buds. An examination of the surface of

a stem in active, growing condition shows a variety of structures, most common of which are **buds** and **leaves.** Leaves are usually broad and flattened, or needle-like, appendages of stems. The point on a stem from which a leaf develops is called a **node;** the section of stem between two successive nodes, an **internode.** Internodes are sometimes very short, as on spur twigs of an apple tree, or, in other species such as willows and sunflowers, they may be several inches long. In the

FIG. 7–3. *Philadelphus*, a shrub.

(Photo by Missouri Botanical Garden.)

upper angle between the point of juncture of a leaf stalk with a stem is located, as a rule, a **bud.** This angle between the leaf stalk and the stem is termed the **leaf axil,** and the buds found in leaf axils are accordingly called **axillary,** or since they occur along the sides of a stem, **lateral buds.** At the tip of each stem or twig is usually located a **terminal bud.** Terminal buds and axillary buds are usually similar in structure and in function; the distinction between them is chiefly one of position in most species of plants. Occasionally buds arise at places other than in the axils of leaves. Buds of this type are called **adventitious.** They sometimes develop as a result of injury; for example, they are frequently found producing young shoots on the stumps of trees that have been felled (Figure 7–4). Structurally, they are like the normal type of buds that occur in leaf axils.

A bud (Figure 7–5) is essentially a convex or cone-shaped mass of meristematic tissue that laterally produces small projections, the **primordia** of leaves, which develop into the mature leaves of the plant as the bud grows. Thus, a bud, since it contains the primordia of leaves, possesses nodes and also very short internodes, and can consequently be regarded as a very much shortened, compact, undeveloped section of a stem. In **naked buds,** the meristematic tissue is exposed to the air without any protective covering other than rudimentary leaves (Figure 7–6); buds of this type occur in most herbaceous plants and in certain woody species in very moist regions of the tropics. In woody stems of the drier portions of the tropics and generally in the temperate zones, buds are covered with overlapping scales, known as **bud scales.** These are modified leaves that grow out from the base of a bud and form a protective coat over the meristematic tissue. These scales are often thick and tough and are frequently, as in cottonwoods, covered with a gummy secretion or, as in some hickories, with a dense growth of hairs. These scales protect the meristematic tissue from desiccation, and to a

(*Photo by C. F. Hottes.*)

FIG. 7–4. Sprouts from adventitious buds on catalpa stump.

certain extent from mechanical injury and various kinds of parasites.

Buds may be classified also on the basis of their activity, their arrangement on the stem, and the kinds of structures they produce. Those buds that grow are called **active** buds to distinguish them from the occasional buds that remain inactive; the latter are called **dormant** buds and are usually axillary in position and situated at some distance below the terminal bud of the twig upon which they occur. Sometimes these inactive buds develop many years after they are formed; they remain embedded in the bark as the stem grows in diameter and under an appropriate stimulus may grow out into branches. Such behavior, of course, occurs only in perennial, woody stems. More frequently, however, dormant buds remain undeveloped during their entire existence. Buds differ, likewise, in their arrangement. In most plants, as in elms

and apples, they are arranged in **alternate** or **spiral** fashion; that is, one bud occurs at each node and the successive buds from the base toward the apex of a stem may be connected by a continuous spiral line. In a lesser, though still rather large number of species, including maples, dogwood, and buckeye, the buds are arranged in **opposite** (Figure 7–9) manner; that is, there are two buds at a node on opposite sides of the stem. The **whorled** arrangement is uncommon, occurring in relatively few plants, such as catalpa, on the stems of which there are three buds at a node more or less equally spaced about the stem. Buds differ also in the nature of the structures they produce. Thus, there are **flower buds,** which produce only flowers, as in roses and morning-glories; **leaf buds,** sometimes called also **branch buds,** which grow out into new lengths of twigs, bearing leaves; and **mixed buds,** such as the buds of buckeye and apple, which produce twigs bearing both leaves and flowers.

Bud Growth. A longitudinal section of a leaf bud, the most common kind of bud in seed plants, shows the convex meristematic region with the rudimentary leaves appearing in succession below the meristematic tip (growing point) of the bud; the largest and oldest leaf primordia are at the base of the bud, with progressively smaller leaf rudiments toward the growing point. These leaf primordia are arranged in spiral, opposite, or whorled manner, just as the leaves are in mature twigs, each with a tiny bud rudiment in its axil. Thus a bud is an inmature shoot possessing a stem, minute leaves, and axillary bud primordia. The axillary bud primordia are not apparent in all species before the opening of the bud, however. The increase in length of a stem is caused largely by the rapid increase in length of the tiny internodes of the terminal bud as the bud develops. In most annual plants and in many woody plants of the tropics, the elongation of the internodes produced by the bud continues through most of the growing season, but in woody plants of cooler regions, the elongation of these internodes occurs chiefly during a few weeks of spring, immediately following the opening of the bud scales. When a leaf bud "opens," its internodes elongate and the leaf primordia enlarge into the mature leaves of the twig. The first terminal bud of a stem develops from the apex of the epicotyl, and as it grows, additional buds are formed in the axils of the leaf primordia of this terminal bud. The end of the growing season of annual plants brings the death of the plant, and the activity of its buds, which are naked, is at an end. In woody plants (the buds of which are usually covered), when a bud opens, the bud scales begin

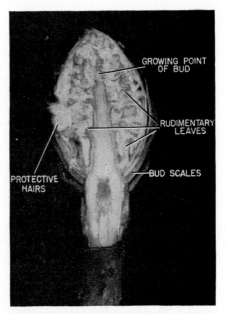

FIG. 7–5. Longitudinal section of horse chestnut bud.

to grow more rapidly on their inner surfaces than on their outer, and, as a result, bend away from the center of the bud. With the separation of the bud scales, the elongation of the internodes of the bud and the enlargement of the leaf primordia begin, and a new section of twig is formed (Figure 7–8). The bud scales usually fall away a short time after they have opened. During the growth season of the new section of twig, the bud primordia that form in the leaf axils begin to enlarge so that at the end of this growing season a new terminal bud, similar in structure to that from which the new section of twig grew, is present at the tip of this stem section, with new axillary buds in all the leaf axils. These buds remain quiescent during the remainder of the summer and throughout the following winter, and with the coming of the next spring they begin to grow in the fashion described above. The buds of woody

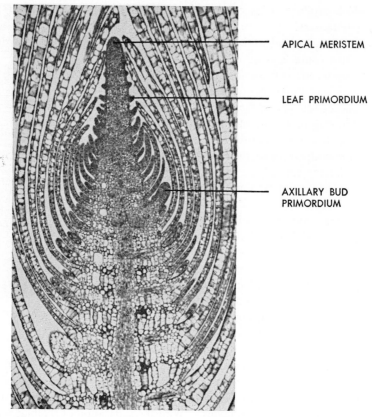

APICAL MERISTEM

LEAF PRIMORDIUM

AXILLARY BUD PRIMORDIUM

FIG. 7–6. *Elodea* shoot tip in longitudinal section, showing leaf and branch primordia and young leaves.

plants are often called **winter buds,** since they live through the winter. The growth of a terminal bud produces elongation of a stem; that of an axillary bud produces a branch or twig of such a stem. When an axillary bud forms a branch twig, this twig develops its own terminal and axillary buds in the same manner as the main stem of which it is a branch. The axillary buds of this branch may grow subsequently and form a further order of branches of the branch twig. Thus, terminal buds produce growth in length of a twig, axillary buds produce branches of that twig. The origin of stem branches may be described as *external* since the axillary buds that produce these branches are located on the surface of the stem. In many plants, the branches formed by the growth of certain axillary buds are **flowers,** which are highly specialized shoots. In such cases the growth of this specialized, reproductive branch ceases; no buds are formed as a rule in the axils of the floral organs and thus no further growth of such a shoot is possible. After fulfilling its reproductive function, the flower usually withers and falls away from the main shoot of which it is a branch.

The form of a whole shoot system is determined in a large degree by the positions, arrangements, and relative activities of the various types of buds. If the axillary buds are opposite, the branches produced by them are opposite; if they are alternate, the branches into which they grow are alternate. If there is a dominant terminal bud with a relatively large number of dormant axillary buds, the branch on which these buds occur will be much elongated with relatively few side branches. If, on the contrary, the terminal bud is slow growing and the axillary buds are active, the stem grows slowly in length and will possess many, relatively fast-growing branches. By applying his knowledge of bud behavior, a horticulturist can control the shape of plants that he is growing. In a plant with an active terminal bud and with slow-growing or dormant axillary buds, the removal of the terminal bud usually stimulates the axillary buds to greater activity, in many cases overcoming their dormancy. Thus, a bushier growth of a plant may be induced by pruning away certain of the terminal buds. In peonies all buds on a stem except the terminal one may be removed, a process called **disbudding,** with the result that the single shoot becomes very tall and erect and the flower that develops from the single bud is much larger than it would be were other flower buds allowed to develop. The reduction of competition among many buds for the food manufactured by the plant places all the food at the disposal of the few remaining buds and thus permits them to form unusually large flowers. Disbudding is a common horticultural practice in the culture of many plants, such as roses, carnations, and asters (Figure 7–10).

Stem Surfaces. An examination of the surface of a herbaceous stem shows relatively few structures other than buds,

FIG. 7–7. Growing point of young oat stem, enveloped by two young leaves.

leaves, and branch shoots of both vegetative and reproductive nature. There may be **hairs,** which are outgrowths of epidermal cells; **stipules,** small projections of tissue at the point of juncture of leaf stalks with the stem; and occasionally **spines,** which may be modified branches, leaves, hairs, or stipules. In the woody twigs of trees and shrubs, however, other structures in addition to the above-mentioned features are present (Figure 7–11). These are **lenticels, leaf scars, bundle scars, bud scars,** and **twig scars.** Lenticels are tiny pores that are scattered over the surfaces of woody twigs. They are usually surrounded by a margin of raised cork tissue; through the lenticels an exchange of gases between the tissues of the stem and the external air occurs. Lenticels are usually circular or nearly so in shape, although in some plants, for example, cherry and peach trees, they are transversely elongated slits. Leaf scars are sometimes apparent in annual plants, if some of the leaves

FIG. 7–8. Stages in the opening of the terminal mixed bud of a buckeye twig.

fall away, but they are especially conspicuous on woody twigs in autumn and
winter. A leaf scar is a mark left when a
leaf stalk breaks away from the twig.
Leaf scars are variable in form in different species; common shapes of leaf
scars are narrow crescents, U's, V's and
sometimes circles and triangles. In the
twigs of the Chinese tree of heaven, the
leaf scars are roughly triangular in shape,
with sides about ½ inch long. In other
woody plants, such as Hercules' club, the
leaf scars are narrow and elongated transversely, frequently attaining a length of
more than an inch. Usually, however,
leaf scars do not exceed ¼ to ½ inch in
length and are most commonly U shaped
or V shaped. Bundle scars appear as tiny

raised dots on the leaf scars. Bundle scars
are the broken ends of **vascular bundles**
(conducting strands) that extend from
the twig into the leaf stalk. When a leaf
falls, these bundles are broken across at
the point of separation of the leaf from
the stem and thus are visible in cross-sec-
tional view within the leaf scars. The
number, size, and arrangement of bundle scars vary in different species of
plants. Bud scars are rings of small, narrow scars left by the bud scales as they
fall away from the base of an opening
bud. These bud scale scars are inconspicuous individually, but the ring that the
several scars form is readily visible. Most
of these bud scars are left by terminal
buds, and each of them marks the place

FIG. 7–9. Opposite buds of *Euonymus alatus*.

FIG. 7–10. Effect of disbudding of chrysanthemums. Both stems in the photograph were taken from the same variety of chrysanthemum. No flower buds were removed from the stem at the left. All flower buds except one were removed from the stem at the right.

at which a terminal bud began its development in a spring season. Since a new terminal bud develops each year from the previous terminal bud of the twig and opens in the following spring, the number of these bud scars on a twig indicates the age of the twig. By counting back from the apex of a stem the number of bud scars present, it is possible to determine the age of any section of the twig. Twig scars are usually circular in outline, are frequently slightly concave, and occur in the axils of leaf scars. They mark the points of juncture of fallen branch twigs with the main twig. If the branch produces a flower instead

of a vegetative twig, the scar left by the fallen fruit (a fruit develops from a flower) is called a **fruit scar.** Such a scar is similar in form and position to the scars left by vegetative twigs. In many species of woody plants, there is a regularity in the rate at which certain of the twigs and branches fall away from the branches from which they arise. This pehnomenon is termed **natural** or **self-pruning** (Figure 7–12) and is especially noticeable in dense stands of trees, the most heavily shaded twigs and branches of which fall away while they are still relatively young.

As woody stems grow in diameter, the smooth, young outer bark is split, partly by the formation of new tissues, partly by rapid diametric growth inside the bark. With cracking of the young bark and the growth of new cork layers, the surface of the branch becomes much roughened in most species of trees and

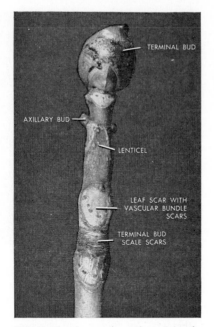
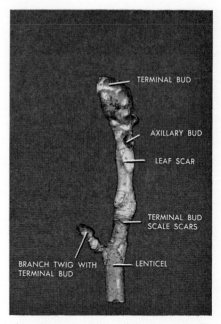

FIG. 7–11. External aspect of buckeye twigs. The photograph on the right illustrates the development of a branch from an axillary bud.

the various structures described above are no longer visible. In some species, such as birch and willow, the bark remains rather smooth, even on old parts of the stem, and some of the structures characteristic of the younger twig surfaces, lenticels principally, are still visible on the bark of old branches.

Many species of plants have stems that differ markedly in structure and function from the common types of aerial stems described in the preceding section. Such stems of special function are termed **specialized** or modified stems.

Most common of these specialized stems are underground, or subterranean stems, of which there are four principal kinds: **rhizomes, tubers, bulbs,** and **corms.** A rhizome is a horizontal stem that grows at or below the surface of the soil, occasionally with its upper surface exposed to the air. Rhizomes, and occasionally other types of specialized

underground stems, frequently resemble roots superficially; they are, however, true stems, for they have nodes, internodes, buds, and leaves. Leaves and buds occur at the nodes of rhizomes, as do also adventitious roots that grow out usually from the lower surfaces of rhizomes. Rhizomes are sometimes slender, as in quack grass, or much enlarged by abundant stores of food, as in iris. The chief functions of rhizomes are reproduction and food storage. Most rhizomes are perennial and thus increase in their length year after year, sending up new plants, or at least new branches at their nodes. If such rhizomes are separated into pieces, as may happen in hoeing or plowing, each segment is able to develop into a new plant and thus increase greatly the number of plants. Because of this behavior and also because of the fact that when rhizomatous weeds are pulled up, fragments of their rhizomes often remain undetected in the soil, plants with stems of this kind are very difficult to eradicate. The propagation of many types of garden plants, such as irises and cannas, is almost entirely by separating large rhizomes into small pieces and planting these.

In some plants, the growing tips of rhizomes become much enlarged as a result of food storage. Such subterranean stems are called tubers, the best known examples of which are the tubers of Irish potato plants. Starch is the most commonly stored food in the tubers, although other carbohydrates, such as **inulin,** are stored in the tubers of certain species. The "eyes" of potatoes are bud clusters; at each node buds are formed in the axil of a single tiny scalelike leaf. The functions of tubers are food storage and reproduction. Under natural conditions, the rhizomes connecting the tubers with the main stem of the potato plant die in the autumn or winter and the tubers, thus isolated in the soil, are able to produce shoots from their buds the following spring. Potatoes are also artificially propagated by tuber segments, called "seed pieces." A tuber is cut into pieces, each with one or more "eyes." These segments are planted and each produces a new plant from one of its "eyes."

A bulb (Figure 7–13) is a single, large, globose bud, with a small stem at its lower end and with numerous fleshy scalelike leaves growing from the upper surface of the small stem, from the bottom of which adventitious roots emerge. Thus, the greater portion of a bulb consists of storage leaves growing from a small, basally situated stem. Bulbs serve primarily for food storage and also for reproduction. Buds frequently develop in the axils of the scale leaves (Figure 7–

FIG. 7–12. Self-pruning in sycamore.

14). These buds resemble the parent bulb, from which they may be separated and used for propagation. Among familiar plants with bulbs are onion, narcissus, lily, and hyacinth.

Corms resemble bulbs superficially in size and form, but their internal structure differs from that of bulbs. The greater portion of a corm is stem tissue; the leaves are usually thinner and much smaller than those of bulbs. As in bulbs, buds occur in the axils of the thin scale leaves, and adventitious roots grow from the lower surface of the stem. Corms function as do bulbs for food storage and reproduction. Well-known plants with corms are gladiolus and crocus.

Aerial stems, or portions of them, frequently perform functions unusual in normal types of aerial stems. In various climbing plants, such as grape and Boston ivy, some of the twigs are modified into climbing organs called **tendrils.** In some plants, the aerial stem grows in

FIG. 7–13. Longitudinal sections of bulbs, showing roots, a small, compact stem, and growing from it, a number of leaves with thickened fleshy bases. In the center of the bulb is a young, growing flower stalk.

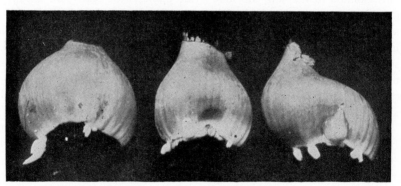

FIG. 7–14. Bulbs forming on bulb scales of amaryllis. Such bulbs are used for the commercial propagation of amaryllis.

spiral, rather than erect, fashion about a suitable solid support; such stems, termed **twiners,** are found in the morning-glory and sweet potato. Creeping stems that grow horizontally above the surface of the soil and that often develop new plants at their nodes, if these touch the soil, are called **runners,** or **stolons.** These occur in strawberry plants (Figure 7–15) and are used as the common method of propagating this species. The thorns of some plants, such as honey locust and Osage orange, are modified twigs; these occur in the axils of leaves and may branch, as in honey locusts. These thorns are doubtless of some importance in discouraging the visits of herbivorous animals. In most species of cactus (Figure 7–16), the leaves are reduced in size, or are transitory, withering away a few days after they are formed. In such plants the stems are green and have assumed the chief function of the missing leaves—namely, food manufacture. Cactus stems also store considerable quantities of water. In some plants, such as onion, **aerial bulbs** are formed. These are similar to subterranean bulbs and when planted in the soil grow into new onion plants. In those onions that produce aerial bulbs, the bulbs form in the **inflorescence** (flower cluster) in place of flowers.

EXTERNAL DIFFERENCES BETWEEN ROOTS AND STEMS

This table presents in summarized form the principal differences between most roots and stems with reference to their external structure and growth habits:

Roots

1. Roots grow downward into the soil.
2. Roots do not have nodes and internodes.
3. Root branches arise internally from the pericycle.
4. The growing points of roots are covered by rootcaps.
5. The characteristic appendages of roots are root hairs.
6. The primary root originates from the hypocotyl of the embryo.

(Photo by A. S. Colby.)

FIG. 7–15. A strawberry plant, *a*, with runners; *b*, and new plants; *c*, developed from the runners.

Stems

1. Stems of most plants grow upward above the soil.
2. Stems have well-marked nodes and internodes.
3. Stem branches arise externally from buds on the surface of stems.

(Photo by Missouri Botanical Garden.)

FIG. 7–16. A cactus garden in California.

4. The growing points of stems are naked or are protected by bud scales.
5. The characteristic appendages of stems are leaves and flowers.
6. The main stem originates from the epicotyl of the embryo, or in part from the hypocotyl.

⫷ SUMMARY

1. Stems arise chiefly from the epicotyls (sometimes in part from the hypocotyls) of embryos.
2. The chief functions of stems of flowering plants are:
   a. Conduction of materials from roots to leaves and from leaves to roots and buds.
   b. The production and support of leaves and flowers.
   c. Food storage.
3. A stem with its leaves is called a shoot.
4. Most stems are aerial; some are subterranean.
5. Herbaceous stems are soft, usually green, with little tough, woody tissue, and usually not much growth in diameter; they are chiefly annual. Woody stems are tough, with well-developed fibers and other types of strengthening cells, are not green, usually show considerable growth in diameter, and are mostly perennial.
6. Stems bear leaves, and in the axils of leaves, buds. The point on a stem from which a leaf or bud arises is called a node. The length of stem between two successive nodes is an internode.

7. Buds that occur at the tips of stems are terminal, those in leaf axils are axillary. Adventitious buds arise in places other than the axils of leaves or the tips of stems.
8. A bud is an undeveloped shoot. A naked bud is covered only by young leaves. A covered bud is protected by overlapping, protective bud scales that are modified leaves.
9. When one bud occurs at a node, bud arrangement is called alternate or spiral. When two buds occur at a node, the arrangement is said to be opposite. When more than two buds occur at a node, the arrangement is called whorled.
10. Leaf buds produce stems and leaves. Flower buds produce flowers. Mixed buds produce stems that bear both leaves and flowers.
11. The opening of a bud results chiefly from the elongation of its internodes and the growth of its leaves. The apex of a shoot is the growing point, the scene of most active growth in a bud.
12. The form of a shoot system is determined largely by the positions and growth activities of its buds.
13. The following structures may be found chiefly on young woody twigs, in addition to buds.
    a. Lenticels—pores in bark.
    b. Leaf scars—left by the falling away of leaves.
    c. Bundle scars—broken ends of vascular bundles in leaf scars.
    d. Bud scars—rings of scars left by the falling away of bud scales.
    e. Twig and fruit scars.
14. Examples of specialized stems are: rhizomes, tubers, corms, tendrils, runners (stolons), and thorns.

⫷⫷⫷ TOPICS AND QUESTIONS FOR STUDY

1. From what part of an embryo does the stem of a seedling originate?
2. Does the hypocotyl ever form a part of a stem? Cite a specific plant as an example and describe how its stem develops.
3. List the functions of stems.
4. What is meant by the term "shoot"? By "shoot system"?
5. Name some plants with aerial stems. With subterranean stems.
6. List as many differences as you can between herbaceous and woody stems.
7. Are annual stems always herbaceous? Explain.
8. What is the major difference between shrubs and trees?
9. Define: node, internode, leaf axil, terminal bud, axillary bud, adventitious bud.
10. Describe the structure of a bud. What is the most important part of a bud from the standpoint of stem growth?
11. What are the functions of bud scales?
12. Distinguish among active, dormant, leaf, flower, and mixed buds.
13. Describe the common types of bud arrangement.
14. Describe briefly the growth of a leaf bud, and name the structures that it produces. What happens to bud scales when a bud begins to grow?

15. When a bud grows, does all its meristematic tissue become differentiated into mature, permanent tissues? Do all buds behave similarly in this respect?

16. What is meant by "terminal bud dominance"? How is a knowledge of this phenomenon important to horticulturists?

17. What is disbudding? What is its effect?

18. Define and describe: lenticels, leaf scars, bundle scars, bud scars, twig scars, fruit scars.

19. What is the function of lenticels? Why are lenticels usually not visible on tree trunks? Name a species of tree in which lenticels are visible on old trunks.

20. Name four types of subterranean stems, and describe their functions and structure.

21. Describe the structure of a potato "eye."

22. The Irish potato is a tuber, but sweet potatoes are roots. What are the differences between them?

23. List the principal structural differences between roots and stems.

8

The Internal Structure
of Stems

The shoot apex within a terminal bud consists of meristematic cells that divide, producing new cells. These meristematic cells, like those of a root tip, are small, thin walled, essentially isodiametric, and possessed of dense cytoplasm with small vacuoles and conspicuous nuclei. Cells newly formed by divisions in the apex soon undergo enlargement, chiefly in a longitudinal direction, and, as their enlargement approaches its maximum, become differentiated into mature tissues, such as xylem and phloem. Thus, roots and stems are similar in the fundamental pattern of growth and in the arrangement of their apical tissues: in both roots and stems, a zone of meristematic cells is located at or near the tip of the organ, a zone of enlarging cells is discernible immediately behind this meristematic tissue, and, behind the zone of enlarging cells, a group of cells undergoing maturation or differentiation is clearly seen. In both stem tips and root tips, then, we may distinguish among a region of cell division, a region of cell elongation, and

a region of maturation of cells. In a young root, the meristematic region (region of cell division) is covered by a protective root cap; in a stem, the meristematic region of the tip is naked, or may be partially or wholly covered by bud scales or immature leaves, as mentioned in the last chapter. In the axils of these young leaves, small outgrowths of tissue develop; these typically become axillary buds.

Differentiation begins very early in stem ontogeny, slight structural changes appearing in the meristematic tissue that underlies the dome-shaped mass of cells at the extreme tip of the stem **(promeristem).** Examination of a longitudinal section of a shoot tip (Figure 8–1) shows the three meristematic tissues that differentiate from the promeristem:

1. **protoderm,** the superficial meristem that gives rise to the epidermis;

2. **procambium,** the provascular meristem, consisting of strands of narrow, slightly elongated cells that develop into primary phloem and xylem;

113

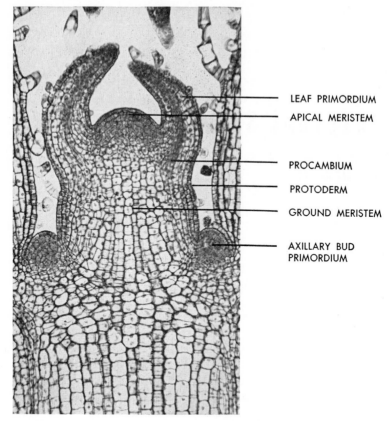

LEAF PRIMORDIUM

APICAL MERISTEM

PROCAMBIUM

PROTODERM

GROUND MERISTEM

AXILLARY BUD
PRIMORDIUM

FIG. 8–1. *Coleus* shoot tip in longitudinal section, showing leaf and branch primordia.

3. **ground meristem,** the meristem that
produces pith and cortex.

With the development of these mineriste-
matic tissues, most of the procambium
differentiates into primary phloem and
xylem. In many species, however, a
single layer of procambial cells may persist, retaining its meristematic condition.
This layer of cells, called the **cambium,**
functions in stems as it does in roots—
namely, in the production of secondary
phloem and xylem.

A study of the anatomical features of
plant stems furnishes convincing evidence of the inseparability of function
and structure in living cells, and of the

intricacies involved in the integration of
physiological activities with the development of the complex tissue systems of
stems. In stems are found strengthening
tissues, composed of cells with greatly
thickened walls of tough, yet elastic cellulose and lignin; conducting tissues
with thinner walls in which are present
numerous perforations and thin areas
(pits) that facilitate the transfer of materials from cell to cell; and thin-walled
cells within which water, foods, and other
materials may be stored. Most of the
movement of materials through stems is
upward and downward. Likewise, most
of the stresses and strains to which stems

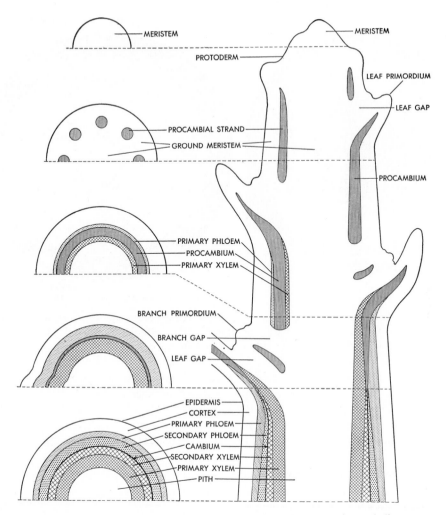

FIG. 8–2. Diagram of longitudinal section (*right*) of a stem tip and diagrams of cross sections (*left*) taken at different levels as indicated by dotted lines.

are subject are exerted in the longitudinal direction. The architecture of stems seems admirably designed to meet these demands. The conducting cells are elongated parallel to the longitudinal axes of stems, and their pits and wall perforations are located in such manner as to make most effective the upward and downward conduction of materials. Further, the strengthening cells are greatly elongated, with tapering ends that fit in

snugly with tapering ends of other strengthening cells and are distributed in such arrangements that they provide maximum resistance to the aforementioned longitudinal stresses.

It was stated in Chapter 7 that stems could be classified into two rather distinct types—**woody** and **herbaceous.** Within these two main types of stems are found many anatomical variations. It is inappropriate to consider in a book of

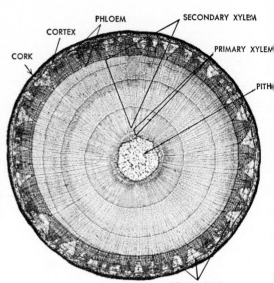

(*Photo by C. F. Hottes.*)

(*From Esau,* Plant Anatomy, *Wiley, 1953. With permission.*)

FIG. 8–3. *Left:* Cross section of oak branch, showing bark, heartwood (dark inner portion), sapwood (light portion between bark and heartwood), vascular rays, and growth rings. *Right:* Cross section of linden (*Tilia americana*) stem.

this type the intricacies of structure of the many varieties of plant stems. In this chapter, we will be concerned with the internal structure and development of only the commonest types of stems of seed plants.

Botanists generally believe that woody stems are more primitive than herbaceous stems. Students, because they commonly think of evolution as always a trend from simple to more complex forms of life, frequently find difficulty in understanding this idea, for woody stems are more complex structurally than herbaceous stems. There is abundant evidence, however, that the first kinds of true seed plants on the earth were perennial, woody stemmed plants and that the annual, herbaceous type of stem is a relatively recent development from the older, woody type. In accordance with this widely accepted modern interpretation, this chapter will describe first the anato-

my of woody stems and later the structure of herbaceous stems.

THE INTERNAL STRUCTURE OF WOODY STEMS

Gross Internal Structure

An examination with the naked eye of a cross **(transverse)** section of a mature woody stem more than one or two years old (Figure 8–3) shows two major groups of tissues: the **bark,** which forms the outer layer of the stem, and the **wood,** or **xylem,** which lies inside the bark. In the center of the stem inside the wood there is discernible in some species a small core of **pith.** Invisible to the naked eye but exceedingly important in the life of the stem is the **cambium,** a single layer of meristematic cells in the form of a continuous circle between the wood and

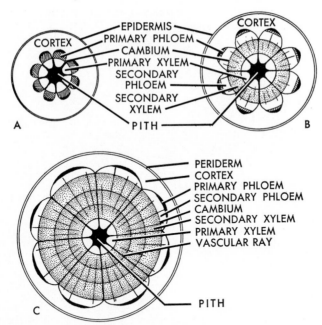

FIG. 8–4. Stages in the development of a woody stem as seen in cross section. A: Primary tissues of the woody stem as seen very early in the first growing season. B: The same stem at the end of the first season of growth. Secondary xylem in the form of a growth ring, and secondary phloem have been formed by the cambium. C: The same stem at the end of three years of growth. There are now three seasonal growth rings.

the bark (Figure 8–4). The cambium layer forms new cells radially, chiefly of the wood, or xylem, and thus causes stems to grow in diameter. The bark is very thin and smooth in young stems but becomes thicker and usually roughened as stems grow older, as a result of the growth activity of the **cork cambium,** a tissue in the outer part of bark. As stated above, the increase in diameter of woody stems results chiefly from the increase in the number of wood cells; although bark becomes thicker with age, its rate of growth is exceedingly slow as compared with that of wood. Thus, as stems grow older, the proportion of wood to bark increases enormously, so that the major part of the volume of the larger limbs and trunks of trees is wood, or xylem. This increase of xylem over bark is in part a result of the fact that all the secondary xylem formed by the cambium is retained within the body of the stem, whereas the outer portion of the bark is slowly and continuously sloughed off.

The Primary Tissues of Woody Stems

In woody stems of the age described in the preceding paragraphs, the tissues present are chiefly of **secondary** origin; that is, tissues produced by the activity of cambium and cork cambium radially in the stem, from the latter part of the first season's growth of the twig through succeeding years. If one examines a cross section of a twig cut in the young part of the maturation region during the early part of the season's growth of that twig, one finds only **primary** tissues present;

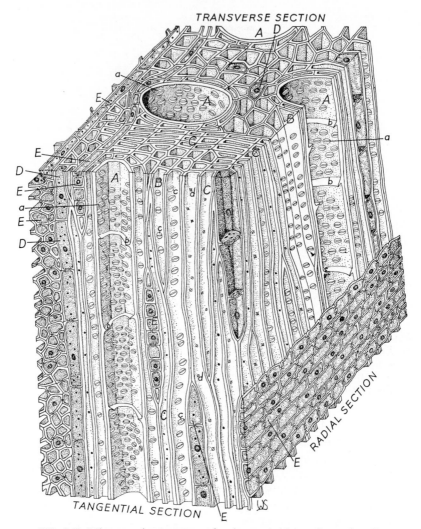

FIG. 8–5. Microscopic structure of oak wood (three dimensional).

A. vessels: *a.* pit in vessel walls;
b. remnants of end walls of vessel elements

B. tracheids: *c.* pits in tracheid walls

C. wood fibers: *d.* pits in fiber walls

D. parenchyma cells

E. vascular rays

that is, tissues formed by growth of the meristematic tissue of the shoot tip and later differentiated into various mature tissues, such as xylem, phloem, etc. These primary permanent structures are:
1. **epidermis;** 2. **cortex;** 3. **phloem;** 4. **xylem;** 5. **pith.** Figure 8–4A shows a transverse section of a woody twig with its primary tissues labeled.*

The epidermis is a single surface layer of cells, the outer walls of which are usu-

---

* The student should refer to Chapter 3 and review the subject of tissue structure before he proceeds with his study of this chapter.

VASCULAR RAY

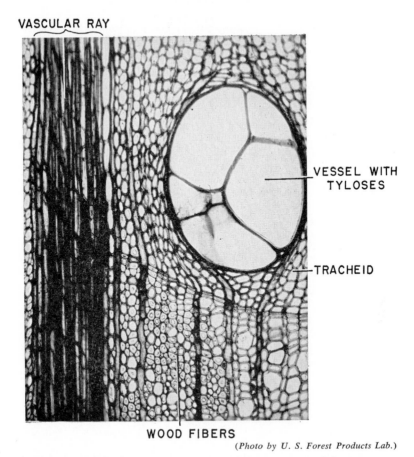

VESSEL WITH
TYLOSES

TRACHEID

WOOD FIBERS

(*Photo by U. S. Forest Products Lab.*)

FIG. 8–6. Highly magnified transverse view of oak wood, showing a large vessel with tyloses.

ally **cutinized** (see Chapter 4) and thus are nearly waterproof. The epidermis is a protective tissue that serves chiefly to prevent excessive evaporation of water from the underlying tissues. The cortex varies in thickness of stems in different species and is composed usually of **collenchyma** or strengthening cells, just under the epidermis, and **parenchyma** cells, which function principally in the storage of food and other materials. The **stele,** or vascular cylinder, is composed of several tissues or groups of tissues: **phloem, cambium, xylem,** and **pith.** Pericycle, the stelar tissue between the phloem and

the cortex, is typically absent from the stems of higher plants.

The phloem lies inside the cortex and consists of **sieve tubes** and their adjoining **companion cells, phloem fibers,** and **parenchyma cells.** Sieve tubes are not individual cells, but are rows of elongated, thin-walled living cells **(sieve tube members)** arranged end to end (Figure 4–7). The end walls (and often side walls) of sieve tube members contain perforations through which cytoplasm passes from one cell to another (although sieve tube members are living, they contain no nuclei at maturity). The wall

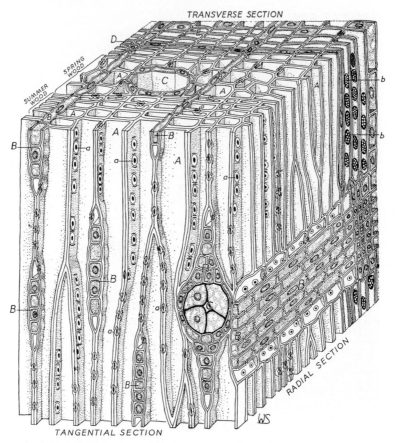

FIG. 8–7. Microscopic structure of a portion of a pine stem (three dimensional).

A. tracheids: *a.* pits in tracheid walls   C. resin canals
B. vascular rays   D. cambium
                E. phloem cells: *b.* sieve plates

perforations promote the passage of foods from one sieve tube member to another and thus are extremely important in the major function of phloem—namely, the conduction of foods, chiefly in a downward direction in stems. Companion cells are living cells that border upon sieve tube members and in some way participate in the conduction of foods in the phloem. Phloem fibers are elongated, tapering, thick-walled strengthening cells, and phloem parenchyma cells are important in food storage. Phloem fibers are of considerable economic importance; linen and Indian hemp fibers, obtained from the stems of flax and Indian hemp plants, are phloem fibers. Linen fibers are used in the weaving of fine textiles and in the manufacture of strong threads and cords, such as those used in making shoes and in binding books. Hemp fibers are used chiefly in binder twine, rope, carpets, mats, burlap bags, and upholstery.

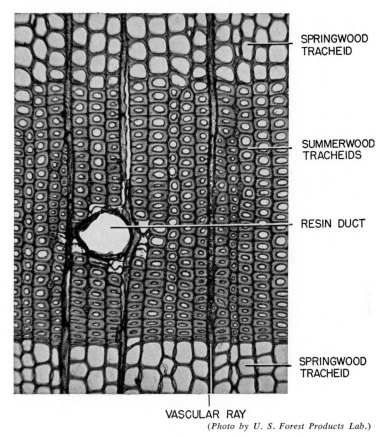

SPRINGWOOD TRACHEID

SUMMERWOOD TRACHEIDS

RESIN DUCT

SPRINGWOOD TRACHEID

VASCULAR RAY

(Photo by U. S. Forest Products Lab.)

FIG. 8–8. Highly magnified portion of transverse section of pine wood, showing portions of two growth rings.

Inside the phloem is the **cambium (vascular cambium),** a single circular row of meristematic cells that are thin walled, elongated, and commonly rectangular as seen in cross section. The cambium is a meristematic tissue, which, by repeated cell divisions, forms secondary phloem tissue on its outer surface and secondary xylem cells on its inner surface. It is chiefly through this production of secondary tissues by the cambium that stems grow in diameter.

Inside the cambium is the **xylem,** or wood, which is composed of **vessels** (Figure 8–5), **xylem fibers, tracheids,**

xylem parenchyma cells, and **vascular rays.** These cell types and cell groups were described in Chapter 4. All these types of cells are found in the wood of most flowering plants. In most gymnosperms, such as pines, however, vessels and wood fibers are not present, the wood being composed almost entirely of tracheids and ray cells (Figure 8–7). There are occasionally other types of structures present in the xylem of some species of woody plants—for example, the **resin canals** of pines and other gymnosperms. The vessels and tracheids conduct water and dissolved substances,

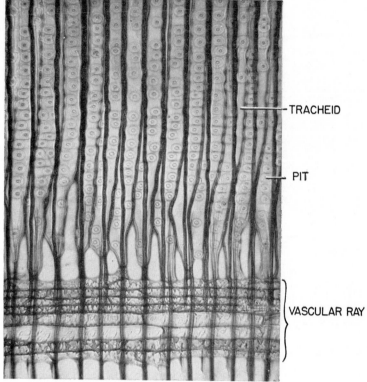

TRACHEID

PIT

VASCULAR RAY

(Photo by U. S. Forest Products Lab.)

FIG. 8–9. Highly magnified radial section of pine wood, showing longitudinal views of tracheids and side view of a ray.

chiefly nutrient solutes from the soil, upward through stems and furnish support to the stem; wood fibers function principally as strengthening and supporting cells, and wood parenchyma cells store food. **Pith,** a tissue located in the center of the stem, is composed of thin-walled parenchyma cells, the function of which is storage of foods. In some species of woody plants, the pith is alive only in the very young twigs, in others it is still alive in older branches of considerable size. **Pith rays** are broad, radially elongated bands of parenchyma cells that extend from the pith outward to the cortex, separating the vascular bundles. In a transverse section of a young twig they have

the appearance of the radiating spokes of a wheel. The first rays that form in a twig are a result of the growth of the terminal meristem in the bud and are thus primary in origin. They function in storage and in lateral conduction. As the cambium grows and forms secondary tissues it produces new rays that are of secondary origin and are called **vascular rays.** These are thought to be similar in function to pith rays.

The epidermis and cortex are continuous layers of cells in a twig of the type described in preceding paragraphs. In such a twig, however, in the early portion of its first season's existence, the xylem and phloem tissues are often not

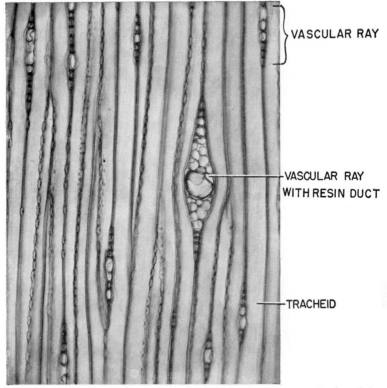

VASCULAR RAY

VASCULAR RAY
WITH RESIN DUCT

TRACHEID

(*Photo by U. S. Forest Products Lab.*)

FIG. 8–10. Highly magnified tangential section of pine wood, showing longitudinal views of tracheids and end views of rays.

arranged in continuous layers, as are the epidermis and cortex, but occur as separate groups of xylem and phloem cells. Each of these groups of primary cells is termed a **vascular bundle** and consists of xylem cells in its inner portion, phloem cells in its outer part, and between the xylem and the phloem, the cambium. This arrangement of the primary xylem and phloem into separate vascular bundles is characteristic of the very young stems of many woody plants but quite unlike the arrangement in young roots in which the discrete strands of primary phloem and xylem are arranged on alternate radii. In some woody species the primary phloem and xylem occur as continuous layers with no marked separation into bundles—that is, as concentric cylinders of tissue. Vascular bundles are arranged usually in a single circle, with the cambium present in the bundles and later extending across the pith rays in a continuous layer connecting adjacent bundles.

As stated previously, all the above-mentioned tissues of a woody twig in the early part of its first season's growth are **primary** tissues; that is, they have been produced as a result of the division of cells in the shoot tip and of the subsequent enlargement and differentiation of these newly formed cells. Especially noteworthy in these processes of differentia-

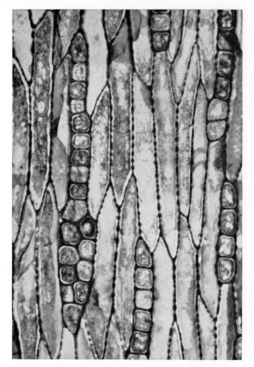

FIG. 8–11. *Juglans* (walnut) cambium in tangential section, showing elongated fusiform initials and smaller ray initials. Beaded appearance of walls is caused by pits.

tion is the fact that one of these primary tissues retains the most characteristic feature of the parent tissue from which it developed—specifically, the cambium is a meristematic tissue and possesses the same ability as the meristematic tissue of the bud, that is, the ability to produce new cells.

The Secondary Tissues of Woody Stems

After the primary tissues are formed in a young twig in the manner described above, little or no further lengthwise growth of this differentiated portion of the stem is possible. The terminal bud that produced these primary tissues continues its growth through the growing sea-

sons of successive years in woody stems (or is replaced by axillary buds that function in the same fashion), each year forming a new stem segment with its primary tissues as described above.

As stated in the preceding section, the primary tissues of a young twig are completed in the first few weeks of the first year's existence of that twig. Also early in the first year of its life, the twig begins to grow in diameter as a result of **secondary** growth that usually continues through a number of growing seasons, often for hundreds or even thousands of years. With each season's secondary growth, the twig or large branch or main trunk increases further in diameter (Figures 8–4C and 8–15).

This secondary growth occurs as a result of the continuing division of cambial cells (Figure 8–11) that produce in a radial direction secondary xylem cells between the primary xylem and the cambium and, also radially, secondary phloem cells between the primary phloem and the cambium. As the secondary phloem develops it presses outward, crushing much of the primary phloem. In most species of woody plants, when the cambium produces new xylem and new phloem it does so along its entire circumference; that is, secondary tissues are produced by the portions of cambium in the vascular bundles **(fascicular cambium)** as well as by the portions lying between adjacent vascular bundles **(interfascicular cambium).** Thus, these secondary tissues are formed in continuous layers, as contrasted with the separate bundles in which the primary tissues may be formed. The continuous nature of the secondary tissues is usually more noticeable in xylem than in phloem. In xylem and also in phloem of some woody stems, the secondary tissues are merely added to the primary

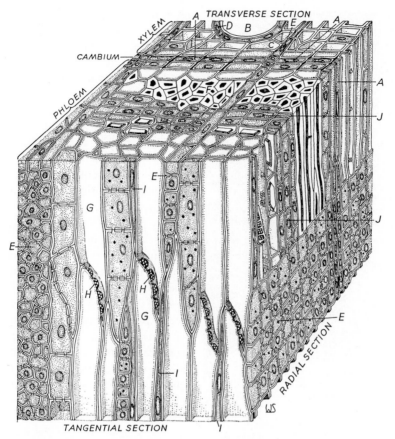

FIG. 8–12. Three-dimensional view of portion of a linden stem.

A. cambium
B. xylem vessel
C. wood fibers
D. xylem parenchyma
E. vascular rays

F. phloem fibers
G. sieve tubes
H. sieve plates
I. companion cells
J. phloem parenchyma

tissues in the vascular bundles, which thus remain separate and distinct throughout the life of the stem. In these, obviously, the secondary tissues are not formed in continuous layers.

The kinds of cells formed by the cambium in its divisions are generally the same as those formed by the meristematic tissue of the bud in the primary tissues that it forms—namely, vessel members, tracheids, wood fibers, and wood parenchyma in the xylem, and sieve

tube members, companion cells, fibers, and parenchyma in the phloem tissue (Figures 8–7 and 8–12). The cambium also produces vascular rays. These parenchymatous structures extend from the phloem inward through the xylem for various distances, the earliest formed (oldest) almost reaching the pith. As woody stems grow in diameter, the number of vascular rays formed by the cambium increases, so that the areas of xylem between such rays remain fairly con-

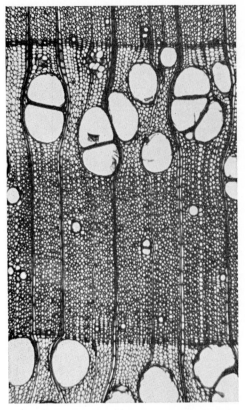

FIG. 8–13. Ring-porous wood of *Fraxinus* (ash) in transverse section. Segment of growth ring is shown in center. Large vessel elements are in springwood, smaller cells below in summerwood.

stant. If new rays were not formed, the distance between first-formed vascular rays at their outer ends would constantly increase as the circumference of the stem increased. The continual formation of new rays by the cambium ensures an adequate supply of rays with reference to the increasing circumference of the xylem and phloem. Although the derivatives of cambium cells are formed chiefly in the radial direction, producing secondary tissue on the inner and outer cambial surfaces, there is also a certain amount of cambial growth in a tangential direction,

as a result of which the actual circumference of the cambium increases. The production of new cambial cells in a tangential direction, then, enables the cambium ring to expand in circumference as it is pushed outward by the xylem with each growing season.

Another group of secondary tissues is produced by the **cork cambium** (Figure 8–14), a meristematic tissue that often has, like the vascular cambium, the form of a continuous ring in the stem, as seen in transverse section. In some species of woody plants, several layers of cork cambium develop; in such stems, the cork cambium layers are not continuous around the stem but occur as tangentially short bands of growing tissue. The roughness of the outer bark of trees is attributable in part to irregular and unequal rates of growth in the numerous patches of cork cambium. The cork cambium usually develops from certain of the parenchyma cells in the outer portion of the cortex. As these cells become meristematic, they produce radially by cell division new cells both on the outer and inner faces of the cork cambium. Those cells formed on the outer surface of the cork cambium become transformed into **cork** cells, which soon become suberized and die. These cork cells prevent the passage of water because of the fatty suberin in their walls, and, as a result, the cells of the cortex and epidermis outside the cork soon die because they are unable to get water. These dead cortical and epidermal cells flake away gradually, partly as a result of rain and wind action and partly because they are split by the outward pressure of the expanding tissues inside them. The cells formed on the inner surface of the cork cambium **(phelloderm)** are similar to some of the primary cells of the cortex and are formed in smaller

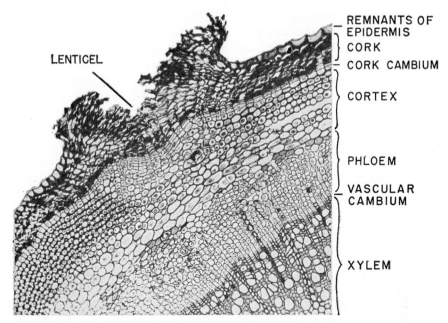

LENTICEL

REMNANTS OF
EPIDERMIS
CORK
CORK CAMBIUM
CORTEX
PHLOEM
VASCULAR
CAMBIUM
XYLEM

FIG. 8–14. Cross section of a portion of a young woody stem, showing periderm, lenticel, and the arrangement of vascular tissues.

numbers than the cork cells outside the cork cambium. The cork cambium, cork, and phelloderm cells are collectively called the **periderm.** Thus as a woody twig grows, the epidermis and outer portion of the cortex, both primary tissues, are cast off, and the protection of the internal tissues of the stem against injury, the attacks of parasites, and excessive evaporation, is assumed by the layers of cork cells. This replacement of stem epidermis and cortex occurs in some species of woody plants during the first year's growth of a twig, in other species, not until several years have elapsed.

The term **bark** is used for the aggregation of all tissues outside the cambium. Thus the young bark of a tree consists of secondary and primary phloem, remnants of the inner portion of the cortex, phelloderm, cork cambium, and cork and epidermal remnants, named in the order of location from the cambium outward.

The term outer bark is applied to all those tissues outside the conducting phloem, that is, the periderm and all the tissues isolated by it. Inner bark is the term applied to the actively conducting phloem. Since the phloem of a woody stem is a tissue of bark, another function of bark is the conduction of substances, chiefly foods, downward into the lower portions of the stem and into the roots. In the outer bark of some species of trees, as in the cork oak, the cork tissue is composed of very distinct layers of cork cells. These layers are usually annual layers; that is, each layer of cork cells is the amount of cork formed by the cork cambium in one season's growth. The periderm of the cork oak tree is the source of commercial cork.

In the young bark of woody stems, **lenticels** (Figure 8–14) are present as tiny raised pores in circular or elongated blisters. As stated in the preceding chapter, lenticels are openings through which gaseous exchange between the internal tissues of a stem and the external air may occur. As a rule, carbon dioxide and other gases formed as physiological by-products diffuse outward through these lenticels, and oxygen moves inward from the external air to the stem tissues. The brownish spongy streaks that traverse bottle corks are the lenticels of the bark of the cork oak. Lenticels develop usually at the places where the pores (stomata) in the stem epidermis are located. A large number of the lenticels of twigs occurs at or near the outer ends of vascular rays. As stems grow older and the young bark is furrowed by the growth of the internal tissues, lenticels are no longer apparent on the surfaces of the bark.

In the temperate zones and also in those tropical regions in which marked wet and dry seasons occur, climatic and other conditions are not suitable for the continued growth of the cambium throughout the year. As a result the cambium experiences alternating periods of activity and of dormancy, or relative inactivity. During each of the active seasons, of which there is usually one per year, the cambium forms a new layer of xylem (wood) and a new layer of phloem. Since the amount of secondary phloem tissue formed in one growing season is relatively small it is difficult, often impossible, to distinguish such seasonal layers in the phloem. In xylem, however, which increases much more rapidly than the phloem, the yearly amounts are visible to the naked eye in transverse stem sections as distinct concentric rings, called growth rings or growth layers (Figure 8–15). A careful examination of each growth ring, in most woody species, shows it to be made up of two fairly distinct bands of xylem cells (Figure 8–13) —an inner portion called the springwood,

in which the vessels and tracheids, especially the former, are relatively large, and an outer portion, the summerwood, in which these cells are much smaller in diameter and thicker walled than those of the springwood. As these names imply, the springwood is the portion of each growth layer formed in the spring of the growing season and the summerwood is that formed during the summer of the same growing period. Springwood appears less dense than summerwood because of its larger cells. The growth ring formed during the first season of a twig's secondary growth is the innermost one, the younger rings being formed in yearly succession, with the youngest ring immediately inside the cambium. It is because of the alternating bands of springwood and summerwood in the growth layers of a woody stem that the rings are so distinct (Figure 8–15).

Since, under ordinary conditions, one ring of xylem is formed each year, the number of such rings in a tree trunk and in a branch indicates the approximate age, respectively, of the whole tree and of the branch. In young twigs in which the first-formed bark has not yet been split, there are thus two methods of determining the age of any portion of the twig—by counting back the number of terminal bud scars from the terminal bud, and by counting the number of growth rings as seen in a transverse section of the twig. The growth of a cambium layer begins as the leaf buds form leaves and continues during most of the period that the leaves are present during the growing season. Thus, there is a correlation between a growth layer and a single crop of leaves. Rarely, as a result of the complete destruction of all the leaves of a tree by insect attack or drought, a second crop of leaves may be formed in one growing

(Photo by U. S. Forest Service.)

FIG. 8–15. Cross section of loblolly pine trunk, showing effect of light upon growth ring thickness. The growth rings inside the *X*'s were formed while the young tree was densely shaded by older trees. The growth rings outside the *X*'s were formed after the older trees had been removed and the young pine trees received abundant sunlight.

season. In such event, a second ring of xylem is formed by the cambium as the new crop of leaves develops, and thus there are fomed in one season *two* xylem rings. For this reason, the number of xylem rings is not always an exact index of the age of a tree, but rather an approximate one. Since the formation of two rings in one season is quite rare, however, the number of rings in most trunks can be regarded as indicating accurately the age of a tree.

The widths of the growth rings in a tree trunk or branches are not uniform. Some rings are very wide, others very-narrow. The differences in ring width in the same stem are attributable to the varying climatic conditions that obtained when the various rings were formed. Probably most effective of the environmental factors influencing ring width is moisture, although such factors as light, temperature, and soil aeration are also important. Growth layers formed in seasons of abundant rainfall are usually wider than those produced in years

(*Photos by C. F. Hottes.*)

FIG. 8–16. *Left:* Fungi growing in sapwood of dead log. Note that the heartwood is free of fungi. *Right:* Fungi on sapwood of dead log.

of drought. The growth rings of small trees shaded by large trees are usually narrow; when the large trees are cut and sunlight is thus able to reach the leaves of the smaller trees, thereby increasing the rate of food manufacture, the new rings become wider. Trees growing in swamps often have narrow rings; if the swamps are drained, thus increasing the oxygen content of the soil, the rings produced in years following the drainage frequently become wider. Especially striking in the relation of growth ring width to these climatic factors is the fact that all individuals of a given species of tree growing under similar environmental conditions produce similar rings in the same season. Thus, a ring formed in a certain season possesses individuality among the other growth rings in the tree, and this individuality of ring structure extends to simultaneously formed rings in other trees of the same species if they have grown under virtually the same conditions. As a result, the same succession of wide and narrow growth rings may be traced in trees of the same species in the same locality. Not only is the total width of a growth layer influenced by the amount of precipitation, but the relative proportions

of springwood and summerwood are affected by the distribution of rainfall through the growing season. Experiments of the U. S. Forest Products Laboratory have shown that the summerwood in certain pines may be considerably increased by providing abundant water in the summer by irrigation.

The widths of growth rings, then, reflect the environmental conditions that obtained when the rings were formed, and it is thus possible by studying the structure of these rings to read something of climatic conditions of past years. Astronomers have made such studies and have found that there is a remarkable coincidence between sunspot cycles and climatic cycles, as evidenced by growth rings. Professor A. E. Douglass, an astronomer of the University of Arizona, and other investigators, have made extensive studies of this type. In his work, Professor Douglass became interested in some of the old Indian pueblos of the Southwestern United States, the ages of which formed for many years a subject of dispute among archaeologists. Douglass made thin sections of wood beams found in the roofs of some of these dwellings and compared them with sections of tim-

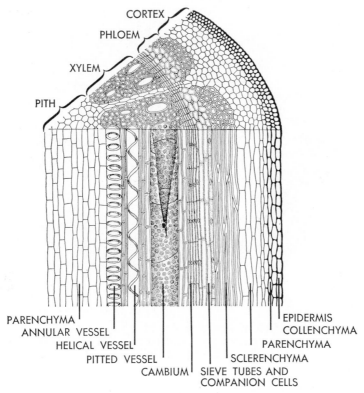

CORTEX
PHLOEM
XYLEM
PITH

PARENCHYMA
ANNULAR VESSEL
HELICAL VESSEL
PITTED VESSEL
CAMBIUM
EPIDERMIS
COLLENCHYMA
PARENCHYMA
SCLERENCHYMA
SIEVE TUBES AND
COMPANION CELLS

FIG. 8–17. Diagrammatic three-dimensional view of a herbaceous dicot stem.

bers of known age. By matching the individualistic growth rings in the sections of known and unknown age, he was able to determine the approximate years in which the roof wood had been cut. Dendrochronologists, specialists who make studies such as the one described above, have recently reported a bristlecone pine (*Pinus aristata*) that is over *4600 years old,* making it the oldest known living individual organism.

As woody stems grow older, physical and chemical changes occur in the oldest growth layers (those nearest the center of the stem) and gradually proceed outward as the growth in diameter of the xylem increases in successive years. In many species the protoplasts of the par-enchyma cells that surround the vessels and tracheids grow through the pits in the walls of these conducting cells. These balloonlike growths **(tyloses)** continue to enlarge until they fill considerable portions of the cavities of the vessels and tracheids, forming plugs that prevent further conduction of water and dissolved substances by the cells. In some trees, tyloses may develop in very young growth layers. The older, nonconducting growth rings contain no living cells and are known collectively as **heartwood;** the younger, actively conducting rings situated outside the heartwood contain many living cells and constitute the **sapwood** (Figure 8–3). The only benefit that heartwood gives to a woody stem is

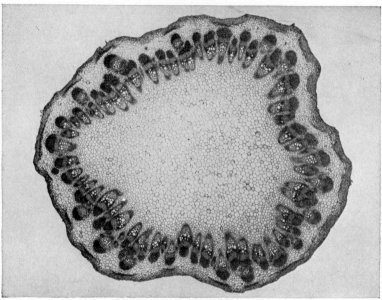

(Photo by Triarch Botanical Products.)

FIG. 8–18. Photograph of a cross section of a herbaceous stem, showing extensive pith in center, ring of vascular bundles, a narrow cortex outside the vascular bundles, and the epidermis on the surface of the stem.

strength and support. Often the heartwood of a tree is burned out or rotted away and yet the remainder of the tree continues to live; so long as the sapwood is intact, conduction of materials upward continues. Trees that have suffered the loss of the heartwood are weakened, however, and are often blown over by winds. Various chemical agents usually not present in sapwood, or present in sapwood in small quantities, become abundant in heartwood: **pigments,** which cause the color of heartwood to darken, **resins,** and **tannins,** bitter substances that discourage the visits of certain wood-rotting organisms. As new growth layers are formed on the surface of the woody cylinder of a tree, the older (innermost) rings of the sapwood are converted into heartwood, usually at about the same rate as the new rings are formed. Thus, the heartwood increases in diameter with the yearly secondary growth of the xylem, whereas the width of the sapwood remains fairly constant in most species.

In the wood of some species of trees, spruce and sycamore for example, the wood is fairly uniform and there is no structural differentiation of wood into heartwood and sapwood, although only the younger growth rings function actively in conduction. Tyloses are absent from the wood of some tree species; they are rare or absent from the wood of pin oak, for example.

These various chemical and physical changes that result in the transformation of sapwood into heartwood increase the weight and usually the hardness and resistance to decay of wood. The tannins and resins (sometimes called **natural preservatives**) often repel insects, fungi, and other wood-destroying organisms, the plugged vessels increase the difficulty of

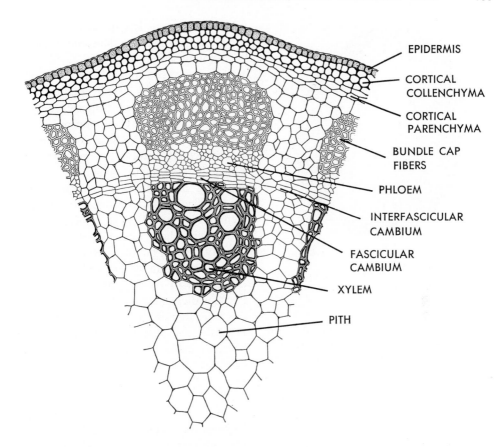

EPIDERMIS

CORTICAL
COLLENCHYMA

CORTICAL
PARENCHYMA

BUNDLE CAP
FIBERS

PHLOEM

INTERFASCICULAR
CAMBIUM

FASCICULAR
CAMBIUM

XYLEM

PITH

FIG. 8–19. Sector of herbaceous dicotyledonous stem (sunflower) as seen in cross section.

penetration of such organisms into the wood, and the absence of living cells reduces the amounts of stored food that might be used by these organisms in heartwood. Thus, heartwood lumber is more durable than that from sapwood and is more valuable for construction purposes, particularly for timbers, poles, and boards that are exposed to the outdoor elements (Figure 8–16).

THE INTERNAL STRUCTURE OF HERBACEOUS STEMS

The flowering plants are classified in two major groups: *monocotyledons* and *dicotyledons*. Monocotyledons, which include corn, wheat, bluegrass, and other grasses, lilies, tulips, irises, and orchids, have one cotyledon in their embryos, flower parts usually in threes, and typically long, narrow leaves with parallel main veins. Dicotyledons, which include oaks, maples, castor beans, potatoes, beans, roses, and sunflowers, have two cotyledons in their embryos, flower parts most often in fours or fives, and leaves principally with networks of veins. Dicotyledons include most woody stemmed flowering plants and, in addition, many thousands of species with herbaceous stems. Monocotyledons are chiefly herba-

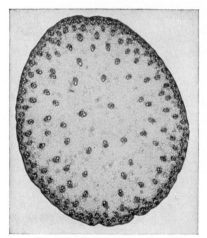

(*Photo by Triarch Botanical Products.*)

FIG. 8–20. Cross section of a monocotyledonous stem (corn).

ceous stemmed plants, although some
monocotyledons (for example, palms)
are trees and shrubs. These two large
groups of flowering plants have fundamental differences in stem structure,
which will be described in the following
sections.

Herbaceous Stems of Dicotyledons

It has been stated elsewhere that the
growth of herbaceous stems is chiefly primary and that ordinarily little or no secondary growth occurs. This is true both
of herbaceous dicotyledonous and of
monocotyledonous stems.

The herbaceous stems (Figure 8–17)
of dicots are strikingly similar to the stems
of many woody plants in their primary
condition, before the beginning of their
secondary growth. In herbaceous dicot
stems, as in young woody twigs in the primary state, the terminal bud in its growth
forms the following primary tissues: epidermis, cortex, phloem, xylem, and pith
(Figure 8–18). The epidermis in herba-

ceous dicot stems is a single layer of protective cells, similar to the epidermal cells
of a young woody stem; the cortex of a
herbaceous dicot is much like that of a
woody twig, but is usually thinner. The
stele is composed of primary phloem,
cambium, primary xylem, and pith, as in
a young woody twig. These stele tissues in
a herbaceous dicot stem are arranged
either in continuous layers, as in fox-
glove, or in the form of separate vascular bundles, as in clover and delphinium
stems (Figure 8–19). In some plants, as
sunflowers, these stele tissues are in the
form of distinct bundles in the young portions of the stem system and in continuous layers in older parts. In some herbaceous dicots, the cambium is a continuous layer that extends as a complete circle
both through and between the vascular
bundles, while in other species, cambium
cells are found only within the vascular bundles, and do not occur between
them.

Thus, in general, the anatomy of herbaceous dicot stems is roughly comparable with that of a young woody twig in its
first year. The most conspicuous difference between the two is in the relative
activity of the cambium: in herbaceous
dicot stems it usually produces little secondary tissue and thus relatively little
growth in diameter, whereas in woody
stems it is very active, producing large
numbers of secondary phloem and secondary xylem cells that bring about a
marked yearly increase in the diameter
of the stem. Herbaceous stems ordinarily
live but a single year, as contrasted with
the usually perennial woody stems, and
hence are smaller and much softer than
woody stems. The pith tissue of herbaceous dicot stems ordinarily occupies a
much larger proportion of stem volume
than it does in woody stems.

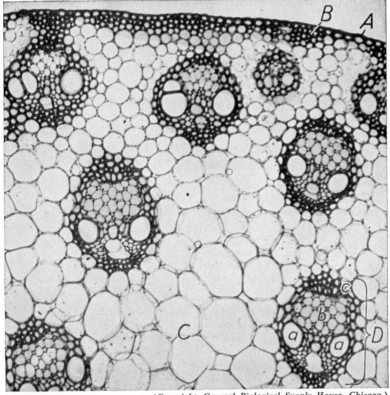

FIG. 8–21. Highly magnified portion of a cross section of a corn stem.

A. epidermis
B. sclerenchyma

C. parenchyma
D. vascular bundle: *a.* xylem; *b.* phloem; *c.* bundle sheath

Herbaceous Stems of Monocotyledons

Most monocot species (with the exception of certain palms and members of the lily family) have no cambium in their stems and thus have no secondary growth, their tissues being entirely primary in origin; that is, they all develop from the cells produced by a terminal bud. The xylem and phloem of monocot stems are never arranged in continuous layers, but are in individual vascular bundles that are usually scattered through the stem rather than arranged in a definite circle as in those dicots with their vascular tissues in separate bundles (Figures 8–20 and 8–21). The vascular bundles are usually surrounded by strengthening cells, which, together with sclerenchyma fibers lying between the outermost vascular bundles and the epidermis, constitute the major strengthening tissues of monocot stems. In the vascular bundles of monocots, as in those of dicots, the phloem is usually in the outer portion of each bundle, with the xylem forming the inner part of each bundle (Figure 8–21). The surfaces of monocot stems are covered by a protective epidermis, as are the stems of herbaceous dicots. Inside the epidermis and among the scattered vascular bundles is an extensive parenchymatous tissue, sometimes called pith or fundamental tissue. This tissue acts primarily as a storage and supporting tissue.

Because of the absence of cambium in most monocots there is relatively little growth in diameter of monocot stems. The small amount of radial growth that does occur is caused by the increase in size of primary cells, rather than by the formation of new cells. Obviously such growth is limited by the capacities of these primary cells to expand and is never great.

LEAF TRACES AND LEAF GAPS

At each node of a stem, vascular bundles separate from the xylem and phloem tissues of the stem, pass out through the cortex, and enter the **petiole,** or stalk of a leaf. These vascular bundles that branch from the vascular system of the stem and enter the petiole are called **leaf traces.** Wherever a leaf trace branches from the conducting tissues of a stem, a small break occurs in the latter. Such an interruption in a portion of stem vascular tissues is called a **leaf gap** (see Figure 24–1). The number of leaf traces that enter a leaf varies in different species of plants; in some species there is only one trace per leaf, in others three, five, or even more. These traces continue out through the petioles and as a result of their branching, form the vein system of the leaf. Thus there is a continuation of the vascular tissues of plants from roots through stems into the leaves and likewise into the buds and flowers of stems.

⫷⫷⫷   SUMMARY

1. A stem grows in length as a result of formation and enlargement of cells produced by meristematic cells at the stem tip.
2. A growing stem tip, like a growing root tip, exhibits a region of cell division, a region of cell enlargement, and a region of cell maturation.
3. As a stem tip grows, it forms three tissue layers: protoderm, which forms the epidermis of the stem; procambium, which develops into primary xylem and phloem; and ground meristem, which forms pith and cortex.
4. Woody stems are generally regarded as more primitive, though structurally more complex, than herbaceous stems.
5. A transverse section of a woody stem shows the following regions:
   a. Bark.
   b. Cambium, just inside the bark.
   c. Xylem (wood), inside the cambium.
   d. Pith in the center of the stem.
6. In young internodes of woody stems in their first season of life, the tissues present are largely primary, that is, formed by growth and differentiation of cells from the bud. These primary structures, in the order of their arrangement from outside in, are: epidermis, cortex, phloem, cambium, xylem, and pith.
7. Primary xylem and phloem are arranged in vascular bundles, or in a continuous layer, with phloem cells almost always outside the xylem cells, cambium between the xylem and phloem.

8. Secondary xylem and phloem are formed by the cambium, xylem cells being formed on the inside of the cambium, phloem outside.

9. After the early part of their first season of life, woody stems consist chiefly of secondary tissues. Growth in diameter of woody stems is thus brought about by the production of secondary tissues by the cambium. Secondary xylem is produced more rapidly by the cambium than is secondary phloem.

10. Phloem tissue consists of sieve tubes, companion cells, parenchyma, and phloem fibers. Xylem consists of wood fibers, tracheids, vessels, parenchyma, and vascular ray cells. In some plants, one or more of these kinds of cells may be absent from the xylem or phloem.

11. Vascular rays are bands of cells extending radially from the xylem outward into the phloem. They originate in the cambium and conduct substances laterally.

12. A meristematic tissue (one or more groups) called the cork cambium develops from parenchyma cells in the cortex and forms cork cells on the surface of woody stems. Large masses of cork cells constitute most of the rough, outer bark of woody plants. The inner bark consists of actively conducting phloem. Cork cambium, cork, and phelloderm constitute the periderm.

13. The outer bark is primarily a group of protective tissues, the inner bark a group of food-storing and food-conducting tissues.

14. In the temperate zones and in those parts of the tropics with marked wet and dry seasons, the xylem is formed by cambium in definite rings, usually at the rate of one per year. These growth rings near the base of a trunk indicate the age of a tree.

15. Each growth ring in most temperate zone woody plants consists of a layer of rather large cells (springwood) and a layer of smaller cells (summerwood).

16. The thickness of growth rings is usually a reflection of climatic conditions (especially rainfall) that obtained when the rings were formed.

17. As woody stems grow older, the innermost (oldest) growth rings die completely, become plugged up, and undergo chemical alterations. These growth layers are known collectively as heartwood. The outermost (youngest) growth rings, which contain some living cells and which remain open and able to conduct materials, constitute the sapwood.

18. Herbaceous stems grow relatively little in diameter and consist chiefly of primary tissues. The xylem and phloem of herbaceous stems are arranged in distinct vascular bundles, or in a continuous layer.

19. Dicot herbaceous stems usually possess cambium and have vascular bundles arranged usually in a single circle or square, as seen in cross section. Monocot stems, which are mostly herbaceous, usually have no cambium (except in palms and certain other plants) and have scattered vascular bundles.

SUGGESTED READINGS FOR INTERESTED STUDENTS

1. Brown, H. P., A. J. Panshin, and C. C. Forsaith, *Textbook of Wood Technology,* Vol. 1. McGraw-Hill, New York, 1949.

2. Esau, Katherine, *Anatomy of Seed Plants.* Wiley, New York, 1960.

3. Schulman, Edmund, "Bristlecone pine, oldest known living thing." *National Geographic Magazine,* Vol. CXIII, No. 3, pp. 354–372, March 1958.

≪← TOPICS AND QUESTIONS FOR STUDY

1. Describe briefly how a stem grows in length.
2. Name and describe the tissues formed by the apical meristem of stems.
3. Describe the interrelations between stem structure and stem functions.
4. Describe the gross structure of a mature woody stem as seen in cross section.
5. Distinguish between vascular cambium and cork cambium, from the standpoint of their location and functions.
6. Distinguish between primary and secondary tissues.
7. Name the primary tissues of a woody stem, describe their location, origin, and structure, and state their functions.
8. Describe the location, structure, and function of vascular rays. Distinguish between pith rays and vascular rays.
9. Name the secondary tissues of a woody stem, describe their location, origin, and structure, and state their functions.
10. Explain how stems grow in diameter.
11. In the life of a woody stem, does the cambium produce more xylem cells or more phloem cells? What is the evidence for your answer?
12. Where is the primary xylem in a stem located with reference to the secondary xylem? Which is older?
13. Where is the primary phloem in a stem located with reference to the secondary phloem?
14. What is the physiological importance of the continuing formation of new secondary vascular rays in the outer part of the xylem?
15. Describe the directions in which cambial growth occurs. Does the circumference of the vascular cambium remain constant throughout the life of a woody stem? Explain.
16. Describe the structure of bark, naming the tissues that compose it, and describing their origin and the types of cells of which they are composed.
17. Name three functions of bark.
18. Explain the factors responsible for the rough, furrowed structure of the bark of many woody stems.
19. Why does bark of trees not become as thick as their xylem?
20. What happens to the stem epidermis during cork formation?
21. Define "growth ring," and describe the major structural features of growth rings.
22. What environmental factors are responsible for the formation of distinct growth rings? Do all species of woody, perennial plants have growth rings? Explain.
23. What are tyloses?
24. Is the number of growth rings in a tree trunk always an exact indicator of the age of that tree? Explain.
25. Describe two ways of determining the age of a twig.

26. Distinguish between heartwood and sapwood, and describe the structural and physiological changes that occur during the transformation of sapwood into heartwood.
27. How do you explain that, despite the rotting away of their heartwood, many old trees are able to live for long periods?
28. Account for the fact that lumber cut from heartwood is usually more resistant to decay than lumber cut from sapwood.
29. Explain this apparent contradiction: heartwood lumber is more resistant to decay than sapwood lumber, yet, in a living tree, the heartwood may rot away, while the sapwood remains living and functioning.
30. Distinguish between monocotyledons and dicotyledons.
31. Name the primary tissues of a dicotyledonous herbaceous stem and describe their origin and structure.
32. Describe the structure of a typical vascular bundle of a herbaceous stem.
33. Describe the formation and extent of development of secondary tissues in herbaceous stems.
34. Contrast the structure and growth of herbaceous dicotyledonous and monocotyledonous stems.
35. Describe leaf traces and leaf gaps.

Wood and the Economic
Uses of Stems

The stem product of greatest usefulness to man is wood. The suitability of various kinds of wood for the many uses to which this product is put is determined largely by the chemical, anatomical, and physical properties of wood. In addition to these fundamental qualities, there are many other factors, chiefly of economic, political, and geographic nature, that determine how, when, and where certain specific kinds of woods are used. A brief discussion of the chemical and physical properties of wood is valuable in understanding the various economic uses that are made of wood.

CHEMICAL PROPERTIES OF WOOD

Water constitutes from 20 to 50 percent of the weight of wood as it is cut from trees. Immediately after being cut, wood begins to lose moisture and continues to do so until its moisture content may become as low as 3 or 4 percent. Of the dry materials in wood, **cellulose** is the chief constituent, occurring in proportions of 60 to 75 percent in various kinds of woods. Cellulose is the major *structural* component of the cell wall and is probably the most abundant organic compound formed in nature. Chemically, cellulose is a carbohydrate having the empirical formula $(C_6H_{10}O_5)_n$. Structurally, the cellulose molecule is composed of numerous glucose sugar units joined to form a chain. Aggregations of cellulose molecules make up the **microfibrils** that form the structural framework of the cell wall. **Lignin,** another important structural component of many cell walls, is deposited in the spaces separating the cellulose microfibrils. Lignin is second to cellulose in quantity, ranging approximately from 15 to 30 percent of the total weight of dry wood. Thus, cellulose and lignin together make up 75 percent or more of all solid materials of wood. Other structural wall components are **hemicelluloses** (noncellulosic carbohydrates of various kinds), certain pectic substances, and minerals. Most woods also contain *nonstructural* materials or **extractives** that may be removed with various solvents without altering structural properties. Examples of these are **resins, gums, oils, dyes,** and **tannins.**

THE PHYSICAL PROPERTIES OF WOOD

Most important among the physical properties of wood is weight, which is expressed usually in terms of **specific gravity** (weight of 1 cubic centimeter of a substance compared with the weight of an equal volume of water, which is 1 gram). In general, the hardness and strength of wood are proportional to the weight of wood, heavier woods being harder and stronger than woods of lighter weight. The specific gravity of *wood substance* is greater than that of *wood,* for wood is wood substance, *plus* a considerable amount of air that is held in its cell cavities. The specific gravities of most woods are less than 1.0; that is, they are lighter than water and will thus float on water. As soon as a piece of wood becomes waterlogged (has its air replaced by water) it sinks because its wood substance is

can balsa wood, the lightest commercially important wood, with a specific gravity of about 0.19, is lighter than cork (specific gravity 0.24) and is widely used in the construction of airplane models, life preservers, and Hollywood movie sets. At the other extreme are lignum vitae from Santo Domingo and tropical ironwood (*Condalia*) with specific gravities of 1.39 and 1.42 respectively. They are among the heaviest woods known. In the list below are presented the specific gravities of a number of important American woods (in dry, or seasoned condition).

All the softwoods on this list have specific gravities of less than 0.41, whereas the hardwoods vary from 0.44 to 0.67 in specific gravity. The term **softwood,** as used here and as interpreted by lumbermen, refers to gymnosperm woods such as pine, spruce, fir, cedar, and redwood, while the **hardwoods** are those of angiosperm trees, such as oaks, maples, beech, ash, and others listed above in the hardwood column.

Hardwoods		*Softwoods*	
Ash, white	.55	Incense cedar	.33
Beech	.56	Bald cypress	.38
Hickory	.67	Douglas fir	.40
Hard maple	.55	White pine	.36
Soft maple	.44	Western yellow pine	.35
White oak	.61	Redwood	.33
Black walnut	.52	White spruce	.32

heavier than water and it no longer has the buoyancy given it by air.

In general, woods of specific gravity less than 0.40 are regarded as light; those with specific gravities of 0.40 to 0.59 are termed moderately heavy; and those above 0.60 are described as very heavy. Most kinds of wood have specific gravities that range from 0.32 to 0.65. There are, of course, some woods that are lighter and some that are heavier. South Ameri-

Another physical property of woods that is important in determining their treatment and ultimate use is their moisture content. The water content of woods, as stated above, varies a great deal in different species. Before woods can be utilized for construction work, for furniture manufacture, and for other finished wood products, their moisture content must be reduced to 10 percent or lower. If this process, known as **seasoning,** is not

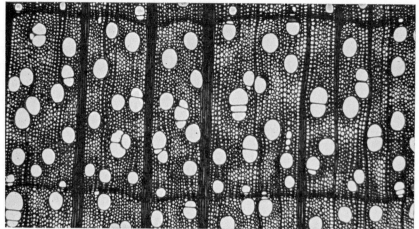

FIG. 9–1.

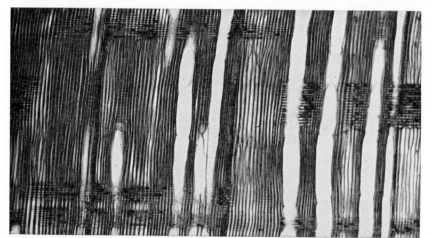

FIG. 9–2.

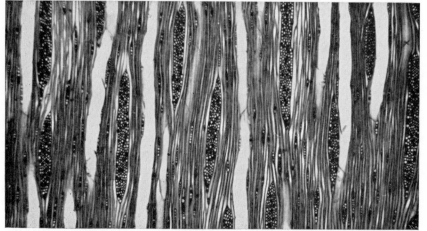

FIG. 9–3.

carefully executed, boards and timbers made from the improperly seasoned wood **warp** and **check.** Warping is an undesired bending or twisting of a piece of wood; checking is the formation of splits along the vascular rays. Both are obviously undesirable occurrences since they result in the loss of shape or cracking of objects made of wood. Seasoning of wood is achieved either by the air drying of boards in well-ventilated stacks or by drying them in special ovens known as **kilns.** As a result of gradual drying under the mechanical pressure of other boards, the stacked boards dry without change of shape—that is, without warping and usually without checking.

The strength and hardness of wood are determined by a number of factors, chief of which are: the specific gravity (weight), relative amounts of springwood and summerwood, presence or absence of tyloses, presence or absence of knots, checks, and decay areas, the degree of seasoning, and the relative numbers, lengths, and arrangement of wood fibers. Heavy woods, with large numbers of long, tightly packed wood fibers, with well-developed summerwood in the growth rings, and with numerous tyloses in the conducting cells are generally stronger and harder than woods of lower specific gravity, fewer fiber cells, etc. The principal reason why gymnosperm woods are softer and weaker than most angiosperm woods is the absence from the former and the presence in the latter of large numbers of thick-walled, heavily lignified fiber cells.

THE DURABILITY OF WOODS

The durability of wood, or the degree to which wood can withstand the forces of decay, has already been referred to in the section on heartwood and sapwood in the preceding chapter. It was stated there that timber and boards made of heartwood are normally more resistant to decay than those made of sapwood, because of the presence of tannins, resins, and other "natural preservatives" in heartwood, the lesser porosity of heartwood, and the smaller quantities of readily available foods in heartwood. Woods vary naturally in their durability. Among very durable woods are red cedar, cypress, black locust, redwood, black walnut, and hickory. Moderately durable are Douglas fir, honey locust, oaks, birch, hard maple, and various pines, while cottonwood, basswood, firs, and willows are exceedingly susceptible to decomposition.

Various methods are employed to increase artificially the durability of wood. These methods are of two types: those in which a protective surface layer is applied to wood to retard the entry of moisture and of organisms, and those in which the wood is impregnated with chemicals that are poisonous or distasteful to organisms and that thus discourage their growth.

WOOD SURFACES

The appearance of wood surfaces, as seen with the naked eye, varies with different species of wood. Each species has its own

---

(Facing) FIG. 9–1. *Acer* (maple) wood in transverse section, showing diffuse porosity. Vascular rays appear as vertical rows of cells. Demarcations between adjacent growth rings appear as wavy, horizontal rows of cells. FIG. 9–2. *Acer* wood in radial section. Vascular rays appear as horizontal rows of cells; vessels as large, clear vertical areas. FIG. 9–3. *Acer* wood in tangential section. Vascular rays appear as small, vertical files of cells and as large, lens-shaped masses of cells.

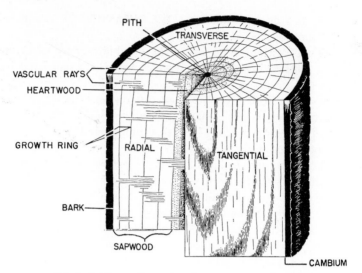

FIG. 9–4. Three-dimensional appearance of a log.

characteristic surface markings, by means of which different kinds of woods may be recognized.

Among the prominent features of such markings are the presence or absence of pores (vessels) and the arrangement of these vessels in woods. Woods of pine, firs, spruce, and other gymnosperms are termed **nonporous** because they lack vessels, in contrast to the **porous** woods of angiosperms in which vessels are usually the largest and most conspicuous xylem elements. In some porous woods, as in hackberry, oak, and ash, the pores differ markedly in size in the springwood and summerwood. Woods in which the vessels are larger and more numerous in the spring wood are called **ring porous** (Figure 8–13). In beech, maple, birch, and other **diffuse-porous** woods (Figures 9–1, 9–2, and 9–3), the vessels are more or less equally distributed throughout both spring- and summerwood and are not so variable in size as in ring-porous woods. The presence or absence of pores, and the distribution of the pores are impor-

tant characters used to identify various kinds of wood.

The term **wood figure** refers to the characteristic surface appearance of wood. The nature of the wood figure is determined by the arrangement and relative numbers and shapes of the constituent cells. Their figure as it is seen on boards or timbers, on table tops, wall panels, etc., varies within the same species of wood, according to the manner in which the boards are cut from the tree (Figure 9–4). In a **transverse** section, as described in Chapter 8, the growth rings appear as concentric circles and the vascular rays radiate from the center toward the circumference of the wood like the spokes of a wheel. Transverse wood surfaces are seen on cut stumps and on the ends of logs, beams, boards, and railroad ties, never as the large surfaces of boards or beams. Wood is not cut transversely into boards because the size of such boards would be limited by the diameter of the tree; furthermore, sections cut transversely, unless they are several

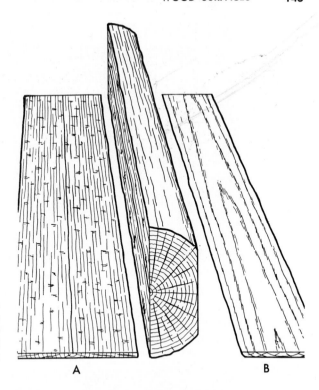

FIG. 9–5. Quarter-sawed (A) and plain-sawed (B) boards from log, illustrating how quarter-sawed (radially sawed) and plain-sawed (tangentially sawed) boards are cut from a log.

A   B

inches or more thick, tend to split along the rays and frequently along the growth rings, so that often the latter begin to separate from each other.

The wood surfaces most commonly visible on the larger expanses of boards, panels, beams, etc., are the surfaces of boards cut longitudinally from the wood of a tree. Such longitudinal sections may be cut in two ways (Figure 9–5): along a radius of the log, that is, from the center to the circumference; or, beginning at the circumference, the boards may be cut one after another lengthwise through the tree, tangentially to a radius of the log. A board cut on the radius, that is, parallel to the rays and across the growth rings, is called a **quarter-sawed** board; one cut at right angles to the rays and tangential to the rings is called a **plain-sawed** or **flat-sawed** board. In radial section (Figures 9–6 and 9–7) the growth rings are seen in

side view and appear as longitudinal streaks, groups of wide streaks (spring wood) alternating with groups of narrow streaks (summer wood); in such a section the vascular rays are seen in *side* view, as horizontal bands, often wavy and irregular in form, running across the growth layers at right angles to the direction of the latter. In quarter-sawed, or radial, sections, the vascular rays constitute the most conspicuous feature of the figure and many woods are quarter sawed to produce boards with the characteristic ray figure. Because only a small number of perfect quarter-sawed boards can be obtained from a log, these boards are rather expensive as compared with plain-sawed boards.

In plain-sawed or flat-sawed boards, the most conspicuous feature is the irregular, alternating light- and dark-colored portions of growth rings. In most boards,

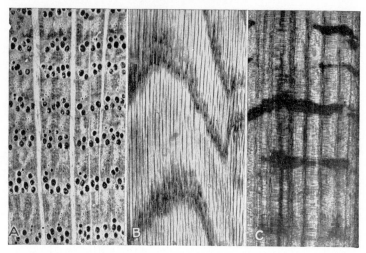

FIG. 9–6 (*above*). Red oak wood (a ring-porous hardwood). A: transverse section; B: tangential section; C: radial section.

FIG. 9–7 (*below*). Yellow birch wood (a diffuse-porous hardwood). A: transverse section; B: tangential section; C: radial section (light portion is sapwood, dark portion is heartwood).

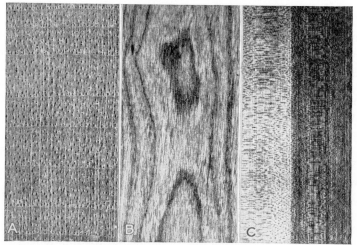

(*Photos by U. S. Forest Products Lab.*)

the *springwood* portions of the growth layers appear dark because their cells are larger and thus reflect less light than do the smaller cells of the *summerwood* portions, which appear lighter. In tangential sections, the cut ends of vascular rays are visible as narrow vertical streaks at frequent intervals in the wavy, growth ring bands. Of these three types of wood surfaces, tangential sections are seen most commonly because a plain-sawed log yields the greatest number of board feet and hence is the most economical method of sawing.

Knots, which frequently appear in boards, are the basal portions of branches that, during the years, have become buried in the wood of the main trunk by the formation of new growth rings over the branch base. The presence of knots usually weakens the boards or beams in which they occur and thus is not a desirable feature in boards, except those used as ornamental paneling.

(Photo by Armstrong Cork Co.)

FIG. 9–8. Bottle corks cut from the cork tissue of the cork oak tree.

THE USES OF WOOD

The uses of wood are so numerous that it is possible within the scope of this book to mention only the more important ones. The chief uses may be arranged in three categories: lumber, pulpwood, and fuel. Lumber includes structural timbers (rafters, joists, mine timbers, pilings, etc.), planing mill products (sashes, doors, wall panels, flooring, etc.), boxes and crates, furniture, veneers, railroad ties, cooperage (barrels and casks), and many others. Wood cellulose obtained from pulpwood finds widespread use in the manufacture of paper, rayon, cellophane, photographic film, synthetic lacquers, and plastics. The process of wood distillation results in the formation of wood alcohol, acetone, wood tar, wood gas, oils, turpentine, and other materials of great industrial value. Cordwood and charcoal are the principal forms in which wood is used as fuel.

OTHER ECONOMIC USES OF STEMS AND STEM PRODUCTS

The stems of plants furnish many materials, other than woods, that are important in our present civilization. Among these are fibers (flax, jute, ramie, Indian hemp, and others), tannins, dyes, perfumes (sandalwood), medicinal substances (quinine, cascara, slippery elm, ephedrine), cork (Figure 9–8), rubber, chicle (for chewing gum), gums, lacquer, turpentine, balsams, spices (cinnamon, sassafras), and foods. Among the important plants that produce abundant quantities of food for man in their stems are: sugar cane, asparagus, sugar maple, sorghum, and Irish potato.

⫷⫷⫷   S U M M A R Y

1. Wood is the most useful to man of all stem products.
2. The most abundant structural constituent of dry wood is cellulose. Second in abundance is lignin. Some nonstructural materials found in wood are resins, gums, oils, starch, dyes, and tannins.
3. Woods vary in their specific gravities from 0.2 to 1.45. Most softwoods (gymnosperm woods) have specific gravities from 0.30 to 0.40; most hardwoods (angiosperm woods) have specific gravities from 0.40 to 0.70. The heaviest

commercial wood is tropical ironwood (specific gravity = 1.42), the lightest is balsa (specific gravity = 0.19).

4. Heavy woods are usually hard, light woods soft.
5. Seasoning is the drying of woods so that they will not warp or check.
6. Factors that determine the hardness of wood are weight, numbers and arrangement of wood fibers, presence of knots, decay areas, etc., and relative amounts of spring- and summerwood.
7. Tyloses are parts of parenchyma cells that grow into the cavities of vessels and tracheids and plug them.
8. The durability of wood is determined in part by the quantities of resins, tannins, and other natural preservatives present.
9. Transverse sections of most woody stems show concentric growth rings, with radially extending vascular rays.
10. Quarter-sawed boards are cut from logs longitudinally along a radius and show the growth rings as vertical, alternating, regular bands of spring- and summerwood, with vascular rays extending horizontally across them as flat, ribbonlike structures.
11. Plain-sawed boards are cut lengthwise tangentially to a radius and show irregular, alternating bands of summer- and springwood, with the ends of vascular rays appearing as streaks in them.
12. Plain-sawed boards are seen most commonly in construction work, because this method of sawing is most economical.
13. Wood is used directly for the manufacture of many industrial products, and is also subjected to wood distillation or chemical treatment to produce many derivative products.
14. In addition to wood, stems furnish fibers, drugs, cork, rubber, gums, resins, spices, foods, and other products.

⫷ SUGGESTED READINGS FOR INTERESTED STUDENTS

1. Brown, H. P., A. J. Panshin, and C. C. Forsaith, *Textbook of Wood Technology,* Vol. I. McGraw-Hill, New York, 1949. Vol. II, 1952.
2. Hill, Albert F., *Economic Botany.* McGraw-Hill, New York, 1952.
3. Jane, F. W., *The Structure of Wood.* Adam and Charles Black, London, 1956.
4. Schery, Robert W., *Plants for Man.* Prentice-Hall, Englewood Cliffs, N. J., 1952.
5. *Wood Handbook,* Agriculture Handbook No. 72, U. S. Government Printing Office, Washington, 1955.

⇶ TOPICS AND QUESTIONS FOR STUDY

1. Name the principal chemical compounds that compose wood, and describe their relative abundance in wood.
2. Describe the relation of the chemical nature of wood to the uses made of wood.
3. Describe briefly the specific gravity characteristics of wood.
4. Distinguish between softwoods and hardwoods, and name several specific woods as examples of each.

5. Describe the processes of wood seasoning, and state the reason for seasoning woods.
6. What is meant by the durability of wood?
7. What are the major factors responsible for the strength and hardness of woods?
8. Describe several methods used to increase the durability of woods.
9. What are the major structural differences between gymnosperm and angiosperm woods?
10. Distinguish between ring-porous and diffuse-porous woods.
11. Describe the relation of wood anatomy to the physical properties and economic uses of woods.
12. Why is it easier to split wood lengthwise than crosswise?
13. Describe the gross appearance of the transverse, radial, and tangential surfaces of a block of wood.
14. Why is commercial lumber never produced by the transverse sawing of wood?
15. Which type of sawing, quarter sawing or plain sawing, yields the greater number of usable boards from a tree? Explain.
16. Why are quarter-sawed boards commonly more expensive than plain-sawed boards?
17. Are there any quarter-sawed boards produced by the plain sawing of a tree trunk? Explain.
18. Describe the origin and structure of knots in wood.
19. What is wood distillation? Name its principal products and look up their commercial uses.
20. Name some of the important commercial products derived from wood cellulose.
21. Name the economically important products, other than wood, that originate from plant stems.

10

The Physiology of Stems and Its Practical Implications

As stated in Chapter 3, the principal functions of aerial stems are: the production and support of leaves and flowers, and the conduction of materials upward, downward, and transversely. The production of leaves and flowers by buds has been described, and the strengthening features of stems have been adequately described in Chapter 8. In addition to these activities, many aerial stems store foods in their tissues, particularly in the parenchyma cells of the xylem, phloem, pith, cortex, and vascular rays.

CONDUCTION OF MATERIALS BY STEMS

The performance of the functions of support, of the formation of leaves and flowers, of food storage, and in some plants, of reproduction, involves processes or forces that are relatively easy to understand. In the conduction **(translocation)** of materials, however, there are many phenomena that have not been entirely elucidated; the problem of the rise of liquids and dissolved substances through

stems and of the paths these substances follow is most complex.

Ascent of Sap. The general term **sap** has been employed both in popular and botanical usage to refer to the water and dissolved materials that move upward, downward, and transversely in stems. Actually, the term is a rather ambiguous one and is used in a variety of ways. Among botanists, the word is applied most commonly to the water and dissolved materials that move upward in the younger growth rings (sapwood) of woody plants, although "sap" is frequently used to refer to the materials moving in the bark and to the watery juices of herbaceous plants and the softer parts of woody plants. In this discussion, the word will be used as synonymous with the ascending water and its solutes in xylem.

It is known that the chief avenue of the upward transport of water and dissolved substances is xylem tissue. Various types of experimentation support this view. The phloem and other tissues external to the

150

cambium may be completely cut away without any appreciable diminution in the upward movement of water and solutes. By careful manipulation of a narrow-bladed scalpel, the xylem of a stem can be completely severed with only a slight injury to the phloem. In this case, wilting of the leaves is apparent in a short time. Thus it is shown that the phloem does not conduct water upward, at least not in sufficient quantities to prevent wilting. If the severed lower end of a stem is placed in a solution of some water-soluble dye, with the remainder of the stem above the liquid, an examination of transverse sections of apical portions of the stem after several minutes or hours have elapsed reveals the presence of the dye only in the tracheids and vessels and occasionally in the parenchyma cells adjoining them. This demonstrates that the upward movement of the colored water has been exclusively through xylem.

It is believed that most inorganic materials (nutrients absorbed from the soil) are carried upward in the xylem, for the removal of the phloem and other tissues outside the cambium does not in most cases interfere with the normal supply of these materials to the leaves. There are some plants in which at least some of these inorganic substances move upward in phloem. It has been demonstrated, for example, that in some trees the removal of the phloem interferes with the movement of nitrogen into the leaves. In most plants, however, the greater portion of the nutrients that reach leaves seems to move upward through the xylem. In addition to mineral nutrients, organic materials, such as sugars, are frequently dissolved in the water that rises through the xylem. Such materials are present in the sap, particularly in the spring in our part of the world, when foods stored in the roots and lower

parts of the stem during the preceding growth season move upward and provide the developing buds with the nourishment that makes possible their growth. After the buds have opened and leaves have reached their mature size, relatively little sugar is found in the ascending solution. In some plants, when fruits are enlarging, sugars in higher concentrations are again present in the ascending sap.

Although botanists have been able to demonstrate rather conclusively that the upward movement of water and dissolved substances is largely through the xylem, they have not been so successful in explaining the cause of this ascent. Tremendous quantities of water pass out into the air by evaporation from the aerial parts of plants. This evaporated water, plus the amounts of water used for food manufacture and growth, rises through the xylem continuously. The rate of ascent is especially rapid during the growing season when plants are in leaf, and there is also a very slow ascent of materials through woody stems even during periods of dormancy. Many external factors of the environment, such as air temperature, humidity, and light intensity, are known to influence the rate of sap rise, but the actual internal causes of this movement are only partly known.

One of the earlier attempted explanations of sap rise is based upon the phenomenon of **root pressure.** When the rate of water loss from the shoot is low and soil moisture is abundant, sap will frequently exude from the stump following removal of the aerial shoot. Such "bleeding" is caused by root pressure that results from osmotic forces developed when living root cells take up solutes against a concentration gradient (active transport). The magnitude of root pressure, which varies considerably in different species of plants and in the same plant with varying internal and external conditions, is usually not much greater than atmospheric pressure and only rarely exceeds 2 or 3 atmospheres. Root pressure alone, however, is insufficient to account for the ascent of sap, for its maximum value under normal conditions, about 3 atmospheres, would be adequate to push sap into the leaves of only herbaceous plants and small trees. Root pressures of more than 12 atmospheres would be required to cause sap to rise in very tall trees, and forces of this magnitude have not been found under normal conditions. There are other objections to the explanation of sap rise on the basis of root pressure. The severed shoots of plants placed with their cut ends in water are usually able to absorb sufficient quantities of water to permit continued growth and food synthesis in the leaves for long periods of time; in such stems, since there are no roots present, there is obviously no root pressure and yet sap rise continues.

Moreover, there is usually very little correlation between the magnitude of root pressure and the rate and volume of sap movement; root pressure may be high in a plant, and yet the sap may simultaneously rise very slowly. Another objection to the suggestion that root pressure is a fundamental force responsible for sap rise is the fact that such pressure is not demonstrable in all species of plants. Still another objection is that, in temperate regions at least, root pressures are usually negligible during the summer when the rate of sap rise is most rapid.

When very fine open glass tubes, or tubes of certain other materials, are placed in a vertical position with their lower ends standing in water, ink, or similar liquids, the liquid rises in them to a level *above* the liquid level in the con-

tainer in which the tubes are standing. The smaller the diameters of the tubes, the higher is the level in them to which the liquids will rise. This rise of liquids in tubes is caused by the capillary or surface attraction between the molecules of the liquid and those of the tube substance. It has been suggested that this force of **capillarity** is involved in the ascent of sap, for xylem tracheids and vessels are hollow structures, roughly similar to the glass tubes in the experiment described above, and their walls are able to absorb and hold water by imbibition. Doubtless, a part of the rise of sap in these conducting elements of xylem is attributable to capillary forces, but the diameters of these tubes and the known forces of capillarity are such that their force could cause a sap rise of only a few inches, or at most a few feet. Thus, capillarity may be regarded as relatively unimportant as a possible cause of sap rise.

Another explanation, largely discounted at present, of sap rise is based upon the action of living parenchyma cells adjoining the conducting elements of the xylem. Several plant physiologists have maintained that a pumping action, caused by rhythmic expansions and contractions of these living cells, is detectable in stems and that their pumping force drives the sap upward. This idea, never widely accepted by botanists, received a mortal blow when it was demonstrated that dead stretches of stems, killed by live steam or by poisons such as picric acid, are still able to conduct sap upward in nearly normal fashion. It is extremely doubtful that such pumping action in living cells actually occurs, but it is certain, of course, that water and solutes pass by diffusion from living cell to living cell. It appears, however, that the presence of living cells in a stem is essential to the continuance of normal sap rise, for stems with dead portions, although they may conduct sap for a time in apparently normal fashion, cannot do so indefinitely. The exact nature of the relationship between living cells and the maintenance of normal sap rise is not known.

The explanation generally considered at present to account most satisfactorily for the ascent of sap is based upon the idea that sap is *pulled* up through vessels and tracheids by forces operative in leaves, not *pushed* up from below. Large quantities of water evaporate from the aerial portions of plants, especially from leaves. When the leaf cells nearest the external atmosphere lose water by evaporation, the colloidal materials of their protoplasm are partially dried, and an increase of osmotic concentration in these cells occurs. Since the colloidal materials in protoplasm possess powerful attraction for water, the partly dried protoplasm of these cells absorbs water, chiefly by colloidal imbibition, partly by the osmotic forces of the leaf cells from adjacent cells with higher water content. These cells in turn, as they undergo partial drying, remove water from cells with higher water content adjacent to them, and thus these imbibitional and osmotic forces, initiated by the evaporation of water from leaf cells, are transmitted from leaf cell to leaf cell. This water deficit in the leaf cells creates a pull on the water in the vessels and tracheids in the leaf veins, a pull that is transmitted downward through the xylem cells of the leafstalk and through the xylem-conducting structures of stem and roots. This pull is transmitted through the water column of a plant because of the tremendous cohesive power of water molecules, which remain together with such great mutual attraction that tremendous power is required to separate them. The

cohesive force of water in columns similar in size to those in xylem vessels has been found to be almost 300 atmospheres, roughly 10 times the pull required to lift sap to the heights of the tallest known trees. The osmotic pressures of the cells of most leaves vary between 20 and 30 atmospheres, more than enough to furnish this pull as water evaporates from them. One investigator has demonstrated very ingeniously the pulling effect of evaporation from leaves by removing a terminal portion, several feet long, from a woody vine and supporting it with its lower end in mercury. When the evaporation of water in the leaves occurred, tensions were exerted on the water columns in the vessels, and these tensions were sufficiently great to cause the mercury to be pulled up into the vessels (because of the adhesive forces between mercury and water molecules) of the stem to a height twice that to which mercury is forced upward by atmospheric pressure.

This theory, known as the **cohesion theory,** is thus based upon several forces and factors all of which have been shown to exist in the shoots of plants: the evaporation of water from leaves; a water deficit created in leaf cells by this evaporation; the passage of water from the xylem cells of the veins into the partly dried leaf cells as a result of colloidal imbibition and osmotic forces; and the transmission downward into the roots of a pull caused by this water deficit, a pull dependent upon the cohesive power of water molecules (Figure 10–1). There are many indirect evidences in support of this theory. It has been shown that negative pressures of as much as 18 to 20 atmospheres exist in the water columns of stems; that is, these water columns are under tremendous tension from above, which tends to attenuate them or draw them out, as a

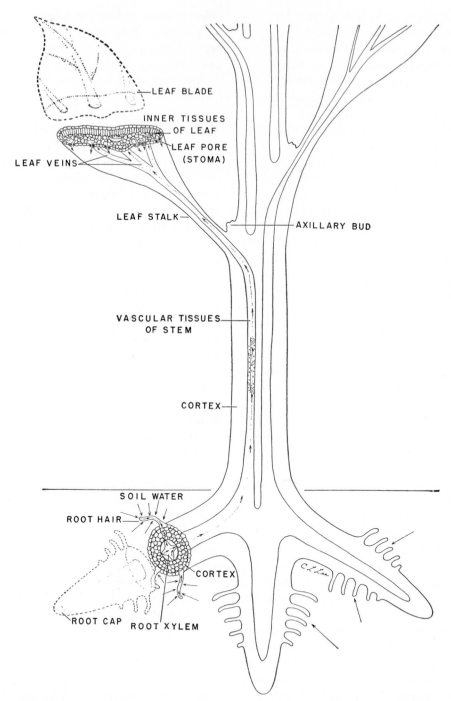

LEAF BLADE

INNER TISSUES
OF LEAF

LEAF PORE
(STOMA)

LEAF VEINS

LEAF STALK

AXILLARY BUD

VASCULAR TISSUES
OF STEM

CORTEX

SOIL WATER

ROOT HAIR

CORTEX

ROOT CAP   ROOT XYLEM

FIG. 10–1. Rise of sap in a plant. The arrows in the soil, root, stem, leaf stalk, and leaf veins indicate liquid water and solutes; the arrows at the leaf pores represent water vapor.

rubber band is stretched when one end is made fast and the other end is pulled with considerable force. These tensions exist in the vessels because, under conditions of rapid evaporation from leaves, roots cannot supply water to the xylem elements as rapidly as the water evaporates from the leaves. In plants with rather transparent stems—for example, pumpkin and balsam—the diametric shrinkage of the xylem vessels in the stem under conditions of water tension can actually be observed under a microscope.

It is also demonstrable that on hot, bright days when evaporation of water from leaves is rapid, the stems of many plants, both woody and herbaceous, actually shrink in diameter, as a piece of rubber tubing will shrink in thickness if one end is closed and suction is applied at the other. The tremendous pull engendered by water evaporation from the leaves creates "negative pressures" or tensions in the water columns, tensions that result in these slight, though definite decreases in stem diameters. Because of these negative pressures air will rush into the conducting cells in which these tensions exist, if incisions are made into a stem. If air bubbles enter a vessel, the upward rise of water in that vessel usually ceases, for the air bubble breaks the water column in the vessel. If the tension in a vessel is lowered, the air bubble may be dissolved and the vessel then resumes its upward conduction of water. When cut flowers are brought into a house, an inch or more of the lower ends of their stalks should be cut off under the surface of the water in the flower bowl or vase. This treatment removes the portions of the stalks into which air bubbles entered when the flowers were cut. With the removal of these air bubbles, the upward movement of water is quickly resumed

and the flowers will not wilt as quickly as they would if some of the vessels in their stalks were plugged by air.

It should be emphasized that the cross walls that occur at intervals in vessels and the end walls of tracheids do not hinder appreciably the rise of sap, for these walls are saturated with water and thus masses of water molecules are continuous from cell to cell through these saturated walls. At night, when evaporation from leaves decreases, the negative pressures in stems fall, and a slight expansion in stem diameters is noticeable as the tension in the water columns is relaxed. Further evidence in support of this theory is found in the structure of xylem vessels, the walls of which are usually thickened, often with rings or spirals; these thickenings are of such nature that they would seem to prevent, not the rupture of the vessels by possible upward pressures from below, but rather the collapse of the vessels as a result of the negative pressures in them—in much the same manner as a metal coil in the wall of a vacuum cleaner tube prevents the collapse of the tube when a "negative pressure" is present inside the tube.

Thus the cohesion theory, which is generally accepted by botanists at present, involves chiefly physical forces in its attempt to explain the rise of sap. It should be remembered, however, that the absorption and movement of water and solutes from the soil into the lower ends of the xylem tissues of roots are brought about by the living cells of root epidermis and cortex, and that living cells in leaves are involved in the evaporation of water and the transmission of the imbibitional forces occasioned by the partial drying of these cells. Thus, the presence of living cells seems to be necessary for normal sap rise, although the forces involved in the upward movement of sap are primarily physical forces, which are, however, subject within limits to physiological control.

It is likely that the evaporation-cohesion force is not the only force operative in the ascent of sap. Root pressure may aid in forcing sap upward for some distance in early spring before buds have opened. Capillary forces in the walls of vessels and tracheids, as mentioned above, doubtless play at least a small role in the upward movement of water. Thus, a variety of physical and vital forces are probably at work in achieving the upward transportation of sap, of which the force produced by evaporation and water cohesion is doubtless the principal one.

As previously described, root pressure causes exudation of sap under certain conditions in some species. However, sap flow from sugar maples results from **stem pressure,** which occurs independently of both root pressure and transpiration. With the onset of cold weather, starch is converted into sugar so that most maple sap contains from 2 to 3 percent sucrose. Toward the end of the winter season when above-freezing daytime temperatures alternate with near-freezing or lower nighttime temperatures, the trees are tapped by drilling a hole into the sapwood. The positive pressure that forms in the stem under such conditions forces the sap out through the hole. An average tree will yield from 10 to 20 gallons of sap per season and may be tapped for many years without apparent injury. There is still considerable speculation concerning the actual mechanism that causes sap to flow in sugar maples. One interpretation suggests that changes in osmotic concentration induced by ice formation, particularly in the outer layers of sapwood, cause some water to move up the trunk; then, after higher daytime temperatures

have warmed the surface tissues and increased the internal pressure, the sap flows out through the opening.

Food Translocation. The translocation of foods, which are manufactured chiefly in leaves, is principally through the living sieve elements of the phloem. The movement of foods in the phloem is chiefly downward except during early spring and also during the events leading to flower and fruit formation when a considerable translocation of food upward into developing buds and flowers occurs. Sugars and various types of proteins are the foods most frequently found in these cells. Several types of experimentation have supplied evidence for the belief that the phloem is the principal food-conducting system of stems. Chemical analyses of xylem and phloem tissues demonstrate that both a greater abundance and a greater variety of foods are found in phloem cells than in xylem cells. Girdling experiments (see p. 163), in which a ring of outer tissues including phloem completely encircling a stem is removed, inward to the xylem, show that conspicuous swellings develop within a few weeks or months immediately above the girdle. These swellings are caused by the accumulation of downward-moving foods that are halted by the interruption of the phloem and that accumulate just above the cut, thus providing nourishment for the rapid growth of stem cells at this point. A complete girdle on the main trunk of a tree usually results in the death of the tree, for the roots, which are unable to manufacture food, depend for their nourishment upon food from the leaves and die of starvation when completely severed phloem halts the downward movement of food. It has been observed that certain aphids and other insects that commonly feed on sap from stems and leaves insert their stylets into sieve tubes more frequently than xylem cells. This behavior is a further indication that more food is found in phloem-conducting cells than in xylem.

Investigations of translocation indicate that there may be a considerable amount of upward movement of organic materials through the phloem, particularly in the spring. During the summer or fall some of the foods moving downward through the phloem are transmitted through the vascular rays to the xylem and stored in the parenchyma and ray cells of the latter tissue. During the early spring some of these foods move upward in part through the xylem, in part upward through the phloem tissue, into which they are carried from the xylem through the vascular rays. In some plants, such as mock orange and sumac, the major part of the upward movement of sugars occurs in the phloem, whereas in other species, such as the sugar maple, the greater quantity of the upward-moving sugars rises through the xylem tissue.

The rate at which foods move through the phloem is far too rapid to be explained by simple diffusion. Of the various theories that have been proposed to account for this relatively fast movement, the **mass flow** (or pressure flow) **theory** is perhaps the most widely accepted by plant physiologists. According to this theory, the sugar produced by photosynthesis in leaf mesophyll cells is moved in a special chemical form across cell membranes by active transport to the parenchyma cells lying adjacent to sieve elements. At or shortly before the time of entry into the sieve tubes, the sugar compound is enzymatically converted to another form (sucrose). The sucrose raises the osmotic concentration within the sieve tubes, thus causing water to move in by

osmosis, which, in turn, causes an increase in turgor pressure. It is the osmotically induced turgor pressure that causes a mass flow of both solute (sucrose) and solvent (water). The flow will continue as long as a turgor pressure gradient exists. A full discussion of the mass flow and other theories of conduction in phloem is, of course, beyond the scope of an introductory text. It should be noted, however, that while no one of the theories is without weak points, each theory does serve as a valuable basis for further experimentation.

A notable feature of the conducting systems of stems is the fact that sieve elements and tracheary elements are remarkably adapted for the translocation of materials vertically (that is, in the direction of the longitudinal axis of stems) but are almost completely unable to carry materials laterally (transversely) in stems. Water, foods, mineral nutrients, and other soluble materials move transversely in stems chiefly through the vascular rays. These vascular rays make intimate contacts with the sieve elements, vessels, and other cells of longitudinal transport. At such points of contact, pits in the walls of the ray cells and those of the sieve elements, vessels, etc., facilitate the interchange of water and solutes among these cells. This transverse conduction by vascular rays is exceedingly important, for it makes possible the movement of foods from the sieve tubes into the dividing cells of the cambium and the enlarging xylem cells of the current growth ring, and also enables foods to pass into the various storage cells of the xylem and phloem. There is also movement of gases, dissolved in water, through the rays; carbon dioxide moves outward toward the lenticels, and oxygen from the external atmosphere moves inward by

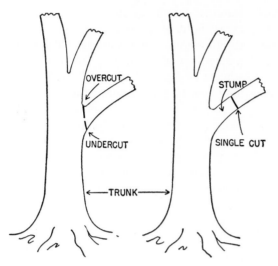

FIG. 10–2. Pruning cuts. *Left:* Branch properly pruned, with undercut made first, followed by overcut; both cuts are parallel to and near trunk. *Right:* Branch improperly pruned; only one cut has been made in such position as to leave a branch stump.

(Photo by C. F. Hottes.)

FIG. 10–3. Healing following pruning of tree limbs.

diffusion through the ray cells and aids in respiratory processes in cambium cells and living cells of xylem and phloem.

PRACTICAL APPLICATIONS OF A KNOWLEDGE OF STEM STRUCTURE AND PHYSIOLOGY

Floriculturists, orchardists, and others engaged in the practical culture of plants find a knowledge of the basic principles of stem structure and physiology indispensable in their work. Although many men engaged in these vocations do not have a theoretical botanical background, they inevitably learn from practical experience the conspicuous features of stem structure and function.

Pruning. The pruning of shrubs and trees involves a knowledge of conduction in stems and of the location and activity of the cambium and cork cambium. The chief purpose of pruning is to remove bro-

ken or diseased branches and thus to prevent the entry and spread of parasites into the main branches or trunks of trees and shrubs. Pruning is also used to give desired shape to ornamental plants, to control or induce flowering, as in grapevines, and to increase the number of branches on a stem by removing the terminal bud. In many plants the terminal bud inhibits the growth of axillary buds of the stem at whose apex it is situated. The fundamental guiding principle in proper pruning is to cut away the branch to be removed as close as possible to the main branch or trunk of which it is an outgrowth, and parallel to the longitudinal axis of the main branch or trunk (Figure 10–2). In order that the growth tissues of a stem may heal a wound, such as one resulting from pruning, phloem cells must be present in such a position that they can conduct food to the healing tissues surrounding the wound. Since the

(*Photos by Missouri Botanical Garden.*)

FIG. 10–4. Treatment of tree trunk cavities (linden). *Left:* Cavity filled with cement and at early stage of marginal healing. *Right:* The same, two years later.

food that moves downward through the phloem cells comes from leaves above, it is essential that there be leaves above the wound in order that food may reach the cambium and cork cambium at the margins of the wound. When a wound is close to a main branch and parallel to it, food moving downward from leaves borne above the wound reaches the cambium and cork cambium around the wound; the growth of protective tissues then begins from the margin of the wound and proceeds inward, until the wound is completely healed by a layer of bark (Figure 10–3). Frequently, pruning jobs are performed carelessly or ignorantly, and an undesired branch is cut away at some distance from the main branch, as a result of

which a stub of several inches is left protruding from the main branch. A wound at the end of a stub is so situated that healing is usually impossible and the beginning of decay is inevitable. In such a case, the healing of a wound at the end of a stub cannot be promoted by foods passing down the phloem of the main branch, for the movement of foods through this phloem is chiefly downward, and the wound is too far from the main branch phloem to receive food for nourishment of the cambium and cork cambium in the stub. As a result of the failure of a wound at the end of such a stub to heal, fungi and insects may enter the exposed sapwood and phloem of the stub and slowly move downward through the wood of the

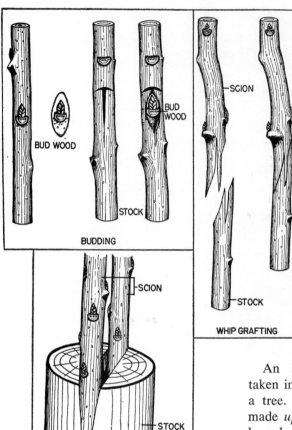

FIG. 10–5. Three common methods of grafting.

stub into the wood of the main branch or trunk. It is then necessary to cut away the diseased tissue and to pack the cavity with concrete, if the tree is to be saved. Thus, a knowledge of the path of food transport and of the situation of the meristematic tissue in stems is a prerequisite to proper pruning technique. After a pruning job is correctly executed, the surface of the wound should be painted immediately. This treatment protects the wound against the entry of parasites while healing is in progress.

An additional precaution must be taken in pruning away large branches of a tree. The first sawing cut should be made *upward* from the underside of the branch, after which a sawing cut may be made downward from the upper side of the branch until it meets the undercut. When both cuts meet, the branch falls away cleanly from the main branch or trunk from which it is being removed. If the sawing is done only from the upper side of the branch, the weight of the branch may cause the branch to be torn away from the trunk as the cut deepens; this may strip off a large mass of bark from the main trunk as the pruned branch falls, thus damaging the trunk.

Grafting. Another practical application of a knowledge of stem structure and physiology is found in grafting, an ancient and valuable horticultural practice in which two freshly cut stem surfaces are bound together so that their cells grow together and thus form an organic union between the two stem pieces. The usual types of grafting involve the union of a basal, rooted stem, the **stock,** and a cutting, or **scion,** which is united with the stock (Figure 10–5).

Certain precautions are essential in the making of a successful stem graft. The stock and scion must be placed together in such a manner that their cambium layers are in contact, for the success of the graft depends in large degree upon a union of the cambial layers of the stock and scion. Successful grafts have been made in monocots, which lack cambium, but usually cambial tissue is essential to stem grafts. The cambium layers do not grow together directly, but are united by the development and growth of a new, connecting cambium in the **callus,** a tissue consisting of large, thin-walled cells that are differentiated from certain living cells of the xylem and inner bark, principally from ray cells. The new cambium cells that develop from callus cells connect the cambium of the stock and of the scion, and new phloem and xylem cells, also differentiated from the callus, connect the xylem and phloem of the stock with those of the scion. From the outer part of the callus new cork cells are formed that merge with those of the stock and scion, covering over the wound with a new layer of water-conserving cells. In a graft, stock and scion must be firmly bound together with twine or tape to prevent movement that would interfere with the process of tissue union (Figure 10–6). The grafted region should be covered with a thick layer of grafting wax to prevent the drying out of the tissues and the entry of fungi. Successful grafts can usually be attained only when stock and scion are members of closely related species or varieties, for only in closely re-

FIG. 10–6. Inarching, a type of grafting.

lated kinds of plants are anatomical features and growth habits similar enough to ensure tissue union at the joined surfaces. Thus, apples can be grafted on apples, plums on peaches, tomatoes on potatoes; but apples scions could not be grafted on oranges, nor plums on walnuts, for the plants in these cases do not have enough structural and behavioral features in common to produce effective union of their stocks and scions.

There are several methods of grafting, most common of which is known as **cleft grafting** (Figure 10–5). In this, a notch is made in a stock, and into the notch is placed the tapering end of a scion, cut to fit the notch. Another common method of grafting, termed **budding,** employs a scion composed usually of a single bud,

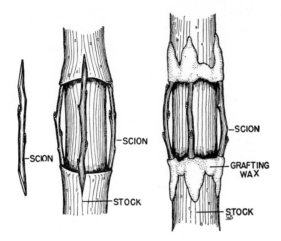

FIG. 10–7. Bridge grafting.

with a small amount of adjacent stem tissue. Budding is often employed when the amount of scion material available is small; a single twig may yield a dozen or more buds, each of which serves as the scion in a separate graft. Budding is used widely in the propagation of various fruit and ornamental trees and shrubs. In some plants, a bud will produce a twig that bears flowers or fruits different in some respect from the others on the same plant; an alteration of this kind in a twig is known as a **bud sport,** or **bud mutation.** Several important cultivated varieties of plants have arisen as bud sports; for example, the Navel orange originated as a bud sport in Brazil in about 1870, and all Navel orange trees now cultivated are descendants of the ancestral mutation. Since the Navel orange is seedless, it is propagated exclusively by grafting, which perpetuates the characteristics of the variety without change. In budding, a T-shaped slit is made in the bark of the stock, which must be young and slender, and a single bud is inserted in the slit in such a way that the flaps of the T close over its margins. The bud is then bound in place and grafting wax applied. Another method of grafting, **bridge grafting,** is used to save trees that have been girdled by the gnawing of porcupines, rabbits, and other animals, or by insects and fungous diseases. The ends of small branches, which are used as scions, are inserted under the bark at the upper and lower borders of the girdle (Figure 10–7). If such a graft is successful, the phloem of the several branches assumes the translocation functions of the destroyed tree bark, and the tree survives.

Grafting is employed for several purposes, among which the following are common:

1. To propagate seedless varieties of plants, such as Navel oranges.

2. To propagate without change hybrid plants, the seeds of which do not all grow into plants like the parents (do not "breed true").

3. To propagate plants, the seeds of which give low percentages of germination.

4. To increase the speed of propagation and induce more rapid fruiting. Many kinds of fruit trees bear fruit within a much shorter time if they are propagated by grafts instead of by seeds.

5. To acclimate species of plants to new environments. For example, culti-

vated apple varieties are frequently grafted on the stocks of Siberian crab apples, the roots of which are less susceptible to the rigors of Siberian winters than are the roots of the cultivated varieties. The roots of plum trees do not grow well in sandy soils, but plums can be successfully grown in such soils by grafting them onto the stocks of peach trees, the roots of which flourish in such soils.

6. To change or control the shape of a plant, as in the umbrella catalpa, Camperdown elm, and others. The maximum stem circumference attained by almond trees is about 5 feet. If almond scions are grafted onto peach stocks, the trunks grow to circumferences of almost 10 feet.

7. To check or eliminate parasites. In France and other parts of Europe, European types of grapes are seriously injured by a kind of root louse that does not attack the roots of American grapes. If scions of European grapes are grafted onto American grape stocks, the European grapes can be grown without damage by root lice.

A common misconception concerning grafting is that it is a method of producing new types of plants. This error has arisen probably because of Burbank's work both with the creation of new varieties of plants and with propagation of plants by means of grafting. Grafting never results in the creation of new kinds of plants. It is exclusively a process of **vegetative** reproduction employed to achieve the continuance of varieties *without change*. New varieties arise naturally by **mutation** (a process of sudden unpredictable change) or they are isolated from other varieties by artificial selection or are developed by cross breeding **(hybridizing).** After new varieties have developed, they are frequently propagated by grafting. Since many such varieties are hybrids, their seeds do not "breed true"; that is, all of them do not grow up into plants like their hybrid parents. In order to maintain and propagate such hybrid varieties, grafting, or some other vegetative method of propagation is employed.

That grafting maintains the separate individualities of stock and scion has been shown by every successful graft. Many closely related varieties of scions may be grafted onto one stock, with the result that separate branches of the grafted plant bear different types of fruits or flowers. There are several well-known apple trees in this country, for example, which have as many as 115 apple varieties grafted to them. Each scion continues to produce apples of its variety, with no mixture of the characteristics of the different varieties. Another interesting type of graft can be made between scions of tomato and stocks of potato (Figure 10–8); the stock continues to produce subterranean tubers, the scion to form typical tomato fruits.

Girdling. Girdling, or "ringing," is another horticultural practice, the success of which depends upon some knowledge of stem structure and functions. As stated earlier, girdling is the removal of a complete ring of bark including phloem down to the cambium or the wood from a branch or trunk of a woody plant. Girdling interrupts the downward passage of food through the phloem and thus causes food to accumulate above the girdle (Figure 10–10). If a girdle is made on a small branch, just below a flower or flower cluster, the fruits produced by the flowers will be unusually large because large amounts of downward-moving food that collect above the girdle pass into the developing fruits. This girdling of small branches is frequently employed in this

FIG. 10–8. Graft of a tomato scion onto a potato stock.
A. *Left:* Young scion grafted onto potato stock. *Right:* A three-week-old graft.
B. A somewhat older graft.
C. Several months later; the scion bears tomato fruits and the stock bears potato tubers.

country to produce extra large grapes or other fruits, chiefly for exhibition purposes. In Europe, girdling is practiced much more extensively than in this country for the production of oversize fruits that command high prices in European hotels and cafés. If, in the girdling of young branches, the cambium is not injured, the girdle is usually healed over by subsequent growth. If a complete girdle is cut through the bark and cambium of a tree trunk, the tree usually dies as a result of root starvation. Girdling of this type is frequently used to kill large numbers of trees preparatory to clearing forest areas for agricultural purposes. Girdling is sometimes employed to force into flowering branches of young trees that are slow in beginning to flower. Removal of a ring of phloem maintains a high concentration of carbohydrates in branches, a condition related to the beginning of flowering in some species of plants, and may also stimulate the development or accumulation of a flower-inducing hormone in girdled branches.

(Photo by Missouri Botanical Garden.)

FIG. 10–9. A chrysanthemum plant with scions of more than eight varieties grafted to it. Notice that each scion produces its own characteristic flower type.

(Photo by C. F. Hottes.)

FIG. 10–10. *Left:* Girdling of a tree trunk by a rope. *Above:* Girdling of a tree trunk by a fence wire.

Stem Cuttings. The vegetative propagation of plants by means of stem cuttings is a horticultural practice that is intimately related to the anatomy and physiology of stems. When stem segments of many species of plants are placed with their lower ends in a suitably moist substance, such as wet sand or soil or, in some species, in water, they develop adventitious roots at these lower ends. Each

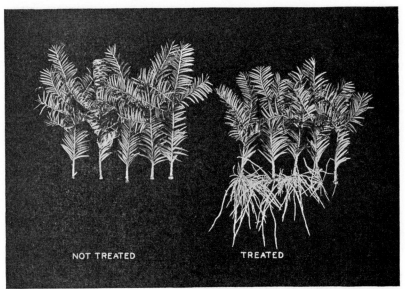

(*Photo by P. W. Zimmerman, Boyce Thompson Institute.*)

FIG. 10–11. Cuttings of yew (*Taxus*). Those on the right were treated with dilute solutions of indolebutyric acid to hasten rooting. Both sets of cuttings were placed in a rooting bench at the same time.

cutting, upon forming new roots, begins to absorb water and minerals rapidly and becomes established as an independent plant. Many important horticultural species are propagated largely or exclusively by cuttings; among these are carnations, geraniums, *Coleus,* chrysanthemums, roses, grapes, and English ivy. Stem cuttings of these plants, together with many others, form roots easily and rapidly. In other species, however, the development of roots proceeds so slowly and unevenly that propagation by means of cuttings is rather unsatisfactory. Treatment of the lower ends of cuttings of many of these plants with plant hormones and related substances in water solutions or in lanolin paste stimulates remarkably the formation of adventitious roots, and thus makes possible the large-scale rooting of cuttings of these species (Figure 10–11). The concentrations of these growth-promoting substances required to accelerate or initiate root formation are remarkably low. For example, a concentration of 1 part of indoleacetic acid in 2000 parts of lanolin is effective in stimulating root production on the cuttings of many species of plants.

In the propagation of plants from stem cuttings, one must take care to reduce evaporation of moisture from the cuttings, for young cuttings, lacking roots, are able to absorb only small quantities of water and would soon wither and die if a compensatory decrease in water loss from aerial parts of the cutting were not made. This reduction in evaporation may be accomplished by removing some of the leaves from cuttings, by keeping the cuttings in a very humid greenhouse, or by placing over the cuttings waterproof containers, such as glass jars, which retain beneath them a very humid atmosphere thereby reducing the rate of transpiration.

Stem Injection. The injection of chemicals into stems is another interesting ap-

plication of a knowledge of stem structure and functions. In many types of soils, iron is not present in forms that can be readily utilized by green plants. The leaves of such plants growing in these soils fail to develop normal green color (**chlorosis**) because iron is required for the manufacture of chlorophyll. It has been found that the deposition or injection of water-soluble iron salts into the sapwood of trees promotes the formation of normal quantities of chlorophyll. Poisons such as arsenic compounds and copper sulfate have been injected into sapwood to kill quickly trees on lands to be cleared for agricultural use and also to thin out dense forests. Several investigators have experimented upon the injection into trees of chemicals poisonous to parasites in the hope of controlling the attacks of such organisms on trees. Lithium salts have been injected into chestnut trees in an effort to check the chestnut blight disease and enable the trees to form protective tissues to surround diseased portions of their stems. The injection of zinc chloride, copper sulfate, and other chemicals into the sapwood of trees has been reported to be moderately effective in reducing the depredations of certain kinds of bark beetles. Research on the use of such chemicals to kill or control fungi and insects in woody plants is not very far advanced and at this time the results of such **chemotherapy** must be considered as inconclusive.

SUMMARY

1. The term sap is applied usually to the water and dissolved substances that rise chiefly through xylem. The term is sometimes used also to refer to substances moving down through phloem.
2. The conducting tissues of stems are xylem and phloem.
3. Xylem vessels and tracheids conduct water, mineral nutrients, and sometimes foods, chiefly upward. Sieve tubes in the phloem conduct foods manufactured in the leaves chiefly downward. There may also be some upward conduction of nutrients and foods in the phloem, especially in early spring in woody plants.
4. The term translocation is applied to the conduction of materials in plants.
5. The principal forces responsible for the rise of sap through xylem seem to be those that develop as a result of the evaporation of water from leaves, the imbibitional forces developed by partially dried leaf cells, the absorption of water from leaf veins by these cells as a result of their imbibitional forces, and the creation of a pull upon the water in the xylem tracheids and vessels. This pull is transmitted downward through stems and roots because of the tremendous cohesive powers of water molecules.
6. Other forces apparently of secondary importance in causing the ascent of sap are root pressure, forces developed within living cells of the xylem, and capillary forces in the walls of tracheids and vessels.
7. According to the mass flow theory, an osmotically induced turgor pressure gradient is responsible for the movement of food in the phloem.
8. Pruning is a practice employed to control the shape of a woody plant or to remove dead or diseased limbs. In pruning, the limb that is to be removed should be cut away parallel to the main branch from which it grows and as close to the main branch as possible to facilitate healing of the wound. Pruning is also employed to control flowering.

9. Girdling is the removal of a complete ring of bark to the cambium or wood. The girdling of small branches of woody plants is employed to produce unusually large fruits or to force limbs into flowering. A girdle on a tree trunk interrupts the passage of food downward through the phloem and results in the starvation and death of the roots and thus the whole tree.

10. Grafting is the uniting of a twig (scion) of one plant upon the stump (stock) of another. The tissues of stock and scion grow together in a successful graft. Grafting is a means of vegetative propagation and does not bring about the development of new types of plants.

11. Grafting is employed:
    a. To propagate seedless varieties of plants.
    b. To propagate plants with seeds of poor germinating power.
    c. To combat plant diseases.
    d. To acclimate plants to new regions and adjust them to different climatic factors.
    e. To decrease the time required for flowering and fruiting.
    f. To change or control the shape of a plant.
    g. To propagate hybrids, seeds of which do not breed true.

12. Plants may be propagated vegetatively by stem cuttings, the basal ends of which, placed in a suitable, moist substratum, form adventitious roots. Growth hormones and related substances are widely used to initiate and accelerate the formation of adventitious roots.

13. The injection of chemicals into stems is often used to correct chlorosis and other types of diseases caused by the deficiency of essential minerals.

SUGGESTED READINGS FOR INTERESTED STUDENTS

1. Gardner, Victor R., *Basic Horticulture,* 2d ed. Macmillan, New York, 1951.
2. Kramer, Paul J., *Plant and Soil Water Relationships.* McGraw-Hill, New York, 1949.
3. Kramer, Paul J., and T. T. Kozlowski, *Physiology of Trees.* McGraw-Hill, New York, 1960.
4. Mahlstede, John P., and E. S. Haber, *Plant Propagation.* Wiley, New York, 1957.
5. Zimmermann, Martin H., "Movement of organic substances in trees." *Science,* Vol. 133, No. 3446, pp. 73–79, January 1961.

TOPICS AND QUESTIONS FOR STUDY

1. Review the major functions of stems.
2. Describe the experimental evidence that indicates that xylem is the major path of sap ascent.
3. Does the removal of a complete ring of bark from a stem interfere with the ascent of sap? Explain.
4. In what portion of the xylem of woody plants does most sap rise occur? In tapping a sugar maple tree, how far into the trunk does the tapper bore? Explain.

5. What substances ascend through xylem cells?
6. What is root pressure? Evaluate root pressure as a cause of sap ascent.
7. What is stem pressure? How does it differ from root pressure?
8. Are living cells in a stem essential for sap conduction? Cite experiments bearing on this problem, and explain your answer.
9. Summarize the presently accepted theory that attempts to explain the ascent of sap, and describe the experimental evidence supporting this theory.
10. Through what tissue does most food translocation occur in stems? Cite experimental evidence in support of your answer.
11. What forces are thought to be responsible for the downward movement of food through phloem?
12. How does transverse conduction occur in stems? What substances are conducted transversely? Describe the relationship between transverse conduction and the structure and location of tissues that bring about such conduction.
13. Studies with a dendrograph, an instrument that measures changes in the diameters of tree trunks, indicate that woody stems decrease in diameter on hot, dry, bright days, as compared with their diameter at night or on cool, humid, cloudy days. Explain.
14. Enumerate the principles of good pruning, and relate them to the physiology of stems. What are the reasons for pruning plants?
15. Define grafting, and state the reasons why grafting is practiced by horticulturists.
16. Describe the precautions that must be taken to ensure a successful graft, and describe briefly the more common types of grafting.
17. What is the special advantage of budding as a type of grafting?
18. If a wire or rope is tightly fastened around a tree trunk or branch, swellings due to accelerated growth appear immediately above the zone of compression. Explain.
19. If a complete girdle of bark is removed from the trunk of a tree, the tree dies, but if a girdle is made on only one branch, the tree does not die. Explain.
20. If a branch is girdled immediately below a flower, that flower may produce an unusually large fruit, but if the girdle is made immediately above a flower, the flower may wilt and fall, without producing a fruit. Explain.
21. A tree may be killed by sapsuckers that drill through the bark. Explain.
22. Will the girdling of a branch interfere with the ascent of water and minerals to its leaves? Explain.
23. Summarize the reasons for girdling plants.
24. Name some important horticultural plants that are commonly reproduced by stem cuttings. How may the formation of roots by cuttings be accelerated?
25. What precautions must be taken to ensure the successful rooting of cuttings?
26. Why is it that some species of plants (for example, some varieties of fruit trees, carnations, and chrysanthemums) are propagated only by grafting, cuttings, or some other vegetative method? Explain.
27. Why are chemicals sometimes injected into stems? Into what tissue should injections be made, if these are to be successful?

11

The Origin and Structure
of Leaves

Leaves are food-making organs and thus are vitally important to plants themselves and likewise to all members of the animal kingdom. All foods used by living organisms (except for a few species of bacteria) are products of leaves or other green parts of plants. **Herbivorous** (plant-eating) animals, such as cattle, sheep, and horses, obtain their nourishment directly from leaves or other plant parts, living or dead; **carnivorous** (flesh-eating) animals, such as lions, tigers, and wolves, derive their food from the tissues of living animals that in turn eat smaller animals or green plants. Fungi and most bacteria are similarly dependent for their nourishment upon foods manufactured by green plants.

THE NATURE, ORIGIN, AND ARRANGEMENT OF LEAVES

Leaves are the most characteristic appendages of aerial stems. They vary enormously in their forms, sizes, and internal structure in different species of plants and to some extent in the same plant. In most flowering plants, leaves are expanded and flattened in form, although occasionally they are needle- or scalelike, nearly cylindrical (as in onions), or of some other shape. There are some types of leaves that are so specialized in structure and in function that they are scarcely recognizable as leaves. Leaves are joined to stems at nodes and usually have buds in their axils. As stated in an earlier chapter, leaves originate as lateral protuberances of the apical meristems of buds. With the opening of a bud, these leaf primordia begin to grow rapidly as a result of cell division, cell enlargement, and cell differentiation until they reach the sizes of mature leaves.

Leaves are arranged on stems in the same manner as buds (Figure 11–1). Leaves are most commonly **alternate,** or **spiral,** in their arrangement, as in elms, lindens, and apples; that is, only one leaf occurs at a node. Less common is the **opposite** arrangement, in which two leaves are at a node, usually on opposite sides of the stem, as in maples, carnations, and buckeye. In the **whorled** arrangement there are three or more leaves at a node, more or less equally spaced around the

170

FIG. 11–1. Leaf arrangement. *Left:* Whorled leaves of veronica. *Center:* opposite leaves of lilac. *Right:* Alternate leaves of redbud.

node; this arrangement occurs in catalpa and in some species of lilies. It is apparent that the arrangement of leaves is such that their weight is more or less equally distributed on all sides of the stem and that there is a minimum degree of mutual shading.

EXTERNAL STRUCTURE OF LEAVES

The most common type of leaf consists of a leaf stalk, or **petiole;** a usually flattened, expanded portion at the end of the petiole, the **blade;** and in some species of plants, such as roses, small green appendages, called **stipules,** at the juncture of petioles with stems. Stipules are absent from the leaves of many plants and in others fall off shortly after buds open. Stipules are seemingly not of fundamental importance in the physiology of most plants. In some species, however, such as the tulip tree, they furnish protection for developing buds in leaf axils (Figure 11–3), and in Japanese quince (Figure 11–2) and in garden pea the stipules, commonly 1 inch or more wide

FIG. 11–2. Alternate leaves of Japanese quince, showing large stipules.

FIG. 11–3. Twigs of tulip tree. A: Stipules. B: Bud scales. C: Leaves.

FIG. 11–4. Corn leaves with parallel venation.

and possessing chlorophyll, manufacture food. Some leaves lack petioles, their blades growing directly from the stem. Petioles are usually slender and cylindrical in form, but in some plants, such as grasses, they may be flattened into **sheaths** that clasp the stem. Petioles conduct water and solutes from stems into leaf blades and transport foods manufactured in the blades downward into the stem. As a result of the ability of petioles to bend, they move the blades that they support into positions in which the maximum areas of the blade surface are exposed directly to light, which is necessary for food manufacture.

Leaf blades are usually flat, thin, and broad, with a conspicuous system of **veins** forming the structural framework of the blades. These veins branch from the apex of the petiole, that is, at the base of the blade, and they are composed of strands of xylem and phloem cells continuous with those of the petiole. Thus, in addition to forming the structural framework

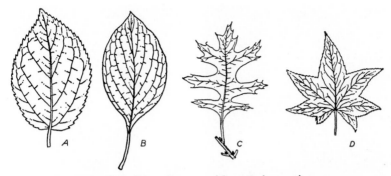

FIG. 11–5. Dicot leaves, with netted venation.

A. toothed leaf   C. pinnately lobed leaf
B. entire-margined leaf   D. palmately lobed leaf

of blades, veins are the ultimate branches of the conducting tissues that pass into leaves from the vascular tissues of stems. The arrangement of veins (**venation**) varies in leaves of different species of plants, but usually conforms to one of two types: **parallel venation** and **net venation.** In leaves with parallel venation, such as those of iris, lilies, and corn, the main veins are parallel with each other and are arranged lengthwise (Figure 11–4). In leaves with net venation, such as those of maple, lettuce, geranium, and bean, the main veins branch from the tip of the petiole in such manner that they are not parallel to each other but form a network (Figure 11–5). There are many variations in these vein arrangements. In banana leaves, for example, the venation is **pinnately parallel;** there is only one longitudinal vein in the blade, a midrib from which a number of smaller veins branch out at the same angle toward the blade margins, in the same fashion as the barbs of a feather extend outward from the central rib. In some net-veined leaves, such as those of elms and oaks, there is one main vein, which is an extension of the petiole; from this main vein the branch veins arise; in a net system of this type the venation is termed **pinnate.** In leaves with **palmate** venation, such as those of sycamore, cucumber, and maple, there are several main veins that branch into the leaf blade from the tip of the petiole. Parallel-veined leaves occur in most monocotyledons, net-veined leaves in dicotyledons.

Leaf blades vary greatly in the degree of their division, their margins, their form, and their size (Figure 11–5). In some plants, for example, clovers, roses, and locusts, the leaf blade is not a single structure but is divided into a number of separate segments. A leaf of this type is termed **compound** and the individual blade segments are called **leaflets** (Figure 11–6). More common than compound leaves are **simple** leaves, in which the blade is a single structure, as in peach, elm, and oak.

The blades of leaves differ also in their margins. The leaves of iris, corn, dogwood, and nasturtium have **entire** margins, that is, smooth margins that lack indentations. In **toothed** and **wave-margined** leaves, the margins are indented respectively by small to moderate-sized teeth, like those of a saw, and by small undulations or rounded teeth. The leaves of elm, cherry, and linden are toothed, those of chestnut are wave-margined.

FIG. 11–6. Compound leaves. *Left:* Pinnately compound leaf of rose, show-ing stipules at base of petiole. *Right:* Palmately compound leaves of horse chestnut.

(Photo by Missouri Botanical Garden.)

FIG. 11–7. Pinnately compound leaves of honey locust tree.

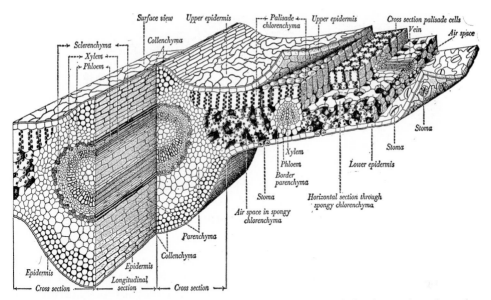

FIG. 11–8. A section of a midrib and a small part of the leaf blade dissected to show the arrangement of the tissues. On the left is a cross section of half of the midrib followed by a longitudinal section, and this by a cross section of the remainder of the midrib and a portion of the blade. The leaf blade on the right is dissected in various ways. The term chlorenchyma is a synonym of mesophyll. (*From* The Plant Kingdom, *by W. H. Brown, Ginn and Company.*)

Lobed leaves are those in which the marginal indentations are deep, often extending inward almost to the main veins, as in maple, sweet gum, and red oak leaves.

The forms of leaf blades vary from **linear,** as in blue-grass and wheat, to **circular,** as in nasturtium, with many intergrading forms, such as **lanceolate** (willows), **heart-shaped** (linden), **ovate** (hackberry), and many others. Leaves differ also in size, from a fraction of an inch in length and width, as in tamarisk, to 12 to 50 or more feet long and 1 to 2 feet or more wide, as in certain palms and in banana plants. These various characters of leaves—size, division of the blade, nature of the margins, blade form, and venation—are important in identifying plants, and, as such, are tools with which botanists may quickly recognize many species of plants.

Of the many variations in leaf form, venation, margins, and shapes, there is apparently no single pattern that renders any one kind of leaf more successful or more efficient than other kinds of leaves. The fact that there exists such diversity in the external structure of leaves attests to an apparent lack of significance in such diversity; all leaves are efficient food-making organs, regardless of whether they are toothed, lobed, simple, or compound, so long as they are well provided with chlorophyll.

THE INTERNAL STRUCTURE OF LEAVES

Microscopic examination of a transverse section of a leaf shows three groups of tissues: **epidermis, mesophyll,** and **veins** (Figures 11–8 and 11–9). The epidermis is a single layer of cells forming the sur-

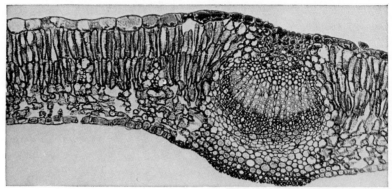

(Photo by Triarch Botanical Products.)

FIG. 11–9. Photomicrograph of a cross section of a lilac leaf. Note the large vein in section.

face skin of the leaf. Its chief functions are the protection of the inner tissues from excessive loss of moisture and the admission of carbon dioxide and oxygen to these internal tissues. In some leaves the epidermis may furnish some protection against the entry of parasites. The outer walls of epidermal cells are frequently thickened and are usually covered with a layer of cutin, a wax that is secreted on the outer surface of the cell walls by the protoplasts of epidermal cells and that is in large part responsible for the effectiveness of the epidermis in conserving moisture. Ordinary epidermal cells are usually lacking in chloroplasts and are colorless; in some plants, however, such as purple cabbage, anthocya-

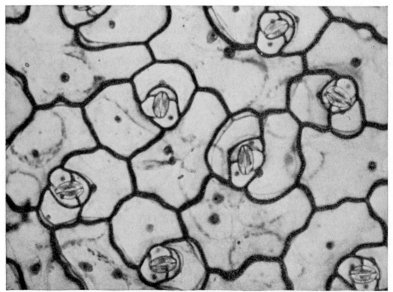

(Copyright, General Biological Supply House.)

FIG. 11–10. Epidermis of *Sedum*, showing guard cells and stomata.

nin pigments are present in the cell sap of leaf epidermal cells. Certain specialized cells of the epidermis contain chloroplasts. These, the **guard cells,** are somewhat bean shaped, as seen in surface view, and occur in pairs, distributed among the more numerous, ordinary epidermal cells, chiefly on the lower surfaces of leaves (Figure 11–10). Each pair of guard cells encloses a small pore, or **stoma** (*pl.* stomata) (Figure 11–11), through which gaseous exchange between the inner tissues of a leaf and the external atmosphere occurs. These paired guard cells expand and contract with changes in their water content, and, as they do so, the size of the stoma that they enclose changes. When the guard cells are expanded, the stomata are open; when the water content of guard cells decreases and they contract, the stomata are nearly or completely closed. Stomata in most leaves are partially or completely open all day

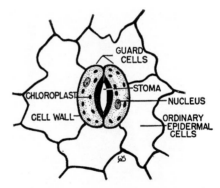

FIG. 11–11. Portion of leaf epidermis.

in both upper and lower epidermal layers, the numbers of stomata are commonly greater in the lower layer. The average areas of most stomata when fully opened are between 0.000092 and 0.0001 square millimeters (remember that a millimeter is $\frac{1}{25}$ inch); clearly, stomatal areas are exceedingly small.

In many plants **hairs** occur as out-

Plant species	Numbers of stomata per square millimeter of leaf surface		Total number of stomata on lower surface of a leaf
	Upper surface	Lower surface	
Sunflower	175	325	1,950,000
Cottonwood	89	132	1,048,000
Olive	0	625	500,000
Birch	0	237	825,000

or during the greater part of the day and are closed or nearly closed during all or most of the night. Stomatal numbers per unit of leaf area vary greatly in different species; also, the numbers of stomata on upper and lower surfaces of the same leaf show considerable differences. Examples of these differences are shown in the above table.

This table indicates the great numbers of stomata in a single leaf and also the occurrence of stomata in some species exclusively on the lower epidermis; in other species, in which stomata occur

growths of leaf epidermal cells, as in tomato and tobacco. In some plants, petunia, for example, the terminal cells of these hairs are glandular and secrete sticky materials that give the leaves a clammy texture. In other species, epidermal hairs soon die and become dry and grayish or white, as in mullein.

The upper and lower epidermal layers of leaves are usually much alike in their detailed structure, except that in most flowering plants, stomata are more numerous on the lower surface, as shown above, and that the cutin layer **(cuticle)**

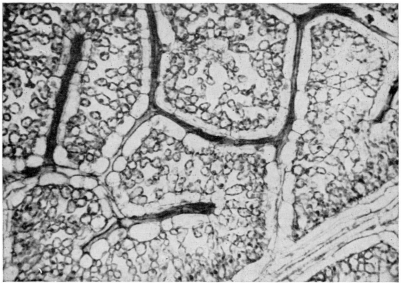

(*Photo by Dr. Richard Armacost.*)

FIG. 11–12. Portion of a leaf of sunflower showing smallest veins and vein endings.

is commonly thicker on the upper epidermis than on the lower. The thicker cuticle and smaller number (or absence) of stomata on the upper surface of a leaf are doubtless an advantageous arrangement, for the upper surfaces of leaves are more directly exposed to the drying action of the sun's rays than are the lower epidermal cells.

The **mesophyll** consists of thin-walled, parenchyma cells (sometimes called chlorenchyma) that contain numerous chloroplasts and is the food-making tissue of leaves. The mesophyll cells nearest the upper epidermis are cylindrical, loosely packed, and arranged at right angles to the leaf surface. These constitute the **palisade** layer of the mesophyll. In the leaves of most plants, there are one or two palisade layers just beneath the upper epidermis. Beneath the palisade cells is a second group of parenchyma cells of different form; these cells are typically quite variable in shape and are also loosely

packed in such manner that there are numerous air spaces among them. These cells constitute the **spongy** layer of the mesophyll. Like palisade cells, spongy cells contain many chloroplasts and thus are food-making cells. The numerous air spaces facilitate gas diffusion through the internal tissues of leaves, for they connect with the spaces underlying the stomata. The type of mesophyll differentiation just described is characteristic of most leaves that grow in a horizontal or oblique position. In some grasses, irises, and other species in which the leaves stand in a more or less vertical position, there are palisade layers under both epidermises, with spongy tissue between them.

Veins are vascular bundles that branch out from the vascular bundles of the petiole at the apices of the latter into the blades, as described earlier. The main veins frequently appear in relief on the lower surfaces of leaves and often as shal-

(*Photo by Missouri Botanical Garden.*)

FIG. 11–13. Plant of *Mesembryanthemum tigrinum,* showing water-storage leaves.

low depressions in their upper surfaces. Each vein consists of both xylem (vessels and tracheids) and phloem (sieve tubes, chiefly), which conduct, respectively, water and minerals upward into leaf blades and foods manufactured in mesophyll downward into the petiole for transfer to the stem and roots. In leaves of most plants, the xylem cells form the upper portion of the veins, the phloem cells the lower portions. Each vein is surrounded by a group of cells, known as a **bundle sheath,** which gives support and strength to the vein; these cells are commonly thick walled. The degree of branching of leaf veins is such that no mesophyll cell is far removed from any part of a veinlet. It has been estimated that there may be as many as 25,000 veinlet endings within 1 square inch of leaf surface (Figure 11–12).

SPECIALIZED LEAVES

There are several kinds of leaves that perform functions other than food manufacture or in addition to food manufacture and that possess corresponding structural features reflecting these specialized functions. Of most common occurrence among the various kinds of specialized leaves are the protective **bud scales** of many woody plants, described in an earlier chapter. In barberry and certain species of cacti, **spines** are morphologically specialized leaves, for they bear buds in their axils; these spines are probably of some value in discouraging the visits of grazing animals. In black locust, the spines of which occur in pairs, at the points of junction of petioles and stems are modified stipules. In onion and lily bulbs, the **bulb scales** are leaves specialized for the storage of food. The leaves of *Portulaca* ("flowering moss"), of *Sedum* and other members of the live-forever family, and of century plants, are very thick and succulent because of the large quantities of water they store (Figure 11–13). The leaves of some plants function wholly, or in part, as **tendrils** (Figure 11–14), structures that twine

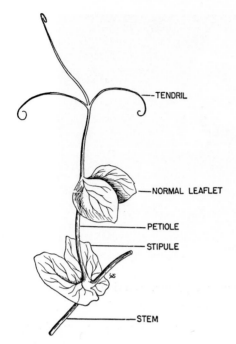

FIG. 11–14. Compound leaf of pea.

ies of insects and other small animals. These plants are chlorophyllous and thus make their own food; their use of animal tissues as a source of food is merely supplementary to their own food making, and they are able to develop in apparently normal fashion without digesting insects, if their roots receive the required mineral nutrients. In some species of these plants, the leaves apparently secrete enzymes that digest the soft parts of insect bodies; in other species, bacteria inhabiting the insectivorous leaves produce these digestive enzymes.

The pitcher plants have leaves that are tubular or pitcher shaped and that hold a liquid containing enzymes. Insects attracted to the pitchers by their colors or odors crawl into them over a number of stiff downward-pointing hairs inside the pitcher. When they attempt to crawl out, they are frequently unable to climb up-

about solid objects and thus aid in supporting their weak stems. In peas, some of the leaflets of the compound leaves are slender tendrils. Among the leaves of seed plants there are some that provide for **vegetative reproduction,** as well as for food manufacture (Figure 11–15). Plantlets forming at the leaf notches of *Bryophyllum* become detached from the leaf, fall to the soil, and, if their roots reach moisture, grow into new plants.

Doubtless the most highly specialized and most amazing of all kinds of specialized leaves are the **insectivorous** or **carnivorous** leaves of about 200 species of angiosperms. These plants grow principally in bogs, the soil of which is either deficient in certain essential elements or contains these elements in forms not readily available to green plants. Insectivorous plants secure certain of these elements by trapping and digesting the bod-

FIG. 11–15. Development of plantlets in leaf notches of air plant (*Bryophyllum*).

FIG. 11–16. A tropical pitcher plant (*Nepenthes dominii*).

cases requiring only 3 or 4 minutes for completion. The fluid with which the bodies of insects are covered contains digestive agents that convert the nitrogenous substance of the insect into forms that the leaves can utilize (Figures 11–20 and 11–21).

The Venus'-flytrap has leaf blades along the margins of which are 12 to 20 bristly teeth, about ½ inch long. On the inner (upper) surface of the blade are several slender hairs that are sensitive to contact. If an insect, alighting on the leaf, touches the sensitive hairs, a stimulation is initiated that causes the two

ward over the bristly hairs and, after becoming exhausted, fall into the liquid and are drowned, following which the soft portions of their bodies are digested and absorbed by leaf cells. Some of the Malayan species (Figure 11–16) have leaf pitchers that are 18 inches long and may hold a quart of liquid. There are pitcher plants in the United States, of which the Sarracenias (Figures 11–17 and 11–18) occur in bogs in many of the midwestern and eastern states. In one species of *Sarracenia,* leaves may be a yard in length.

The sundews are another interesting group of insectivorous plants. In these, the leaf blades possess many glandular hairs that grow upward from their upper surfaces. These tentacles secrete sticky substances containing digestive enzymes. When an insect alights on one of these leaves, it is smeared by the mucilaginous secretions of the glands at the tentacle tips. Simultaneously, some of the tentacles, which are sensitive to contacts of as little as 0.000822 milligram (0.0000000-287 ounce), bend inward and surround the body of the insect. The movement of these tentacles is very rapid, in some

FIG. 11–17. A pitcher plant (*Sarracenia*) in flower. Note the pitcher-shaped leaves; from northeastern United States.

FIG. 11–18. Two sectioned leaves of *Sarracenia*. Note bristles and dead insect remains.

(Photo by C. F. Hottes.)

(Photo by C. F. Hottes.)

FIG. 11–20. Plants of sundew (*Drosera rotundifolia*). The circle in the lower right corner is the rim of a half-dollar.

(Photo by C. F. Hottes.)

FIG. 11–19. Western pitcher plant (*Darlingtonia*), from Oregon.

FIG. 11–21. Leaves of sundew (*Drosera rotundifolia*).

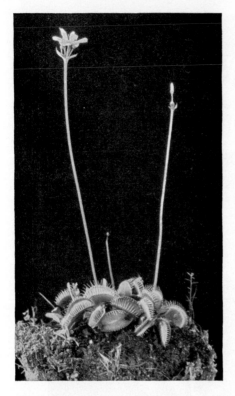

FIG. 11–22. Plants of Venus'-flytrap (*Dionaea*).

of these glands secrete juices that digest the bodies of captured insects. One of the species of this type is used in rural districts of Portugal as a substitute for fly paper. The plants are hung in doorways and, by means of their sticky leaf secretions, firmly hold insects that alight upon them.

There are many superstitions about these insectivorous plants, chief of which is that there exist plants able to entrap the bodies of large mammals, including man. Occasionally stories of this nature find their way into the columns of tabloids, but they have never been authenticated by reputable scientists. The known carnivorous plants limit their prey to small insects, occasional crustaceans, and infrequently very small amphibia.

ECONOMIC IMPORTANCE OF LEAVES

The fundamental importance of leaves to man rests upon their ability to make foods and vitamins that he can utilize as sources of nutriment for himself and for his domesticated animals. Of the many kinds of plants that furnish food for cattle, sheep, and horses, most valuable are the grasses, which form dense mats of leafy vegetation over vast stretches of the prairies of the world. Important plants, the leaves of which are used directly by man as a source of food, are artichoke, cabbage, collards, Brussels sprouts, broccoli, celery, endive, lettuce, rhubarb, spinach, Chinese cabbage, and water cress. Economically important products other than foods are derived from the leaves of many other species. Among such materials are tannins (from sumac leaves), dyes (indigo and henna), aromatic oils for perfumes, soaps, spices, and flavoring extracts (geranium, citronella, bay, marjo-

halves of the leaf to move together, in the same manner as a book is closed. The marginal bristles interlock and the insect is securely held within the trap. Glands on the inner surface of the leaf then digest the entrapped body. After digestion is completed, the leaf opens again, ready for another victim. The time required for the closing of the leaf halves is very brief, frequently as brief as 1 second (Figures 11–22 and 11–23).

In many other species of insectivorous plants, there are no highly specialized leaves of the types described above. In such species, the surfaces of the leaves are covered with sticky, glandular hairs, upon which insects become glued. Some

FIG. 11–23. Stages in the capture of a fly by a leaf of Venus'-flytrap.

ram, peppermint, sage, spearmint, thyme, parsley, wintergreen, and tansy), drugs (belladonna, cocaine, digitalis, eucalyptus, witch hazel, and senna), tobacco, tea, chlorophyll (used as a dye in foods, soaps, candles, and beverages), and waxes used in polishes for furniture, shoes, and automobiles.

⫷⫷⫷ SUMMARY

1. The chief function of leaves is food manufacture.
2. Leaves are usually flattened, expanded structures, although in some plants they are needle- or scalelike.
3. Leaves develop as lateral protuberances of the growing points of buds.
4. Leaves are arranged in the same manner as buds: spiral (alternate), opposite, and whorled. Buds are formed in the axils of leaves.
5. A typical leaf consists of a petiole (stalk), blade, and, in some species, a pair of stipules at the base of the petiole.
6. Leaves vary greatly in their sizes, forms, margins, venation, and degree of division of their blades.
7. Parallel-veined leaves are characteristic of most monocots, net-veined leaves of most dicots.
8. The surface layer of cells of leaves is the epidermis.
9. Between upper and lower epidermises of leaves are the mesophyll tissues. These consist typically of vertically elongated cylindrical palisade cells, situated usually in one or two layers beneath the upper epidermis, and a spongy layer, located below the palisade cells. The spongy tissue consists of loosely packed, rather irregular cells with numerous intercellular spaces. Extending through the mesophyll are veins that branch out from the apex of the petiole or its continuation in the blade, the midrib.
10. Epidermal cells usually have cutinized outer walls and serve primarily in protecting the mesophyll against excessive drying. Occurring in pairs in the epidermis are green guard cells, each pair enclosing a pore, or stoma, through which gas exchange occurs.
11. The mesophyll cells are rich in chlorophyll and are the chief food-making cells of a leaf.
12. The xylem cells of veins conduct water and minerals into leaves, and the phloem cells of veins conduct foods downward into stems.
13. Examples of structurally and functionally specialized leaves are: bud scales, certain types of spines and tendrils, bulb scales, storage leaves, and insectivorous leaves.

⫷⫷⫷ SUGGESTED READINGS FOR INTERESTED STUDENTS

1. Darwin, Charles, *Insectivorous Plants*. Murray, New York, 1884.
2. Esau, Katherine, *Anatomy of Seed Plants*. Wiley, New York, 1961.
3. Lloyd, F. E., *Carnivorous Plants*. Ronald Press, New York, 1942.

←←← TOPICS AND QUESTIONS FOR STUDY

1. Describe the origin and development of leaves, and state their major functions.
2. Name and describe some common types of leaf arrangement.
3. Why is the fact that all leaves do not grow from one side of a stem important?
4. Describe the external structure of a typical angiosperm leaf.
5. What are the functions of stipules?
6. Distinguish between parallel venation and net venation. Are venation differences of any importance in plant classification and identification? Explain.
7. Distinguish between pinnate and palmate venation.
8. What is the physiological importance of leaf veins?
9. Distinguish between simple and compound leaves. Do you think that either of these types of leaves is better or more efficient than the other? Explain.
10. How do you most frequently identify different species of flowering plants, by their leaves or their flowers? Explain.
11. Describe the structure of the epidermis of a typical leaf. What is the significance of the cuticle?
12. Describe the structure of guard cells, and state their relation to stomata and stomatal behavior.
13. If one coats the upper surface of a detached leaf of rubber plant with Vaseline and places it on a laboratory shelf, the leaf wilts and dries out completely in two or three days. If one coats the lower surface of a detached rubber plant leaf, then places it on the shelf, it remains moist and turgid for a week or more. Explain.
14. Describe variations in the distribution of stomata on leaf surfaces, and comment upon the significance of this distribution.
15. What is the meaning of "mesophyll"? Describe the structure of mesophyll of a typical angiosperm leaf.
16. What is the major function of mesophyll tissues?
17. Name five kinds of specialized leaves and list their functions.
18. Describe the structure of leaf veins.
19. Some types of specialized leaves are similar structurally and physiologically to certain types of specialized stems. State how you would determine whether such structures are leaves or stems.
20. List some of the economically important uses of leaves and leaf products.

12

The Physiology of Leaves

LEAF FALL

The leaves of **deciduous** plants fall off the branches at the end of their growing season, as contrasted with those of **evergreens,** in which the leaves persist for several seasons, often for four years or longer. Evergreens do not retain the same leaves always, but shed them gradually. Leaf fall, technically termed **leaf abscission,** involves more than the physical separation of a leaf from a branch; it includes complex structural and physiological changes that, in effect, prepare the plant in advance for this event. Prior to

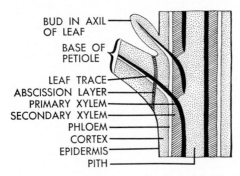

BUD IN AXIL OF LEAF
BASE OF PETIOLE
LEAF TRACE
ABSCISSION LAYER
PRIMARY XYLEM
SECONDARY XYLEM
PHLOEM
CORTEX
EPIDERMIS
PITH

FIG. 12–1. Portion of twig and petiole, showing position of abscission layer.

188

actual leaf drop, a **separation,** or **abscission, layer** is formed across the base of the petiole in a region called the **abscission zone** (Figure 12–1). This layer is only a few cells thick and is characterized by structural weakness attributable, in part, to chemical alteration of cell walls and intercellular material. A somewhat thicker **protective layer** is formed by deposition of suberin and other substances in intercellular spaces and walls of cells situated beneath the separation layer. The factors responsible for these changes are not completely understood. Evidence indicates that the **photoperiod,** or relative duration of night and day, to which plants are exposed is a major factor in the initiation of abscission. A decrease in production of auxins (a kind of growth-regulating substance) in leaves is also believed to promote abscission. The existence of a special abscission hormone has recently been proposed; since then, two investigators have succeeded in isolating from cotton burs a hormone **(abscisin)** that has accelerated abscission in experimental plants. A decrease in available soil moisture is another factor involved in leaf abscission in some species, as, for example, in many tropical regions with marked alternation between wet and dry seasons and in temperate zones in periods of serious drought.

The separation layer begins to disintegrate shortly after its formation, as a result of the separation or the dissolution of its cells, or both. Disintegration continues until the leaf is held to the stem merely by the vascular bundles of the petiole. With the repeated swaying caused by winds and also as a result of frost action, the vascular bundles break and the leaf falls. In woody plants, the protective layer is later replaced by periderm that forms beneath it. It should be emphasized that frost is not a factor that initiates the formation of a separation layer, since the differentiation of this layer commonly precedes the first frosts of autumn and occurs in tropical regions where there is no frost.

THE COLORS OF LEAVES

The predominating green color of leaves is caused by the presence of the pigment chlorophyll, which is essential in food synthesis. All higher plants and some of the algae contain chlorophyll that consists of two closely related pigments, **chlorophyll** *a* and **chlorophyll** *b*. For the sake of convenience, these two pigments are commonly referred to by the single name chlorophyll. Chlorophyll *a* ($C_{55}H_{72}O_5N_4Mg$) constitutes about three fourths of the total chlorophyll of leaves and is bluish green in color. Chlorophyll *b* ($C_{55}H_{70}O_6N_4Mg$) is a yellowish green. Light is a necessary factor in chlorophyll synthesis in most plants. When seedlings of these plants are grown in darkness, they do not become green. Moreover, when healthy green plants are placed in the dark, they lose their green color and become yellowish, or **etiolated.** Chloroplasts contain, in addition to chlorophyll, pigments belonging to a class of compounds called the **carotenoids.** The carotenoids include a relatively large group of yellowish pigments, the **xanthophylls,** and a much smaller group of yellowish orange ones, the **carotenes.** Two very common carotenoid pigments found among green plants are **lutein** (a xanthophyll) and **beta-carotene.** Carotenoids are usually present in relatively small quantities as compared with chlorophyll; hence, their colors are usually masked. When larger amounts of xanthophyll and carotene pigments are present, the leaves may appear yellowish green.

Chlorophyll and carotenoid pigments are insoluble in water and occur chiefly in plastids. Infrequently they may be found dispersed in the cytoplasm, but never in the cell sap. The physiological role of carotenoids in plants is poorly understood. Experiments have shown that in certain groups of plants, the carotenoid pigments in chloroplasts absorb light energy that is then contributed to the photosynthetic process. The carotenoids in chromoplasts impart bright coloration to many flowers, fruits, and seeds. Thus, they probably aid in attracting insects, birds, and other animals that are agents of pollination and seed dispersal.

The red, blue, lavender, and purple colors of various plant parts are attributable principally to water-soluble pigments known as **anthocyanins.** These pigments belong to a group of organic compounds called **glycosides,** which, upon partial decomposition, yield sugar (usually glucose) in addition to a nonsugar component. Anthocyanins are found dissolved in cell sap and are never present in plastids. These pigments occur commonly in the petals of flowers and are also frequently present in leaves (wandering Jew, purple cabbage), roots (garden beet), fruits (grapes), and occasionally in stems. Little is known about the direct significance of these pigments in the physiology of plants. The widespread occurrence of such colored compounds in flowers indicates that they are probably important in attracting insects that are necessary for pollination.

When abscission and protective layers form, tyloses may grow in the vascular bundles and impede the conduction of materials into and away from leaf blades. Through such interference with the translocation of nitrogen, magnesium, iron, and other substances into leaves, chlorophyll synthesis is retarded. It is believed by some plant physiologists that bright light causes the decomposition of chlorophyll in leaves and that the decrease in movement of the above-mentioned elements into leaves prevents the synthesis of new chlorophyll in place of that destroyed by light. This explanation is scarcely tenable, however, since there is no clear evidence that light destroys chlorophyll in living leaf cells. At present, all that we can justifiably say is that in late summer and autumn, certain factors, not thoroughly understood, cause leaf chlorophyll to decompose more rapidly than carotene and xanthophyll; the latter pigments, persisting longer than chlorophyll, and freed from the masking effect of the more abundant chlorophyll, become apparent, causing leaves to exhibit yellowish and golden colors.

The flaming red and purple colors characteristic of the autumn leaves of sumacs, hard maples, sweet gums, and numerous other species of plants are attributable to the formation of anthocyanins not previously present in the leaves, probably as a result of the accumulation of certain waste products. The details of the development of these pigments are not known, but their appearance is correlated with the presence of considerable quantities of sugars in leaves. Light seems to promote the formation of these red pigments, as do also very sudden drops in temperature. If the main vein of a leaf is severed in early autumn, the portion of the blade beyond the cut becomes a deeper red than other portions of the leaf, for the disjunction of the vein prevents sugars from leaving this part of the leaf and thus promotes anthocyanin formation. The sudden decrease in temperature usually accompanying frost inhibits the removal of sugars and often deepens the colors of the anthocyanins in leaves, but the frequent appearance of yellow, orange, and red colors *before* the first frost indicates that frost is not essential to the development of these hues.

With the death of all the cells of leaves, these various pigments decompose and leaves become brown.

PHOTOSYNTHESIS

Photosynthesis is the fundamental process of food manufacture in nature and is the primary physiological process performed by leaves. Sugar, one product of photosynthesis, is important for its direct use in the plant and for its use in the manufacture of all other foods and organic compounds in plants and animals. Thus, photosynthesis makes possible the existence of all plants (except a few species of bacteria) and all animals. If any one physiological process of plants can be designated as "most important," photosynthesis is that process. Such a statement must be made guardedly, however, for without the processes of osmosis,

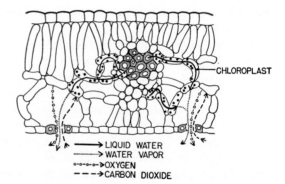

LIQUID WATER
WATER VAPOR
OXYGEN
CARBON DIOXIDE

FIG. 12–2. Cross section of a common type of leaf, showing movement of water and gases during photosynthesis. Water vapor and oxygen leave the leaf through the stomata, while carbon dioxide enters.

translocation, chlorophyll formation, and other physiological activities, photosynthesis could not occur. Evaluated in terms of the importance of its products, photosynthesis may seem more important than these other processes, but since all the physiological changes of living organisms are interrelated, no one can be regarded alone without reference to associated processes.

For many centuries, scholars believed that green plants derived all their nourishment from the organic materials of the soil. This interpretation of plant nutrition, called the Humus Theory, was demonstrated to be false by the work of a Belgian physician, Jean van Helmont, who in about 1630 performed this revealing experiment: he placed exactly 200 pounds of completely dried soil into a vessel and planted in the soil a willow shoot weighing 5 pounds. For 5 years van Helmont added rain water to the soil at regular intervals; he added no fertilizer, nor did he remove any soil during this period. At the end of the 5 years, he removed the willow tree, now grown large, scraped all the soil from its roots, returned this soil to the vessel, removed all water from the willow tree by drying it, and carefully weighed the willow tree. He then dried the soil thoroughly and weighed it. He found that the willow tree

weighed 169 pounds and 3 ounces, a gain of approximately 164 pounds during the 5-year interval, and that the soil weighed 199 pounds and 14 ounces, indicating a loss of only 2 ounces during the same period. Van Helmont concluded that the willow tree built its substance from water alone, a conclusion directly opposed to the Humus Theory. Although his critical experiment demonstrated the falsity of the Humus Theory, van Helmont's explanation of his results was only in part correct, since he did not know of the role of carbon dioxide in the synthesis of organic matter by plants. Now it is universally accepted by scientists that the Humus Theory is untenable, that green plants fashion most of their solid materials from water of the soil and carbon dioxide of the air in the process of photosynthesis and in subsequent syntheses, and that green plants absorb relatively small amounts of solid substances (mineral nutrients) from the soil.

The distinctive features of photosynthesis are these:

1. Photosynthesis is an energy-requiring process; it uses light as the source of energy and thus can occur only when light shines upon plant tissues.

2. Photosynthesis transforms light energy into chemical energy.

3. The green pigment chlorophyll is

the principal light-absorbing material of most plants.

4. The raw materials, or reacting substances, in photosynthesis are carbon dioxide, absorbed from the air, and water, absorbed chiefly from the soil.

5. The principal food product of photosynthesis in higher plants is the carbohydrate glucose.

6. Oxygen in molecular form is released from green plant tissues in the process.

7. Photosynthesis is not a single, simple chemical reaction, but is rather a series of many complex chemical reactions, some of which are only imperfectly known.

8. Photosynthesis is important in the entire world of living organisms in two fundamental ways: 1. It is the only major process of food manufacture in the world; 2. It is the only major source of oxygen in the earth's atmosphere at the present time.

The Course of the Process. Photosynthesis may be represented by this simplified chemical equation:

epidermis. Carbon dioxide dissolves easily in water and thus readily enters the green mesophyll cells of leaves through their moist cell walls. As photosynthesis proceeds, the absorption of carbon dioxide molecules by mesophyll cells results in a lowered concentration of carbon dioxide molecules in the air of the intercellular spaces of the mesophyll. The concentration of carbon dioxide molecules, then, is higher in the air surrounding the leaf, and carbon dioxide molecules, according to the laws of diffusion, continue to diffuse into the leaf through the stomata.

The energy that is essential to photosynthesis is absorbed by chlorophyll in chloroplasts and is normally supplied by sunlight. The chloroplasts are membrane limited and contain small, chlorophyll-bearing bodies **(grana)** embedded in a colorless matrix, or **stroma.** Electronmicrographs show the grana to consist of flattened vesicles or sacs **(lamellae)** aligned in such a way that they bear a superficial resemblance to a small stack of coins (Figures 12–3, 12–4). The mem-

$$6CO_2 \;+\; 6H_2O \;+\; 673kcal \;\rightarrow\; C_6H_{12}O_6 \;+\; 6O_2\uparrow$$
$$\text{(carbon dioxide)}\quad\text{(water)}\quad\text{(light energy)}\qquad\text{(glucose)}\quad\text{(oxygen)}$$

This equation simply indicates the raw materials and products and the proportions in which they occur. It shows that for a net input of 6 molecules of carbon dioxide and 6 molecules of water, there is a net output of 1 molecule of sugar and 6 molecules of oxygen. It further shows that 673 kilocalories (kcal) of energy are utilized in the process (a kilocalorie is the quantity of energy required to raise the temperature of 1000 grams of water 1°C).

The carbon dioxide used in photosynthesis in higher plants enters leaves by diffusion through the stomata of the leaf

branes that form the lamellae are believed to be composite structures, each consisting of two films of protein between which are a layer of chlorophyll and a layer of fatty material. Some lamellae extend through two or possibly more grana.

Of the light that strikes a leaf, a portion is reflected from leaf surfaces, a portion passes through the leaf without being absorbed, and a portion is absorbed by green cells of the leaf. Experiments have indicated that only 0.5 to 2 percent of the total light energy absorbed by a leaf is actually converted into the chemi-

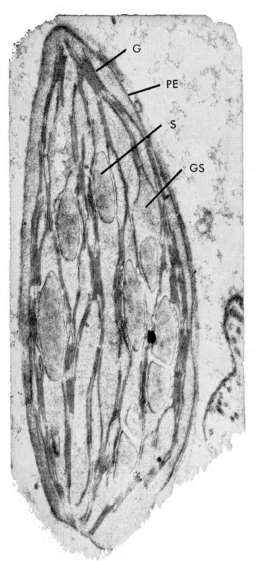

FIG. 12–3. Electronmicrograph of chloroplast of *Isoetes howellii*. G, granum; PE, plastid envelope; S, starch grain; GS, ground substance. (20,000 ×.)

cal energy of foods in photosynthesis. If sunlight passes through a glass prism (or at certain angles through droplets of moisture, as in a rainbow), it is separated into its component types of visible light as a continuous colored light band called a **spectrum;** a sunlight spectrum shows red, orange, yellow, green, blue, and violet light. If sunlight passes through a chlorophyll solution, then through a prism, the resulting spectrum shows chiefly green, yellow, and some orange color, indicating that the chlorophyll has absorbed most of the red and blue-violet light rays. The rays that are most completely absorbed by chlorophyll are most effective in photosynthesis. Leaves are green principally because green light is both reflected and transmitted by chlorophyll. Only a very small amount of green light is absorbed.

As stated earlier, photosynthesis is not a single chemical reaction but a complex series of reactions not all of which are understood. A diagrammatic summary of its principal steps is presented in Figure 12–5. The process is subdivided into **dark** and **light reactions.** A dark reaction may

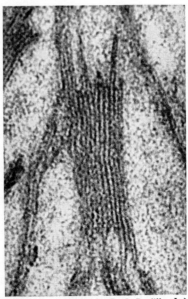

FIG. 12–4. Detail of granum indicated by G in Figure 12–3. (82,-000 ×.)

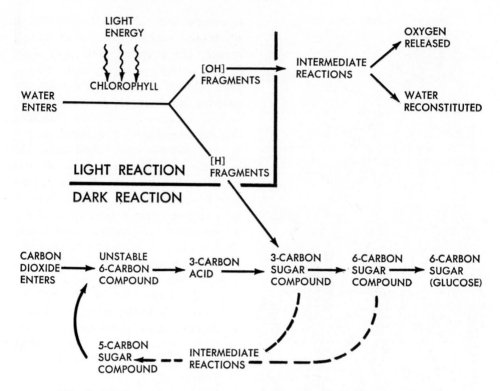

FIG. 12–5. Diagrammatic summary of photosynthesis. Explanation in text.

be described as purely chemical in that the reaction rate is doubled with each 10°C increase in temperature, whether in darkness or light. This characteristic applies to photosynthesis when light, carbon dioxide, and other factors are adequate, that is, not *limiting* the process by their shortage. On the other hand, the light reactions are *photochemical* because they require only light energy in order to proceed and are unaffected by changes in temperature (within limits). When the intensity of light is low enough to be a limiting factor, the rate of photosynthesis is not influenced by changes in temperature.

Chlorophyll has been shown to participate in at least two major photochemical processes in which light contributes energy to chlorophyll molecules and this energy is transferred to energy-trapping compounds. One of these processes yields a compound that provides readily available energy for use in various metabolic functions of the cell. The other is associated with the fragments formed by the cleavage, or **photolysis,** of water molecules. The energy of the excited chlorophyll is used in the removal of hydrogen from water. The water molecule is believed to be split into two parts, one of hydrogen [H], and one containing oxygen and hydrogen [OH]. Through intermediate reactions, the [OH] fragments are combined to form water and molecular oxygen. The hydrogen removed from water in the light reaction enters into a temporary chemical union with molecules of a carrier compound. The photochemical processes allow photosynthesis to perform a dual function: the conversion of light energy to a form immediately available for use in the cell, and the use of light energy in the manufacture of food that is completed in the dark reactions.

The dark reactions are carried out in the stroma of the chloroplast. Here carbon dioxide (a 1-carbon compound) is combined with another compound containing the 5-carbon sugar, ribulose. This reaction is believed to produce an unstable 6-carbon compound that quickly decomposes to form two molecules of phosphoglyceric acid, each of which contains three carbon atoms. The hydrogen removed from water is transferred via the carrier compound to the 3-carbon acid to produce a 3-carbon sugar compound. Two of these 3-carbon sugar compounds are then combined to form a single molecule of a 6-carbon sugar compound that, subsequently, can be converted to glucose.

The speed at which sugar is manufactured in photosynthesis varies in different species of plants and with changing environmental conditions. In bright light and warm temperature, leaves of most plants manufacture sugars at the rate of 0.5 to 1.8 grams (a gram is about $\frac{1}{28}$ ounce) per hour per square meter (slightly more than a square yard) of leaf surface. These values represent averages and may fluctuate from hour to hour during the day. The sugar manufactured in photosynthesis may be utilized in a variety of ways. Some of it is oxidized ("burned") to provide energy for living cells, some is converted into starch, the most common storage carbohydrate food in plants, and some of it is used to form cellulose, proteins, fats, and other compounds necessary for growth and for the formation of new protoplasm.

In most species of plants, as sugar molecules are formed in photosynthesis, they are converted almost immediately into starch that accumulates as small grains in leaf cells during the light part of the day. This behavior is advantageous, for starch is insoluble in water and thus does not affect the osmotic properties of cells, as sugar does. Furthermore, the conversion of sugar into starch results in a decrease in volume; that is, the starch does not occupy as much space as do sugars. During the night, when photosynthesis does not take place, much of the starch stored in the mesophyll cells during the day is transformed back into sugars, a portion of which is translocated through the veins and petioles to the stems and other portions of plant bodies to be utilized in various processes that will be described in the next chapter.

Factors Influencing Photosynthesis. Photosynthesis, as a complex of chemical and physical reactions involving phenomena both inside and outside a plant, is affected by a variety of factors. Among those factors that exert direct influences upon photosynthesis and that have been extensively studied are: the chlorophyll content of leaves, the intensity of the light shining upon leaves, the availability of moisture, and the carbon dioxide content of the air.

The synthesis of chlorophyll depends upon a number of factors: the availability in suitable form of the chemical elements that constitute the chlorophyll molecule; the presence of light; the activity of certain chemical regulators; and hereditary factors. The carbon, hydrogen, and oxygen of chlorophyll molecules are derived from sugars. The first chlorophyll synthesized in a seedling is formed at the expense of foods stored within the seed. As the seedling grows and begins to carry on photosynthesis, its subsequently formed chlorophyll is built up from sugars manufactured as a result of the seedling's photosynthetic activity. The nitrogen and magnesium present in chlorophyll are derived from nitrate and magnesium ions absorbed by roots from the soil. Iron also is essential to chlorophyll formation, although it is not a part of the chlorophyll molecule. When plants become yellowish as a result of deficiency of magnesium or iron or nitrogen in the soil, they are termed **chlorotic.** If plants do not receive light, most of them fail to form chlorophyll and thus are white or pale yellowish, and they show certain structural peculiarities, such as weak, sappy stems and undeveloped leaves. This condition is known as etiolation.

Light intensity influences photosynthesis. When plants grow in exposed situations in full sunlight, they carry on photosynthesis effectively; plants that grow in densely shaded locations, for example, on a forest floor, may have a low photosynthetic rate because of the low intensity of light that reaches them. Different levels of photosynthetic activity may occur in different leaves on the same plant, a condition that is at least in part related to light intensity differences, for leaves at stem tips ordinarily receive more light than leaves borne lower on a branch in a position shaded by other branches and leaves.

Ordinarily, unless they are in a period of extreme drought, plants receive enough water for photosynthesis. So long as their tissues are turgid and water is being absorbed by roots and translocated into leaves, plants do not suffer variations in their photosynthesis as a result of minor fluctuations of water in their mesophyll cells.

Carbon dioxide makes up approximately 0.03 to 0.04 percent, or 3 to 4 parts per 10,000 parts, of air. Carbon dioxide is added to the air as a result of the combustion of fuels, of volcanic action, of rock weathering, and of plant and animal respiration. Simultaneously some of the carbon dioxide in the air is used in photosynthesis, so that the proportion of this gas in the air fluctuates but little. Green plants ordinarily have abundant light, chlorophyll, and water for photosynthesis, but the supplies of CO_2 available to them are limited by the small concentration of this gas in the atmosphere. Because the speed of the photosynthetic process under conditions of abundant light and moisture is usually limited by the low concentrations of carbon dioxide available, carbon dioxide is often termed the "limiting factor" in photosynthesis. It has been shown experimentally that an increase of as much as 20 times in the normal atmospheric concentration of carbon dioxide induces a corresponding increase in the rate of photosynthesis in some plants. Several greenhouses in this country are equipped with devices to increase the carbon dioxide content of their air, for a more rapid rate of photosynthesis results in more rapid growth and frequently in greater yields of flowers, fruits, vegetables, and other crops. Experiments have also shown that the yield of certain field crops is increased if the air about them is enriched by the addition of carbon dioxide from pipes laid in or on the ground. Such "aerial fertilization" is still largely experimental. It should be emphasized that, although carbon dioxide is commonly the limiting factor in photosynthesis in plants growing in full sunlight and with readily available moisture, other factors may become limiting agents of this process. Thus, on the poorly illuminated floor of a forest, light, rather than carbon dioxide, may limit the rate of photosynthesis.

Leaves as Photosynthetic Machines. The leaves of most plants may be considered as rather efficient photosynthetic mechanisms. They are usually broad and thin, and thus light penetrates readily all cells of the mesophyll. Their epidermal layers contain numerous stomata, through which carbon dioxide diffuses into the intercellular spaces of the mesophyll. These spaces afford ready paths of diffusion of carbon dioxide to all green cells of leaves. The cuticles of leaves aid in the conservation of water, which is a raw material of photosynthesis, and in the maintenance of turgidity, which is a necessary condition for rapid and continuing photosynthesis. Further, the numerous ramifications of the vein systems carry water to all cells of leaves. Finally, the numerous chloroplasts of the mesophyll cells constitute the machinery in which the manufacture of sugar occurs.

Each stoma is enclosed by a pair of guard cells, in which turgor changes produce expansion or contraction of the cells and thus open or close the stoma. Guard cells characteristically contain chloroplasts. The inner walls of the guard cells, that is, the walls bordering upon the stoma, are frequently much thicker than the outer walls, those that touch upon other epidermal cells. When the turgor pressure within the guard cells increases, the outer, thinner walls expand more rapidly than the thick inner walls and pull the inner walls away from each other, thus opening the stoma. With a decrease in the turgor pressure, the thick inner walls straighten and move toward each other, closing the stoma. The factors re-sponsible for turgor changes in guard cells are not fully known. An explanation of stomatal opening favored by many physiologists suggests a sequence of events beginning with illumination of the plant. The light induces photosynthesis in guard cells and, as a result, sugar is formed. Sugar in these cells is also produced by the enzymatic conversion of starch. The increase in the concentration of sugar raises the osmotic concentration within the cells, causing, in turn, the osmotic uptake of water. With the uptake of water, there is a concomitant increase in turgor pressure that expands the cells and opens the stomata. The stomata of most plants are usually open to the greatest extent during the day; during this time, photosynthesis proceeds actively. At night, the concentration of sugars within guard cells decreases and some water leaves the guard cells that contract and close the stomata. In some leaves (for example, those of potato), stomata may be open for part of the night.

TRANSPIRATION

Transpiration is the evaporation of water from the aerial parts of plants, especially the leaves. This process goes on at all times, except possibly when the air is saturated with moisture during or immediately following rains. The quantities of water lost by transpiration are often very great. It has been determined that a single sunflower plant during a growing season of approximately 140 days loses about 145 pounds of water by evaporation from its aerial portions, an average daily loss of more than 1 pint of water. A single corn plant has been found to lose by transpiration over 50 gallons of water (more than 400 pounds) during its life span of 100 days. An acre of corn plants, transpiring in this same degree, evaporates into the air over 300,000 gallons (about 1200 tons!) of water in a 100-day growing season. Calculations of the quantities of water transpired by large apple trees indicate that a single, full-grown apple tree loses by evaporation as much as 1800 gallons of water in a growing season of about 6 months. The tremendous amounts of water vapor transpired by such extensive masses of vegetation affect air temperatures, increase the moisture content of the air, and thus influence the frequency and quantity of rainfall.

Ordinarily about 90 percent or more of the water that evaporates from leaves passes out into the air through the stomata; the remainder of the water vapor lost diffuses outward through the lenticels and the cuticle. These three types of transpiration are termed **stomatal, lenticular,** and **cuticular transpiration,** respectively. The relative amounts of water vapor lost by these methods show that stomatal transpiration is by far the most abundant and hence the most important.

The actual conversion of liquid water into water vapor does not occur at or through the stomata, for the latter are merely openings in the epidermal layer. Liquid water passes into vapor from the wet walls of the mesophyll cells at the places where such walls are exposed to the intercellular spaces. As water vapor collects in these spaces, it moves outward through the stomata into the external air, in accordance with the laws of diffusion.

Transpiration proceeds more rapidly during the day than at night. This is chiefly because the stomata of most plants are open widest during the day and also because the environmental factors that prevail during the day favor rapid evaporation of water. At night, when stomata are partially or wholly closed and when temperatures are lower than during the day, the rate of transpiration is considerably less. The nocturnal rate of evaporation from leaves is frequently from 3 to 20 percent of the daytime rate.

The principal external factors that influence the rate of transpiration in plants are light, temperature, humidity, wind velocity, and soil factors.

Transpiration is more rapid in bright light than in diffuse light or in darkness, partly because certain light rays raise the temperature of leaf cells and thus increase the rate at which liquid water is transformed into vapor, partly because bright light causes opening of stomata.

High temperatures favor more rapid transpiration, not only because evaporation and diffusion occur faster in warm air but also because warm air is capable of holding more water vapor than is cold air. At moderate or low temperatures, the rate of transpiration is markedly less than it is when the temperature of the surrounding air is high.

When the external atmosphere is very humid, the evaporation of water from leaves is reduced, for the difference in water vapor concentration in the inner spaces of leaves and in the outside air is so slight that the net outward diffusion of water molecules from leaves is very slow. The rate of transpiration is roughly proportional to atmospheric humidity; thus, the drier the air, the more rapid is the rate of evaporation from leaves. It is known that plant organs, particularly leaves, become larger when they grow in humid atmosphere than in dry air. The greater the atmospheric humidity, the lower the rate of transpiration and the greater is the amount of water retained within the plant.

Where there are no breezes, the motionless air near transpiring leaves becomes very humid and, as a result, the rate of water evaporation decreases. Moving air currents continually bring fresh, drier masses of air in contact with leaf surfaces and thus maintain a high rate of transpiration. However, the rate of transpiration is not directly proportional to wind velocity, for closure of the stomata frequently begins when the wind velocity exceeds 25 or 30 miles per hour, and thus the transpiration rate may be lowered at high velocities.

Soil temperature, the solute concentration of the soil solution, the water content of the soil, and other soil factors influence the rate of transpiration indirectly in that they affect the rate at which roots absorb water. If plants cannot absorb water readily, the rate of their transpiration is correspondingly low. If water is more easily absorbed, the transpiration rate is higher.

Other factors of importance in controlling transpiration are those inherent in the physiological and structural organization of plants. Among these internal factors regulating transpiration is stomatal behavior. It might seem at first consideration that plants can control in large degree the rate of water evaporation from their leaves by closing their stomata, for these apertures are easily regulated by their surrounding guard cells. However, the stomata of plants are singularly ineffective in reducing water vapor loss, for so long as leaves are turgid and are exposed to light, their stomata remain open. Only when leaves begin to wilt or the guard cells lose their turgidity are the stomata completely closed. One investigator has estimated that nearly all the reduction in transpiration caused by stomatal closing occurs when the stomata have closed to about 2 or 3 percent of their full apertures. Thus, stomatal regulation of

transpiration occurs only after guard cell closing is well advanced; such control may be regarded as only partially effective.

The colloidal materials in protoplasm hold water very tenaciously, and when transpiration has proceeded for some time at a rapid rate, the water-retaining power of these colloids frequently causes a marked decrease in transpiration rate. Many desert plants, such as various species of cacti and acacias, have colloidal mucilaginous materials in large quantities in their tissues.

Structural modifications in many species of plants growing in desert soils of low water content frequently conserve water. Plants that grow in such regions and that possess structural features that reduce transpiration are termed **xerophytes** to distinguish them from **hydrophytes** (plants growing in water) and **mesophytes** (land plants growing in soils with moderate amounts of available moisture). Among the characteristic structural features that conserve water in xerophytes are: heavy layers of cutin on leaves and stems, reduced numbers of stomata, stomata sunken in cavities below the surfaces of leaves, abundance of water storage tissues, and reduction in size of or absence of leaves. Some xerophytes produce leaves during the rainy season and lose them as soon as dry weather begins.

The question of the importance of transpiration to plants is a much debated one. It has been suggested that transpiration lowers the internal temperatures of leaves on hot days, since evaporation of liquids is known to exert a cooling effect. Numerous measurements of the temperatures of leaf tissues show conflicting results and seem to justify only one general conclusion; namely, that in some species of plants, transpiration lowers the temperature of leaves on hot days several degrees below that of the surrounding air, and that in the leaves of other species of plants a cooling effect of transpiration is not demonstrable.

It has been argued by some plant physiologists that transpiration may be regarded as having a positive beneficial effect in plants in that it furnishes the pull in leaves that is principally responsible for the rise of sap. It should be emphasized, however, that if there were not such tremendous water loss from leaves, plants would not need to lift such large quantities of water into their leaves. It appears that in most plants less than 10 percent of the total water absorbed by the roots and passed through stems is actually used in photosynthesis and in the maintenance of turgor. In many tropical plants, which grow in almost constantly saturated air, transpiration is slight and sap rise is slow, yet sufficient water as-

cends to the leaves to maintain photosynthesis and growth.

It is sometimes stated that rapid transpiration favors a correspondingly rapid absorption of nutrient ions from soil. There is little experimental evidence in favor of such a supposition, although it is true that rapid transpiration promotes the upward movement of ions in the xylem *after* they have entered roots.

The chief disadvantage to plants of transpiration lies in the fact that it frequently causes excessive loss of water, resulting in wilting and often death. If the rate of water absorption by roots equals or exceeds that of transpiration, no wilting occurs, but if transpiration overbalances water absorption, wilting is inevitable.

Transpiration is sometimes called "unavoidable," a statement that is doubtless true, for plants have no way of preventing the escape of water vapor from the leaves when their stomata are open. It should

FIG. 12–6. Fruit trees in Utah growing behind a windbreak of Lombardy poplars.

FIG. 12–7. Guttation in strawberry leaves.

be emphasized here that the primary importance of stomata is their admission to mesophyll cells of the carbon dioxide necessary for photosynthesis, not the regulation of water loss. Stomata are open and admit carbon dioxide during the light hours of the day. In the intake of carbon dioxide, plants must expose wet cell walls to the air; carbon dioxide molecules become dissolved in the water of the cell walls and diffuse into the enclosed protoplasm. Simultaneous with the intake of carbon dioxide is the unavoidable escape of water molecules from the leaf cell walls and their diffusion from intercellular spaces of leaves through stomata into the outside air.

Transpiration and Plant Cultivation. Farmers, horticulturists, and others engaged in large-scale plant culture employ certain practices that control water balance. One of the commonest of these is the removal of weeds from the vicinity of cultivated plants. Weeds, like other plants, transpire and thus deplete water supplies of the soil. When weeds are removed, the water

in the soil that they would have used is reserved for the use of the desired plants. Weeds are removed for other reasons as well: they shade cultivated plants and thus interfere with their photosynthetic activities, they use soil nutrients that are thus lost to crop plants, and they crowd and frequently stunt root growth of cultivated plants.

Horticulturists whitewash their greenhouses during the summer to reduce the intensity of sunlight and to lower the greenhouse temperature. They usually water the walks, floors, and walls of the greenhouses several times during hot summer days to maintain a high degree of humidity in the air. These practices result in a decrease in the rate of transpiration of plants growing in these houses.

When horticulturists propagate plants from cuttings, they remove some of the leaves before planting the cuttings or they cover them with glass jars. The reduction of leaf surface in the first case diminishes water loss from the cuttings and thus prevents wilting. The glass jars exclude air currents and maintain humid air around the cuttings, thus decreasing transpiration, and at the same time allow light to reach the leaves, which can thus manufacture sugars.

One of the major reasons for windbreaks of trees (Figure 12–6) planted about fields and gardens, particularly in regions of dry summers and frequent winds, is to break the force of the hot winds and thus to prevent excessive transpiration from the leaves of cultivated plants growing behind the windbreaks. In addition windbreaks offer protection against the mechanical force of strong winds.

GUTTATION

Guttation is the exudation of water in liquid form by aerial parts of plants, chiefly leaves. Guttation occurs usually when environmental conditions are such as to check transpiration, particularly during cool nights following hot days when the air is very humid and soil water is abundant. Drops of water appear along the margins of leaves, usually as a result of exudation through special glands known as **hydathodes.** Guttation occurs frequently in the leaves of strawberries (Figure 12–7) and roses at night or in the early morning hours. In many plants, guttation is never apparent and in others it occurs only rarely. The exudation of water droplets is a direct result of root pressure within a plant; high atmospheric humidity and abundant available soil moisture favor the development of root pressure and the process of guttation. Guttation should be considered a resultant of another physiological process, not as a process of positive physiological significance in plants.

⋘ SUMMARY

1. Deciduous trees and shrubs lose their leaves at the end of each growing season. Evergreens shed small numbers of their leaves at intervals and thus always have some leaves on their stems.
2. Leaves fall as a result of the development of an abscission layer across the base of the petiole and the subsequent disintegration of this layer.
3. The predominant green color of leaves is due to the presence of chlorophyll. In autumn, chlorophyll disappears from deciduous leaves, and the yellowish pigments, xanthophyll and carotene, masked earlier by chlorophyll, become apparent. The formation of red and purple pigments in leaves in autumn follows the development of anthocyanins and is related to the accumulation of sugars in leaves.
4. Photosynthesis is the manufacture of carbohydrate food from carbon dioxide and water, a process in which light energy is transformed into chemical energy through the action of chlorophyll. In addition to food synthesis, photosynthesis converts light energy to a form immediately available for use in the cell.
5. The carbon dioxide utilized in photosynthesis is derived from the air; the water, from the soil. Carbon dioxide enters leaves through stomata.
6. Chlorophyll, consisting of two pigments, chlorophyll *a* and chlorophyll *b,* absorbs light energy and then transmits it to energy-trapping compounds.

7. Red and blue light are most effectively absorbed by chlorophyll and are most effective in photosynthesis.

8. Water is split into [H] and [OH] fragments. [H] units are combined with organic compounds in the synthesis of food. [OH] units react to produce molecular oxygen and water.

9. Photosynthesis is influenced by various factors, including chlorophyll content of mesophyll cells, light intensity, water supply, and carbon dioxide content of the air. Carbon dioxide most often limits the rate of photosynthesis.

10. Chlorophyll may fail to develop in leaves as a result of lack of chemical elements required for its synthesis, or as a result of insufficient light. Chlorotic plants are yellowish because of chemical deficiencies; etiolated plants are pale, with weak stems and undeveloped leaves, because of inadequate light.

11. Transpiration is the loss of water vapor from the aerial parts of plants.

12. An excess of transpiration over water absorption leads to wilting and often death.

13. Transpiration varies with changes in light intensity, wind velocity, atmospheric humidity, temperature, and other external factors.

14. Certain internal factors, such as leaf anatomy, imbibitional forces of protoplasmic colloids, etc., influence the rate of transpiration.

15. Hydrophytes are plants that grow partly or wholly submerged in water; xerophytes grow in soils of low moisture content; mesophytes grow in soils of moderate available moisture content.

16. Transpiration apparently provides the principal force responsible for the rise of sap. However, if there were not such tremendous water losses from leaves by transpiration, plants would not need to lift such large quantities of water into their leaves.

17. The chief importance of stomata and guard cells lies in their admitting carbon dioxide to the interior of leaves. They are not very effective in regulating transpiration until leaves begin to wilt.

18. Various methods are used by horticulturists and farmers to prevent excessive transpiration from the leaves of cultivated plants.

19. Guttation is the exudation of water in liquid form by aerial parts of plants. It is a result of high turgor pressures within plant tissues.

⫷ SUGGESTED READINGS FOR INTERESTED STUDENTS

1. Bassham, J. A., "The path of carbon in photosynthesis." *Scientific American*, Vol. 206, No. 6, pp. 88–100, June 1962.

2. Esau, Katherine, *Anatomy of Seed Plants*. Wiley, New York, 1960.

3. Galston, Arthur W., *The Life of the Green Plant*. Prentice-Hall, Englewood Cliffs, N. J., 1961.

4. Lehninger, Albert L., "How cells transform energy." *Scientific American*, Vol. 205, No. 3, pp. 63–73, September 1961.

5. Meyer, B. S., D. B. Anderson, and R. H. Böhning, *Introduction to Plant Physiology*. D. Van Nostrand, Princeton, N. J., 1960.

≪← TOPICS AND QUESTIONS FOR STUDY

1. Distinguish between deciduous and evergreen plants.
2. Describe briefly the causes of leaf fall. To what extent does frost influence leaf fall? Explain.
3. Name the principal leaf pigments and describe their colors. Which of these pigments occur in flowers or other plant parts?
4. How are these pigments distributed in the cell?
5. Explain briefly the causes of the familiar autumnal coloration of leaves. To what extent does frost influence this coloration?
6. What is the dual function performed by photosynthesis?
7. What is the Humus Theory? What is its present status?
8. What conditions must be present in a plant and in its environment in order that photosynthesis may occur?
9. What are the raw materials of photosynthesis? What are its products?
10. Compare a leaf and the process of photosynthesis with a factory and its operations.
11. State a simple, balanced chemical equation that indicates the raw materials and products of photosynthesis.
12. What are the sources of the carbon dioxide of the atmosphere? What is the usual concentration of carbon dioxide in the atomsphere?
13. Would you expect the carbon dioxide concentration of the soil air to be greater or lower than that of the air above the soil? Explain.
14. What process accounts for the movement of carbon dioxide into leaves? Explain.
15. Describe briefly the structure and operation of guard cells.
16. What is a "limiting factor" in any physiological process? What is usually the limiting factor in photosynthesis? How would you demonstrate this experimentally?
17. Do other factors ever become limiting factors in photosynthesis? Name some of these potentially limiting factors and describe the conditions under which they may become limiting.
18. What is "aerial fertilization"?
19. What is the source of the water used in photosynthesis? How does it reach leaves?
20. What happens to the light energy that reaches a leaf? About what percentage of this energy is transformed into the stored energy of foods in photosynthesis?
21. Distinguish between a light and a dark reaction.
22. Why is chlorophyll green?
23. What light rays are most effectively absorbed by chlorophyll?
24. Describe two ways in which photosynthesis is essential to the animal kingdom.
25. List several ways in which the carbohydrate formed in photosynthesis is utilized by plants.
26. State two reasons why excessive grazing by sheep may kill forage grasses.

27. Perennial weeds, such as dandelions, may be killed by repeatedly cutting off their leaves, before the latter enlarge. Explain.
28. Explain this statement: "Potato beetles attack chiefly the leaves of the potato plant; as a result, the tubers are greatly reduced in size and food value."
29. State the reasons why leaves may be regarded as effective photosynthetic machines.
30. What is chlorosis? How may this condition be corrected?
31. Name the conditions essential to chlorophyll synthesis.
32. Distinguish between chlorosis and etiolation.
33. Explain this statement: "Most of our machines and engines are powered by photosynthesis." Can you think of any machines that are not powered by photosynthesis? Explain.
34. Define transpiration.
35. Where in a leaf does water evaporation occur?
36. List the principal environmental conditions that influence transpiration, and describe how they affect this process.
37. What is the relation of stomata to transpiration? Is the major function of stomata and guard cells the control of transpiration? Explain.
38. Distinguish among hydrophytes, mesophytes, and xerophytes, compare the conditions under which they grow, and describe their structural and physiological differences.
39. Comment upon the significance of transpiration in the physiology of plants.
40. Criticize this statement: "Transpiration has a beneficial function in plants, since it provides the force that causes ascent of sap."
41. Describe some of the precautions that are taken to reduce transpiration in the cultivation of plants.
42. If you plant a rootless cutting in soil, should you cover the cutting with a glass jar or a tin can? Explain.
43. Distinguish between transpiration and guttation. What environmental conditions favor guttation?

Metabolism

Metabolism is the total of all the chemical changes involved in the physiological activities of living organisms. Certain phases of metabolism involve the synthesis of foods and other organic substances used for energy and for the construction of tissues; photosynthesis, as already stated, is the fundamental food-building process of green plants. Other phases of metabolism involve the breaking down of certain foods and the accompanying release of their stored energy in the process of **respiration.** Protoplasm is in a continual state of change; certain of its chemical components are being synthesized as others are being transformed and broken down. Thus, the maintenance of protoplasm and the processes of growth involve unending metabolic activity. All metabolic activities of plant cells involve transfers of energy. The ultimate source of energy involved in these metabolic processes is, of course, sunlight, which is transformed into chemical energy of carbohydrates in the process of photosynthesis. When foods are oxidized in the process of respiration in living cells, their stored energy is released and is used in

repair, growth, movement, and reproduction. Photosynthesis is a basic metabolic process of green plants, a process upon which all other metabolic processes are dependent.

THE MINERAL NUTRITION OF GREEN PLANTS

The Essential Soil Elements

Sixteen elements are known or suspected by plant physiologists to be essential for the normal metabolism of green plants. Three of these (carbon, hydrogen, and oxygen) are obtained chiefly from air and water. The remaining 13 elements are taken in from the solid matter in the soil and include nitrogen, phosphorus, potassium, sulfur, calcium, iron, magnesium, boron, zinc, manganese, copper, molybdenum, and chlorine. These soil elements, or soil nutrients, are absorbed not in elemental form but as ions that diffuse into root cells or are taken in by active transport as a result of the expenditure of energy by root cells.

The ions originate from the dissociation of various kinds of molecules in soils. Thus, magnesium sulfate molecules ($MgSO_4$) dissociate into magnesium ions (Mg^{2+}) and sulfate ions (SO_4^{2-}); potassium nitrate molecules (KNO_3) dissociate into potassium ions (K^+) and nitrate ions (NO_3^-). When a molecule dissociates, two kinds of ions result: a **cation** bearing one or more positive electric charges, and an **anion** bearing one or more negative electric charges. In the dissociation of potassium nitrate for example, the cation is K^+, the anion is NO_3^-. The essential elements absorbed as anions, and their principal ionic forms, are: nitrogen as nitrate ions (NO_3^-), phosphorus as phosphate ions ($H_2PO_4^-$), sulfur as sulfate ions (SO_4^{2-}), boron as borate ions ($HB_4O_7^-$), molybdenum as molybdate ($HMoO_4^-$), and chlorine as chloride (Cl^-). The essential elements absorbed by roots as cations, and their principal ionic forms, are: potassium (K^+), calcium (Ca^{2+}), magnesium (Mg^{2+}), iron (Fe^{3+}), manganese (Mn^{2+}), zinc (Zn^{2+}), and copper (Cu^{2+}). In addition to these, other ions may be absorbed by roots; for example, ammonium (NH_4^+), aluminum (Al^{3+}), carbonate ions (Co_3^{2-} and HCO_3^-), and others. The relative quantities of ions absorbed by plants from the soil vary with differences in the chemical and physical properties of soils and also with different species of plants. Chemical analyses of plant protoplasm indicate that carbon, hydrogen, and oxygen ordinarily constitute more than 92 percent of living protoplasm. This means that the remaining 8 percent, or less, consists of nitrogen, iron, phosphorus, and others listed in the preceding paragraphs. Of the soil nutrients, nitrogen is usually absorbed in larger quantities than all other soil nutrients combined; nitrogen ordinarily makes up about 1 to 2 percent of living protoplasm. Of the other soil nutrients, sulfur, phosphorus, calcium, potassium, and magnesium are required in much smaller quantities than nitrogen. The remaining seven elements (iron, zinc, boron, molybdenum, manganese, copper, and chlorine) are required in such relatively minute quantities that they have become known as the **trace elements,** or **micronutrients.** The contrasting term, **macronutrients,** is applied to the other essential elements.

Determining the Essentiality of Soil Elements. The fundamental researches upon the essential nature of the various soil elements in the nutrition of green plants utilized an experimental technique known as water culture. In this procedure, plants are grown, not in soil, but in distilled water, in which mineral salts are dissolved. Glazed earthenware jars or hard-glass vessels are used to hold the solution. By omitting various mineral salts and thus various chemical elements, plant physiologists have been able to determine the effects of such omissions upon plant growth; if the omission of a particular element from a water culture results in stunted growth of tops, poorly developed root systems, failure of chlorophyll formation, or some other structural or physiological abnormality, it may be safely assumed that the element is essential for the normal nutrition of the plant (Figure 13–1). When a particular element is present in insufficient quantities in a soil, the soil is said to suffer from a deficiency of that element. Green plants growing in such a soil and exhibiting abnormalities as a result of the deficiency of an essential element are said to be suffering from a **deficiency disease.** A variation of the water-culture technique is that of sand cultures, in which quartz sand or gravel, from which all soluble materials have been removed by chemical treatment and

(*Photo by Swift & Co.*)

FIG. 13–1. Water cultures, showing growth of petunia plants in complete

repeated washing, is placed in the culture jars, along with a suitable water solution of chemicals. Sand cultures have one great advantage over water cultures, namely, that plants in sand cultures stand erect without any external support, whereas plants in water cultures must usually be supported above the jars so that their roots dip into the solutions.

The term **hydroponics** has been applied in recent years to growth of plants in water and sand cultures. The solutions used in hydroponic culture must contain all the essential elements for the normal growth and development of green plants and must contain them in the proper proportions and in usable forms. The hydroponic growth of plants has received wide

nutrient solution and in solutions lacking various essential elements.

attention in popular magazines, and many amateur gardeners have utilized this method of growing plants. Large-scale hydroponic growth is being practiced by some commercial plant growers in this country. Roses, tomatoes, gladioli, snapdragons, lettuce, carrots, and potatoes are among commercially important crops that thrive in water and sand cultures (Figure 13–2). The hydroponic culture of plants has certain advantages, among which are these: 1. The chemical composition of the nutrient solution may be carefully controlled, so that the most suitable kinds and concentrations of nutrients may be provided for each crop. 2. There are no soil colloids present to immobilize any of the nutrients through

(*Photo by W. F. Gericke.*)

FIG. 13–2. Tomatoes growing in hydroponic tanks.

adsorption. 3. Frequent replacement of hydroponic solutions prevents the accumulation of possible toxic organic decomposition products such as often occur in soils. 4. In hydroponic cultures, conditions are relatively unfavorable for the growth of bacteria, higher fungi, and other organisms that may cause diseases of crop plants. 5. Through pumping devices, the solutions may be circulated and aerated, thus ensuring a regularity of aeration not possible in soils. 6. No tilling is required. 7. There is no weed growth in hydroponic cultures.

Although hydroponic gardening may be satisfactorily and profitably carried on as home gardening or commercial greenhouse projects, this method of crop culture must be regarded as an adjunct to field soil culture, not as a new technique that will replace soil culture.

Physiological Functions of Soil Elements. The functions of the various soil elements in plants are not fully known, but the work of plant physiologists has produced rather precise information concerning the importance of some elements. The detailed study of these functions cannot be appropriately included in a course in elementary botany; hence, only a brief list of some of the known or supposed functions of these elements will be included here.

1. *Magnesium* is a constituent of chlorophyll and is thus essential to chlorophyll manufacture and photosynthesis. It is also associated with certain regulatory compounds (enzymes). Plants growing in magnesium-deficient soils are a pale, greenish-yellow, a condition known as chlorosis. In some plants, purplish-red leaves with green veins indicate magnesium deficiency.

2. *Nitrogen* is a constituent of proteins, chlorophyll, nucleic acids, and many other organic compounds in plants. Green plants growing in nitrogen-deficient soils most commonly exhibit chlorosis in their older leaves, that is, the leaves farthest from the shoot tip.

3. *Sulfur* is a constituent of some proteins and is thus generally distributed throughout the plant. It also occurs in certain enzymes, glycosides, and other compounds. When sulfur is deficient in a soil, the plants are frequently yellowish and stunted.

4. *Phosphorus* is a constituent of some proteins, of energy-trapping compounds, nucleic acids, and other organic substances. It participates in many physiological activities including photosynthesis, respiration, and reproduction. Phosphorus deficiency generally retards growth and, in some plants, causes a purplish coloration in leaves and stems.

5. *Calcium* is a constituent of cell walls and of intercellular cementing substance. It is also known to influence cell membrane permeability. Calcium deficiency seriously affects the tissues in the tips of roots and shoots, and results in pronounced growth abnormalities. The adhesion of the tips of developing leaves is a symptom of calcium deficiency in corn.

6. *Potassium* is apparently not a constituent of the compounds synthesized by green plants. It seems to function in a regulatory manner, influencing photosynthesis, carbohydrate translocation, protein synthesis, and other activities. The principal symptoms of potassium deficiency in many plants include growth retardation, progressive chlorosis that begins along the margins of older leaves and gradually spreads to the younger parts of the shoot, and the premature loss of leaves.

7. *Iron* is a constituent of some enzymes and plays a role in respiration and in chlorophyll synthesis (although iron is not a constituent of chlorophyll). Iron deficiency frequently causes chlorosis, especially in the tissue between the veins of young leaves.

8. The functions of *zinc, boron, molybdenum, manganese, copper,* and *chlorine* are inadequately known, but these elements seem to be involved primarily in the regulation of various physiological activities. Thus, copper is part of several enzyme systems and is thought to play an important part in protein utilization and respiration; zinc is necessary for auxin synthesis; molybdenum is involved in an

(*Photo by A. L. Lang.*)

FIG. 13–3. Illustrating effects of fertilizer applications on crop growth. *Left:* Corn plants growing in soil regularly treated with a complete fertilizer. *Right:* Corn plants growing in soil to which no fertilizer has been added.

enzyme system that reduces nitrates; manganese is important in chlorophyll synthesis and in several oxidation-reduction reactions; and boron is thought to be associated with the translocation of sugars. Least known is the ·part played by chlorine in plant metabolism. Some evidence suggests that this element is associated with photosynthesis.

Deficiency diseases may be reduced or eliminated by the addition of suitable mineral nutrients in the form of fertilizers to soils (Figure 13–3). In some plants, nutrient deficiencies may be corrected by spraying solutions of the appropriate essential nutrients on leaves, a practice commonly referred to as "leaf feeding." An interesting factor in the mineral nutrition of plants is the toxicity of certain essential elements when these are present in soils in excess. For example, zinc, boron, and manganese are essential in minute concentrations, but in larger quan-

tities become poisonous to most green plants. The enormous amounts of soil nutrients sold each year are used primarily to force greater crop yields and, at the same time, to prevent deficiency diseases. In the United States, more than 20,000,-000 tons of commercial fertilizers are purchased annually. Most of this total consists of various blends of three macronutrients: Nitrogen (N) in organic or inorganic form, phosphorus measured in terms of phosphoric oxide (P_2O_5), and potassium measured in terms of potash (K_2O).

In several of the paragraphs above, the locations of the first symptoms of particular deficiency diseases are mentioned. These locations are related to the metabolism of the deficient elements. For example, a plant may utilize calcium so that it cannot be withdrawn from the tissues into which it has been incorporated. The calcium is therefore immobile in the plant, and if calcium becomes deficient during the growing season, the deficiency disease shows up first in the growing points of the plant. Nitrogen can be removed from old plant parts and transported to the meristem. In case of deficiencies, nitrogen is removed from old leaves and brought to the shoot tip. The deficiency disease appears first in older leaves because the mobile nitrogen is withdrawn from the older plant parts in favor of the growing points.

FOODS AND FOOD SYNTHESES

The word "food" is frequently used to designate all types of substances that enter the bodies of living organisms and are used by them. In this sense, "food" is commonly used by florists, horticulturists, and farmers to refer to the inorganic materials absorbed by plants from soil. Most botanists prefer a more restricted use of the word "food"—to refer, namely, to *those organic compounds synthesized by living plants and used to supply energy and to construct and repair living tissues.* In terms of this more limited definition, nutrient ions, water, and carbon dioxide absorbed from the soil and air by plants are not foods, but are the *raw materials* from which green plants make foods. As stated in the preceding chapter, foods contain chemical energy, derived from the energy of the sun's rays. The synthesis of foods from the simple, inorganic substances of the soil and air thus requires energy, which is stored in sugars and other compounds in the process of photosynthesis. There are three kinds of foods manufactured by living organisms from raw materials of the kinds described above: **carbohydrates, fats,** and **proteins.**

Carbohydrates. Carbohydrates are always composed of carbon, hydrogen, and oxygen, with the hydrogen and oxygen in the same proportion (2 to 1) as they are in water. Most carbohydrates in plants contain in their molecules 6 carbon atoms or some multiple of 6: common carbohydrates in plants are glucose, or grape sugar ($C_6H_{12}O_6$); fructose, or fruit sugar ($C_6H_{12}O_6$); sucrose, or cane sugar ($C_{12}H_{22}O_{11}$); maltose, or malt sugar ($C_{12}H_{22}O_{11}$); and starch and cellulose, both with the basic formula ($C_6H_{10}O_5$)$_n$. The fact that different carbohydrates (for example, glucose and fructose) may have the same chemical formula means that the differences between them are attributable to differences in the *arrangement* of their constituent atoms, *not* to differences in the kinds or number of their atoms. Many carbohydrates, such as sugars, are soluble in water and can thus be moved readily from one part of a plant to other parts. Starch, however, is insoluble in water and thus cannot be translocated in plants unless it is converted into sugars. Starches are the commonest reserve carbohydrates in plants and are found stored in the form of small colorless grains in the cells of fruits, such as bananas, in the cells of seeds, such as corn and wheat, and in the cells of various types of roots (carrots) and stems (potato tubers) (Figure 13–4). Sugars are also stored in considerable quantities in the tissues of certain plants, as in sugar cane, sugar beet, and sugar maple. The chief uses of carbohydrates in plants are: to supply energy, to furnish materials from which other organic substances, especially fats and proteins, are made, and to build the structural framework of plants (cellulose).

Fats. Fats and oils are similar to carbohydrates in that they are composed of the same chemical elements: carbon, hydrogen, and oxygen. The arrangement of

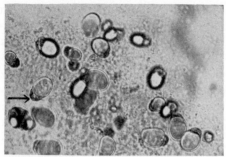

(*Photo by W. N. Stewart.*)

FIG. 13–4. Starch grains forming in chloroplasts of *Pellionia* stem. The arrow indicates a chloroplast.

the atoms of these substances in fat molecules differs markedly from that in carbohydrate molecules, and the proportion of hydrogen to oxygen in fats is much higher than the 2 to 1 ratio of carbohydrates. The chemical formulas of two plant fats, stearin and palmitin, are respectively $C_3H_5(CO_2C_{17}H_{35})_3$ and $C_3H_5(CO_2C_{15}H_{31})_3$. From these formulas can be seen the relatively small proportion of oxygen in these substances. It is largely because of this low percentage of oxygen that fats are able to provide about twice as much energy as sugars, weight for weight, for fats can be oxidized to a greater extent. In plants, fatty substances occur most frequently as oils; that is, they are liquid at ordinary temperatures. All fats and oils are insoluble in water. Fats are chiefly reserve foods that are stored in various plant structures, especially seeds (peanut, coconut, castor bean) and fruits (banana, avocado, paw-paw). When these reserve foods are about to be utilized, they may be converted into sugars. Certain complex fatty compounds are constituents of living protoplasm, particularly of cytoplasmic membranes, and are thus important in membrane permeability and absorption phenomena.

Fats are derived from glycerol (glycerine) and fatty acids; when they are digested in living cells, their molecules break down into the constituent glycerol and fatty acids. The fat content of plant tissues is closely related to the carbohydrate content. Thus, in the maturing of many kinds of seeds, the carbohydrates decrease as the fats simultaneously increase. Also, in the germination of many seeds, the fatty foods decrease and carbohydrates increase, apparently at the expense of the fats.

Proteins. Proteins are the most complex organic substances in living organisms. Their molecules are exceedingly large, as is shown by two plant proteins, **zein** from corn and **gliadin** from wheat, the formulas of which are respectively $C_{736}H_{1161}N_{184}O_{208}S_3$ and $C_{685}H_{1068}N_{196}O_{211}S_5$. The molecular weights of some proteins approximate 500,000 as compared, for example, with 342 for sucrose and 180 for glucose. Proteins, like fats, are made from carbohydrates and thus always contain carbon, hydrogen, and oxygen, as do carbohydrates. In addition to these chemical elements, proteins always contain nitrogen and frequently also contain sulfur or phosphorus, or both. The nitrogen, phosphorus, and sulfur in proteins are derived chiefly from nitrate, phosphate, and sulfate ions absorbed from the soil.

In the synthesis of proteins, the carbon, hydrogen, and oxygen derived from carbohydrates are combined in complex chemical reactions with nitrogen to form **amino acids,** which may be regarded as the building blocks from which protein molecules are constructed. As shown in Figure 13–5A, an amino acid has two chemically reactive **functional groups:** a carboxyl, or acid, group (COOH), and an amino, or basic, group (NH₂). It has, in addition, a characteristic side group

(*R*) that is different in each of the 20-odd amino acids isolated from plant tissues. For example, in the simplest amino acid (glycine), *R* represents a single hydrogen atom; in another (alanine), it represents CH_3. Plants are able to synthesize all the amino acids required in their metabolism. From these compounds, the hundreds of proteins occurring in the plant are synthesized as a result of the chemical linkage of amino acid molecules with other amino acid molecules. The union of two amino acids, a process involving the removal of a molecule of water and the formation of what is termed a peptide bond, is schematically outlined in Figure 13–5B, C. Proteins consist of many amino acids joined to form chains, and are characterized in large part by the kind, number, sequence, and spatial relationships of these components.

Proteins form the fundamental structure of protoplasm, and thus are found in all living cells. Many proteins are stored as reserve foods in plant cells, usually in the form of distinct bodies called **aleurone grains.** Aleurone grains are especially abundant in certain cells of grains, such as corn and wheat. Reserve proteins occur in large concentrations in many other types of seeds, such as beans, peas, and soybeans. The proteins stored in seeds are used chiefly in the formation of protoplasm in new cells when seeds germinate. The chief function of proteins is the construction and repair of protoplasm. Proteins may also be used as sources of energy, but such utilization ordinarily occurs only after available carbohydrate and fat reserves have been exhausted.

HETEROTROPHIC NUTRITION

Plants that manufacture their own foods from simpler substances are called **auto-**

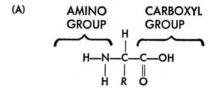

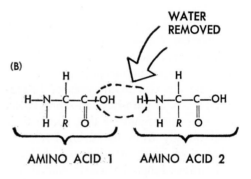

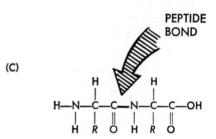

FIG. 13–5. A: A diagrammatic representation of an amino acid. B and C: Illustrating the union of two amino acids.

trophic; those that depend upon ready-made, externally supplied foods are **heterotrophic.** Most important and most common of autotrophic plants are those that manufacture their basic foods by photosynthesis—in other words, all green plants. There are several species of photosynthetic bacteria that, although they lack chlorophyll, contain purple or green pigments and are able to synthesize their own food from carbon dioxide and hydrogen sulfide (H_2S). Some other species of bacteria are able to manufacture their own food by **chemosynthesis,** a process in which energy for food synthesis is obtained by various oxidation or reduction reactions that the organisms carry out. For example, certain bacteria oxidize free sulfur to sulfate, while others reduce sulfate to sulfide. Still others use iron and nitrogen compounds as substrates for oxidation or reduction reactions. However, the number of species of autotrophic bacteria is small as compared with that of more advanced autotrophic plants.

There are two main types of heterotrophic plants: **parasites** and **saprophytes.** Parasites are organisms that obtain their food directly from the living bodies of other organisms. Beechdrops, dodders, and various fungi that cause animal and plant diseases are examples of parasites. Some species of plants are partial or semi-parasites. Mistletoe, for example, contains chlorophyll and can therefore manufacture food; however, it obtains water and mineral nutrients from the trees upon which it grows. Saprophytes are organisms such as breadmold, Indian pipe, most kinds of mushrooms, and puffballs, which obtain their food from the dead bodies or waste products of living organisms, or from other nonliving organic materials. Many species of very adaptable organisms can live either parasitically or saprophytically. Certain fungi behave as parasites when they attack the living tissues of their **host** (the organism that they parasitize) but later live saprophytically upon the dead tissue of the host.

The curious and unusual methods of obtaining supplementary food employed by insectivorous plants deserve mention again in connection with the other methods by means of which plants make or acquire foods.

ORGANIC COMPOUNDS OTHER THAN FOODS

Plants produce, in addition to carbohydrates, fats, and proteins, a great variety of other organic substances. Some of these (chlorophyll, xanthophyll, carotene, anthocyanins, suberin, and others) have already been discussed. Only a few other groups of organic substances remain to be considered in this introductory text.

Enzymes. A **catalyst** is a chemical agent that controls the rate at which a chemical reaction occurs. The catalyst itself is not used up in the process that it promotes and does not appear in the products of the reaction. Catalysts are also highly efficient in that only minute quantities are required to speed the reaction of much larger quantities of substrate material. Many types of catalysts are used in promoting large-scale chemical reactions in industry; for example, in the manufacture of sulfuric acid from sulfur dioxide and oxygen, platinum is the catalyst that hastens the reaction. In the absence of catalysts, many chemical reactions proceed slowly or not at all.

Living cells produce their own catalysts in the form of special proteins, or **enzymes,** that play an important part in the regulation of physiological processes, including photosynthesis, digestion, and respiration. As organic catalysts, enzymes have certain characteristics in addition to those mentioned above. For example, they have a higher *specificity* than most inorganic catalysts; that is, a particular enzyme usually catalyzes only a single reaction. Metallic platinum, on the other hand, can hasten the rate of a variety of reactions. Much of the enzyme's high specificity may be attributed to the kind of protein comprising the enzyme molecule. Some enzymes can function only when they are associated with a nonproteinaceous **coenzyme.** Inorganic materials such as copper and iron, and organic compounds such as vitamins are known to function as coenzymes. Another characteristic of enzymes is their sensitivity to heat. Many of them are weakened or inactivated at temperatures of 160°F, and most of them are quickly destroyed by temperatures near the boiling point of water (212°F).

Vitamins. These are complex organic compounds, most of which are synthesized only by plants. Although the chemical structure of some vitamins is known and the laboratory synthesis of certain vitamins has been accomplished, information concerning their specific functions in plants is rather meager. It is probable that most vitamins contribute to the formation of enzymes, or function as coenzymes (see above). Some are believed to function in growth regulation, while other vitamins or vitamin derivatives serve as hydrogen carriers in respiration.

Hormones. These are organic compounds synthesized by living protoplasm and involved principally in the regulation of certain processes of growth and development. A fuller account of these hormones and of their behavior follows in the chapter on growth (Chapter 14).

Essential Oils. These are organic compounds that occur widely in plant tissues and that are generally regarded as waste products of plant metabolism. Although they are called "oils," they are chemically different from true oils and fats; most of them are members of a group of organic compounds called **terpenes,** which are made up of carbon and hydrogen only, with no oxygen. The essential oils are aromatic substances that are responsible for the characteristic odors and flavors of many plant parts, such as fragrant flowers, mint leaves, cinnamon bark, clove buds, sandalwood, nutmeg seeds, and pine needles. The essential oils are economically important in perfumes and cosmetics, food flavoring, varnishes, medicines, and many other products. Essential oils in some plants become partially or wholly oxidized into substances called resins, of which turpentine, balsams, and copals are examples.

Organic Acids. All living plant cells contain organic acids of various types. Among the common organic acids of plants are citric, malic, oxalic, pyruvic, succinic, tannic, and tartaric acids. These are variously important in plant metabolism. Some organic acids are obviously waste products of certain metabolic activities of plants, and often accumulate in sufficient concentrations in plant tissues to give them a sharp, sour taste (for example, oxalic acid in rhubarb and sourdock leaves). Also, the sour or tart taste of many fruits is the result of relatively high organic acid content (for example, malic acid in apples, citric acid in lemons and grapefruit). Tannic acid is probably a metabolic waste product that accumulates in certain plant tissues and becomes transformed into tannins. Tannins occur in many types of wood (chestnut, oak), in bark (hemlock, oaks), in leaves (tea, sumac), and in seeds and unripe fruits (acorns, persimmons, plums, bananas). Tannins are important economically in the tanning of animal hides and in the manufacture of tannin inks. Some organic acids are intermediate products in respiration and may be oxidized with the release of energy.

DIGESTION

Digestion is the process whereby foods that are insoluble in water or are very complex chemically are converted into foods that dissolve readily in water or that are simpler chemically. Digestion of insoluble storage products is prerequisite to translocation, for only water-soluble foods can be moved from one part of a plant to other parts. It is also important as a preliminary to other processes, such as respiration, that ordinarily occur only when the foods involved in them are dissolved in water.

Digestion proceeds in virtually all living cells, but is especially active in cells that store considerable quantities of foods. Thus, it is a conspicuous feature in most seeds, tubers, rhizomes, and other storage structures, particularly when they are beginning or resuming growth after a dormant period. The principal kind of digestion that occurs in green plants is **intracellular;** that is, it proceeds within the protoplasm of cells. In some plants, such as many fungi and insectivores, digestive enzymes diffuse out of the cells that produce them and thus act upon foods external to the cells in which they developed. This type of digestion, which also occurs in cotyledons, is termed **extracellular.**

Digestion involves the uptake of water during the conversion of complex into simpler foods, as is shown by the equation representing the transformation of malt sugar to grape sugar:

$$C_{12}H_{22}O_{11} \quad + \quad H_2O \quad \rightarrow \quad 2C_6H_{12}O_6$$
(malt sugar)   (water)   (grape sugar)

Thus, from the chemical standpoint, digestive processes are processes of **hydrolysis.** The mere physical addition of water to complex foods in the cell is not sufficient to cause their transformation into simpler foods, for these complex substances are so stable that they require the action of enzymes to bring about their alteration.

The action of some hydrolytic enzymes is reversible; that is, they not only convert complex foods into simpler ones, but they may also build up the corresponding complex foods from the simpler types. The enzyme **maltase,** for example, digests maltose (malt sugar) into glucose (grape sugar) and is also able to synthesize maltose from glucose molecules. The reversible action of some enzymes is very important in translocation and food storage. An insoluble food in one part of a plant may be digested by a particular enzyme into soluble food, which may then be moved to some other portion of the plant and converted back into insoluble form by the same enzyme.

Kinds of Digestive Enzymes. There are many dozens of digestive enzymes present in plant cells, each with its specific function. Only a few of the more important digestive enzymes will be cited here. These enzymes are usually classified into three major groups, which, with representative enzymes of each group, are the following:

1. **Carbohydrate-digesting enzymes:** these include the following widely distributed enzymes:
    a. **Amylase** (diastase), which catalyzes the digestion of starch to maltose (malt sugar);
    b. **Invertase,** or **sucrase,** which catalyzes the digestion of sucrose (cane sugar) both to glucose (grape sugar) and to fructose (fruit sugar);
    c. **Maltase,** which catalyzes the digestion of maltose to glucose.

2. **Fat-digesting enzymes:** these enzymes, called **lipases,** catalyze the digestion of fats to fatty acids and glycerol and also catalyze the synthesis of fats from fatty acids and glycerol; in other words the lipases are reversible in their action. Lipases are especially active in the germination of fatty seeds.

3. **Protein-digesting enzymes:** these include the **proteases,** which catalyze the digestion of proteins into amino acids and also promote the synthesis of proteins from amino acids. Proteases, like lipases, are reversible in their action.

Economic Importance of Enzymes. Enzymes, chiefly those from plants, are important in many industrial processes; in some of these the hydrolytic activities of living tissues are employed, in others the enzymes are extracted from the living cells and are then allowed to act upon certain substances of economic significance. The following partial list of uses made of enzymes attests to their great economic value: the preparation of sizing for textiles and paper; the removal (retting) of fibers from the stems of flax, hemp, and other plants; the degumming of silk; the preparation of skins for tanning; the manufacture of glycerin; the brewing and clarification of beer; the clarification of syrups and pectin solutions; the making of bread; cheese manufacture; the production of syrup from sweet potatoes and corn; the manufacture of soy sauce; the fermentation of pulp to remove it from cocoa seeds; the preparation of medicinal diastase and pepsin for human digestive disturbances; and the manufacture of infant foods. In the brewing of beer, barley grains (or other types of cereal grains) are most commonly used as a source of carbohydrates. The grains are soaked in warm water and germinated; during this sprouting, the amylase in the grains becomes active and converts the stored starch into maltose, a sugar that is readily acted upon by yeasts and converted into alcohol. Sprouted barley is known in the brewing industry as malt. A protease enzyme, papain, from leaves and fruits of the tropical pawpaw (papaya) is used to tenderize meats, since the enzyme digests some of the meat proteins. Papain is sometimes used medicinally for patients whose own proteases show diminished activity.

RESPIRATION

Photosynthesis is the process that converts the energy of light into the stored chemical energy of foods; respiration is the process that converts this stored energy into energy available for the synthesis of fats, proteins, and other organic compounds, for growth, reproduction, movements, active transport, and other energy-requiring processes. Respiration is fundamentally a process of oxidation; that is, it involves the addition of oxygen to, or the removal of hydrogen from, the material undergoing respiration, as a result of which energy is liberated. The oxygen that is involved in the oxidative processes of respiration may be derived from free, atmospheric oxygen that, dissolved in water, enters the cells of plants, or it may be oxygen that is transferred from one type of chemical compound to another. Respiration is frequently compared with the burning of wood or coal, which releases in the form of heat and light the energy stored in these materials. Obviously, the comparison is a crude one, for oxidation in living organisms occurs at slower rates and at lower temperatures than those involved in the combustion of fuels, and is subject to controlling factors unlike those involved in the burning of coal and wood. Of the energy released from foods by respiration, a portion escapes from the bodies of living organisms as heat; the remainder is used to provide the energy necessary for energy-using physiological processes, such as those mentioned above.

Respiration is sometimes defined as the intake of oxygen and the release of carbon dioxide by organisms, or is used synonymously with "breathing." Such uses of the word "respiration" are confusing and should be abandoned. The fundamentally significant feature of respiration is that it is a chemical process that goes on in *all living cells;* the central characteristic of the process is a chemical reaction of oxidation, not the exchange of oxygen and carbon dioxide, which is merely incidental to the chemical process itself. The use of "respiration" in such terms as "artificial respiration" is inexcusable physiologically. The word that should be employed here is "breathing."

Respiratory processes vary somewhat in different kinds of plants, but all types of respiration have certain common attributes: the chemical breakdown of foods, the release of energy as a result of such breakdown, transfers of oxygen and hydrogen among foods and other substances involved in respiration, and the production of carbon dioxide. The rate and intensity of respiration may be measured in terms of certain of these attributes. For example, the heat released in respiration is a rough index of respiratory intensity; most commonly, the quantity of carbon dioxide released by respiring tissues and organs is used to measure respiratory activity.

Aerobic Respiration. In this type of respiration, which occurs in most kinds of plants, organic compounds, chiefly sugars, are oxidized in the presence of oxygen, with the result that energy is released and carbon dioxide and water are formed, as indicated by this equation:

$$C_6H_{12}O_6 + 6O_2 \rightarrow 6CO_2 + 6H_2O + \text{energy}$$
(glucose) (oxygen)   (carbon   (water)
                     dioxide)

In aerobic respiration, the energy released is approximately the equivalent of the energy absorbed in photosynthesis and utilized in the manufacture of glucose. Thus, from the standpoint of energy transformation, respiration balances photosynthesis.

The gaseous exchange between green plants and the external atmosphere during the day is different from such exchange at night. During the day, both photosynthesis and respiration occur in leaves. Photosynthesis uses carbon dioxide and releases oxygen, whereas respiration uses oxygen and releases carbon dioxide. Photosynthesis proceeds more rapidly, however, than respiration, so that the carbon dioxide produced in respiration is immediately used in green tissues in photosynthesis. The oxygen released in photosynthesis is in excess of that used by respiration, so a part of this oxygen escapes into the outer air. Thus, during the day, green plants give off oxygen and take in carbon dioxide. This makes it appear as though only photosynthesis were going on, for the gaseous exchange during the day is the characteristic gaseous exchange of photosynthesis. Actually, however, both photosynthesis and respiration occur during the day, but, so far as gaseous exchange is concerned, photosynthesis masks respiration because it goes on more rapidly. At night, photosynthesis ceases and respiration continues. Thus, at night, green plants give off carbon dioxide and take in oxygen, a condition exactly the reverse of that during the day.

As stated above, respiration releases energy, some of which, in the form of heat energy, is often measurable. In the growth of flower clusters of certain tropical plants called aroids and in masses of sprouting seeds, temperatures are occasionally as much as 80°F higher than those of the outside air. Respiration proceeding rapidly in a poorly ventilated space may generate sufficient heat to cause fire. For example, if moist hay is stored in a tightly walled barn loft, the respiration of living hay cells and of the bacteria and molds that grow upon the hay may develop enough heat to cause the hay to burst into flame. Frequently the burning of barns is attributable to this "spontaneous combustion." In many ways, aerobic respiration has the reverse effect of photosynthesis, as is indicated in the table below.

Anaerobic Respiration. Anaerobic respiration occurs in the absence of free oxygen (or in the presence of very small quantities of oxygen). It makes use of the same foods that are respired aerobically, expecially sugars. Instead of oxidizing foods completely to carbon dioxide and water, anaerobic respiration usually forms carbon dioxide and some organic compound, such as ethyl (grain) alcohol or lactic acid. Anaerobic respiration releases less energy from the same quantity of sugar than does aerobic respiration because one of its products (the organic compound) is incompletely oxidized. In sufficiently high concentrations, the organic substances resulting from anaerobic respiration are often toxic to the organisms that produced them. Yeast plants may produce alcohol to a concentration of 12 to 16 percent before their growth is inhibited. One of the factors that restricts the growth and reproduction of many bacteria is the accumulation of the toxic products of their anaerobic respiration.

The most familiar example of anaerobic respiration is the **alcoholic fermentation** of sugars by yeasts, which are minute one-celled fungi. Yeasts derive their energy from the anaerobic respiration of sugars, releasing carbon dioxide and ethyl alcohol in the process. Even in the presence of free oxygen, yeasts continue to produce alcohol; that is, they are unable to complete a process of aerobic respiration because they lack certain chemical regulators essential to aerobic respiration. In the presence of free oxygen and the alcohol produced by yeasts, certain bacteria will oxidize the alcohol to acetic acid. These bacteria, often present on the skins of grapes and other fruits, convert

Photosynthesis	*Respiration*
1. Absorbs water and carbon dioxide	1. Releases water and carbon dioxide
2. Liberates oxygen	2. Absorbs oxygen
3. Makes sugar (and other compounds)	3. Breaks down sugar (and other compounds)
4. Increases dry weight of tissues	4. Decreases dry weight of tissues
5. Stores energy in foods	5. Releases energy from foods
6. Proceeds in green cells only	6. Proceeds in all living cells
7. Proceeds only in light	7. Proceeds in light or darkness

wines (fermented fruit juices) to vinegar.

Anaerobic respiration is important to man in many ways. The manufacture of industrial alcohols, alcoholic beverages, and vinegar, the spoilage of many types of foods, the manufacture of cheese and other dairy products and of sauerkraut, and the preparation of ensilage (fermented green plant material, such as chopped cornstalks and leaves) in silos are the results of processes of anaerobic respiration by microorganisms. Much of the decomposition of dead plant and animal bodies in soil and water and of their waste products is attributable to the anaerobic respiration of these materials by certain anaerobic bacteria and fungi. These anaerobic organisms produce certain organic compounds as their respiratory products and, in so doing, obtain energy necessary for their life processes. Aerobic soil organisms may then respire the organic products of anerobic organisms, obtaining energy in the process and forming water and carbon dioxide as their respiratory products. The processes of decomposition result in the ultimate restoration to the soil and air of the simple substances that constitute the organic compounds of plant and animal bodies, and are thus important in maintaining soil fertility.

Relation of Aerobic to Anaerobic Respiration. Anaerobic respiration is apparently of general occurrence in living cells. In many lower organisms, such as yeasts and some bacteria, anaerobic respiration is the only type of respiration normally carried on, and these organisms, called **anaerobes,** commonly live only in the absence of free oxygen. Most higher plants respire anaerobically for a time, at least, if they are deprived of oxygen. When higher plants are deprived of oxygen for a few hours, their tissues develop small

amounts of some of the intermediate products (for example, acetaldehyde) of anaerobic respiration. Also, when seedlings in air are given fermented sugar solutions, their respiration rate increases, indicating that they can respire products of alcoholic fermentation. Although higher plants may respire anaerobically, they can live normally only in the presence of oxygen. If such plants are kept in oxygen-free atmosphere for more than two or three days, they begin to show growth abnormalities as a result of the accumulation of toxic products of their anaerobic respiration. Corn seedlings, for example, under anaerobic conditions for so short a time as 48 hours, suffer severe injury. One effect of the waterlogging of soil is the accumulation in and around roots of toxic products of anaerobic respiration. Some investigators have reported traces of alcohol in soil water around plant roots under anaerobic conditions.

The Chemical Mechanism of Respiration. Respiration is not a single chemical reaction but is rather a group of intricately organized and integrated reactions of great complexity. Thus the equation

$$C_6H_{12}O_6 + 6O_2 \rightarrow 6H_2O + 6CO_2 + energy$$

for aerobic respiration is only a generalized representation of reacting substances and final products and does not indicate the long series of intermediate chemical reactions constituting the complete process of anaerobic respiration.

The principal chemical steps in respiration are shown in schematic outline in Figure 13–6; the many intermediate compounds and reactions have been omitted. In the first reaction, glucose is converted into a phosphorus-containing compound, glucose phosphate. Through intermediate reactions, the glucose is transformed to fructose and another phosphate group is

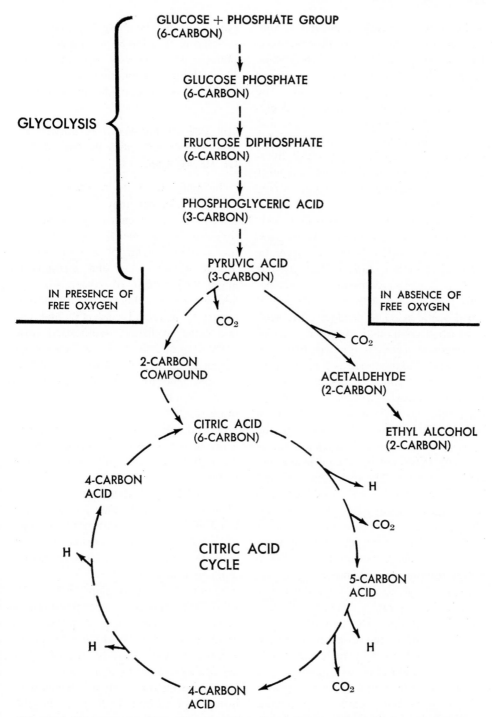

GLUCOSE + PHOSPHATE GROUP
(6-CARBON)

GLUCOSE PHOSPHATE
(6-CARBON)

FRUCTOSE DIPHOSPHATE
(6-CARBON)

PHOSPHOGLYCERIC ACID
(3-CARBON)

PYRUVIC ACID
(3-CARBON)

GLYCOLYSIS

IN PRESENCE OF
FREE OXYGEN

IN ABSENCE OF
FREE OXYGEN

CO_2

CO_2

2-CARBON
COMPOUND

ACETALDEHYDE
(2-CARBON)

CITRIC ACID
(6-CARBON)

ETHYL ALCOHOL
(2-CARBON)

4-CARBON
ACID

H

H

H

CO_2

CITRIC ACID
CYCLE

5-CARBON
ACID

H

4-CARBON
ACID

CO_2

FIG. 13–6. Schematic outline of some major chemical steps in respiration. Explanation in text.

added to form fructose diphosphate. Subsequent reactions convert this 6-carbon fructose compound to the 3-carbon phosphoglyceric acid, which, in turn, is chemically changed to **pyruvic acid.** The foregoing group of reactions, called **glycolysis,** does not require free oxygen and thus may be completed under anaerobic conditions. In addition, glycolysis liberates a relatively small amount of energy that is transferred to energy-trapping compounds.

The final group of reactions in aerobic respiration is completed only in the presence of free oxygen. With the enzymatic removal of carbon dioxide from pyruvic acid, a 2-carbon compound is formed. This is combined with a 4-carbon acid (oxaloacetic acid) to produce citric acid, a 6-carbon compound. Another series of intermediate reactions removes hydrogen and carbon dioxide and, as a result, produces a 5-carbon acid. Again hydrogen and carbon dioxide are removed through chemical steps to form another 4-carbon compound (succinic acid). Through the subsequent removal of hydrogen, oxaloacetic acid is formed and the **citric acid cycle** is completed. The hydrogen given off in aerobic respiration is combined with free oxygen to form water. The most significant aspect of the aerobic mechanism is the fact that it liberates relatively large amounts of energy that are transferred to energy-trapping compounds.

Figure 13–6 also illustrates the major steps in the respiratory chemistry of alcoholic fermentation. The first phase, glycolysis, occurs in the absence of oxygen (as it may in flowering plants) and results in the production of pyruvic acid. Carbon dioxide is then removed from pyruvic acid to form the 2-carbon compound, acetaldehyde. In the final reaction, hydrogen is added to acetaldehyde to form ethyl alcohol. The energy liberated in the process is transferred to trapping compounds. The relatively low energy yield of alcoholic fermentation is attributable to the incomplete oxidation of glucose.

THE USE OF RADIOACTIVE ELEMENTS AND HEAVY ISOTOPES IN THE STUDY OF METABOLISM

In addition to its common form, a chemical element may occur in forms having similar chemical properties but different atomic weights. For example, the common form of oxygen has an atomic weight of 16 and accounts for about 99.7 percent of oxygen atoms. In addition to O^{16}, there are two naturally occurring heavier forms (O^{17} and O^{18}) and three artificially synthesized forms (O^{14}, O^{15}, and O^{19}). These heavier and lighter forms are called **isotopes.** Artificial isotopes tend to be highly unstable; in their spontaneous transformation to more stable forms, they emit radiant energy and are spoken of as **radioactive.** Most of the naturally occurring isotopes are either stable or only slightly radioactive.

A widely used technique of studying plant nutrition and other phases of metabolism is the use of radioactive isotopes of certain chemical elements. In some suitable form these are placed in the medium in which roots grow, or are otherwise introduced into plant bodies. The subsequent movement and physiological behavior of radioactive compounds in plant tissues may be studied by photographic methods or by the use of a Geiger-Muller counter or some similar device for measuring radioactivity. Radioactive isotopes of carbon, hydrogen, phosphorus, sulfur, and other elements have been used in investigations of absorption,

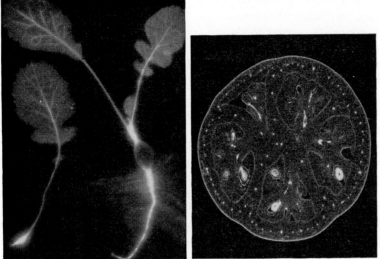

(*Photo by American Smelting & Refining Co.*)

FIG. 13–7. Autoradiographs showing accumulation of radioactive material in radish plant (*left*) and tomato fruit (*right*).

translocation, photosynthesis, and other activities, and have produced much information about these phenomena. The use of radioactive elements has demonstrated the rapid exchange of potassium and phosphorus by living cells during absorption, a phenomenon that was unknown before the use of these "tracer" elements (Fig. 13–7).

Nonradioactive isotopes also are used in the attack upon physiological problems. For example, a study of photosynthesis involving the use of water containing the heavy oxygen isotope, O^{18}, showed that all the oxygen liberated in this process comes from water and that the oxygen that enters into carbohydrates is derived from carbon dioxide.

SUMMARY

1. Metabolism is the total of all chemical changes that occur within living organisms. It includes food manufacture, food transformations, and food breakdown with energy release.
2. The essential elements for growth of green plants are carbon, hydrogen, oxygen, nitrogen, phosphorus, potassium, sulfur, calcium, iron, magnesium, boron, zinc, copper, manganese, molybdenum, and chlorine. Deficiencies in the supply of these elements result in deficiency diseases.
3. Plants may be grown in water solutions of essential soil elements. This type of plant culture is called hydroponics.
4. A food is an organic substance that furnishes energy or is used in building protoplasm. Three classes of foods are carbohydrates, fats, and proteins.
5. Carbohydrates supply energy, build cell walls, and are the sources from which fats, proteins, and other organic compounds of plants are constructed. Carbohydrates consist of carbon, hydrogen, and oxygen, with twice as many

hydrogen atoms as oxygen atoms in each molecule. Carbohydrates include sugars, starches, and cellulose.

6. Fats are chiefly storage foods and constituents of protoplasm. Fats contain carbon, hydrogen, and oxygen, with a lower proportion of oxygen to hydrogen than in carbohydrates. Fats result from the reactions of glycerol with fatty acids.

7. Proteins are the chief solid constituents of living protoplasm and contain carbon, hydrogen, oxygen, and nitrogen, and often phosphorus or sulfur or both. Proteins result from the linkage of amino acid molecules.

8. Autotrophic plants manufacture their own food by photosynthesis or chemosynthesis. Heterotrophic plants are unable to make their own food; they are parasites (which obtain foods from tissues of other living organisms) or saprophytes (which obtain foods from dead or nonliving organic matter).

9. Organic compounds other than foods produced by plants include chlorophyll, carotenoids, enzymes, hormones, vitamins, organic acids, essential oils, and others. Some of these perform vital functions, others are metabolic wastes.

10. Enzymes are highly specific, proteinaceous catalysts that promote a great variety of reactions.

11. Vitamins are complex compounds, many of which function as coenzymes.

12. Organic acids may be metabolic waste products, or intermediate compounds in food syntheses and respiration.

13. Digestion is the conversion of complex or water-insoluble foods into simpler or water-soluble foods. Digestive processes are processes of hydrolysis.

14. Respiration is the chemical breakdown of food with the release of energy, which is used in processes of growth, reproduction, active transport, etc. Some energy is dissipated as heat from the plant's surface.

15. The foods most commonly respired are sugars. Respiration always results in destruction of foods, release of energy, transfers of hydrogen and oxygen among various organic compounds, and production of carbon dioxide.

16. Aerobic respiration occurs in the presence of free oxygen and its chemical products are carbon dioxide and water. In some ways it may be regarded as opposite to photosynthesis.

17. Anaerobic respiration occurs in the absence of free oxygen and its chemical products are carbon dioxide and some organic compound, such as alcohol or an organic acid. It occurs in many types of lower plants (for example, yeasts) and in higher plants also.

18. Aerobic respiration is not a single chemical reaction but is a complex of chemical processes that may be separated into two groups: 1. Glycolysis, in which simple sugars are transformed through phosphorus mechanisms into pyruvic acid and which is anaerobic. 2. A cyclic group of aerobic reactions in which pyruvic acid is transformed through a series of organic acids into carbon dioxide and water.

19. Energy is transferred to energy-trapping compounds during the course of reactions in both groups of processes.

20. Considerably more energy is liberated in aerobic respiration than in anaerobic.

21. Respiration in higher plants, lower plants, and animals involves many similar chemical reactions.

⫷ SUGGESTED READINGS FOR INTERESTED STUDENTS

1. Allfrey, V. G., and A. E. Mirsky, "How cells make molecules." *Scientific American,* Vol. 205, No. 3, pp. 74–82, September 1961.
2. Bonner, James, and Arthur W. Galston, *Principles of Plant Physiology.* Freeman, San Francisco, 1952.
3. Doty, Paul, "Proteins." *Scientific American,* Vol. 197, No. 3, pp. 173–184, September 1957.
4. McElroy, William D., *Cellular Physiology and Biochemistry.* Prentice-Hall, Englewood Cliffs, N. J., 1961.
5. *Plant Diseases.* The Yearbook of Agriculture, U. S. Government Printing Office, 1953.
6. Salle, A. J., *Fundamental Principles of Bacteriology,* 5th ed. McGraw-Hill, New York, 1961.
7. *Soil.* The Yearbook of Agriculture, U. S. Government Printing Office, 1957.

⫷ TOPICS AND QUESTIONS FOR STUDY

1. Define metabolism.
2. It has been said that the plant kingdom is a link between the nonliving world and the animal kingdom. Explain.
3. Name the soil elements that are essential for the normal development of green plants.
4. In what chemical forms do these elements occur in soils?
5. Name the principal cations and anions absorbed by plant roots?
6. What is meant by "dissociation"? Explain.
7. Which soil element is absorbed in greatest quantity by plants?
8. Describe the relative abundance of the various essential elements in plant protoplasm.
9. Describe the experimental demonstration of the essentiality of the various elements.
10. Define the term "hydroponic."
11. List the known or supposed physiological functions of the micronutrients in plants.
12. What practical applications have resulted from studies by plant physiologists of the mineral nutrition of plants?
13. Why is the burning of dead leaves, straw, and other plant residues biologically wasteful?
14. Define "food" as the word is used by biologists.
15. Name the classes of foods, characterize them chemically, and state their major functions in the physiology of plants.
16. Distinguish between autotrophic and heterotrophic nutrition. Name and describe the types of heterotrophic nutrition.

17. Name some of the organic compounds, other than foods, found in plants, and describe their physiological importance.
18. Define digestion and describe its physiological importance in plants.
19. Digestion is a "hydrolytic, catalytic phenomenon." Explain what is meant by this statement.
20. Define enzymes and describe their characteristic properties.
21. What is a coenzyme?
22. Name several plant enzymes and describe their work.
23. Describe the ways in which enzymes are important in agriculture and industry.
24. Give a general, biological definition of respiration.
25. What is the original source of the energy released in respiration?
26. Describe the energy transformations that occur in photosynthesis and respiration.
27. What forms of energy are released in respiration?
28. Contrast fully photosynthesis with respiration.
29. Describe the gas exchange that occurs in green leaves during the day and at night.
30. Distinguish between aerobic and anaerobic respiration.
31. Why does anaerobic respiration release less energy than aerobic respiration?
32. Describe the agricultural and industrial importance of anaerobic respiration.
33. Explain how yeasts cause the "raising" of dough.
34. Describe briefly the chemical pathways involved in respiration.
35. If damp hay is stored in a poorly ventilated barn, the mass of hay may burst into flame. Explain.
36. The dry weight of a seed (that is, the weight of its solid matter) is greater than that of the seedling it produces, if the latter grows in complete darkness; the dry weight of the seedling is greater than that of the seed, if the seedling has leaves and is grown in light. Explain.
37. Why do seeds stored in a cool place retain their viability longer than seeds stored at a high temperature?
38. In the commercial growth of many greenhouse plants, the night temperature is often kept 10 to 15 degrees lower than the day temperature. Explain the reason for this practice.
39. In pools of water standing in fields about the roots of plants, traces of alcohol have been detected. Explain.
40. What is the most convenient way of measuring the respiration of plants? What precautions must be taken in the study of respiration in a green plant, which are not necessary in the study of respiration of fungi? Explain.
41. Describe briefly some of the physiological discoveries made through the use of isotopes.

14

Growth and Irritability

THE NATURE OF PLANT GROWTH

The word "growth" usually signifies to the layman increase in size. To biologists, however, growth is a complex phenomenon with many more implications than mere enlargement. The biological interpretation of growth includes both quantitative and qualitative concepts. Quantitatively, growth is an irreversible increase in size of a cell, tissue, organ, or organism, and is usually accompanied by an increase in the amount of protoplasm and in dry weight. The qualitative aspect of growth, sometimes called development, includes all the structural changes that occur as growth proceeds. Three fairly distinct growth phases are recognized: first, the formation of new cells by the processes of mitosis and cell division; second, the enlargement of the newly formed cells; and third, the differentiation or maturation of these enlarging cells into the mature tissues of a growing organ. There are no sharp lines of demarcation among these stages of growth; each phase merges gradually into the next. The terms "cell division," "cell enlargement," and "cell differentiation" refer to these characteristic stages in a continuous process. Ex-

tremely important in the growth of living organisms are the coordination of physiological activities and the subordination of these activities to the growth plan of each species, whereby differentiation and the orderly development of tissues and organs occur. Growth without coordination results in **hypertrophy,** the formation of abnormal growths, such as tumors and galls. Various internal maladjustments and external conditions, such as insect or fungus attacks, may interrupt normal growth processes and thus cause hypertrophies.

Growth occurs ordinarily only when food-making activities of plants exceed food-consuming processes, for the formation of new cell walls and protoplasm requires food both for construction and for energy. Thus, photosynthesis is prerequisite to growth. If respiration exceeds photosynthesis through a period of days or weeks, food utilization exceeds food manufacture and growth conspicuously declines. Under such conditions, there may occur a considerable decrease in volume of plant organs and in weight of protoplasm. Thus, growth is closely related to plant nutrition; only when sufficient quantities of cellulose for wall building, sugars

229

for energy, and amino acids and proteins for the construction of protoplasm are present in living tissues can growth occur.

Growth Rates and Measurement. The rate at which growth occurs varies in different species and in different organs, if growth is measured in terms of increase in size, as is frequently done. In some plants, such as desert junipers and cacti, the rate of growth is exceedingly slow, so slow, in fact, that measurement of growth is almost impossible except over a period of many months or years. In other plants, the growth rate may be phenomenally rapid; for example, the young leaf sheath of banana grows for a time at the rate of almost 3 inches per hour; wheat stamens for a brief time grow at the rate of 1.8 millimeters (about $\frac{1}{14}$ inch) per minute, and bamboo stems have been observed to grow as much as 2 feet per day. In most species of plants the rate of growth lies between these extremes. The rate of growth depends upon a complex of factors: the hereditary nature of the plant, temperature, nutrition, water supply, and many others to be discussed later. Most commonly growth begins slowly, then enters upon a period of rapid enlargement, following which it gradually decreases until no further enlargement occurs.

Distribution of Growth. Growth does not simultaneously occur in all parts of plant bodies, but as indicated in earlier chapters, proceeds chiefly in certain tissues, known as meristematic tissues. These are normally the growing points of the tips of roots and the buds of stems, the cambium, cork cambium, and root pericycle. The growth of roots and stems is **indeterminate,** which means that the meristematic tissues of the buds and root tips do not become completely transformed into mature, differentiated tissues but retain their meristematic character, continuing to

cause growth of the stems and roots for as long as those organs live. These small masses of meristematic tissues in buds and root tips are called terminal meristems; they do not themselves increase in volume, but form new tissues that are left behind; as they carry on this growth activity the growing points are carried upward (in buds) or downward (in roots) by the tissues they have produced. A striking example of indeterminate growth is furnished by palm trees. In a palm, such as the coconut tree, the terminal bud, which continues its growth for the entire life of the tree (a period of many years), is a direct continuation of the meristematic tissue of the epicotyl of the embryo. The growth of cambium in woody stems may be regarded also as indeterminate in nature. Some plant organs, upon reaching their mature sizes, cease their growth and enlarge no more, all their meristematic cells having been transformed into differentiated, mature tissue. Such growth, called **determinate,** is characteristic of leaves, flowers, and fruits.

In many plants, certain differentiated cells, particularly parenchymatous cells, occasionally undergo a process of **dedifferentiation;** that is, they are transformed from matured cells into meristematic cells and are capable of further growth that may result in the production of adventitious roots, buds, etc. In all these growing parts of plants, the same sequence and pattern of growth phases occur—cell formation, cell enlargement, and cell differentiation.

INTERNAL FACTORS AND PHENOMENA ASSOCIATED WITH PLANT GROWTH

Growth is a resultant of numerous physiological processes, including the absorption of water and of soil nutrients, the manufacture of food, the digestion, translocation, and assimilation of food, the release of energy by the process of respiration, the construction of cell walls from pectic substances and cellulose, mitosis, and regulating influences of plant hormones. Growth is, therefore, affected by the diverse internal and external factors that influence these metabolic activities. These factors will be considered briefly in this and the next section of this chapter.

The internal factors that affect growth are chiefly those inherent in the protoplasm of a species (hereditary factors), or that have been previously induced in the protoplasm by external factors. It is not always easy to distinguish between internal and external factors in their effects on growth; for example, the amount of food stored in the roots of a perennial plant is an important internal factor in determining in large part the features of the next season's growth. The food thus stored, however, depends upon the amounts of water, light, carbon dioxide, etc., available at the time when it was synthesized in the preceding growing season.

Hereditary Nature of Plants

The hereditary potentialities of individual species of plants are important internal factors that regulate growth. Some species of trees, such as poplars and willows, grow very rapidly in the presence of favorable external conditions; pines, white oaks, and sweet gums exposed to similarly advantageous conditions grow much more slowly. Morning-glories are by nature twining vines with weak stems, and although their rate of growth may be markedly influenced by variations in their external environment, they always remain weak-stemmed twiners. The buds of black-locust trees produce leaves that are pinnately compound; the rate of growth of such leaves is subject to environmental variations, but the compound nature of the leaves cannot be changed by alterations in moisture, temperature, etc. The time of flowering of tobacco plants may be shifted by changes in the daily duration of light to which they are exposed, but the plants always remain recognizably tobacco plants, with the traits and potentialities of the tobacco species. Thus, variations in environmental factors can induce certain changes in gross structure, anatomical features, reproductive phases, etc., but the degree and quality of these changes are limited in the final analysis by that most important internal controller—the hereditary nature of the species. Such a constitution is always liable to amendment, but never to fundamental change.

Growth Regulators

Plant **hormones** constitute another of the important internal mechanisms that regulate plant growth. Characteristically, a hormone is synthesized in one region of the plant and is translocated to another region where, in extremely minute amounts, it exerts a physiological effect. Although the existence of a growth-regulating substance had been postulated as early as 1881 by Charles Darwin, it was not until 1926 that such a substance was isolated from plant material. About ten more years elapsed before investigators were able to determine its chemical identity: **indoleacetic acid,** an organic compound of the formula $C_{10}H_9O_2N$. Unfortunately, the minute amounts of indoleacetic acid (IAA) in a plant could not be accurately determined with usual chemical techniques. Investigators finally devised a suitable test for hormone activity by measuring the response of *living tissue* to hormone, a technique known as **bioassay.** A widely used bioassay for IAA and related growth substances is the **Avena test,** so named because seedlings of oat (*Avena sativa*) are employed in its use. The hormone to be tested is collected in a small agar block that is then placed on one side of the tip of a decapitated oat coleoptile. The growth substance moves down into the tissues immediately beneath the agar block and stimulates the cells of that region to elongate. This, in turn, produces a curvature in the coleoptile. The degree of curvature is a measurement of hormone activity, since the response of living coleoptile tissue is almost directly proportional to the amount of hormone present. The development of this now standardized test has greatly facilitated research efforts.

In recent years many different growth-promoting substances have been extracted from plants. Some of these behave like indoleacetic acid—that is, cause curvature of oat coleoptiles—and, together with IAA, are called **auxins.** Another group of growth-promoting substances, the **gibberellins,** lack this property. Auxins, gibberellins, and synthetic regulators will be discussed in more detail in subsequent paragraphs. Another class of regulatory substances includes those that *inhibit* growth. Some natural and synthetic inhibitors are known; however, our information on the nature and mode of action of inhibitors is meager since research in this field is still in its infancy.

Auxins. Auxins are synthesized chiefly in young, physiologically active parts of plants, such as root and shoot apices. In these regions, an amino acid (tryptophan) is enzymatically converted into indoleacetic acid, which is then translocated to other parts of the plant. Experiments have shown that auxin transport is polarized; that is, it moves away from root and shoot apices but cannot move toward them. The specific effects of auxins upon the metabolic activities of plant cells are not well understood, but some of them are known at least in part. One of the cellular phenomena influenced by auxins is the structural alteration of the wall, which enables a cell to take up more water and increase its size. Here, the auxins seem to affect deposition of new cellulose microfibrils among the older microfibrils of the wall and also to increase the extensibility of young cell walls.

Auxins regulate many growth and developmental processes of plants. Some of the more fundamental of these processes are:

1. Tissue and organ growth generally seems to be regulated by auxins. The growth of buds, the enlargement of leaf primordia, the growth of flower buds into mature flowers, cambial growth, and the growth of roots are some of the processes under auxin control. Researches on the effects of auxins upon these growth phenomena have led to rather important commercial applications. For example, the treatment of stem cuttings, particularly the more basal parts, with solutions, pastes, or powders containing small concentrations of plant auxins, or chemically related substances, promotes rapid and extensive rooting of cuttings (Figure 14–1). This method is now used on an extensive commercial scale to hasten the formation of roots on stem cuttings of hard-to-root cultivated plants.

2. Cell division in some tissues seems to be regulated by auxins. Cell division of the cambium, for example, is stimulated by auxins diffusing downward in stems

NOT TREATED   TREATED

(*Photo by P. W. Zimmerman, Boyce Thompson Institute.*)

FIG. 14–1. Effect of a growth-promoting substance, indolebutyric acid, on the rooting of cuttings of American holly (*Ilex*). *Left:* Cuttings placed in cutting bench without treatment. *Right:* Cuttings treated with indolebutyric acid, then placed in cutting bench for same length of time as plants at left.

from apically situated buds and young leaves. The beginning of division of cambial cells in woody stems usually coincides with the beginning of bud growth; at this time, auxin production by the developing buds increases rapidly. The application of hormones to the tips of decapitated stems accelerates the division of cambial cells located in more basal portions of the stems.

3. Abscission of leaves, flowers, and fruits is in part controlled by auxins. The abscission of leaves, for example, is the result in part of a decrease in supplies of hormones moving from leaf blades downward through leaf petioles. If a leaf blade is removed from a petiole and an auxin preparation is applied to the cut end of the petiole, abscission of the petiole is delayed, often for a long period of time. Abscission of fruits is apparently also related to diminishing auxin supply; if young fruits are sprayed with solutions of growth substances, their fall is often retarded. This fact has been applied commercially to delay premature fruit drop in apple trees (Figure 14–2); spraying of young apple fruits with auxins prevents premature fruit drop, a major source of fruit loss. When high concentrations of such sprays are used upon fruits, abscission of some immature fruits may be promoted, resulting in a thinning out of fruits; this effect is sometimes valuable in preventing overproduction of fruit, which may weaken a plant or cause it to bear a negligible crop in the year following a heavy crop production.

4. The development of fruits from the ovaries of flowers and the ripening of ovules into mature seeds after fertilization are controlled in part by auxins. The first evidence that chemical regulators play a role in fruit development was secured in 1910 by a plant physiologist who discovered that, if a water extract of orchid pollen grains (in lieu of the pollen grains themselves) was placed on orchid ovaries, the ovaries enlarged just as though they had been pollinated; these ovaries,

(Photo by U. S. D. A. Plant Industry Station.)

FIG. 14–2. The effects of hormonelike substances in retarding fruit drop. *Top:* An untreated apple tree, showing extensive, premature fruit drop. *Bottom:* An apple tree of the same variety, whose young fruits were sprayed with a hormonelike substance. Note that there has been almost no fruit drop.

ins and related growth substances, when applied to ovaries of flowers in liquid sprays or in a lanolin paste or injected into the ovaries, cause the development of ovaries into seedless fruits (Figure 14–3). This phenomenon has been demonstrated in a number of species of plants. Watermelons, tomatoes, and squashes are particularly sensitive to this treatment and develop parthenocarpic fruits readily when subjected to it. There is a close relation between the fertilization of ovules and the growth of the ovary into a ripened fruit, a relation that is doubtless hormonal. In most species of flowering plants, ovaries do not develop into fruits unless the ovules are fertilized and mature into seeds; the sizes of the fruits are usually related to the numbers of seeds that develop within them. These phenomena may be interpreted on the basis of movement of auxins from developing seeds into ovary tissues.

5. Various **correlation** phenomena are the result of auxin-induced effects. Correlation may be defined as the mutual interaction of plant parts. For example, in many kinds of stems, the terminal bud is the dominant bud—that is, it grows more rapidly and is physiologically more active than the lateral buds; the dominance of the terminal bud prevents or retards the development of lateral buds. This correlation phenomenon, called bud inhibition, may be demonstrated strikingly in a potato tuber. If a whole potato is planted, only the terminal cluster of buds develops into sprouts, the lateral buds remaining inactive; if the tuber is cut into several pieces, all or most of the lateral buds, removed from the inhibitory effects of the terminal bud cluster, sprout. Similarly, in aerial stems, the development of branches is related to this **apical dominance.** So long as the terminal

of course, contained no seeds, since no fertilization of ovules had occurred. More recent studies have shown that aux-

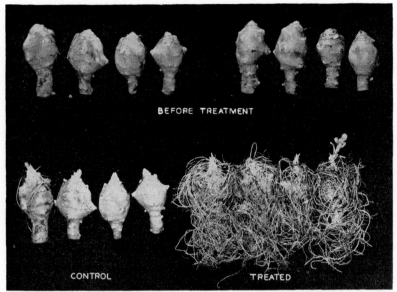

(*Photo by P. W. Zimmerman.*)

FIG. 14–3. Tubers of Jerusalem artichoke (*Helianthus tuberosus*), showing acceleration of development following treatment with a growth substance. *Upper row:* Tubers before treatment and planting. *Lower row:* Tubers after a period of growth; the four tubers at left were soaked in water for 24 hours before planting, four tubers at right were soaked in a dilute solution of naphthaleneacetic acid for 24 hours before planting.

bud is present, the lateral buds usually develop slowly or remain dormant; the removal of the terminal bud commonly results in growth of the lateral buds. Auxin interactions between terminal and lateral buds are responsible for this bud correlation.

6. Flowering of plants appears to be related to hormone activity. Information concerning the hormonal initiation of flowering is still meager, since it has not been possible to isolate chemically a flower-inducing hormone, or to demonstrate conclusively that the known auxins are related to flower production.

7. Many of the movements of plant organs in response to environmental stimuli are the result of changes in the concentrations and distribution of auxins in various tissues. For example, when a stem is illuminated more brightly on one side than on the other, a bending of the stem toward the light occurs. This reaction, called **phototropism** (see p. 246), is partially explained by the fact that some of the auxin moving down the more brightly illuminated side of the stem is inactivated by exposure to light. There is also evidence to suggest that some auxin migrates from the lighter to the darker side of the stem. The higher concentration of auxin on the darker side causes more rapid growth of those tissues and, consequently, curvature of the stem toward the light source.

Gibberellins. Japanese rice farmers have long been familiar with the "foolish seedling" disease in which the shoot of a rice plant becomes extremely elongated. The cause of this disease, infection by the sac

(*Photo by Michigan State University.*)

FIG. 14–4. Asparagus plot, showing clear area at right in which a chemical weed killer, related to indoleacetic acid, has destroyed all weeds; area at left and in background has not been treated with weed killer.

fungus *Gibberella fujikuroi,* was discovered in 1926 and about ten years later, the growth-promoting substance was isolated and named **gibberellin.** It was not until after World War II that American investigators began intensive studies of this hormone and its effects on plant growth and development. To date about ten different gibberellins have been isolated, some from the fungus only, some from seeds of certain green plants, and one from both of these sources.

As was previously shown, plants treated with auxins exhibit a variety of responses. This is also true for plants treated with gibberellin. The commonest effect is extreme elongation of the stem. On an experimental basis, gibberellin has also been used to increase cambial activity, to inhibit the development of floral and vegetative buds, and to shorten the period of dormancy of seeds of some species. One of the most surprising responses to gibberellin treatment is the induction of flowering in long-day plants that are on a short-day photoperiod. Photoperiodism is discussed later in this chapter and in Chapter 15.

The practical applications of research upon growth regulators illustrate an important feature of scientific work, namely, that many of the economically valuable procedures in agriculture and industry are the results of the labors of scientists who explore the secrets of nature to satisfy their intellectual curiosity, without compulsion to seek practical benefits. The plant physiologists who made the fundamental discoveries concerning plant hormones were motivated simply by their consuming desire to learn more of plant growth, not by a wish to make cuttings root more rapidly or to cause apples to cling longer to the branches of their parents. We now know many of the physiological functions and operations of auxins and many of the intricacies of plant growth; new practical applications of this knowledge are still being developed and will probably continue to expand in the future with further basic research on growth regulators. Consider one of the practical benefits of such research—the use of 2,4-D (2,4-dichlorophenoxyacetic acid) and related compounds as selective weed killers. Some of these substances are toxic to broad-leafed plants and have little or no effect upon most monocotyledons, such as cereal crops and lawn grasses. Thus, they may be sprayed or dusted upon lawns and fields of wheat, corn (Figure 14–4), rice, oats, and other cereals, with killing effects upon dandelions, plantains, bindweeds, milkweeds, poison ivy, and other noxious weeds, without damaging the valuable grasses. These growth substances have an exaggerated hormonelike effect upon susceptible plants; they stimulate respiration and accelerate the depletion of stored carbohydrates, until the plants die of physiological exhaustion.

It should be emphasized that plant hormones do not bring about their effects in a simple, direct manner but that their functions are related to, and dependent upon, other physiological processes. Thus, auxin activity is related to respiratory processes that release from foods the energy required for growth. Also, the growth of cells requires such substances as cellulose, sugars, and proteins that are used in the synthesis of cell walls and protoplasm. In the absence of these structural materials, hormone-controlled processes cannot be carried on.

Food Reserves

As stated in the introductory paragraph, the nature and concentration of food reserves stored in a plant influence various aspects of growth. Although these food reserves occur within the plant body and may thus be regarded as internal growth factors, their original synthesis depends upon various external factors obtaining at an earlier period of the plant's development. The food reserves of plants are especially important in affecting the growth of embryos in seed germination, the rate and extent of root development on cuttings, and new growth of perennial plants in the spring, as in the development of sprouts from underground stems such as potato tubers.

THE EXTERNAL FACTORS THAT INFLUENCE GROWTH

The principal external factors that affect growth and configuration of plants are **light and other types of radiations, temperature, moisture, soil nutrients, foods, oxygen, carbon dioxide and other gases, poisons, gravity,** and **the attacks of parasites.** A noteworthy feature of this list is the fact that most of these environmental conditions that influence plant growth likewise exert profound effects upon the development of animals. The susceptibility of all living organisms to the same features of their environments is another indication of the fundamental unity of all living protoplasm.

These factors of the external environment affect plants in various ways: they influence the rate of growth of their tissues; they affect food manufacture, digestion, respiration and other physiological activities; they exert influences upon the form and structure of certain organs (limited, of course, by the internal organization of each species); they affect reproduction; and, if they act in different intensity from different directions, they frequently induce movements of various plant organs.

Light and Other Radiations. The sole source of energy for green plants is the radiant energy from the sun. The visible portion of this radiation, called **light,** is the most important type of radiation in plant life. Light affects the germination of certain kinds of seeds, photosynthesis,

the rate of growth of various organs, the synthesis and distribution of auxins, the initiation of reproduction, transpiration, the sizes of various plant organs, the activity of enzymes, the synthesis of chlorophyll, and the physicochemical condition of certain protoplasmic proteins. Many species of plants are very exacting in their light requirements. Grasses, sunflowers, goldenrods, tomatoes, and milkweeds thrive under bright, direct sunlight and grow poorly in diffuse, dim light. Most ferns and mosses, and many woodland wildflowers, grow best in low light intensities and are retarded in their growth or killed by the intensity of full sunlight. Still other plants, such as columbines, phlox, periwinkles, and roses, are tolerant of wide ranges of light intensity and grow well both in bright and diffuse light.

Light has pronounced morphological effects upon the leaves and stems of plants. Plants that grow in darkness are characterized by long, succulent, weak stems, undeveloped leaves, and pale, yellowish, chlorophyll-less tissues; this condition is called **etiolation.** Excessive intensities of light frequently cause a stunting of stems and of leaves. Plants grown in moderate light intensities usually have longer internodes, with larger, more succulent, less tough leaves than those growing in intense sunlight. Most of us have observed that leaves growing in shade, such as tree leaves growing on inner, shaded branches, are appreciably larger and more tender than those growing in full sunlight. Several species of crop plants, such as tobacco and lettuce, are frequently cultivated under cheesecloth screens to reduce the intensity of light reaching them, and thus to produce larger, more succulent leaves.

The duration of daily exposure to light profoundly affects various developmental

FIG. 14–5. Milmi (*Amaranthus edulis*), a food plant of the Andes mountains, is a short-day species. Plant at left was grown on 8-hour daily photoperiods. Plant in center was grown in 14-hour daily photoperiods. Plant at right was grown on 24-hour daily photoperiods. Note that only the plant grown on short photoperiods has flowers.

(*Photo by R. B. Withrow.*)

FIG. 14–6. Photoperiodism in China Aster, a long-day plant. Plant at left received normal short winter days, plus 9 hours each night of electric illumination of 10 foot-candles intensity. Plant in center received same treatment, except that the intensity of the night electric illumination was only 0.1 foot-candle. Plant at right received normal short winter days without night illumination.

processes in plants. Most striking of the effects of daily **photoperiods** upon plants is that upon the onset of flowering. Certain species of plants (for example, poinsettias, most chrysanthemums, certain soybean varieties, cosmos, asters, dahlias, violets) produce flowers only when the daily photoperiod is shorter than a critical length, usually about 14 hours; these are called **short-day plants** (Figure 14–5). Other species (for example, lettuce, beets, spinach, wheat, clovers, delphiniums, gladiolus, coreopsis) flower only when the daily photoperiod is longer than a critical length; these plants are termed **long-day plants** (Figure 14–6). If short-day plants are exposed to long photoperiods, they do not produce flowers but continue to grow vegetatively, or their flowering is much delayed. If long-day plants are exposed to short photoperiods, they fail to flower, or their flowering is long delayed. Some species of plants, termed **indeterminate** species, flower irrespective of the photoperiods to which they are exposed; examples of such plants are buckwheat, tomatoes, carnations, cotton, and dandelion. The photoperiodic mechanism will be discussed in the next chapter.

The ecological aspects of **photoperiodism** are worthy of brief mention. In tropical and subtropical regions, where the day length usually does not exceed 13 or 14 hours, most native species are short-day plants; in high latitudes (north and south of 60°), the native species are largely long-day; in the temperate zones, both long-day and short-day plants occur, the long-day species usually flowering in late spring and early summer, the short-day species in early spring or late summer and autumn. Indeterminate species, which flower under widely different photoperiods, are widely distributed over the earth's surface. Daily photoperiods also affect certain purely vegetative activities; for example, many potato varieties form few tubers in long days but undergo rapid tuberization in short photoperiods (temperature is also involved in tuber formation in potatoes); soybeans undergo tuberization when the photoperiod is shortened below the optimum for stem growth or flowering; yams experience extensive tuberization under short days but show little tuberization under long photoperiods. Research upon the photoperiodic responses of plants has led to important applications in practical plant growing; for example, by controlling photoperiods through the use of shading or of supplemental electrical illumination at night, commercial growers can accelerate or delay the flowering of greenhouse crops. Complete shading of most chrysanthemum and poinsettia plants during a portion of the long days of summer accelerates flowering, while supplemental illumination of these species by electric lights at night prolongs vegetative growth and causes later flowering. The flowering of snapdragons, stocks, and other long-day plants may be hastened during the short days of autumn, winter, and early spring by supplemental electric illumination at night.

Temperature. Growing plants are constantly influenced by variations in the temperature of the soil in which they grow and of the surrounding air. Most species of plants in active condition develop best in temperatures between 70° and 90°F and cease growth when air and soil temperatures approach freezing or rise much above 100°F. Dormant (relatively inactive or resting) structures, such as seeds or spores, with low water content are much more resistant to extremes of temperature than are actively growing organs. The maximum, minimum, and optimum (best) temperatures for seed germination and plant growth vary, of course, with different species of plants, with age, with other environmental conditions simultaneously operative, etc. In general, plants of tropical and subtropical origin have higher temperature requirements than do those of higher latitudes. Thus, rubber, quinine, and orange trees require higher temperatures for their best growth than do apple, pine, and birch trees, which are natives of the north temperate zone.

Plants that are able to survive exposure to subfreezing temperatures are termed **hardy.** Elms, apple trees, maples, irises, pines, and strawberries, for example, are hardy in the Middle West. Hardiness is fundamentally an inherent characteristic of different species, although it is subject to considerable modification by varying environmental conditions. Winter hardiness depends upon several physiological factors—increased soluble carbohydrate content of tissues, great stability of protoplasmic proteins, reduced water content of tissues, and a high proportion of colloidally bound water, which is incapable of freezing. The hardiness of many kinds of plants such as cabbage, tomatoes, and alfalfa may be increased by suitable manipulation; thus, cabbage plants moved from a warm greenhouse directly to outdoor temperatures slightly below freezing suffer pronounced cold injury; if cabbage plants are first moved from a warm greenhouse to a cool greenhouse or a cold frame with a temperature of about 35° to 40°F, and are kept at the cool temperature for 5 or 6 days, they are then able to withstand outdoor temperatures slightly below freezing for several days without injury. Many other species of plants may be subjected to this **hardening** treatment with a similar beneficial re-

sult, namely, increased ability to withstand low temperatures. Plants may also be hardened by severe pruning, which deprives them of actively growing parts that are especially susceptible to cold injury, and by manipulation of photoperiods to reduce vegetative growth and to cause storage of soluble carbohydrates.

Temperature has many other effects upon plant growth that are too numerous and too complex for discussion in an elementary textbook. In some species, for example, susceptibility to disease varies with different temperatures. Another striking temperature effect is found in the differentiation of flower buds; certain plants, such as varieties of winter wheat, beets, cabbage, and celery, do not flower if they are grown continuously at temperatures of 70°F or above; brief low temperature exposures **(vernalization)** are needed for formation of flower primordia in these plants. Temperature is also an important factor in ending the dormancy of their flower buds; grown in subtropical climates in the absence of low winter temperatures, apple and peach trees normally do not flower. Other species of plants flower only at higher temperatures; rice and cotton usually do not flower unless they are exposed to temperatures above 80°F.

Water. The importance of water in the life of plants has been considered in earlier chapters. The relation of plants to water is complex and involves problems of osmosis, water transport, transpiration in relation to water absorption by roots and to wilting, atmospheric conditions, etc. The amounts of water available to plants influence markedly their growth and form. Since water is one of the raw materials of photosynthesis, its availability is related to the quantities of food manufactured in plants. The growth of cell walls and the formation of new protoplasm depend directly upon the amount of food formed in photosynthesis. Chiefly through its effects upon these processes and upon the turgor of cells, the water supply of plants influences growth rate and the ultimate size attained by various tissues and organs.

Most species of plants possess minimum, maximum, and optimum soil moisture concentrations that influence their growth. Plants may be stunted in their development by too much water as well as by too little. In mesophytes, a scarcity of water results in stunted growth because of reduced food synthesis and assimilation; an excess of water in the soil may likewise stunt growth through the exclusion of oxygen necessary for root development; growth is best promoted by moderate supplies of water that are sufficient for rapid food manufacture and assimilation and yet do not exclude oxygen from the soil. In addition to its effect upon the rate of growth, water supply frequently exerts a direct influence upon specific morphological features of plants. For example, the roots of corn plants grown in water cultures do not produce root hairs; in damp soil or in saturated air, root hairs develop in great abundance. In several species of water plants, leaves borne above the surface of the water are morphologically very different from those produced below the water surface; this structural difference is apparently related to dissimilar conditions of the aerial and submerged habitats.

Gases. Oxygen is required for normal root growth and for respiration, and its absence is soon indicated by abnormalities in growth. Carbon dioxide is a raw material of photosynthesis and hence its presence is necessary for the manufacture of carbohydrates. A moderate increase in the carbon dioxide content of air usually accelerates photosynthetic activity. If the percentage of atmospheric or soil carbon dioxide becomes excessive, plants may be injured as a result. Some other gases influencing plant growth are sulfur dioxide, ethylene, and carbon monoxide, which escape into the air from smelters, factories, etc., usually as products of the combustion of coal and of other fuels involved in industrial activities. These gases frequently cause serious injury to plant tissues and often kill plants, particularly evergreens, which are more susceptible than most other plants to such injury because they retain their leaves during the winter, when the smoke and gas content of the air near congested industrial centers is highest. Plants are exceedingly susceptible to small traces of illuminating gas. One of the reasons for the poor growth of many kinds of plants in houses is the presence in the air of minute amounts of illuminating gas escaping from stoves and other appliances. These traces of gas are so small that they are harmless to human beings, but they stunt the growth of plants and cause premature fall of leaves, retardation of growth, and often death. Extremely low concentrations of ethylene gas hasten the ripening of fruits and are used commercially to speed the ripening of citrus fruits, bananas, and other kinds of fruits.

Chemical Agents in Soils. The quantities and kinds of nutrient elements available to plants exert tremendous influences upon growth, for the failure of plants to obtain the elements necessary for food syntheses, chlorophyll formation, the construction of protoplasm, and other metabolic activities results in pronounced physiological aberrations. The effects of deficiencies and excesses of these essential nutrients upon plant growth have been briefly described in the preceding chapter and will not receive further attention here.

In addition to these essential nutrients, soils often contain substances that are toxic to plants and that may cause their injury or death. Some of these toxic compounds are inorganic substances of mineral derivation; compounds of selenium, copper, and other elements occur in some soils in sufficient concentrations to injure plants. Some toxic inorganic compounds accumulate in soils as a result of certain agricultural and industrial practices; for example, arsenic residues from insecticidal sprays sometimes reach sufficient concentrations to cause injury to plants. Some toxic substances in soils are organic compounds produced by the decomposition of dead plants and their parts, and animal bodies; these substances often stunt the growth of plants or otherwise adversely affect them. An interesting feature of the toxicity of such organic compounds is the fact that the poisonous compounds produced by the decomposition of dead leaves, roots, fruits, and other parts of one species are usually more toxic to other plants of the same species than they are to plants of other species. Thus, the growth of successive crops of oats on the same soil results in a progressive deterioration of later oat crops, despite the periodic addition of fertilizer; if, after a crop of oats is harvested, clover, corn, or some other crop is grown in the same soil, no harmful effects of the decomposition products of oats upon the second crop are apparent. The formation of toxic organic decomposition products in soils is an important factor in crop rotation, and may likewise play an important ecological role in cyclic fluctuations of plant populations in nature.

Other Living Organisms. Higher plants are frequently attacked by parasitic fungi, worms, insects, and other living organisms. Such attacks exert profound effects upon the growth and structure of the attacked plants. The harmful effects of parasites are the results of several physiological disturbances: the theft of food from the tissues of parasitized plants, destruction of leaves and the consequent reduction of the food-making ability of the host plants, stoppage of vascular tissues and interference with sap rise and food translocation, injury to roots and thus abnormalities in absorption, etc. The attacks of parasites often result in accelerated local growth of host tissues, with the formation of galls and tumors.

The growth of plants is affected also by higher animals. The trampling of hoofs of cattle, sheep, and other domesticated animals injures the shoots of grasses, churns up and destroys their roots, and often causes their death. Also, the browsing of animals exerts marked effects upon plants; domesticated herbivorous animals eat the leaves of plants and thus reduce their photosynthetic activity. Rabbits, porcupines, and other wild animals eat bark and frequently girdle the trunks of young trees, causing their death.

IRRITABILITY IN PLANTS

General Nature of Irritability. Irritability, one of the most characteristic properties of living protoplasm, is a twofold phenomenon involving first, sensitivity to stimuli, and second, reaction or response to these stimuli. A stimulus may be defined as an environmental factor or event that exerts an effect upon living protoplasm. The stimuli that induce the movements or reactions of plants are principally those mentioned in the preceding section of this chapter—light, water, gravity, chemicals, etc. When these external factors are diffuse or when they are more or less equally distributed about a plant, their usual effects are upon growth rates and form, as described in the preceding section. If, however, these stimuli are concentrated in certain parts of the environment and are thus more powerful on one side of a plant organ than on another, they affect growth rates and other physiological activities very unequally in various parts of the growing organs. As a result, movements, or changes in position of the organs subjected to such stimuli, are brought about.

Plant reactions or movements are usually too slow to be observed by the human eye but that they actually occur can be demonstrated by time-lapse motion picture photography or, more simply, by observing reacting plants at intervals of several hours and noting changes in position of the various organs. All kinds of plants exhibit reactions to environmental stimuli. The reactions of plants differ in their speed, direction of movement, the nature of the mechanisms that bring them about, and in other respects. Despite the many variations among the diverse kinds of plant movements, there are certain features common to most kinds of reactions, chief among which are reception of stimuli, the transmission of growth hormones, and changes in certain cells or tissues that actually bring about a reaction or movement.

Reception of Stimuli by Plants. The reception of stimuli by plants is frequently compared with the reception of warmth and cold by human skin in that it is usually rather diffuse; there are no morphologically differentiated receptive structures in most plants, and the reception of external stimuli is therefore a somewhat general function of many tissues. Generally, all portions of leaf blades are sensitive to light, and all plant organs are sensitive to temperature changes, to moisture, and to many other stimuli. In certain plants, there are definitely localized groups of cells that act as sensory or perceptive zones. In most roots, for example, certain cells are apparently more effective than other root cells in detecting the stimulus of gravity, if roots are placed in a horizontal position. Intact primary roots in a horizontal position soon begin to turn downward, but if their tips are cut off before the roots are placed on their sides, no bending occurs until a new root tip is regenerated. This behavior indicates that reception of the stimulus of gravitational force by roots is largely limited to these special root tip cells. Similarly, in many kinds of plants, the stimulus of light is received more readily by certain groups of cells than by other cells. In the seedlings of grasses, such as oats and corn, only the tip of the young sheath, which encloses and protects the young leaves, receives effectively the stimulus of light. If this tip is cut off or shaded and only the cells below the tip are exposed to light, little or no bending of the sheath occurs. If the tip is illuminated, however, the stimulus is received and a pronounced bending toward the light results. In the leaves of the Venus'-flytrap, only the sensory hairs on the inner surfaces of the leaves are able to receive contact stimuli. Thus, in some plants, there are somewhat localized or specialized sensory zones or structures, as described above. Usually, these sensory zones are not highly specialized morphologically, except in such cases as the sensory hairs of the flytrap, but differ chiefly in a physiological manner from the other cells surrounding them.

Effects of Stimuli on Plants. In most animals, stimuli directly affect sense organs, from which the effects of the stimuli are transmitted to muscles or other reactive parts by nerves. In plants, as in animals, a stimulus may be received by one part of the body, while the reaction may occur in some other part. In leaves, for example, the blade receives a light stimulus and the petiole reacts by bending; thus, there may be a transmission of the effect of a stimulus from one part of a plant to another part. In plants no specialized structures comparable with nerves and muscles exist; thus, the effects of stimuli in causing plant reactions must involve other types of physiological mechanisms. In most plants, when a stimulus acts, its immediate effect is a change in the distribution of growth hormone in plant tissues, causing different parts of an organ to receive different concentrations of hormone; these variations of hormone concentrations result in unequal growth rates in different parts of an organ, and the organ thus bends toward or away from the stimulus. In some plant reactions, physiological changes other than differences in growth hormone distribution occur; in the movements of Venus'-flytrap leaves and of *Mimosa* ("sensitive plant") leaves, contact stimuli appear to release a special substance that induces rapid changes in turgor pressure in specialized cells; these turgor changes, rather than unequal growth rates, cause movements of the leaves.

Growth hormones move through protoplasm and cell walls of various plant tissues and are capable also of moving through conducting structures of xylem and phloem. Plasmodesmata, the protoplasmic strands that connect the protoplasm of adjacent cells, apparently facilitate the movement of hormones.

The Kinds of Reactions in Plants. Plants exhibit many kinds of reactions to stimuli.

FIG. 14–7. *Top:* Positive phototropism in geranium; notice that the stems and petioles have turned toward the source of illumination at the upper left. *Bottom:* Leaf-mosaic of geranium, a result of phototropic bendings of the petioles.

These reactions are classified chiefly on the basis of the physiological mechanisms

FIG. 14–8. Successive stages in the positive phototropic bending of a bean seedling. Exposures were made on the same plate at intervals of 40 minutes.

FIG. 14–9. *Top:* Positive geotropism in primary root of bean. *Bottom:* Negative geotropism in young stem of bean plant.

that bring them about. A detailed discussion of these many reactions is inappropriate in an elementary botany textbook; therefore, only a few of the more common and more interesting types of reactions, chiefly those occurring in flowering plants, will be discussed:

1. **Growth reactions,** in which the movement or reaction results from differences in growth rates in different parts of an organ; these growth rate differences arise from unequal distribution of growth hormones. Growth reactions are limited

chiefly to young, enlarging parts of plants (Figures 14–7 through 14–10).

a. *Tropisms* are growth responses to unidirectional stimuli, that is, stimuli that affect one portion of a plant more strongly than another. Tropisms are common throughout the plant kingdom; they occur in many fungi, in mosses and ferns, and in all seed plants. Since tropisms result from differences in growth rates in different parts of organs, they are usually rather slow, requiring from one hour to several days or longer for their completion. Tropisms are named on the basis of the stimuli that initiate them. Thus, **phototropism** is the growth reaction of plant organs to light, **geotropism** is the growth reaction to gravity, **chemotropism** to chemical agents, etc. In phototropism, stems and leaves usually bend toward light, roots may bend away from light; in geotropism, stems usually bend upward away from the earth's gravitational force, while roots usually bend downward. A reaction toward the source of a stimulus is a **positive reaction,** one away from the stimulus is a **negative reaction;** thus, the bending of a stem and leaves toward light is positive phototropism, while bending of roots away from light is negative phototropism. Tropisms constitute the chief means of advantageous adjustment of most plants to environmental factors. It is obviously advantageous in the life of a plant, for example, that stems and leaves usually grow upward and toward light and that roots grow downward into the soil as a consequence of their geotropic reaction. In studying tropisms, students should take care that they do not attribute foresight or purposeful reaction to plants. One should not say that plants bend toward the light *in order* to secure light, which they need, or that roots grow downward *in order* to reach the soil. A more nearly scientific interpretation is this: stems grow toward light because light is a stimulus that affects their growth in such a way as to cause them to bend toward it, and roots grow downward because gravitational force influences their growth in such a manner that they bend downward.

b. *Nastic movements* are growth responses to stimuli that affect all parts of the plant to a more or less equal degree, for example, temperature and diffuse light. Such movements occur most frequently in the opening of buds and the growth of young leaves and petals, and result from differences in growth rates of tissues on the upper and lower surfaces of these organs. Thus, when the upper surface of a petal grows more rapidly than the lower surface, the petal bends outward from the center of a flower into a more or less horizontal position.

2. **Turgor reactions,** in which the reaction results from changes of turgor pressure of certain tissues of plant organs.

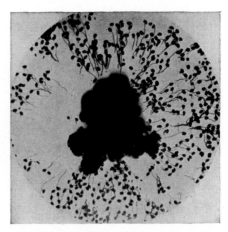

FIG. 14–10. Chemotropism in pollen tubes, which are shown growing toward a crushed stigma.

These changes of turgor pressure are usually rapid, so that turgor movements may be completed within a fraction of a second, or, at most, within a few seconds. In contrast with most growth movements, turgor movements in many species of plants seem to have little advantageous significance for the plants in which they occur. Unlike most tropisms, turgor movements are reversible; that is, when the stimulus has disappeared, the plant organ returns within a brief time to its original position before stimulation.

a. *Sleep movements* occur chiefly in leaves of various plants, such as clovers, beans, locusts, wood sorrel, and peas, and result from turgor changes, induced by alterations of light intensity, usually in specialized tissues at the bases of leaflets and leaves. In white clover, for example, leaflets assume a horizontal position in bright light and move upward into a nearly vertical position as light disappears; wood sorrel leaflets occupy a horizontal position during the day, assume a vertical hanging position at night, and return to the horizontal position at sunrise. Sleep movements appear to involve

FIG. 14–11. Sleep movements in *Oxalis stricta. Left:* Day position of leaflets. *Right:* night position of leaflets.

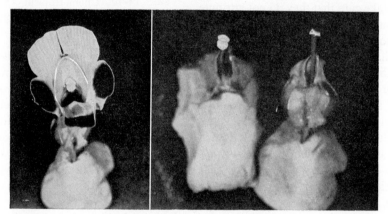

FIG. 14–12. *Left:* Flower of *Torenia,* showing 2-lobed stigma in center of corolla tube. *Right:* Unstimulated and stimulated stigmas of *Torenia* (corollas removed).

no known benefits to plants (Figure 14–11).

b. *Contact movements* are turgor movements, chiefly of leaves and flower parts, that result from contact stimuli. The closing movements of the leaf halves of the Venus'-flytrap are contact turgor movements; this reaction is one of obvious advantage to this species, since it increases the effectiveness of insect trapping. The rapid movement of certain flower parts, such as the stigmas (the tips of the pistils, the innermost floral parts) of *Torenia* flowers, are turgor movements

that are beneficial in promoting insect pollination. In the flowers of *Torenia,* catalpa, and trumpet creeper, the two-lobed stigmas are sensitive to contact and fold together quickly when they are touched (Figure 14–12). If the stigmas are not covered with pollen during their stimulation, they open after a several minutes' closure; if, however, as normally occurs, the stigma lobes are covered with pollen, they remain closed, securing the pollen grains firmly between them. Doubtless most spectacular of all turgor movements is the rapid in-folding of the

FIG. 14–13. The sensitive plant, *Mimosa pudica. Left:* Plant in unstimulated condition. *Right:* Two seconds after plant was struck by a pencil.

leaflets and the sudden drooping of the whole leaves of the sensitive plant, *Mimosa pudica* (Figure 14–13). This leaf reaction, which is initiated by various stimuli, such as sudden contact and rapid temperature change, is completed within a few seconds. After one leaf drops and folds its leaflets, other leaves above and below the stimulated leaf react successively in similar fashion. After a period of some minutes, the leaves return to their original positions. It appears that these spectacular reactions of *Mimosa* leaves possess little if any biological significance. Experiments on *Mimosa* plants indicate that stimulation of a leaf releases or activates a chemical agent that moves rapidly to other leaflets of the plants, inducing them to respond in the same manner as a stimulated leaf.

⋘ SUMMARY

1. The growth process has both qualitative and quantitative aspects. The qualitative aspects include all the structural changes that accompany growth—formation, enlargement, and differentiation of new cells into the permanent tissues of the plant. Quantitatively, growth is an irreversible increase in size of a cell, tissue, organ, or organism and is usually accompanied by an increase in dry weight.

2. Growth continues only when the total of food-making activities exceeds the total of food-consuming processes.

3. The rate of growth varies in different species of plants and in different organs of the same plant.

4. Growth in plants occurs principally in root tips, buds, cambium, cork cambium, and root pericycle. The more or less continuous growth of root tips, buds, and

cambium is called indeterminate growth. The growth of leaves, flowers, and fruits, which ceases upon maturity, is called determinate.

5. Growth is influenced by a number of internal conditions—the hereditary nature of the plant, supply of growth hormones, reserve foods, vitamins, etc.

6. Hormones are naturally occurring growth-regulating substances. Characteristically, they are synthesized in one part of a plant and translocated to other parts where very small amounts of the regulators produce physiological effects.

7. Indoleacetic acid is the best known plant hormone and, together with related compounds, forms a class of growth substances called auxins. Auxins influence many growth processes, such as cell division, root formation, abscission, fruit development, and correlation phenomena.

8. Another class of plant hormones, the gibberellins, also influences many growth processes, for example, stem elongation, cambial activity, bud development, and flowering in some species.

9. Several practical applications have been made of growth regulators: in the rooting of cuttings, the production of seedless fruits, the prevention of premature fruit drop, and weed killing.

10. The production of new tissues by such organs as stem cuttings, rhizomes, and tubers is roughly proportional (within limits) to the quantities of food reserves within the organs.

11. Growth of plants is influenced by many external factors, among which are light, temperature, water, gases, chemical agents, and other living organisms.

12. Irritability, a characteristic property of living protoplasm, involves the reception of stimuli by plants and reactions of plant organs to those stimuli. The principal stimuli that initiate plant responses are light, chemical agents, water, gravity, gases, and contact.

13. The reception of stimuli by plants is chiefly diffuse; that is, many tissues are sensitive to stimuli. In some plants, morphologically and physiologically specialized structures receive stimuli.

14. Various stimuli bring about the unequal distribution of growth hormones in plant organs or cause the release of special substances that initiate reactions. The unequal distribution of growth hormones leads to differences of growth rates in different parts of organs and thus to bending reactions.

15. Plant movements of higher plants may be classified into two categories: 1. Growth movements, which result from unequal rates of growth in different parts of organs. 2. Turgor movements, which are brought about by changes in the turgor pressure of certain tissues following stimulation.

⋘ SUGGESTED READINGS FOR INTERESTED STUDENTS

1. Andus, L. J., *Plant Growth Substances,* 2d ed. Interscience Publishers, New York, 1959.

2. Galston, Arthur W., *The Life of the Green Plant.* Prentice-Hall, Englewood Cliffs, N. J., 1961.

3. Leopold, A. Carl, *Auxins and Plant Growth.* University of California Press, Berkeley and Los Angeles, 1955.

4. Meyer, B. S., D. B. Anderson, and R. H. Böhning, *Introduction to Plant Physiology*. D. Van Nostrand, Princeton, N. J., 1960.
5. Mitchell, John W., "Fundamental developments in the field of plant growth regulators." *Bull. Torrey Bot. Club*, Vol. 88, No. 5, pp. 299–312, 1961.
6. Sinnott, Edmund W., *Plant Morphogenesis*. McGraw-Hill, New York, 1960.
7. Went, Frits W., *The Experimental Control of Plant Growth*. Ronald Press, New York, 1957.

⋘ TOPICS AND QUESTIONS FOR STUDY

1. What are the quantitative and qualitative concepts associated with a biological interpretation of growth?
2. Why is food essential to growth?
3. Describe briefly the methods of measuring the growth of various plant organs.
4. In what sense is the measurement of dry weight increase a better criterion of growth than increase in fresh weight, increase in length, or increase in some other dimension?
5. May growth occur in plants without increase in size? Explain.
6. Describe the structure of meristermatic cells.
7. Describe the changes that occur in enlarging and differentiating cells.
8. Indicate the locations of the principal meristems in higher plants.
9. Characterize indeterminate growth, and contrast it with determinate growth.
10. List the principal internal factors that influence plant growth.
11. Describe the importance of heredity as a determiner of plant growth.
12. Define each of the following terms: hormone, auxin, bioassay, coleoptile.
13. Describe the Avena test for auxin activity.
14. What is the cause of "foolish seedling" disease of rice?
15. Describe some of the effects produced by treatment with gibberellin.
16. Name one way in which gibberellins differ from auxins.
17. What horticultural applications have been made of the results of hormone research?
18. Describe the relation of hormones to plant movements.
19. Name and describe briefly the principal effects of light upon plant development.
20. Define photoperiodism, and classify flowering plants on the basis of their photoperiodic responses.
21. Comment briefly upon the ecological aspects of photoperiodism.
22. What practical applications have been made of photoperiodic studies? Explain how the study of photoperiodism may be agriculturally important in selecting crops for cultivation in different parts of the world.
23. Describe briefly the relation of temperature to flowering.
24. What is the effect of reduced transpiration upon plant growth?
25. Why are lettuce and tobacco sometimes grown under cloth?
26. In what ways is water important in the lives of plants?
27. What are the effects of industrial gases upon plant growth?
28. Name some of the organisms that parasitize flowering plants.
29. In what ways do these parasites harm the plants upon which they grow?

30. What effects do grazing animals exert upon plants?
31. How would you account for the fact that grazing animals eagerly eat some species of plants but avoid others?
32. Name the principal external stimuli to which plants are sensitive.
33. Distinguish between positive and negative reactions of plants.
34. Describe briefly the reception of stimuli by plants.
35. Describe the physiological effects of stimuli upon plants.
36. Name and describe briefly several growth movements of plants.
37. On what basis are tropisms classified? Name three plant tropisms, name the effective stimulus for each, and describe their importance in the lives of plants.
38. List and describe briefly the chief differences between turgor movements and growth movements.
39. Name and describe several types of turgor movements and comment upon their importance in the lives of plants.

15

The Structure and Functions of Flowers

PHYSIOLOGY OF REPRODUCTION IN FLOWERING PLANTS

The activities thus far considered in flowering plants are termed **vegetative activities.** They involve the absorption of raw materials from the atmosphere and the soil, the synthesis of foods and other complex organic substances from these raw materials, the translocation of foods, the release and utilization of the potential energy of foods, and the processes involved in growth, differentiation, and reaction. Vegetative processes serve primarily in maintaining the life of the individual.

The **reproductive activities** of flowering plants, on the contrary, do not involve directly the absorption of raw materials and the elaboration of organic compounds therefrom, but are centered upon the propagation of the species through the formation of offspring. Ordinarily, vegetative activities begin in sprouting seeds and continue for a varying period of time before reproduction commences.

The reproductive processes of flowering plants may be divided into two categories: **asexual** or **vegetative reproduc-**tion, and **sexual reproduction,** which is typically associated with seed formation. Vegetative reproduction includes the production of new plants by runners, rhizomes, tubers, bulbs, and corms, the development of new individual plants as root suckers, and various human-controlled processes such as grafting, layering, and the rooting of cuttings of stems and leaves. Sexual reproduction involves the fusion of a male gamete, or **sperm,** with a female gamete, or **egg,** in the ovules of flowers; this fusion process, called **fertilization,** results in the formation of a fertilized egg, or **zygote,** that develops into the embryo of a seed.

The Initiation of Flowering. One of the major unsolved problems in the study of plant physiology is that of the factors responsible for the beginning of flowering. For a long time, plant physiologists regarded flowering as the result of the accumulation of food reserves within the vegetative organs of plants; according to this interpretation, the production of flowers requires large quantities of food, and is able to begin only when a sufficient amount of food has been synthesized and stored. This explanation of the cause of

253

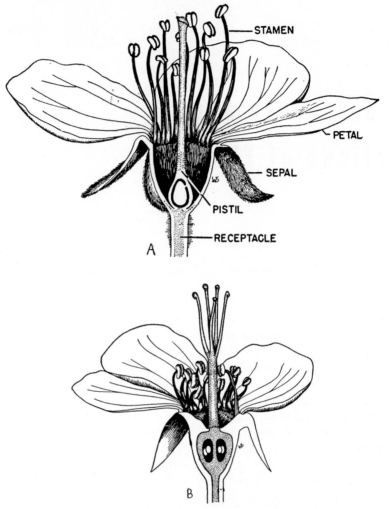

FIG. 15–1. Longitudinal sections of complete flowers.
A: With superior ovary (plum). B: With inferior ovary (apple).

flowering is acceptable so far as it goes, for flower formation does require the mobilization of foods in flower buds; but it is inadequate, since it does not explain many of the phenomena associated with flowering.

Our knowledge of the reproductive process was greatly advanced in 1920 with the discovery of photoperiodism (Chapter 14), a factor of prime impor-tance in the induction of flowering. Sub-sequently, the efforts of many investiga-tors have yielded considerable data on the physiological and morphological changes associated with floral initiation, including hormone activity and, most recently, the first substantial clues regarding the timing mechanism inherent in photoperiodism. The following account of flowering in cocklebur summarizes some of the events as they are presently understood. It should be kept in mind, however, that much research remains to be done.

Photoperiod, or more correctly, the length of the night, is a principal factor in the control of flowering in cocklebur (*Xanthium*). Cocklebur is a short-day plant; that is, it requires a regime of short days alternating with longer periods of continuous darkness in order to flower. The dark period must be continuous, for if it is interrupted by even a brief flash of light, no flowers are produced. Investigation of this phenomenon by researchers in the U. S. Department of Agriculture showed that exposure of the plant to a flash of red light was more effective in prevention of flowering than exposure to other colors. They also learned that brief exposure to longer wavelength (far red) light when applied immediately after a flash of red light, would reverse the inhibitory effect, thus permitting the plant

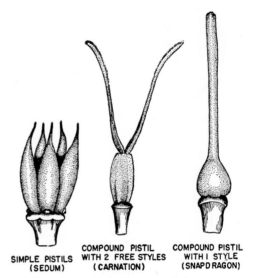

SIMPLE PISTILS (SEDUM)   COMPOUND PISTIL WITH 2 FREE STYLES (CARNATION)   COMPOUND PISTIL WITH 1 STYLE (SNAPDRAGON)

FIG. 15–3. Types of pistils.

to flower. These investigators were later able to demonstrate the existence of a photosensitive protein pigment that they named **phytochrome.** Exposure to red light changes phytochrome to an enzymatically active form that inhibits flowering; exposure of the active form to far-red light converts it to the inactive, noninhibitory form. Of special significance is the fact that, in darkness, the inhibitory form of phytochrome changes *spontaneously* to the noninhibitory form. In some plants this occurs at a rate that diminishes the amount of active pigment by one half every 2 hours. To date, phytochrome has not been isolated for chemical analysis; accordingly, its reactions with other compounds are unknown. There is little doubt, however, that the spontaneous conversion of this pigment in darkness from its active to its inactive form is one of the chief controlling factors of floral initiation.

Another physiological aspect of the flowering process involves hormonal activity, as has been convincingly demon-

(Photo by Chicago Natural History Museum.)

FIG. 15–2. Model of grapefruit flowers.

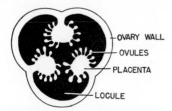

- OVARY WALL
- OVULES
- PLACENTA
- LOCULE

PARIETAL PLACENTATION

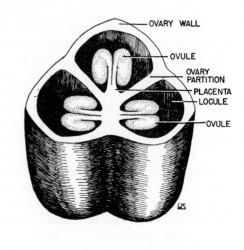

- OVARY WALL
- OVULE
- OVARY PARTITION
- PLACENTA
- LOCULE
- OVULE

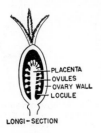

- PLACENTA
- OVULES
- OVARY WALL
- LOCULE

LONGI-SECTION

FIG. 15–4. *Left:* Two types of placentation. *Right:* Section of lily ovary, showing axile placentation.

CROSS SECTION

FREE CENTRAL PLACENTATION

strated by experiments on grafted cockle-burs. A cocklebur plant growing under a regime of long days and short nights will not flower; conversely, one growing under short-day and long-night conditions does produce flowers. When two plants growing under these respective regimes are grafted together, a flowering stimulus is transmitted from the short-day plant to the long-day plant causing the latter to flower. Further experimental evidence indicates that the stimulating agent is synthesized in leaves. The chemical nature of this flowering hormone, tentatively named **florigen,** is unknown, since it has yet to be isolated and identified. Moreover, the relationship between florigen and the pigment phytochrome is unknown at present. The stimulus, regardless of its nature, influences the conversion of the vegetative shoot apex into a floral primordium.

A balance between the carbohydrate and nitrogenous constituents of the tissues of some species of plants seems to be related to the beginning of flowering. A high carbohydrate content in relation to nitrogen content seems to favor early flowering in some species; in others, a shift in carbohydrate-nitrogen ratio appears to occur after flower production has begun.

Other factors of the external environment also exert some effect upon the beginning of flowering. Thus, plants growing in fertile soils and therefore supplied with all essential nutrients are more likely to undergo normal flowering than plants growing in poor, exhausted soils. Also, temperature is an important external factor in the flowering of most species of plants; as stated in the last chapter, for example, cotton plants require a fairly high minimum temperature before they

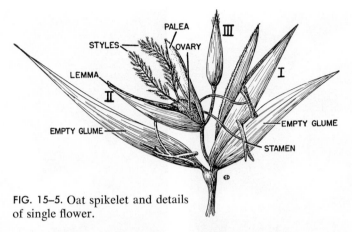

FIG. 15–5. Oat spikelet and details of single flower.

flower, while other species may flower at much lower temperatures. Some species of plants, for example, winter cereals, require an exposure to low temperatures for early flowering. Many species of plants come into flower quickly when some environmental condition, or combination of conditions, assumes an unfavorable aspect; sudden drops in temperature, drought, and sometimes crowding by other plants often act as stimuli to flowering.

THE DEVELOPMENT AND STRUCTURE OF FLOWERS

In the angiosperms, the characteristic reproductive structures are **flowers.** A flower is regarded by botanists as a specialized shoot, some parts of which are directly involved in reproduction, others of which are only indirectly concerned with reproductive activity. Some of these floral organs are leaflike in development and structure, whereas others have the developmental and anatomical characteristics of stems.

Flowers develop from **buds,** as do vegetative shoots. Some buds produce only flowers (elm, morning-glory, poplar); others produce both flowers and leaves

(buckeye, apple), and bring about increase in the lengths of stems in addition. Flowers differ from vegetative shoots in that there is virtually no elongation of their internodes, as a result of which floral organs are bunched together and are not distributed at obvious intervals along the floral axis. Moreover, growth of the flower is **determinate,** that is, no further apical growth occurs after the floral parts have been formed, whereas apical growth of the vegetative shoot is **indeterminate.** Flowers also differ from vegetative shoots in that buds normally do not develop in the axils of floral organs as they do in the axils of green leaves of vegetative twigs. The parts of a flower develop as lateral protuberances of a bud growing point in much the same way as do foliage leaves. The lowermost floral organs usually develop first, followed in order by the more apically situated parts, those nearest the tip of the bud enlarging last. The tip of a floral stalk, from which floral organs grow, is called the **receptacle.**

The most familiar types of flowers, such as those of snapdragons, morning-glories, roses, irises, and petunias, are **complete** flowers; that is, they bear on their receptacles four kinds of floral or-

FIG. 15–6. *Left:* Staminate flowers of walnut. *Right:* Pistillate flowers of walnut. These flowers are imperfect. (About 4 times natural size.)

gans: 1. **sepals,** 2. **petals,** 3. **stamens,** and 4. **pistils** (Figure 15–1). Botanists commonly regard these structures as highly modified leaves. The outermost (lowermost) of these are the sepals, which, in most kinds of flowers, are small, green, leaflike structures. The sepals enclose and protect the other floral organs in the bud before they are fully developed. The sepals collectively are called the **calyx.** Above (inside) the sepals are the usually showy, conspicuous, often brightly colored **petals,** known collectively as the **corolla.** The number of petals in a flower is usually the same as that of the sepals, or sometimes a multiple of the sepal number. In buttercups, for example, there are 5 sepals and 5 petals. Single roses have 5 sepals and 5 petals; in double roses

with many petals, the number of petals is usually a multiple of 5. Petals serve primarily to attract insects, the visits of which are important in the reproductive functions of flowers. Petals secure the attention of insects in several ways. The bright colors of many flowers are attractive to insects. The petals of some flowers have glands (**nectaries**) that secrete **nectar,** a sweetish liquid much desired by bees and other kinds of flower-visiting insects. The odors of the essential oils and other substances produced by the petals of many species of plants constitute another means of luring insects to flowers. In many species, floral fragrances are very pleasant to the human sense of smell; the characteristic odors of jasmine, rose, lavender, sweet pea, carnation, and

(*From* Taxonomy of Flowering Plants *by C. L. Porter. San Francisco: W. H. Free-man and Company, 1959.*)

FIG. 15–7. Flower of *Lilium philadelphicum,* a monocotyledon.

other flowers arise from substances secreted by petals. Many of these substances are of importance in perfume manufacture. In a few species, such as skunk cabbage and Dutchman's pipe (*Aristolochia*), the floral odors are very strong and exceedingly unpleasant, sometimes in such a degree that they cause nausea in human beings. These offensive odors attract chiefly the kinds of insects that commonly visit decaying animal flesh and other rotting, ill-smelling organic matter. Many flowers of this type are reddish brown in color and frequently resemble animal flesh. The insects, such as bees, that visit pleasantly scented flowers are not attracted by flowers of the latter type.

Inside (above) the petals are the **stamens,** which produce **pollen grains.** A stamen consists usually of a slender stalk, or **filament,** that bears at its apex a single, enlarged, often more or less cylindrical or ovoid **anther.** Within anthers develop the pollen grains that later lead to the formation of male reproductive cells, or **sperms.** In the center of a complete flower is a **pistil** (or pistils), which consists usually of three fairly distinct portions—an enlarged basal **ovary,** within which the seeds are formed; an elongated, slender **style,** which rises from the top of the ovary; and at the top of the style, a slightly enlarged **stigma,** upon which pollen grains fall or are brought, previous to the fertilization of the imma-

FIG. 15–8. The bilaterally symmetrical flowers of the dove orchid, a monocotyledon. The head of the "dove" is the column, which is a structure composed of a pistil, bearing a functional stamen near its apex.

ture seeds, or **ovules.** Stigmas are frequently very rough or bristly, and sometimes they are covered with a sticky fluid, as a result of which pollen grains are more securely held on the stigmatic surfaces. A pistil is composed of one or several **carpels,** or ovule-bearing organs. A pistil made up of one carpel, as in the flowers of peas, beans, and buttercups, is called a **simple pistil.** In the flowers of tulips, snapdragons, lilies, and many other species, two or more carpels are fused to-

gether into a single **compound pistil** (Figure 15–3).

Inside the ovary of a pistil are structures called **placentae,** to which the ovules are attached, each by a short stalk or **funiculus,** and which usually are of the same number as the carpels in the pistil. The arrangement of placentae in an ovary varies in different species of plants; some of the common types of placentation are illustrated in Figure 15–4. The number of ovules in an ovary varies from one, as in corn, to many hundreds, as in foxgloves, or more than a million, as in some orchids. An ovary cavity, within which ovules develop, is called a **locule.**

Sepals and petals are termed the **accessory parts** of flowers because they are not directly concerned with reproduction processes. Stamens and pistils are the **essential parts** of flowers for they are involved directly in the production of seeds. The accessory parts are frequently of indirect importance in reproduction in that they may attract insects, which are necessary for the pollination of many types of flowers.

The four kinds of floral organs described above—sepals, petals, stamens, and pistil(s) are present in all complete flowers. Not all flowers are complete, however; in some plants, such as anemone and clematis, there are sepals, stamens, and pistils present, but no petals. In oat flowers, stamens and pistils are present, but sepals and petals are lacking (Figure 15–5). In corn and willows, there are two kinds of flowers, some that bear stamens, others that bear pistils; in both types, neither sepals nor petals are present. All flowers, such as those of willow, corn, clematis, and anemones, that lack one or more of the four kinds of floral organs, are called **incomplete.** Species, such as willow, corn, walnut, and cottonwood (Figure 15–6), in which the stamens and pistils are produced in separate flowers, are said to have **imperfect flowers.** Imperfect flowers that bear stamens are termed **staminate,** those that contain pistils are called **pistillate flowers.** In willows, cottonwoods, hemp, and many other species, staminate flowers and pistillate flowers are borne on separate plants, a condition described as **dioecious.** The staminate and pistillate flowers of other species, such as walnut, oaks, and corn (Figure 15–6), are produced by the same plant: such plants are **monoecious.** Tulips, lilies, roses, sweet peas, and orchids have flowers in which stamens and pistils are present in the same flower; such flowers are termed **perfect flowers.** A flower may be perfect but incomplete; for example, oat flowers are perfect because they bear both stamens and pistils, and they are incomplete, because they lack sepals and petals. All imperfect flowers are obviously incomplete.

There are many other kinds of variations in the structure of flowers of different species of angiosperms. The numbers of parts, the sizes and colors of petals, the relative position of the various floral organs, the degree of fusion among parts, are chief among the varying characteristics of the flowers of different species of plants.

The flowers of monocotyledons (about 50,000 species) generally have their flower parts in 3's or multiples of 3. In tulip flowers, for example, there are 3 sepals, 3 petals, 6 stamens, and a pistil of 3 fused carpels. In iris flowers, the same numbers of parts are found, except that there are only 3 stamens. The same basic numbers of parts are found in most other monocot families—grasses, amaryllises, bananas, pineapples, palms, and orchids. In dicotyledons (about 200,000 species)

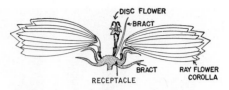

FIG. 15–9. Longitudinal section of a composite inflorescence (sunflower).

flower parts are chiefly in 4's or 5's (Figures 15–1 and 15–2), less frequently in 2's, and in only a few families in 3's. In the flowers of *Sedum* and certain other members of the live-forever family, there are 5 sepals, 5 petals, 10 stamens, and 5 separate, simple pistils. The flowers of evening primroses have 4 sepals, 4 petals, 8 stamens, and a compound ovary of 4 fused carpels. In members of the bleeding-heart family, the flowers have usually 2 sepals, 4 petals, 6 stamens, and a compound pistil of 2 fused carpels. Magnolias and pawpaws are among the relatively few dicotyledons in which the sepals and petals are in multiples of 3.

Petals vary greatly in their size, color, and arrangement in flowers. In buttercups, petunias, and roses, the petals are equal in size and are equally spaced in position, so that the flowers of which they are parts are built on a circular plan, as viewed from above. This type of symmetry is termed **radial symmetry** (Figure 15–1). In other flowering plants, such as sweet peas, snapdragons, orchids, and mints, the petals vary in size and are unequally spaced, so that flowers of this type are constructed upon a right-and-left plan rather than a circular plan. This right-and-left plan of floral construction is called **bilateral symmetry** (Figure 15–8).

In many flowers, such as roses and magnolias, the floral organs are all separate and distinct from each other. The flowers of petunias, phlox, and sunflowers, on the contrary, show a considerable

FIG. 15–10. Composite head of goatsbeard, in which all flowers are ray flowers.

degree of fusion among their floral organs. In petunia and phlox flowers, the petals are fused into trumpet-shaped and tubular corollas, respectively. In sunflowers, the petals are fused and the stamens are likewise fused by their anthers into a tube around the style. The degree of fusion of various flower parts thus differs widely among different species of flowering plants.

In some kinds of flowers such as magnolias and water lilies, the floral organs are arranged in **spiral** fashion on the receptacle; that is, all the floral organs from lowermost to uppermost can be connected by a continuous, spiral line or several spiral lines. In lilies, phlox, and many other species, the flower parts are arranged in distinct circles or cycles upon the receptacle and cannot be connected by a spiral line. This **cyclic** arrangement of parts is more common than the spiral arrangement among flowering plants.

Flowers vary also in the positions of their ovaries with respect to the places of attachment of sepals and petals on their receptacles. In snapdragons and morning-glories, the sepals and petals are attached to the receptacle just *beneath* the point of attachment of the ovary to the receptacle. In evening primroses and honeysuckles, in contrast, the sepals, petals, and stamens grow out from the *top* of the ovary, which is sunken in the receptacle. Ovaries of the first kind—those situated above the points of origin of sepals and petals—are termed **superior ovaries.** Those ovaries of the second type, with sepals and petals arising at their crests, are called **inferior ovaries** (Figure 15–1).

Flowers vary also in their relative positions on the plants that produce them. In magnolias, most roses, and tulip trees,

FIG. 15–11. Inflorescences of dogwood (*Cornus florida*). Each inflorescence consists of several very small flowers subtended by 4 large, white bracts.

each flower is solitary, borne on a single stalk at some distance from other flowers. In snapdragons, lilacs, and asters, several or many flowers are borne in a cluster. These flower clusters, or **inflorescences,** differ markedly in the numbers of flowers they bear, the numbers and arrangements of their branches, and in other respects.

A type of inflorescence called a **head** is characteristic of members of the daisy, or composite family (Figures 15–9 and 15–10). In a head, the flowers are small and are tightly crowded on a flattened or convex, disc-shaped compound receptacle. The corollas of the marginal flowers on these discs are much enlarged and brightly colored in most composites. These **rays** are commonly and errone-

ously called petals. Each of these so-called petals of a sunflower head, for example, is really the corolla of a ray flower. The flowers that occupy the central part of a sunflower head have much smaller, less conspicuous corollas than do the ray flowers; further, disc flowers are radially symmetrical, whereas ray flowers are bilaterally symmetrical. In sunflowers, as in many other composites, the disc flowers produce seeds, while the ray flowers are sterile. A whole sunflower is thus not a single flower, but an inflorescence bearing many dozens of tiny flowers. In some composites, for example, dandelion and goatsbeard, the inflorescence is made up entirely of ray flowers (Figure 15–10); in other composites, for example, ageratum and blazing star, the head is composed entirely of disc flowers.

In many kinds of inflorescences, special, leaflike structures called **bracts** grow out from the main stalk **(peduncle)** of the inflorescence (Figure 15–11). A bract may grow from the base of the peduncle, or from the juncture of each individual flower stalk **(pedicel)** with the peduncle in such fashion that the flower is in the axil of its bract, just as a vegetative twig is in the axil of a leaf. These bracts are sometimes small, as in snapdragons, or they may be large and brightly colored, as in poinsettias. There is commonly a gradual transition from typical foliage leaves to bracts; one may find a graded series of such structures in snapdragons, foxgloves, and poinsettias, in which there are leaves intermediate between the green leaves and the bright red bracts. Bracts sometimes attract insects or offer protection to flowers, but commonly they seem devoid of function.

The flowers of grasses deserve brief description because of the abundance of grasses in the earth's vegetation and of

(Photo by Missouri Botanical Garden.)

FIG. 15–12. An inflorescence of banana, showing the large terminal bud of the inflorescence, and the clusters of bilaterally symmetrical flowers with inferior ovaries that ripen into the edible bananas of commerce. Flowers are borne in the axils of bracts.

the great economic importance of grasses. A grass inflorescence bears flowers in separate, small clusters called **spikelets** (Figure 15–5). At the base of a typical spikelet is a pair of chaffy bracts called **sterile glumes.** A slender, short stalk projects above the glumes, and at its joints other pairs of bracts are borne. The larger bract of each of these pairs is the **lemma,** the smaller the **palea.** Within each such pair is borne a single flower; in most grasses a flower consists of a single pistil with two feathery, long styles and of three stamens with long, slender filaments. In a few species, the flowers are imperfect, as in corn, the pistillate flowers of which are borne on the ears, the staminate in the tassels. A spikelet may bear only one flower, as in barley, or several flowers, as in oats. Pollination of grass flowers is by wind, the long, feathery styles effectively capturing wind-borne pollen (Figure 15–13) shed by the long, dangling stamens that protrude beyond the enveloping bracts. The "chaff" of many grains consists of lemmas and paleas that adhere to the grains. Threshing removes these chaffs, freeing the grains.

These many diverse features of flower structure furnish the chief criteria used to distinguish among various species of flowering plants and to classify such plants into related groups. On the basis of their study of plant fossils, of the anatomy of flowers of living plants, of the developmental histories of flower parts, and of other features of floral structure, botanists have demonstrated that evolution has occurred among the angiosperms and that certain types of floral structure are to be regarded as primitive, others as more advanced. In the table on page 265 are listed some of the primitive and advanced characters of flowers.

A   B   *(Photo by O. T. Bonnett.)*

FIG. 15–13. A: An oat spikelet, showing two flowers ready for pollination. B: A fully developed oat flower, showing *a.* styles, *b.* a filament,
and *c.* anthers.

Primitive Characters	*Advanced Characters*
1. Large, variable numbers of parts	1. Smaller, constant numbers of parts
2. Spiral arrangement of parts	2. Cyclic arrangement of parts
3. Solitary flowers	3. Flowers in inflorescences
4. Parts separate	4. Parts partly or wholly fused
5. Superior ovaries	5. Inferior ovaries
6. Radial symmetry	6. Bilateral symmetry

Among plants that are considered to have primitive or intermediate types of flowers are magnolias, buttercups, barberries, tulip trees, and roses. Species that have more advanced types of flowers are mints, petunias, snapdragons, morning-glories, potato, and sunflower.

THE POLLINATION OF FLOWERS

Pollination is the first of a series of processes that result in the formation of seeds and thus is exceedingly important in the lives of angiosperms. Pollination in angiosperms is the transfer of pollen grains from an anther to a stigma. The transfer of pollen from the anther of a flower to the stigma of a flower of another plant is **cross-pollination.** In **self-pollination,** pollen is carried from an anther to the stigma of the same flower or to another flower of the same plant. In some species (for example, orchids), only cross-pollination occurs; in others (for example, peas), self-pollination is the rule.

Flowers that produce seeds following self-pollination are termed **self-fertile,** while those that form seeds only as a result of cross-pollination are **self-sterile.** Flowers of pears, grapes, and apples are

FIG. 15–14. Portion of staminate inflorescence of corn, showing dangling stamens.

chiefly cross-pollinated; if cross-pollination fails, self-pollination of these flowers often occurs, with the result that some fruits and seeds are formed; these are usually fewer and sometimes smaller than fruits and seeds resulting from cross-pollination. Horticulturists advise the establishment of beehives in or near orchards to ensure cross-pollination of flowers of fruit trees so that the fruit crop may be large and of superior quality.

The natural agents of pollination are most commonly **wind** and **insects,** less frequently **birds** and **water,** rarely bats, snails, and other animals. Bees, butterflies, and moths are the most common insect visitors of flowers (Figure 15–15). Various kinds of birds, particularly hummingbirds in search of nectar, are important in pollinating flowers of some spe-

cies. In most flowering plants, insects are the most common agents of pollination. Insect-pollinated and wind-pollinated flowers have certain fundamental structural and behavioral differences that reflect their different modes of pollination. Wind-pollinated flowers, such as those of cottonwoods, oaks, corn, wheat, and cattails, are usually borne in rather dense clusters, produce copious pollen, and have stigmas that are greatly enlarged or that are equipped with long hairs that catch and hold pollen grains as they are blown through the air (Figure 15–16). Flowers of roses, orchids, apples, and sunflowers, which are pollinated by insects, generally possess rather large and showy petals, produce nectar or aromatic substances or both, form smaller quantities of pollen than do wind-pollinated

(Photo by C. F. Hottes.)

FIG. 15–15. Bees entering snapdragon flowers.

flowers, and usually have stigmas that are smaller than those of wind-pollinated flowers and that lack bristles and hairs (Figures 15–1 and 15–2). Many insect-pollinated flowers lack showy corollas but have brightly colored sepals (four-o'clock), showy stamens (willow, eucalyptus), or large bracts (dogwood, poinsettia). In composites, the flowers are tiny, but the heads in which they occur are usually conspicuous, chiefly because of the large corollas of the ray flowers, and thus attract insects.

A cross section of an anther shows usually four pollen sacs, within which the pollen grains are produced. When an anther reaches maturity, the pollen sacs open, usually by longitudinal slits, and the pollen grains are thus exposed and are ready for transfer to a stigma.

In many species of plants, it seems that greater vigor is shown by the offspring of cross-pollinated flowers than by those of self-pollinated flowers. This fact, together with the facts that the flowers of most species of angiosperms are cross-pollinated and that there exist in these flowers many modes of behavior and highly specialized devices to ensure cross-pollination, indicate that this type of pollination seems to be a rather highly advanced type. Among the ingenious methods that ensure cross-pollination or make it more effective are the following: imperfect flowers (Figures 15–6, 15–17), chemical incompatability between pollen and stigma of flowers on the same plant, differences in time of maturation of stigmas and stamens (Figures 15–18, 15–19), and specialized floral structure that keeps

(*Photo by O. T. Bonnett.*)

FIG. 15–16. Tip of mature style ("silk") of corn, showing pollen grains.

the stamens out of proximity to the stigma in the same flower.

FERTILIZATION IN FLOWERS

After pollen grains (Figure 15–20) are deposited on a stigma, swellings appear in the thin places in their walls. The pollen grains absorb water and other materials from the stigma and use these substances, together with the foods stored within them, in the production of **pollen tubes** (Figure 15–21). Each pollen grain

normally produces a single tube, which grows downward through the style. The lengths attained by pollen tubes vary in different species of plants, depending upon the lengths of the styles through which they must grow. In some flowers, such as those of willow and beet, the styles are only about $\frac{1}{10}$ inch long and the pollen tubes are accordingly short. In some lilies, the styles are 5 inches long, and in the pistillate flowers of corn, the styles (silks) are frequently 16 to 20 inches long, with pollen tubes necessarily somewhat longer. In many short-styled flowers only a few hours are required for the complete growth of pollen tubes, whereas in many long-styled species, several weeks may be required for the full growth of pollen tubes. The length of the style is not always a controlling factor in determining the time required for a pollen tube to complete its journey through the style; in oak flowers, for example, pollen tubes require several months to grow through the styles, which are about $\frac{1}{8}$ inch long, whereas in corn, the pollen tubes often complete their growth through more than a foot of style within 36 hours.

Pollen tubes continue their downward growth through the style until they reach the ovary cavity, within which the ovules are contained. The pollen tubes grow along the inside of the ovary wall until they reach the ovules, which they enter. Although many pollen tubes reach an ovary, only one pollen tube usually enters each ovule. Each pollen grain contains a **tube nucleus** and a **generative cell,** and these enter the pollen tube when it is formed. The tube nucleus, which usually precedes the generative cell in the growing tube, is not directly involved in fertilization but controls the growth of the pollen tube. At some time during the development of the tube, the generative cell

FIG. 15–17. Inflorescence bases of jack-in-the-pulpit (*Arisaema*). *Left:* Staminate flowers from inflorescence of male plant. *Right:* Pistillate flowers from inflorescence of female plant. The enveloping sheaths are bracts.

undergoes a single mitotic division, forming two **sperms,** or male gametes, which are directly involved in fertilization in the ovule.

As stated earlier, a pistil is composed of one or more carpels. Each bears ovules along its margins, which are turned inward longitudinally and fused along their line of meeting into a hollow, more or less cylindrical form. If the simple pistil (a single carpel) of a pea is opened along the line of marginal fusion and is spread out flat, it bears a striking resemblance

to a foliage leaf, from which it differs in that it has ovules attached to its edges. A carpel is regarded by many botanists as a leaf or as a structure similar in its development to a leaf and engaged in reproductive rather than vegetative activities. In compound pistils, 2 or more carpels are fused together into 1 pistil. In some species, such as lilies, there are as many cavities in the ovary of the compound pistil as there are carpels; in a lily ovary, there are 3 fused carpels, each fundamentally like the 1-carpellate pistil

FIG. 15–18. Flowers of *Cleroden-dron. Left:* The stamens are mature, the style is immature and is still curled downward. *Right:* Stamens have shed their pollen and have begun to dry up, and the style is now erect and capable of receiving pollen.

FIG. 15–19. Plantain inflorescence. The young flowers (upper half of spike) have mature white styles and immature stamens. The older flowers (lower half) have mature stamens and pollinated, dried styles.

of pea, but combined into a compound pistil with 3 separate cavities, within which the ovules are borne. In other species, carpel fusion is such that there are no walls between the carpels; the ovary of such a pistil, though it is composed of 2 or more carpels, has but a single cavity. In most flowering plants, the number of styles or of style or stigma branches coincides with the number of carpels in their pistils. In lilies, for example, there are 3 stigma branches and 3 carpels in a pistil, in cherry flowers 1 style and 1 carpel, in morning-glories 2 style

branches and 2 carpels. There are some exceptions to this correspondence; in a tomato flower, for example, there is a 2-carpellate pistil, with but a single, unbranched style.

An ovule, or undeveloped seed, is attached to the inside of the ovary in which it is borne by a short stalk (Figure 15–4). The outer cells of an ovule form one or two fairly distinct layers termed **integuments,** which, after fertilization, become the **seed coats** of the seed. At one end of an ovule, there is a tiny pore, the **micropyle,** in the integuments. Inside the in-

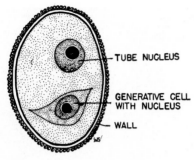

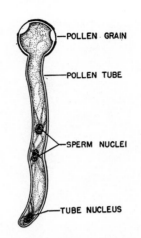

FIG. 15–20 (*above*). Pollen grain (*Lilium*).

FIG. 15–21 (*right*). Germinating pollen grain with pollen tube.

teguments and other outer cells of an ovule is a somewhat ovoid **embryo sac** (Figure 15–24), which usually occupies the greater part of the volume of an ovule. A typical embryo sac at the time when it is ready for fertilization contains the following structures: an **egg cell** (female gamete) and 2 **synergid cells** at the micropylar end of the embryo sac, 2 **polar nuclei** in the central region, and 3 **antipodal cells** opposite the micropylar end. (See frontispiece and Figure 28–1A.)

When a pollen tube, after its growth down a style, reaches an ovule, it penetrates the micropyle and enters the embryo sac, into which it discharges a portion of its contents, most important of which are the 2 sperms. One of the sperms fuses with the egg in the embryo sac, a process called **fertilization.** The other sperm fuses with the 2 polar nuclei of the embryo sac to form the **endosperm nucleus.** The process of fusion of a sperm with the polar nuclei is termed triple fusion. The remaining 5 cells of the embryo sac (3 antipodals and 2 synergids) usually disintegrate after fertilization is completed. The term **double fertilization** is applied to the two fusion processes in which the sperms engage.

After fertilization, the ovary usually begins to enlarge into the **fruit,** and, as it does so, the ovules also grow. As stated in Chapter 14, pollination and fertilization are stimuli that initiate the enlargement of the ovary. The **zygote** (fertilized egg) by numerous cell divisions and differentiation processes becomes the embryo of the seed. The endosperm nucleus grows into the **endosperm tissue** (food storage tissue) of the seed. Simultaneously, the integuments grow and harden to form the seed coat.

The complex series of events involved in pollination and fertilization in flowers is as follows, in summary form:

1. Pollen grains are transferred from a stamen to a stigma by wind, insects, or some other agency (pollination).

2. Pollen grains absorb water from the stigma and produce pollen tubes, which grow down through the style into the ovary.

3. Each pollen tube has a tube nucleus, which controls the growth of the tube, and a generative cell, which divides into 2 sperm cells.

4. A pollen tube enters an ovule through the micropyle, a pore in the integuments of the ovule.

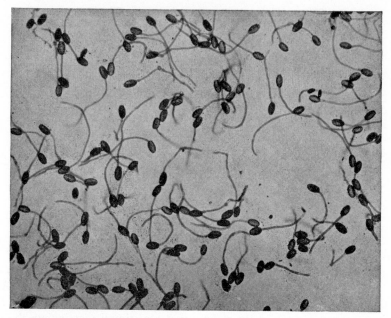

FIG. 15–22. Germinating pollen grains, with their pollen tubes.

5. In an ovule there is an embryo sac, which at the time of fertilization contains an egg cell and 2 synergid cells at the micropylar end, 3 antipodal cells at the opposite end, and 2 polar nuclei in the central part of the sac.

6. A pollen tube entering the embryo sac discharges its 2 sperms into the sac.

7. One sperm fertilizes the egg, forming a zygote, which by subsequent growth develops into the embryo of the seed.

8. The other sperm fuses with the polar nuclei, forming the endosperm nucleus, which after numerous mitotic divisions gives rise to the endosperm or food storage tissue of the seed. The developing seed enlarges as a result of growth of the endosperm and of the embryo and the movement of food into it, the integuments harden into the seed coat, and the fruit undergoes enlargement. As the ovary enlarges, stamens, petals, and often the sepals wither and fall. In some fruits, such as pea pods and apples, the sepals and often some stamens persist and may be found as dried structures at one end of the fruit.

9. When the fruit reaches maturity, it splits open, or, if there is no definite splitting, its walls disintegrate, and the now-mature seeds are freed.

The enlargement of ovaries into fruits and of ovules into seeds requires much food. Soluble foods, such as sugars, amino acids, and simple proteins, move rapidly through vascular tissues that connect flower parts with stems into the cells of the ovules and of the ovary walls. When these foods reach their destination, they may be converted into insoluble storage foods, such as starches, complex proteins, and fats. In this process, the water content of maturing ovules and often fruits decreases markedly, so that mature seeds contain a low percentage, usually not more than 10 percent, of moisture.

The maturation of fruits and seeds often has an inhibitory effect upon the growth of vegetative organs, especially of annual and biennial plants, usually leading to their death—in annuals at the end of one season of growth, in biennials during the second season of their lives; in some perennials, such as century plants (*Agave*), there is a vegetative period of 5 to 60 or more years, following which the plants flower once and die. If the maturation of seeds and fruits in such plants is prevented by the removal of flowers as they appear, there is usually no inhibition of vegetative growth, which may continue for many weeks or months. Many of us have practiced the gardener's advice "to keep picking the sweet pea flowers if you want the plants to keep flowering." This valuable admonition applies not only to sweet peas, but to pansies, stocks, larkspurs, and many other garden annuals as well. It has long been thought by plant physiologists and horticulturists that this inhibition of vegetative growth and the frequent death of plants following seed and ovary maturation are the result of exhaustion by the rapidly growing seeds and fruits of food reserves stored in vegetative organs. However, there is evidence to indicate that this inhibition must be at least in part attributable to some physiological cause other than exhaustion of food reserves. It has been suggested that young, developing fruits produce a hormone that in some manner retards vegetative growth; there is insufficient information as yet concerning the nature of this supposed hormone or the manner of its action.

Usually the development of ovules into seeds and the growth of an ovary into a fruit follow only after pollination and fertilization have occurred. In most species of flowering plants, the failure of

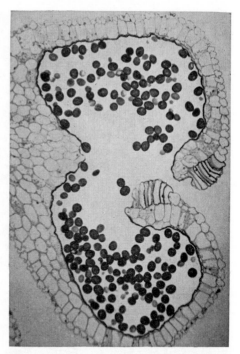

FIG. 15–23. Portion of *Lilium* (lily) anther in transverse section, showing numerous pollen grains.

pollination results in a failure of fruit and seed production. This phenomenon frequently occurs if pollinating insects are not active, or if destruction of pollen occurs. In many kinds of fruit trees, if heavy rains fall during the time when pollen grains are maturing, the pollen grains are washed out of the flowers, pollination does not occur, and, as a result, few or no flowers "set fruits." The action of pollen upon ovaries is as least twofold: the pollen grains produce the sperm cells that fertilize the eggs within the ovules and thus lead to the development of embryos within the seeds, and they stimulate a hormonal reaction that controls the enlargement of ovaries into fruits. If an extract of pollen grains is prepared and is placed upon the stigmas of flowers instead of pollen grains, ovary enlargement

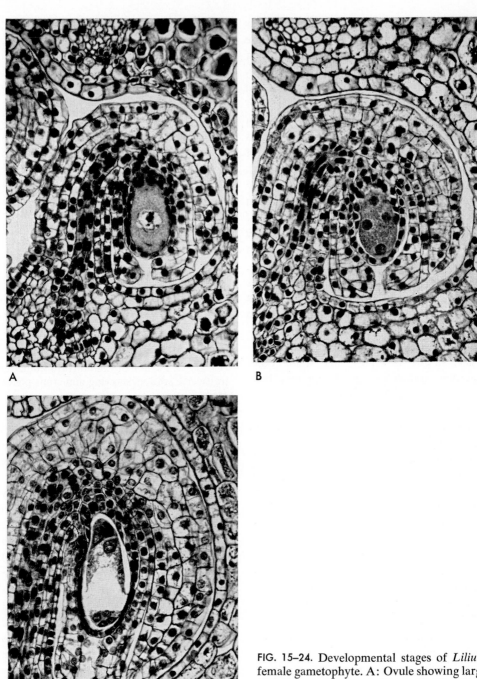

A

B

FIG. 15–24. Developmental stages of *Lilium* female gametophyte. A: Ovule showing large diploid megaspore mother cell. B: Ovule showing 4 haploid megaspore nuclei. C: Ovule showing 8-nucleate stage, 4 triploid nuclei above, and 4 smaller, haploid nuclei below.

C

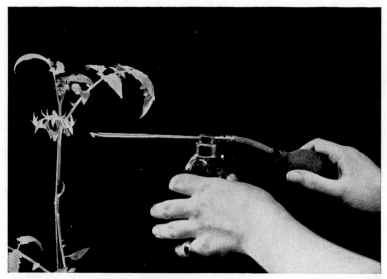

FIG. 15–25. Method of spraying tomato flowers with growth substances to produce parthenocarpic fruits.

commonly occurs. The same result, as described in the last chapter, may be obtained by spraying growth-promoting substances upon, or injecting them into, ovaries of many species of plants. This type of fruit development is called **induced** or **artificial parthenocarpy;** this treatment leads to the production of seedless fruits that are often more succulent and more desirable than normal, seed-containing fruits (Figure 15–26). Some kinds of plants produce seedless fruits naturally, that is, without treatment of their pistils with growth-promoting substances; in navel oranges, bananas, and pineapples, for example, ovaries normally develop into seedless fruits, a type of fruit development called **natural parthenocarpy.**

Now that our study of the biology of flowering plants has brought us back to the subject of seeds, students should review seed structure and germination.

SUMMARY

1. Leaves, stems, and roots function primarily in maintaining the life of the individual plant, though some of them carry on reproduction by rhizomes, runners, tubers, etc.
2. Seed formation involves a sexual process and is the function of flowers.
3. The causes of flowering are not fully known, but they involve the accumulation of foods, the exposure of plants to suitable photoperiods, and the development of floral hormones. Suitable temperatures, nutrient supplies of the soil, and other external factors affect flowering.
4. A flower is interpreted as a reproductive shoot bearing organs, some of which are similar to leaves in their origin and structure, others to twigs.
5. A complete flower consists of a receptacle, to which are attached 4 kinds of

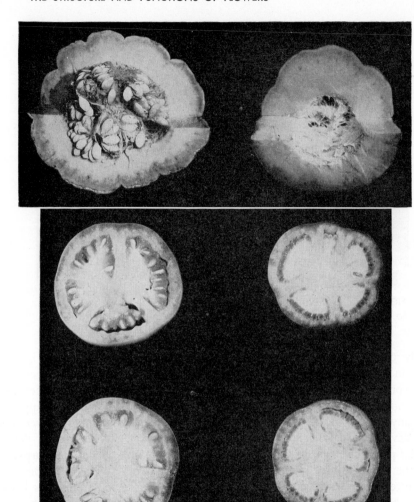

(*Photo by P. W. Zimmerman, Boyce Thompson Institute.*)

FIG. 15–26. Cross sections of melon and tomato fruits. Fruits at the left were developed by normally pollinated flowers and contain seeds. Fruits at right are parthenocarpic, without seeds, as a result of treatment of ovaries with beta-naphthoxyacetic acid, a growth substance, instead of pollination.

floral parts: sepals (calyx collectively), petals (corolla collectively), stamens, and pistil(s). A pistil consists of one or more carpels. The enlarged base of a pistil is the ovary; this contains ovules that develop into seeds after fertilization.

6. Sepals protect the inner parts of young flowers, petals attract insects, stamens produce pollen grains, and carpels produce ovules.

7. There are many variations in the structural and physiological features of

flowers: numbers of parts, size and form of parts, color, kinds of parts present, etc.

8. Flowers develop from buds, the floral parts arising as lateral protuberances of the growing points of buds.

9. A flower cluster is an inflorescence.

10. Pollination is the transfer of pollen grains from a stamen to a stigma. Self-pollination is the transfer of pollen from a stamen to the stigma of the same flower or another flower on the same plant. Cross-pollination is the transfer of pollen from a stamen to the stigma of a flower on another plant. Cross-pollination is the more common.

11. Pollination is brought about mainly by insects and wind, to a lesser extent by water, birds, and other agents.

12. Many kinds of flowers have specialized mechanisms or modes of behavior that attract insects or increase the effectiveness of insect pollination.

13. Fundamental structural differences occur between wind-pollinated and insect-pollinated flowers.

14. The events that occur from pollination through fertilization and seed development are summarized on pages 271 and 272.

15. A fruit is a matured ovary, a seed is a matured ovule.

16. The maturation of fruits and seeds often inhibits the growth of vegetative organs and sometimes leads to the death of plants, especially of annuals and biennials. The cause of such death is probably twofold: depletion of food reserves, and activation of hormones with an inhibitory effect.

17. Pollen affects ovaries in two ways: it provides the sperms that bring about fertilization in the ovules, and it stimulates the formation or activity of auxins that induce the enlargement of ovaries into fruits.

18. The enlargement of a fruit without pollination and fertilization is called parthenocarpy. Parthenocarpy occurs naturally in some fruits, in others it can be induced by the application of auxins to the pistil.

⋘ SUGGESTED READINGS FOR INTERESTED STUDENTS

1. Borthwick, H. A., and S. B. Hendricks, "Photoperiodism in Plants." *Science,* Vol. 132, No. 3435, pp. 1223–1228, October 1960.

2. Downs, R. J., H. A. Borthwick, and A. A. Piringer, *Light and Plants,* U. S. Dept. of Agriculture Misc. Pub. No. 879, Government Printing Office, Washington, D. C., 1961.

3. Foster, A. S., and E. M. Gifford, Jr., *Comparative Morphology of Vascular Plants.* Freeman, San Francisco, 1959.

4. Galston, Arthur W., *The Life of the Green Plant.* Prentice-Hall, Englewood Cliffs, N. J., 1961.

5. Hillman, William S., *The Physiology of Flowering.* Holt, Rinehart and Winston, New York, 1962.

6. Salisbury, Frank B., "The flowering process." *Scientific American,* Vol. 198, No. 4, pp. 108–117, April 1958.

⟪⟪← TOPICS AND QUESTIONS FOR STUDY

1. Contrast the vegetative with reproductive activities of flowering plants.
2. Indicate the order in which these activities occur in the life of a flowering plant.
3. Describe several methods of vegetative reproduction. In what ways does such reproduction differ from reproduction by seeds?
4. Summarize the present state of our knowledge concerning the physiological causes of flowering. Cite specific experiments as evidence.
5. Describe briefly the development of flowers.
6. Distinguish between complete and incomplete flowers.
7. Name and describe the organs of a complete flower and state their functions.
8. How do flowers attract insects?
9. Distinguish among carpel, pistil, simple pistil, and compound pistil.
10. Define placentation.
11. What are ovules? Describe the structure of an ovule.
12. What is the major difference between flowers of monocotyledons and those of dicotyledons?
13. Distinguish between radial and bilateral symmetry. Name several specific plants to illustrate each type of floral symmetry.
14. Distinguish between spiral and cyclic arrangement of flower parts.
15. Distinguish between superior and inferior ovaries.
16. Summarize the major differences among flowers.
17. Describe in detail the structure of a composite inflorescence (head).
18. Describe the structure of a grass spikelet and of a grass flower.
19. List and describe briefly the structural differences between primitive and advanced types of flowers.
20. Define pollination, and list the principal agents of pollination.
21. Distinguish between self-pollination and cross-pollination.
22. Nursery catalogs frequently advise that a person desiring to have a fruit tree in his garden should buy two fruit trees and plant them in close proximity. Explain.
23. Horticulturists advise keeping beehives in or near orchards. Explain.
24. List the principal differences between wind-pollinated and insect-pollinated flowers.
25. List and describe briefly some of the features of flowers that promote cross-pollination.
26. List and describe (in the order of their occurrence) all the events that take place in the reproductive processes of flowers, from the time of pollination through the formation of mature seeds.
27. What is double fertilization?
28. It is often stated that the female has more effect upon the endosperm of a seed than the male. Explain.
29. Fruit trees may flower profusely but form few fruits. Describe the conditions that might be responsible for this.

30. After a season of heavy fruiting, fruit trees may produce very light fruit crops during the next year. Explain.
31. When DDT is extensively used outdoors as an insecticide, fruit production in nearby orchards may be reduced, even though DDT may not reach the trees. Explain.
32. Name and describe two effects of pollen upon pistils.
33. Distinguish between natural and artificial parthenocarpy. Name some plants that produce naturally parthenocarpic fruits.

16

Fruit Development and Structure

FRUIT DEVELOPMENT

As described in the preceding chapter, a fruit is a matured **ovary** and a seed is a matured **ovule,** which is produced inside a fruit. The term "fruit" in its technical botanical sense is thus any kind of ripened ovary within which seeds are formed, and includes such diverse structures as bean and pea pods, squashes, grapes, peaches, corn grains, tomatoes, dandelion "seeds," cucumbers, and watermelons. The popular usage of "fruit" differs somewhat from the botanical usage, in that it refers only to matured ovaries that are sweet and more or less pulpy. According to this popular definition, only grapes, peaches, and watermelons of the above list are fruits; bean and pea pods, corn, squashes, tomatoes, and cucumbers are popularly termed "vegetables," although botanically they are ripened ovaries or fruits.

The development of an ovary into a fruit is a complex phenomenon that involves many physiological activities. As described in the chapter on growth, growth hormones play an important role in fruit development. Pollen grains con-

tain auxins that directly stimulate the growth of ovaries, or initiate a chain of reactions that cause an increase in the auxin concentration of ovary tissue and thus stimulate ovary growth. The development of ovaries into fruits involves many other physiological changes. Foods of various types are translocated into ovary tissues, some of them accumulating in the ovary tissues, others moving into the growing ovules. Sugars, amino acids, soluble proteins, and other foods commonly increase in ovary tissues during ripening; the increase of sugar supplies in maturing fruits is responsible for the sweetness of many fruits, such as grapes, peaches, and bananas. The sugar content increases in the early development of corn and wheat grains (one-seeded fruits), then decreases with maturity as the sugars are converted into starch. In avocados and olives, fats and oils accumulate in large quantities in the growing tissues. The accumulation of water is often very great in fleshy fruits, such as tomatoes and watermelons; in others, such as string beans and walnuts, the water content of the fruit decreases sharply as maturity is reached. Coincident with these changes in food and water content there is often a change in the pigmentation. In tomatoes, for example, chlorophyll disappears and is replaced by carotenoid pigments as the fruits approach maturity. In Concord grapes, Jonathan apples, and many types of plums, anthocyanin pigments accumulate as ripening progresses and give the fruits their characteristic bluish, purplish, or reddish colors.

The physiological processes involved in the late stages of fruit ripening are even less understood than those occurring in the early stages of fruit development. It was discovered some years ago that ethylene, a gas, hastened the ripening of citrus and other types of fruits, a discovery that was soon applied in a practical manner to the accelerated commercial ripening of green fruits by brief storage of such fruits in chambers containing a very low concentration of ethylene. More recently it has been demonstrated that normally ripening fruits, as well as flower parts, leaves, and other plant organs, produce ethylene in minute quantities. Thus, the so-called "artificial ripening" of fruits by ethylene treatment is seemingly only an acceleration of a normal physiological ripening process. The physiological significance of ethylene production in fruit ripening is not known.

FRUIT STRUCTURE

As an ovary ripens into a fruit, its wall **(pericarp)** often becomes differentiated into three rather distinct layers of tissues: the **exocarp, mesocarp,** and **endocarp.** The exocarp is the outermost layer and consists usually of a single layer of epidermal cells, although in some species it may consist of several cell layers. The mesocarp is the middle layer of tissue and varies in thickness from a single layer of cells to a mass of tissues several inches thick. The endocarp, or innermost layer of the pericarp, likewise varies greatly in structure, texture, and thickness in the fruits of different species.

There are many different kinds of fruits, which are classified principally on the basis of their structure and of the number of ovaries comprising them. A classification of some common types of fruits and brief descriptions of them follow:

    I. **Simple Fruits** (Figures 16–1 through 16–8). A simple fruit consists of a single ripened ovary. The fruits of most angiosperms are simple fruits. The major types of simple fruits are:

      A. **Fleshy fruits,** in which all or most of the pericarp is soft and fleshy at maturity. Seeds escape from fleshy fruits as a result of the decomposition of the fleshy tissues.

        1. **Berry,** in which the entire pericarp is mostly fleshy throughout. Examples: grape, banana, tomato, watermelon, orange, cucumber, currant.

        2. **Drupe,** in which the exocarp is a thin skin, the mesocarp is thick and fleshy, and the endocarp hard and stony. The endocarp ("stone" or "pit") encloses 1, rarely 2 or 3 seeds. Examples: peach, plum, olive, cherry, apricot.

      B. **Dry fruits,** in which the entire pericarp becomes dry and often brittle or hard at maturity.

FIG. 16–1. Berries. Tomato (above) with thin exocarp, and orange (below) with thicker, leathery exocarp.

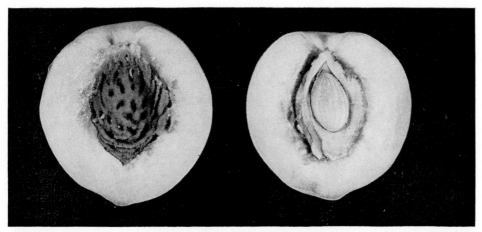

FIG. 16–2. Drupe of peach. *Left:* Section of fruit showing intact pit (endocarp) and fleshy mesocarp. *Right:* Section of fruit with pit split open to show single seed.

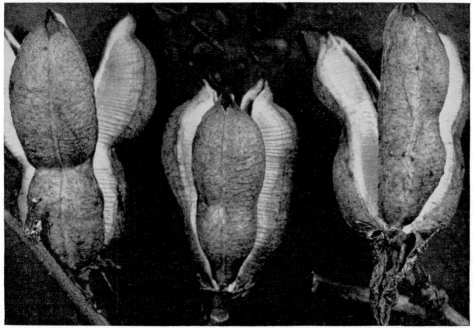

FIG. 16–3. Capsules of *Yucca.*

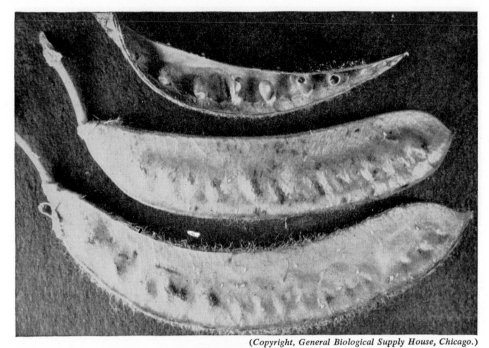

FIG. 16–4. Legume fruits of broom (*Cytisus*).

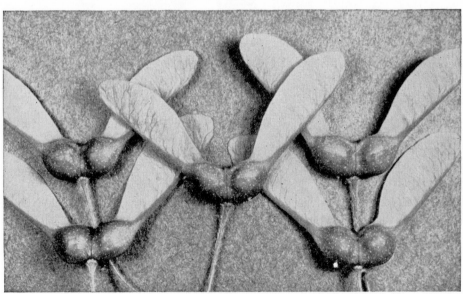

FIG. 16–5. Samaras of maple (*Acer*).

FIG. 16–6. Nuts of hazel.

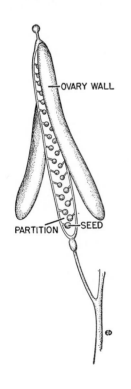

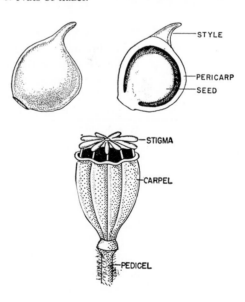

FIG. 16–7 (*above*). *Top:* Achenes of buttercup. *Bottom:* Capsule of poppy.

FIG. 16–8 (*left*). Silique.

285

FIG. 16–9. Aggregate fruits of raspberry. Note the styles extending from the small drupes.

1. **Dehiscent fruits,** which split open along definite seams or at definite points at maturity. Contain several to many seeds.
    a. **Legume,** consisting of 1 carpel, which splits open along 2 seams. Examples: pea, bean, locust.
    b. **Follicle,** consisting of 1 carpel, which splits open along 1 seam. Examples: larkspur, columbine, peony.
    c. **Capsule,** consisting of 2 or more fused carpels and splitting open in various ways. Examples: lily, snapdragon, tulip, violet.
    d. **Silique,** consisting of 2 fused carpels that separate at maturity, leaving a persistent partition between. Examples: mustard, shepherd's-purse, cabbage.
2. **Indehiscent fruits,** which do not split open along definite seams or at definite points at maturity. Usually contain only 1 or 2 seeds.
    a. **Achene,** bearing only 1 seed which is separable from ovary wall, except at point of attachment of seed to inside of pericarp. Examples: sunflower, buttercup, dandelion, smartweed.
    b. **Caryopsis,** or **grain,** bearing only 1 seed, the coat of which is completely fused to the inner surface of the pericarp. Examples: corn, wheat, oats.

FIG. 16–10. Multiple (compound) fruit of pineapple.

    c. **Samara,** a 1- or 2-seeded fruit, the pericarp of which bears
    a flattened winglike outgrowth. Examples: elm, maple, ash,
    wafer ash.

    d. **Nut,** a 1-seeded fruit, much like an achene, but with a much
    thickened, very hard pericarp. Examples: acorn (oak),
    hazelnut, chestnut.

  II. Aggregate Fruits. An aggregate fruit is a cluster of several to many
ripened ovaries produced by a single flower and borne on the same
receptacle. The individual, ripened ovaries may be drupes (as in
raspberries and blackberries, Figure 16–9), achenes (as in buttercups,
Figure 16–7), etc.

 III. Multiple (Compound) Fruits (Figure 16–10). A multiple fruit is a
cluster of several to many ripened ovaries produced by several flowers
crowded on the same inflorescence. As in aggregate fruits, the fruitlets
of a compound fruit may be drupes, berries, nutlets, etc. Examples:
mulberry, Osage orange, pineapple.

 IV. Accessory Fruits. Accesory fruits are structures that consist of one or
more ripened ovaries together with tissues of some other floral part,
such as calyx or receptacle. In an accessory fruit, these additional
tissues are often extensively developed to the point of constituting the
major part of the structure popularly called the "fruit." Among familiar accessory fruits are strawberries (Figure 16–12), in which the
individual fruits are achenes, borne upon an extensively developed,
sweet, red, succulent receptacle. Another common type of accessory
fruit is a **pome** (Figure 16–11), exemplified by apples and pears, in
which the matured ovaries (sections of the core) are surrounded by
enlarged receptacle and calyx tissues in which large amounts of food
and water are stored. Thus, in strawberries, apples, and pears, the
edible portions are not true fruits; that is, they are not the matured
ovaries, but they are stem and calyx tissues in which or upon which
the matured ovaries, or true fruits, are embedded.

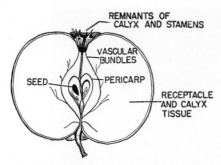

FIG. 16–11. The apple is a pome (accessory) fruit.

It is obvious from a study of the above classification and descriptions that the common names of many kinds of fruits do not indicate their correct botanical nature. Thus, blackberries and raspberries are not berries, but are aggregates of tiny drupes; the mulberry is not a berry, but a multiple fruit composed of tiny nutlets that are surrounded by fleshy sepals; the strawberry is not a berry; neither is it, in the strict botanical sense, a fruit, but a much enlarged receptacle, bearing upon its convex suface an aggregation of dry fruits, the achenes. An apple is not merely a fruit, but is a true fruit (the core, plus a thin layer of fleshy tissues immediately surrounding it) embedded in an extensive mass of edible fleshy, succulent tissue, which is stem and calyx tissue. The popular term "nut" is, in most cases, not properly descriptive of the botanical nature of the fruits to which it is applied. Thus, a peanut is not a nut, but is a legume fruit. A walnut is not a nut, but a drupe, the fleshy husk of the walnut being the outer part of the pericarp, and the walnut "shell" the inner part of the pericarp; the "meat" of a walnut is the seed, with two large, much-convoluted cotyledons, a tiny epicotyl and hypocotyl, and a thin, papery seed coat. A Brazil nut is a seed, borne along with several other seeds in a large, thick-walled capsule; a coconut is a drupe; and an almond shell is the "stone" (hardened endocarp) of a drupe, with a single seed, rarely more!

ECONOMIC IMPORTANCE OF FRUITS

The importance of fruits as sources of food for man is so obvious that it needs little comment. Many fruits consist largely of water, with very small quantities of sugars, other foods, minerals, vitamins, and other organic compounds in their tissues. Such fruits are important in the human diet chiefly for their flavor and for the vitamins they contain. Apples, pears, cherries, oranges, watermelons, and many other fruits of this type have little food value in terms of calorific content. Avocados, bananas, cereal grains, and plantains, on the other hand, contain high concentrations of starches and fats and thus possess high food value, as well

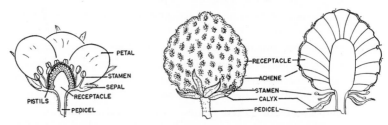

FIG. 16–12. *Left:* Longitudinal section of strawberry flower. *Right:* Accessory fruit of strawberry: whole fruit and section.

(Photo by Missouri Botanical Garden.)

FIG. 16–13. Peanut plant, showing the fruits (legumes) that develop underground after the flowers, which are borne and pollinated above the soil, bend downward, burying the young fruits.

as the accessory dietary advantages derived from vitamins and minerals.

Many products other than foods are supplied to man by fruits. Dyes (Persian berries, sap green), oils (castor oil, palm oils), waxes (bayberry and myrtle waxes), vegetable ivory (from the hard fruits of several palm species), drugs (morphine from the opium poppy, cubebs from a climbing Asiatic pepper), and spices (allspice, capsicums or red peppers, black pepper, vanilla, anise, caraway, dill) are among the economically important products of fruits.

⋘ SUMMARY

1. A fruit is a matured ovary.
2. The maturing of an ovary into a fruit involves a series of complex physiological activities, including the acceleration of tissue growth under the influence of auxins, the translocation of foods and often water into fruits, and changes in pigmentation.
3. In some little known manner, ethylene appears to be involved in fruit ripening.
4. A fruit wall is called a pericarp. A pericarp may consist of three tissue layers: exocarp (outer layer), mesocarp (central layer), and endocarp (inner layer). The relative development, texture, and other features of these layers vary in the fruits of different species.
5. A classification of fruits is presented in this chapter.
6. The common names of fruits frequently do not indicate their botanical nature.

7. Fruits are important to man in many ways. They provide food, drugs, dyes, waxes, spices, and other products.

◄◄◄ SUGGESTED READINGS FOR INTERESTED STUDENTS

1. Bonner, James, and Arthur Galston, *Principles of Plant Physiology*. Freeman, San Francisco, 1952.
2. Esau, Katherine, *Anatomy of Seed Plants*. Wiley, New York, 1961.
3. Porter, C. L., *Taxonomy of Flowering Plants*. Freeman, San Francisco, 1959.

◄◄◄ TOPICS AND QUESTIONS FOR STUDY

1. Contrast the popular and scientific meanings of "fruits."
2. Describe the physiological processes involved in the growth of an ovary into a fruit.
3. Explain the fact that some fruits become sweeter as they ripen (for example, bananas), while others (for example, corn grains) become less sweet as they mature.
4. Describe the effects of fruit growth upon the vegetative organs of some plants, and explain the physiological causes of these effects.
5. Comment upon the relation of ethylene to fruit ripening.
6. Define pericarp, and describe the structure of a typical pericarp.
7. Distinguish among simple, aggregate, and compound fruits, and name specific plants to illustrate each type.
8. Describe the structure of each of the following types of fruits: berry, drupe, legume, follicle, capsule, achene, caryopsis, samara, nut. Name specific plants to illustrate these fruit types.
9. What are accessory fruits?
10. Describe the structure of a pome, and name some pome fruits.
11. Describe the structure of a strawberry "fruit."
12. List the economically important products derived from fruits.

17 ⫷⫷-⫷⫷-⫷⫷-⫷⫷

Genetics and Plant Breeding

One of the most striking qualities of living protoplasm is its ability to beget protoplasm of the same kind. When a plant or animal reproduces, its offspring are always like their parents in their fundamental character. Robins produce more robins; snapdragons produce seeds that grow into snapdragon plants. The tendency of progeny to resemble their parents in all fundamental features of structure and behavior is called **heredity.** All organisms inherit the characteristic attributes of their species from their parents. Not only are they recognizably members of the same species as their parents, but they often inherit certain peculiarities and thus resemble their parents more than they do other individuals of the same species. Despite the fact that all organisms are fundamentally like their parents, they usually differ from them in certain minor respects. No child is ever a perfect duplicate of his mother or father; he is a member of the human species, as are his parents, and he may show a marked resemblance to one or both of them but he is at the same time an individual who is different, if ever so slightly, from them. White elms are all white elms, yet each tree is an individual living organism that differs in some quality or degree from other white elms. This tendency of organisms to differ from their parents is called **variation.**

Variation. Variations within a certain plant or animal species are of three common types: variations induced by **environmental conditions,** variations resulting from **hybridization** (breeding together of organisms differing from each other in one or more features), and variations resulting from **mutations.** Plants of the same species often vary from each other as a result of being subjected to different environmental conditions. Plants grown in poor soils do not grow so large or produce so much food as plants of the same species that grow in fertile soils. Plants exposed to bright sunlight manufacture more food than those growing in dim light, and thus have greater dry weights. These variations caused by differences in moisture, light, soil nutrients, and other environmental factors are not inherited;

FIG. 17–1. Gregor Mendel (1822–1884), Austrian monk, who developed the fundamental principles of genetics.

that is, they are not transmitted to the offspring of the plants subjected to the varying environmental conditions. The seeds of Bonny Best tomatoes, whether they are from tall plants grown in fertile soil, or stunted plants in poor soil, usually produce plants of the same quality if they are planted and allowed to grow under similar environmental conditions. The variations induced by environmental factors are thus not a part of the inheritance of the species and are limited in their extent and quality by the hereditary characteristics of the species.

The second type of variation, resulting from hybridization, is the product of the breeding of closely related, though somewhat different, types of organisms. This "crossing" of two different varieties or types of parents often results in offspring with different characteristics, since the offspring may exhibit a combination of characteristics of both parents.

The offspring resulting from a cross between two individuals differing in at least one characteristic is called a **hybrid.** Variations resulting from hybridization differ from environmental modifications in two major ways: first, the determiners of these variations in hybrids are carried in the sex cells of the parents, whereas environmentally induced variations are ordinarily limited to the body cells of organisms: second, variations resulting from hybridization are heritable, whereas environmentally induced variations are apparently not inherited.

Defined broadly, mutations are changes in the genetic material that can be detected and that are not attributable to ordinary gene recombination. These changes are frequently difficult to recognize, but in some organisms they are so marked that the offspring that arise by mutation often seem to be new varieties or even new species.

GENETICS

The field of biology that treats of heredity and variation is called **genetics.** It is one of the younger fields, since there was little exact knowledge of the principles of inheritance prior to 1900.

The Studies of Mendel

The foundation of modern genetics was laid by an Austrian monk, Gregor Mendel, who in 1866 published the results of his important experiments on inheritance in garden peas. The value of Mendel's experiments was not recognized until 1900, some years after his death, when several biologists discovered the significance of the experiments described in his brief publication. Mendel's work differed from that of his predecessors in that he studied the inheritance of a single characteristic at one time, instead of attempting to trace the inheritance of a number of traits simultaneously, a task of great complexity. Mendel proceeded differently in another respect, in that he kept very accurate records of the pedigrees of every plant with which he worked. He knew the parents, grandparents, great grandparents, and the more remote ancestors of every individual plant involved in his experiments. Mendel established another precedent in genetics: he studied not only the *kinds* of variations that developed from his cross-breeding experiments but also the *numbers* of the types of offspring produced. Thus, his study was both *qualitative* and *quantitative,* a fundamental feature of the scientific method of investigation.

For his study, Mendel chose peas because they grow quickly from seed to maturity, because the hybrid offspring are fertile, and because their flowers are normally self-pollinated. This latter feature was an important one in his choice, for foreign pollen from unknown sources usually does not reach the stigmas of pea flowers and thus cannot introduce unknown factors into breeding experiments. Finally, he investigated only characteristics that were constant and clearly recognizable.

The methods used by Mendel in performing his crosses are the same methods employed today. In order to prevent self-pollination, he removed the immature stamens from a pea flower that was to serve as the female parent. Next he placed on the stigma pollen from the plant being used as the male parent. He then covered the hand-pollinated flowers to prevent foreign pollen from reaching the stigma and fertilizing the eggs in the ovules. In such experiments, it is im-portant to know whether a particular characteristic can be transmitted by both egg and sperm. Mendel determined this in each case by making a **reciprocal cross** in which the parents are reversed. For example, when the experimental cross consisted of applying pollen from a dwarf plant to the stigma of a tall plant, the reciprocal cross was made with pollen from the tall plant and the stigma of the dwarf variety.

Following such cross-pollination, the ovaries produce seeds. These seeds, when planted, grow into the first generation of offspring from the cross, called the **first filial generation,** or F_1 generation. The F_1 individuals, after normal self-pollination, produce offspring that constitute the F_2 or **second filial generation;** the offspring of the F_2 are known as the F_3 generation, etc.

Monohybrid (Single-character) Crosses. In one of his experiments, Mendel crossed a race of garden peas that were tall (6 to 7 feet in height) with a race of peas that were dwarf ($\frac{3}{4}$ to $1\frac{1}{2}$ feet in height). The seeds from this cross grew into an F_1 generation, all plants of which were tall. This was surprising, for Mendel expected that the plants in this first filial generation would be intermediate in height between the parents of the cross. Mendel then permitted these tall F_1 plants to be self-pollinated, and in the resulting F_2 generation, he found that 75 percent of the plants were tall and 25 percent were dwarf (Figure 17–2). The actual count was 787 tall and 277 dwarf plants; that is, the F_2 ratio of tall to dwarf plants was $3:1$. Mendel allowed these dwarf individuals to carry on self-pollination, and he found that in the F_3 generation all the progeny of the F_2 dwarf individuals were dwarf. However, when the tall individuals of the F_2 were permitted to carry on self-pollination, one third of them always pro-

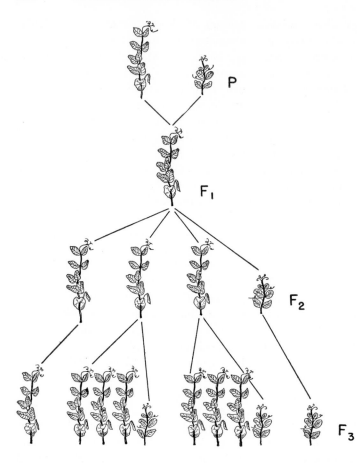

FIG. 17–2. Diagram illustrating one of Mendel's monohybrid crosses in the case of dominance of tallness over dwarfness. See text for explanation. *P* indicates the original parental generation.

duced tall pea plants in the F_3, while two thirds produced tall and dwarf plants in the F_3 in a 3:1 ratio as had the plants of the F_1 generation.

Law of Unit Characters. On the basis of this and similar experiments, Mendel concluded that there must be determiners in a plant that control the inheritance of characters such as height. These determiners he called factors. He concluded that these factors must occur in *pairs,* because from the F_1 he recovered both tall and dwarf individuals in the F_2, and, therefore, the F_1 individuals must have had a tall factor and a dwarf factor. These conclusions are sometimes referred to as the **Law of Unit Characters.** In modern

form, this law states that the characters that constitute an individual are controlled in inheritance by factors or **genes,** and that these genes occur in pairs. At the time of Mendel's work, nothing was known of chromosomes or genes; the word "gene" was not suggested until after Mendel's death.

Law of Dominance. Mendel concluded further, on the basis of the cross just described and of similar crosses, that one gene in a pair may mask the expression of the other. When he crossed a tall pea plant with a dwarf, all the F_1 plants were tall, but both tall and dwarf types appeared in the F_2. Thus, the F_1 plants must have carried a gene for dwarfness,

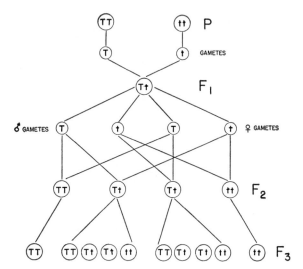

FIG. 17–3. Diagram representing gene behavior in a cross between homozygous tall and dwarf pea plants. *T* represents the gene for tallness, *t* the gene for dwarfness. See text. *P* indicates the original parental generation. The F₂ gametes and their crossing combinations have been omitted.

which was obscured by the one for tallness in the F₁ plants. This conclusion of Mendel's is known as the **Law of Dominance,** which may be stated thus: one gene in a pair may mask, or inhibit, the expression of the other. In the cross described above, the factor for tallness is the **dominant** gene; the dwarf factor that is suppressed by the dominant is the **recessive** gene.

Figure 17–3 is a diagram representing Mendel's cross between tall and dwarf pea plants. Capital letter *T* is the symbol that represents the gene controlling tallness; lower case *t* represents the gene controlling dwarfness. The tall parent is shown as *TT* because these hereditary factors occur in pairs; similarly, the dwarf parent is shown as *tt*. Each of these parents produces gametes that contain only *one* factor of each pair—a result of the process of meiosis, to be explained in a subsequent section. The tall parent produces only gametes with one *T*, or one factor for tallness; the dwarf parent produces gametes with *t*, or one factor for dwarfness. The gametes unite in pairs at fertilization and produce zygotes, which have both factors

and which develop into new individuals, those of the F₁ generation. The plants of the F₁ generation are shown as *Tt;* that is, each F₁ plant bears in its cells one gene for tallness and one for dwarfness, derived from the tall and dwarf parents, respectively. At maturity, the F₁ plants produce male and female gametes. Half the male gametes have *T,* the gene for tallness, half have *t,* the gene for dwarfness. Similarly, half the female gametes have *T,* half have *t.* Following self-pollination, the gametes unite at random and produce zygotes that grow into the plants of the F₂ generation. In this random combination, a male gamete with *T* may unite with a female gamete with *T,* thus producing an F₂ individual with *TT;* or, a male gamete with *T* may unite with a female gamete with *t,* producing an F₂ plant with *Tt.* Also, a male gamete with *t* may unite with a female gamete bearing a *T* gene, forming a plant with *Tt,* and a male gamete with *t* may fertilize a female gamete with *t,* producing an offspring with *tt.* These are the only four possible combinations resulting from the union of these gametes. The plant with *TT* is tall because it has only genes for tallness. The two plants with *Tt* are also tall, since, the *T* gene dominates the recessive *t* gene. The plants with *tt* are dwarf because they possess only genes for dwarfness. Thus, there are three tall plants and one dwarf pea plant in the F₂ generation, or a ratio of 3:1. In his experiments, Mendel permitted these F₂ plants to carry on self-pollination, and the individuals with *TT* always produced tall individuals. Similarly, the plants with *tt* always produced dwarfs. The individuals with *Tt* behaved like the F₁ plants, producing tall and dwarf plants in a ratio of 3:1.

This experiment shows that individuals similar in external appearance, or **phenotype,** may actually differ in their genetic constitution, or **genotype.** It is frequently necessary in breeding experiments to know which of the phenotypically similar offspring are **homozygous,** that is, contain identical genes, and which are **heterozygous,** or contain a dominant and a recessive gene. This may be determined by backcrossing the unknown hybrid with a homozygous recessive, a procedure known as a **test cross.** If homozygous dominant *TT* is crossed with homozygous recessive *tt,* all the offspring will be tall; if the heterozygous *Tt* is crossed with *tt,* half the resulting offspring will be tall and half will be dwarf.

Law of Segregation. Mendel's work led also to the establishment of the **Law of Segregation,** which states that the genes making up pairs are separated from each other prior to the formation of gametes. In other words, only one gene of each pair goes into a given sperm or egg (Figure 17–3).

Dihybrid (Two-character) Cross. A dihybrid cross is one between two individuals differing in two distinct characteristics. For example, one of Mendel's ex-

periments involved a cross between two varieties of peas, one of which had seeds that were yellow and round, the other, seeds that were green and wrinkled. Mendel found that yellowness and roundness were dominant, greenness and wrinkledness recessive. As Figure 17–4 illustrates, the genes of one parent may be represented by *YY RR,* those of the other parent by *yy rr.* The parent with the dominant traits produces gametes with *YR,* the other produces gametes with *yr.* When these gametes unite, the zygotes bear the genes *Yy Rr;* phenotypically, the plants produced by these zygotes all have yellow, round seeds, because of the dominance of yellowness and roundness; these F₁ plants may be described as heterozygous yellow and heterozygous round. Both the male and the female gametes produced by heterozygous F₁ plants are of four types: *YR, Yr, yR,* and *yr.* Following self-pollination, the gametes combine at fertilization to produce zygotes. The results of chance combinations of the various types of gametes are shown in Figure 17–4. Nine of the F₂ plants have yellow, round seeds, 3 have yellow, wrinkled seeds, 3 have green, round seeds, and 1 has green, wrinkled seeds. Thus, the phenotypic ratio of the F₂ plants is 9:3:3:1.

Law of Independent Assortment. On the basis of this dihybrid cross, Mendel concluded that the entrance of the yellow factor and round factor together into a cross does not mean that they remain together when the gametes are formed by the F₁ plants. This conclusion is called the **Law of Independent Assortment,** which, in modern form, states that the genes representing two or more contrasting characteristics are segregated to the gametes independently of each other, and that these gametes then combine with each

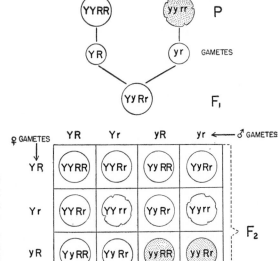

FIG. 17–4. Diagram representing a cross between two varieties of peas that differ in two characters. *Y* represents the gene for yellowness, *y* the gene for greenness, *R* the gene for roundness, and *r* the gene for wrinkledness. The parents are a plant with yellow, round seeds and a plant with wrinkled, green seeds. Yellowness and roundness are dominant over greenness and wrinkledness. (See text.)

other at random at the time of fertilization.

The Cytological Basis of Inheritance

Every organism that develops as a result of sexual reproduction begins its existence as a single cell termed a zygote, which is the product of the fusion of gametes. All the traits that parents transmit to their offspring are carried in these gametes; therefore, the gametes constitute the sole hereditary link between parents and offspring. The fundamental characteristics of an organism are thus mapped out for its entire life at the time when the zygote is formed. As stated earlier in the chapter, the expression of these hereditary features is frequently modified by environmental conditions, but the fundamental nature of the hereditary characteristics is normally not altered by external factors. We may say, then, than an organism inherits from its parents certain structural and func-

tional *potentialities;* the development of these potentialities is conditioned largely by the mode of life of the individual.

There is no doubt that most hereditary determiners are carried by the chromosomes in cells. Convincing evidence in support of this statement comes, in part, from close parallels in the behavior of genes, as determined by various breeding experiments such as those mentioned earlier, and in the behavior of chromosomes, as determined by observation with the microscope. Studies of the sexual cycle of a plant in relation to its chromosomes show that at fertilization, two sets of chromosomes are combined in a single cell (zygote). One set comes from the paternal parent by way of the male gamete, or sperm; the other set is contributed by the maternal parent in the female gamete, or egg. Each of the paternal chromosomes has a matching counterpart in the maternal chromosome complement. The members of such matching pairs are said to be **homologous.** The number of chromosomes in a gamete is called the **haploid,** or n number, while the number of chromosomes in the fertilized egg, or zygote, is the **diploid,** or $2n$ number. In onions, for example, each gamete contains 8 chromosomes and the diploid zygote contains 16. The multicellular plant body that develops from the zygote is essentially a diploid structure, since all or most of its cells contain 2 sets of homologous chromosomes—copies of the originals brought together at fertilization. In each mitotic division, the chromosomes are duplicated without undergoing qualitative change. In this way, the morphological identities of chromosomes are preserved, as is the genetic information they carry. Diploid body cells do not function as gametes, however. In all sexually reproducing organisms, there occurs at some time prior to gamete formation a process called **meiosis,** in which the diploid chromosome number is reduced to the haploid number. In angiosperms this process occurs in the formation of microspores in anthers, and in the formation of megaspores in ovules. Meiosis is just as essential to sexual reproduction as is the process of fertilization, for in the absence of either, the sexual cycle cannot be completed. Moreover, meiosis plays a significant role in inheritance by recombining genes in various ways. In contrast with mitosis, in which there is one chromosomal duplication and one nuclear division, meiosis involves one duplication and two divisions. Chromosomal duplication in meiosis is thought to occur most commonly in early prophase of the first meiotic division (prophase I) or in the preceding interphase. Following duplication, each chromosome consists of two chromatids.

Prophase I affords visible evidence of two characteristic meiotic events: **pairing** and **crossing over** (Figure 17–5). In pairing, homologous chromosomes come together in a zipperlike manner and soon lie parallel to each other along their entire length. Each part of one chromosome is adjacent to the corresponding part of the other member of the homologous pair. The visible evidence of crossing over is an exchange of matching *segments* of two homologous chromatids; that is, two of the four chromatids break at the same gene locus, with the result that a chromatid of one chromosome will carry a corresponding portion of a chromatid from the other chromosome, and vice versa. The exact time when crossing over occurs is not known with certainty; however, crossovers are visible under the microscope after the chromatids have become shorter and thicker. At metaphase I, the chromosomes are arranged in the equatorial region of the cell; in anaphase I, the members of a homologous pair of chromosomes migrate to opposite poles. Anaphase is usually followed by telophase, during which the nuclear membranes are formed. The second meiotic division then follows a brief interphase. This second division bears a superficial resemblance to mitosis; but, of course, the chromatids that separate are not necessarily perfect duplicates. Meiosis ends with the completion of telophase II. The single duplication and two divisions of meiosis have produced four nuclei, each with the haploid number of chromosomes. The gametes that are formed subsequently are derivatives of these haploid meiotic products. Union of gametes at fertilization produces a diploid zygote and initiates the next reproductive cycle. The genetic significance of meiosis lies in the "reshuffling" of genes. This is accomplished in part by the random separation of homologous

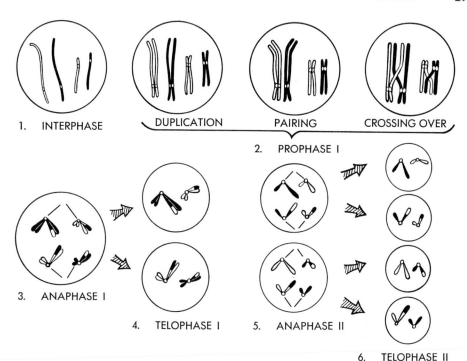

1. INTERPHASE DUPLICATION PAIRING CROSSING OVER

2. PROPHASE I

3. ANAPHASE I

4. TELOPHASE I 5. ANAPHASE II

6. TELOPHASE II

FIG. 17–5. Schematic representation of meiosis. Interphase shows two pairs of homologous chromosomes; that is, $2n = 4$. In telophase I, each cell contains two chromosomes, each consisting of 2 chromatids. The four haploid cells shown at telophase II each have two chromosomes. Metaphase I, prophase II and metaphase II have been omitted.

chromosomes in anaphase I and II. Not all the chromosomes that came from the male parent go to a particular cell, and not all the chromosomes from the female parent go to a particular cell. Rather, chance determines which of the chromosomes moves to which of the cells. Further reassortment of genes is brought about by crossing over, to be discussed in a later section.

During the fertilization process, the respective haploid chromosome sets come together in the zygote. When a homozygous individual forms gametes, these are all of the same type, because the homologous chromosomes that are separated in reduction divisions are alike; that is, they carry identical genes. In the production of gametes by a heterozygous organism, however, the chromosomes that separate at reduction division do not all bear similar genes, for they have been contributed to the heterozygous individual by different types of parents. Thus, the gametes produced by heterozygous organisms are of different kinds with respect to various genes they carry rather than of the same kind, as in homozygous organisms. As the result of the chance unions of the different kinds of gametes formed by hybrids, different characters are brought together and thus different types of offspring are produced.

The control of characters in inheritance

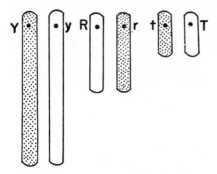

FIG. 17–6. Diagram illustrating the location of genes on chromosomes. The gene for the yellow condition of seeds (*Y*) is located on one of the paired chromosomes, while the homologous gene for green seeds (*y*) is located on the homologous chromosome. The genes for the round and wrinkled conditions are located on another set of chromosomes, etc.

is the function of genes, which are located on the chromosomes (Figure 17–6). In the garden pea, the gene controlling roundness of seeds is located on one chromosome, and the gene controlling wrinkledness is located on the homologous chromosome. On another pair of chromosomes, there are the gene for yellowness and the gene for greenness, on the third pair of chromosomes the gene for tallness and the gene for dwarfness. There are striking parallels between the genes and the chromosomes. Thus, the genes occur in pairs, just as do the chromosomes. These genes occur in pairs, because half of them come from the male parent and half come from the female parent. Likewise, there is a segregation of factors prior to the formation of gametes, and there is a similar segregation of chromosomes during meiosis. Finally, just as there is independent assortment of genes, so there is independent assortment of chromosomes.

The Chemical Basis of Inheritance

As the carriers of hereditary traits, chromosomes have been intensively studied in an effort to determine the chemical basis of inheritance. Analyses have shown the principal constituents of chromosomes to be proteins and two kinds of nucleic acids: deoxyribonucleic acid (DNA) and ribonucleic acid (RNA). The nucleic acids account for approximately 40 percent of the total, of which about 1 percent is RNA. One of the fundamental problems, then, was to determine which of these materials bore the hereditary determiners.

Convincing evidence that DNA carried the genetic information was presented in 1944. This work was based on extensive studies of pneumococci, the bacteria that cause pneumonia. Each of these pathogenic cells has a thick outer capsule of polysaccharide material. The numerous strains of pneumococci are recognized on the basis of certain genetically controlled properties of their capsules. When cultured on agar, the virulent strains produce smooth colonies. Occasionally, there arises a mutant form that lacks a capsule and produces colonies described as rough. In addition, the rough forms are nonvirulent. Rough mutants may occasionally mutate back to the smooth form, producing capsules characteristic of the original strain. For example, cells of smooth strain II may mutate to rough, which may then revert to smooth II. It was found by earlier workers that when a *mixture* of heat-killed smooth III bacteria and living rough bacteria derived from strain II was injected into a mouse, the mouse contracted the disease. Living pneumococci recovered from the animal were found to be virulent *smooth III*. This strain did not arise through mutation, for rough could mutate only to smooth II. However, under the influence of the heat-killed cells, there occurred a heritable **transformation** from one genetically controlled strain to another. Years of research were required in order to learn the identity of the transforming agent, which has been shown to be deoxyribonucleic acid. It is now thought that the DNA carrying the genetic information relating to capsule formation is incorporated into a rough cell. This cell (and its descendants) then synthesizes a capsule according to the new "instructions." Other examples of genetic transformation in bacteria have been described, but, to date, none has been discovered elsewhere in the plant or animal kingdoms.

Molecules of DNA are very large and are constructed in a way that enables them to contain an enormous amount of "coded" information and to undergo **replication,** that is, exact duplication in every detail. They are composed of units called **nucleotides,** each of which includes a phosphate group, a 5-carbon sugar **(deoxyribose),** and one of four different nitrogenous bases. Two of the bases **(adenine** and **guanine)** belong to a class of compounds called purines; the other two **(cytosine** and **thymine)** are pyrimidines. The nucleotides are linked together by bonds between sugar and phosphate groups, to form long strands or chains. Attached to each sugar unit is a base (Figure 17–7A). The DNA molecule is believed to consist of two strands of nucleotides, coiled to form a double helix (Figure 17–8). The strands are arranged in such a way that each base on one strand is "paired" with a complementary base on the other strand. Weak hydrogen bonds hold these base pairs (and, therefore, the two strands) together. Further, adenine pairs only with thymine (A—T

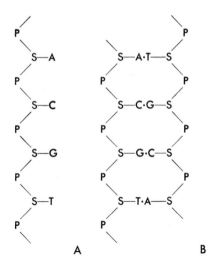

FIG. 17–7. A. Diagram illustrating a portion of a strand of nucleotides. P represents a phosphate group; S, a sugar; A, adenine; C, cytosine; G, guanine; T, thymine. B. Diagram showing a portion of the DNA double helix. A pairs only with T, C pairs only with G. Dots between base pairs represent hydrogen bonds.

and T—A), and cytosine only with guanine (C—G and G—C), as shown in Figure 17–7B. The number of ways in which these four different pairs of bases (or, more accurately, pairs of nucleotides) can be arranged along the length of the double helix is literally enormous. Therefore, it is the *sequence* of base pairs that imparts the tremendous capacity for variation among DNA molecules.

As was mentioned previously, the double helix configuration allows the DNA molecule to be replicated. Evidence indicates that replication involves the unwinding of the two strands of nucleotides, each strand serving as a template and directing the synthesis of its new complementary strand. Since a particular purine can pair only with a particular pyrimidine, the newly formed strand is an exact copy of the one that formerly occupied the same position.

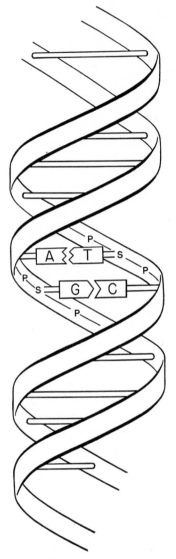

FIG. 17–8. Diagram representing a portion of the DNA double helix. "Backbone" of each strand formed from phosphate (P) and and sugar (S) groups. Cross bars represent base pairs (A-T, T-A, G-C, and C-G), two of which are shown at center. (Based on Watson and Crick model.)

Through a series of far-reaching experiments, two researchers—George Beadle and Edward Tatum—were able to demonstrate a close relationship between genes and biochemical reactions. This work was done with the mold *Neurospora*. Normal spores of *Neurospora* may be germinated and molds grown on chemically defined, minimal culture medium; that is, a substrate containing only those nutrients essential for the growth of the organism. Mutations were induced in normal spores by x-ray treatment, after which the spores were transferred to enriched culture medium that contained the nutrients of minimal medium plus other amino acids and vitamins. Following germination and mold growth, a portion of each mold was subcultured on minimal medium where, it was found, some were unable to grow. Each mutant form was later shown to require, in addition to the nutrients in minimal medium, one other substance that prior to mutation it was able to synthesize. For example, the mutation of a particular gene prevented the organism from synthesizing the amino acid citrulline; another specific gene mutation prevented the formation of another amino acid, arginine.

The biosynthesis of these compounds is a stepwise process, each step of which is enzymatically regulated. It has been postulated that a given gene directs the synthesis of a particular enzyme that, in turn, catalyzes a specific reaction. This is called the one-gene, one-enzyme hypothesis. The genetic information needed to control enzyme synthesis resides in DNA. However, protein synthesis occurs chiefly in the cytoplasm in association with ribosomes (Chapter 4). It appears that the transfer of information from chromosome to ribosome is mediated by ribonucleic acid. RNA differs from DNA by having the 5-carbon sugar **ribose** instead of deoxyribose, and by having the nitrogenous base **uracil** instead of thymine. Formed under the direction of DNA (which prob-

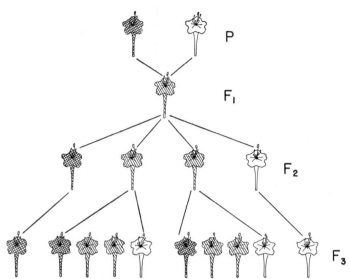

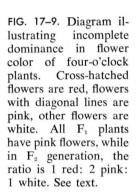

FIG. 17–9. Diagram illustrating incomplete dominance in flower color of four-o'clock plants. Cross-hatched flowers are red, flowers with diagonal lines are pink, other flowers are white. All F_1 plants have pink flowers, while in F_2 generation, the ratio is 1 red: 2 pink: 1 white. See text.

ably serves as a template), this "messenger" RNA combines with ribosomes. Other types of RNA ("transfer" RNA) are believed to associate with amino acids in the cytoplasm. For each kind of amino acid, there is a particular kind of transfer RNA. Amino acid-transfer RNA units move to the ribosome where they are aligned in the sequence prescribed by ribosomal RNA, which is thought to function as a template. In a final step, the amino acids are joined through peptide bonds to form a protein molecule.

Some Other Genetic Mechanisms

Incomplete Dominance. Genetic studies made after Mendel's work have shown that while dominance occurs in many cases, it is rarely if ever absolute. It is now known that dominance may be influenced by a variety of external and internal factors and that the phenotypic expressions of offspring are commonly intermediate between the phenotypes of their parents. This may be illustrated by a cross between red-flowered and white-flowered four-o'clocks. In these plants, red flowers are the expression of a homozygous dominant condition (RR), and white flowers, a homozygous recessive condition (rr). However, all the F_1 offspring (Rr) are pink-flowered (Figure 17–9). When two of the pink F_1 plants are crossed, the resulting F_2 ratio is 1 red, 2 pink, and 1 white.

Multiple Genes. The blending effect obtained in crossing four-o'clocks resulted from the interaction of only two genes. A far more common cause of blending is the interaction of multiple, incompletely dominant genes. This may be illustrated by a cross between two varieties of wheat, each of which has four genes that influence coloration of the kernels. A plant homozygous for dark red kernels ($R_1R_1R_2R_2$) is crossed with one homozygous for white kernels ($r_1r_1r_2r_2$). All the F_1 offspring produce kernels of a medium red color ($R_1r_1R_2r_2$). However, most of the F_2 progeny have kernels of various shades of red. Analysis of the F_2 reveals a phenotypic ratio of 1 dark red: 4 red: 6 medium red: 4 light red: 1 white. These re-

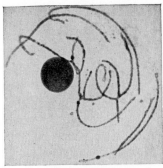

(Photo by M. M. Rhoades.)

FIG. 17–10. Chromosomes in a microspore (pollen) mother cell of corn. The large black object is the nucleolus.

sults reflect the cumulative effect of R genes for redness, as follows:

$RRRR$ = dark red
$RRRr$ = red
$RRrr$ = medium red
$Rrrr$ = light red
$rrrr$ = white

With each additional pair of interacting genes, there is an increase in the number of F_2 phenotypes and, therefore, an increase in variability among the offspring. But in terms of expected numbers of individuals, the proportions of F_2 phenotypes change rapidly with an increase in pairs of interacting genes. For example, when only 2 genes interact, the probability of obtaining an F_2 individual similar to one of the homozygous parents is 1 in 4; with 4 genes, it is 1 in 16; with 6, it is 1 in 64; with 8, it is 1 in 256; etc. This explains why geneticists, when dealing with large numbers of multiple genes, find it difficult or virtually impossible to recover in the F_2 a single individual similar to one of the parental types. It also explains why earlier workers who knew nothing of this genetic mechanism were unable to account for their experimental results.

Linkage. An exception to Mendel's law of independent assortment was discovered when it was shown that certain groups of genes tended to be inherited together. This behavior is attributable to the fact that each gene of a particular group is located on the same chromosome. Since a chromosome moves in meiotic division as a unit, all the genes on that chromosome move together. This phenomenon, in which certain genes (and the characteristics they determine) are inherited in groups, is called **linkage.** The genes that are borne on the same chromosome are said to be linked. It was a remarkable accident that, even though Mendel studied seven pairs of characters in peas, all the genes of these characters were located on different chromosomes and therefore showed no linkage; thus, Mendel found no exceptions to independent assortment.

Crossing Over. Shortly after the discovery of linkage, it was found that the characteristics whose genes are on the same chromosome do not always remain linked. This phenomenon is explained by crossing over. As described earlier, the cytological basis for crossing over lies in the interchange of segments of homologous chromatids. The effect of crossing over on the distribution of genes is diagrammatically illustrated in Figure 17–11. Crossing over may be regarded as an exception to linkage, which in turn is an exception to independent assortment.

Through careful analysis of crossover data, it has been possible to determine the locations of specific genes on a chromosome and thus to construct "chromosome maps." The positions of genes may be deduced by determining the percentage of crossing over. If two genes are close together, there is less chance for a crossover between them than if they are more distantly separated. Therefore, if

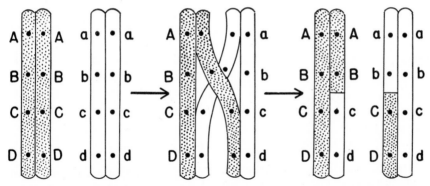

FIG. 17–11. Diagram illustrating crossing over. To the left are two homologous chromosomes, each consisting of two chromatids. The letters *A, B, C, D* indicate genes with their homologs *a, b, c, d.* In the center of the figure, the chromosomes are shown at synapsis (pairing), with one chromatid twisted over a chromatid from the other chromosome. The portion to the right shows the distribution of genes following exchange of segments between the two chromatids.

the percentage of crossing over between two particular genes is high, those genes are thought to be relatively far apart. On the other hand, if the percentage is low, the two genes are thought to be relatively close together.

Sex Inheritance. One might suppose, since genes control the inheritance of various characteristics, that there might be a gene controlling the characteristic of sex. Such, however, is not the case. In animals and in some plants, there are sex-determining chromosomes. In a human, for example, the diploid number is 46. Two of these chromosomes are **sex chromosomes;** the remaining 22 pairs are called **autosomes.** The two sex chromosomes in the female are similar and are designated X chromosomes. Males have one X chromosome, and a dissimilar Y chromosome. As can be seen in Figure 17–12, the female produces only gametes with single X chromosomes, whereas the male gametes are of two types, one with a single X chromosome, the other with a Y chromosome. These gametes fuse at random and thus, when two gametes with

X chromosomes unite, a female results, and when a gamete with an X chromosome unites with a gamete with a Y chromosome, a male results. Males and females are thus produced in a ratio of 1:1. A similar mechanism is known to operate in some dioecious plants.

Mutations. As defined earlier, mutations are changes in the genetic material that can be phenotypically detected and that are not attributable to ordinary gene recombination. These changes are frequently difficult to recognize, but in some organisms they are so marked that the offspring that arise by mutation often seem to be new varieties or species. The characters that develop by mutation are usually passed on by mutating organisms to their offspring; that is, they are heritable and persist from generation to generation as permanently established variations. Mutations occur in plants raised from seeds, or they may develop from individual buds on a stem. These are known respectively as **seed mutations** and **bud mutations.** In a mutation that develops in a bud, the twig that grows

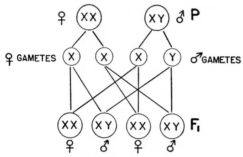

FIG. 17–12. The inheritance of sex in certain dioecious plants, or in man. The female has two X chromosomes and the male has an X and a Y chromosome. See text for further details.

from the bud differs in some manner from all other twigs of the plant. Many important varieties of cultivated plants have had their origins in mutations. Among these are navel oranges, certain varieties of Boston ferns, weeping willows, nectarines, many kinds of double-flowered plants, and some sweet pea and chrysanthemum varieties. Bud variations are usually propagated by bud grafting or other means of asexual propagation.

It is known that many mutations are due to changes in single genes and it is in this sense that most geneticists use the term mutation. Other mutations are produced by the development of extra sets of chromosomes. Plants with extra sets of chromosomes are known as **polyploids;** those with $3n$ chromosome numbers are called triploids, those with $4n,$ tetraploids, etc. Other mutations are caused by a single extra chromosome produced by imperfect reduction division; still other mutations are produced by the inclusion or omission of fragments of chromosomes, or by the inversion of pieces of chromosomes. Mutations occur in nature as well as in the laboratory, although the rate of production is apparently not very high. It is possible

to induce mutations experimentally by various radiations and by the use of certain chemicals, such as colchicine and mustard gas, as well as by severe temperature changes. It should be emphasized, however, that these mutations are haphazard and are not predictable.

PLANT BREEDING

One of the important techniques of plant breeding is **selection,** a very old method of improving the quality of domesticated organisms. It is based upon the fact that organisms of the same species or variety vary among themselves and tend to pass on to their offspring many of these variations. It is a matter of common knowledge, for example, that certain families of human beings rank unusually high in intelligence and that the members of successive generations of these families generally possess superior mental ability. In other families, low intelligence prevails and is a common feature of its members through many generations. Some plants are more resistant to diseases than others of the same species and their offspring sometimes inherit, in part at least, the greater resistance of their parents. Some plants yield better crops than other plants of the same species and often pass this more desirable feature on to their progeny. From a large group of plants of the same variety or species, the individuals that possess the desired qualities in greatest degree are selected. Their seeds are planted and selections again made from the plants that their seeds produce. This selection process is often continued through many generations until a superior type of plant, with respect to a single character or group of characters, is isolated. Luther Burbank (1849–1926) employed this method with conspicuous success in the development of the giant Shasta daisy and the "stoneless" plum. The production of the latter illustrates the method of selection. First, Burbank selected from a large collection of plums one which had a thin "pit" or stone. He permitted this tree to carry on pollination and to set fruit. Then, he chose from this tree a few plums that had the thinnest stones. The seeds from these he planted, and when the resulting trees fruited, he again selected the fruits with the thinnest stones. These were planted and when the resulting trees matured, Burbank again selected the fruit with the thinnest "pits." After several selections of this type, he produced a plum with an extremely thin stone; this was marketed as a "stoneless" plum. In this method, advantage is taken of all the desirable variations and modifications, and the undesirable types are discarded.

In some kinds of plants, the practice of selection entails difficulties. Sometimes selected varieties gradually revert back to less desirable ancestral forms and thus the process of selection must be carried on constantly to assure a continuance of superior varieties. Further, the rate of progress in selection toward a desired type is often very slow, so that long periods of time are required in some plants to achieve the wanted improvements. In spite of these limitations, selection has developed many valuable types of plants, such as Reid's Yellow Dent corn, Leaming corn, Red Fife wheat, and various oat and tobacco varieties. Of course, an intelligent breeder, while carrying on this work, is alert for the appearance of any desirable mutations or "sports," which he would then select for further work. He would also carry on hybridization to achieve recombinations of characters.

Inbreeding. Another method of plant breeding is illustrated by the work of a breeder who desires to obtain a variety of plant that is both productive and resistant to a destructive disease. He first selects those plants that produce very large yields, and then permits them to carry on self-pollination. This procedure of selection followed by self-pollination might be carried on for several generations. This type of breeding in which self-pollination is carried on or in which closely related individuals are crossed is known as **inbreeding.** By this method a **pure line** is established; that is, the plants become more or less homozygous for productivity and hence produce offspring that are also highly productive. There are dangers in inbreeding, for, as a result of this crossing of closely related individuals, undesirable recessive characters may appear. However, if the stock is good and lacks these recessives, the method is successful.

Hybridizing. While this pure line of very productive plants is being developed, the breeder has been carrying on similar procedures with plants selected for desirable resistance until he has obtained a more or less pure line for disease resistance. He then crosses the two lines, thus obtaining offspring with a combination of disease resistance and high productivity. In addition, the offspring resulting from a cross between two such inbred lines usually show a marked increase in vigor and productivity, a result called **hybrid vigor.**

Similar methods are used in the production of **hybrid corn,** which is the product of a cross between two or more carefully inbred lines. As is well known, hybrid corn may give a yield much greater than that of the parent varieties. Yet, if the seed produced by plants grown

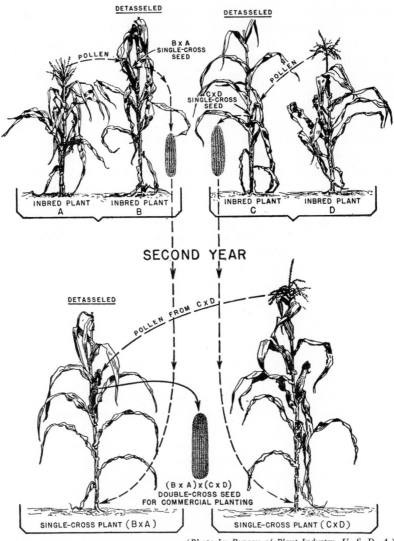

SECOND YEAR

(Photo by Bureau of Plant Industry, U. S. D. A.)

FIG. 17–13. Crossing to produce hybrid corn. The plants A, B, C, and D are the offspring of four inbred lines. Strain A is crossed with strain B, C with D. The products of these two crosses are then crossed to produce the hybrid corn seed, which is planted.

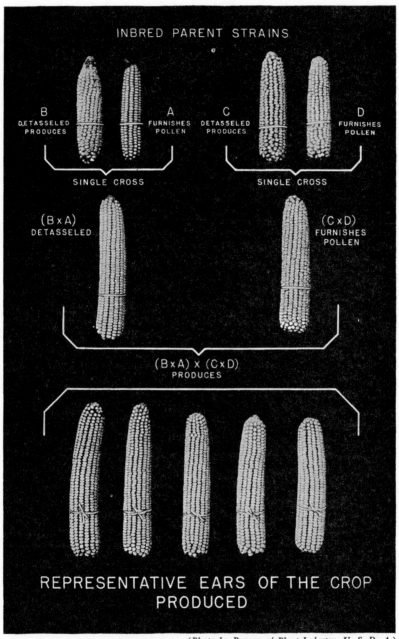

INBRED PARENT STRAINS

B
DETASSELED
PRODUCES

A
FURNISHES
POLLEN

C
DETASSELED
PRODUCES

D
FURNISHES
POLLEN

SINGLE CROSS

SINGLE CROSS

(B × A)
DETASSELED

(C × D)
FURNISHES
POLLEN

(B × A) × (C × D)
PRODUCES

REPRESENTATIVE EARS OF THE CROP
PRODUCED

(Photo by Bureau of Plant Industry, U. S. D. A.)

FIG. 17–14. Corn ears illustrating the crosses represented in Figure 17–13.

from hybrid corn grains is planted, the crop is very poor. This illustrates another characteristic of hybrids of this type; that is, their seeds are low in productivity and they do not breed true to the parent type, for in the reproductive process, assortment of genes occurs and hence their offspring are of different types. Thus, desirable hybrids must be propagated vegetatively by cuttings or grafting, or must be produced repeatedly. Such vegetative propagation is used in reproducing hybrid fruit trees, rosebushes, carnations, and many other types of plants that have been developed as a result of cross-breeding or hybridizing. Corn plants cannot, however, be propagated by such methods. Farmers must purchase fresh hybrid corn seed each year (Figures 17–13, 17–14).

Mutation. In all these methods, the alert breeder is constantly on the watch for desirable mutations, for these are the only really "new" characters and types that appear; selection of desirable variations can only be carried so far, and hybridization merely recombines old characters. Mutations are thus the new traits that are the stepping stones for the production of new types of plants; mutations also play a similar role in the production of new species in nature. The Shirley poppy, dwarf sweet peas, numerous double-flowered plants, as well as the red dogwood, have appeared as a result of mutation.

⫷ SUMMARY

1. Heredity is the tendency of offspring to resemble their parents; variation is the tendency of organisms to differ from their parents.
2. Variations may result from changes in environmental conditions, from hybridization, and from mutations. Organisms inherit potentialities; the environment affects the development of these inherited potentialities.
3. A genetic hybrid is the offspring resulting from a cross between two parents differing in at least one characteristic.
4. Mendel crossed tall peas with dwarf peas. All the F_1 peas were tall, and when these were permitted to self-pollinate, the F_2 plants were in a ratio of 3 tall to 1 dwarf. When the F_2 peas were self-pollinated, the dwarf pea plants always produced dwarf pea plants. One third of the tall peas always produced tall peas, the other two thirds produced tall and dwarf plants in a 3 to 1 ratio, as did the F_1 plants.
5. Mendel's laws may be summarized as follows. (1) Law of Unit Characters: Genes control the inheritance of characters, and these genes occur in pairs. (2) Law of Dominance: One gene in a pair may mask the expression of the other factor. (3) Law of Segregation: Only one gene of each pair goes into sperm or egg. (4) Law of Independent Assortment: The genes representing two or more distinct characters are distributed to the gametes independently of one another, and the gametes then fuse randomly in fertilization.
6. A gene that is expressed is called a dominant gene, a gene that is masked is called a recessive gene. The external appearance of an organism is referred to as its phenotype, while its genetic constitution is known as its genotype. When the two genes of a pair are similar, they are said to be homozygous (TT or tt); when the two genes of a pair are unlike, they are said to be heterozygous (Tt).

7. Monohybrid crosses involve two parents differing in one character, a dihybrid cross involves two organisms differing in two characters. In the latter, the F_2 ratio is $9:3:3:1$, in the case of two dominants.

8. Every cell in a flowering plant body is a descendant of the zygote that resulted from the fusion of egg and sperm. Each of these gametes contributes a set of chromosomes, and hence the zygote has two sets of homologous chromosomes; that is, it is $2n$ or diploid, whereas the gametes are n or haploid. The zygote undergoes mitosis, in which the chromosomes are duplicated. In meiosis, the diploid or $2n$ chromosome number is reduced to the n or haploid chromosome number of the gametes.

9. In meiosis, homologous chromosomes duplicate and then pair. Chromatid segments of homologous chromosomes are interchanged in a process called crossing over. In the first division of meiosis, the homologous chromosomes (each consisting of two chromatids) separate. In the second division, the two chromatids separate and move to different cells. Thus, the four cells produced by these two divisions have the haploid or n chromosome number.

10. Genes are apparently located on chromosomes in linear order. The following are some of the similarities that occur between the genes and the visible chromosomes: both are duplicated, both are in pairs, both are segregated in meiosis, and both undergo independent assortment.

11. Chromosomes consist chiefly of proteins, DNA, and RNA; of these, DNA has been shown to carry the genetic information.

12. A molecule of DNA is viewed as two strands of nucleotides forming a double helix. Each nucleotide consists of a phosphate group, a 5-carbon sugar, and one of four nitrogenous bases: adenine, thymine, cytosine, and guanine. The first two of these bases (adenine and thymine) can pair only with each other; the other two (cytosine and guanine) can pair only with themselves. The information carried by DNA is believed to be coded according to the sequence of base pairs.

13. DNA in the chromosome directs the synthesis of "messenger" RNA, which then passes to ribosomes in the cytoplasm. The "instructions" transferred by the messenger RNA are followed in the formation of specific proteins. The so-called one-gene, one-enzyme hypothesis postulates that the DNA of a given gene directs the synthesis of a specific enzyme that then controls a particular biochemical reaction.

14. In incomplete dominance both genes are expressed phenotypically, neither gene masking the expression of the other.

15. Multiple gene inheritance produces blending among the offspring through the cumulative effect of more than two genes that influence the same trait. This mechanism is far more common than incomplete dominance between two genes.

16. Linkage, or the inheritance of characters in groups, is due to the location of genes for these characters on the same chromosome. Linkage is an exception to independent assortment.

17. Crossing over is an exception to linkage and is the result of exchange of parts

between homologous chromosomes. Crossing over results in the separation of some genes that were linked.

18. Sex in some dioecious plants and in animals is determined at the time of fertilization by sex chromosomes. In the usual type of chromosome behavior, the presence of two X chromosomes produces a female, while an X and a Y chromosome result in a male plant or animal.

19. Defined broadly, mutations are the changes in the genetic material that can be detected phenotypically and that are not attributable to ordinary gene recombination. They may result from changes in genes or from chromosome aberrations such as extra chromosomes or sets of chromosomes. Experimentally they may be induced by various radiations, by treatment with various chemicals, and by severe temperature changes.

20. Selection is the choosing of desirable individuals generation after generation for breeding purposes. Hybridization results in recombination of characters. Inbreeding is the crossing of closely related organisms, leading to the production of a "pure line," that is, a line of organisms that are more or less homozygous for certain desirable traits.

21. Crossing two inbred lines produces offspring with a combination of the characters of the two lines, and, in addition, a special vigor, known as hybrid vigor.

22. Hybrid corn is the product of crossing two or more carefully inbred lines.

23. Hybrid plants do not breed true if they are propagated by seeds. If they are to be propagated without change, they must be reproduced by cuttings, grafts, or some other asexual method.

⋘ SUGGESTED READINGS FOR INTERESTED STUDENTS

1. Allfrey, V. G., and A. E. Mirsky, "How cells make molecules." *Scientific American,* Vol. 205, No. 3, pp. 74–82, September 1961.
2. Beadle, G. W., *The Physical and Chemical Basis of Inheritance.* Condon Lectures, University of Oregon Press, Eugene, Oregon, 1957.
3. Bonner, D. M., *Heredity.* Prentice-Hall, Englewood Cliffs, N. J., 1961.
4. Gardner, E. J., *Principles of Genetics.* Wiley, New York, 1960.
5. Snyder, L. H., and P. R. David, *The Principles of Heredity,* 5th ed. D. C. Heath, Boston, 1957.
6. Sutton, H. E., *Genes, Enzymes, and Inherited Diseases.* Holt, Rinehart and Winston, New York, 1961.

⋘ TOPICS AND QUESTIONS FOR STUDY

1. Why was Mendel more successful than his predecessors in experiments on inheritance?

2. Define the laws of Unit Characters, Dominance, Segregation, and Independent Assortment.

3. Using genetic symbols, work out a monohybrid cross in which one factor is dominant, such as in a cross between tall and dwarf peas. Assuming that the F_1 and F_2 individuals are self-pollinated, carry your analysis through the F_2 and F_3. What is the F_2 phenotypic ratio? What is the F_2 genotypic ratio?

4. Repeat for a dihybrid cross in which two factors are dominant. What is the F_2 phenotypic ratio? The F_2 genotypic ratio?
5. Repeat for a monohybrid cross in which there is incomplete dominance. What are the F_2 ratios?
6. Explain the terms phenotype, genotype, homozygous, and heterozygous.
7. Compare mitosis and meiosis.
8. Define and give an example of bacterial transformation.
9. Describe the composition of the DNA double helix.
10. How might replication of DNA occur?
11. What special significance has the sequence of base pairs in a DNA molecule?
12. What is the one-gene, one-enzyme hypothesis?
13. What is "messenger" RNA? "transfer" RNA? What are their roles in protein synthesis?
14. Define and explain linkage and crossing over.
15. Explain the mechanism of sex inheritance. In view of your knowledge of sex determination, comment upon the belief that a mother may "will" the sex of her unborn child; that environmental conditions may influence the sex of a child.
16. Discuss mutations with reference to their nature, causes, examples, and horticultural and evolutionary significance.
17. Explain the methods of selection, inbreeding, and cross-breeding.
18. Explain how hybrid corn is produced. Why is it important that hybrid corn seed be secured each season, rather than using the seed from the previous year's crop?
19. Why are hybrid fruit trees propagated by vegetative methods rather than by seeds?
20. Discuss the respective roles of environment and heredity in determining the traits of organisms.

18

The Principles of Plant Classification

THE CLASSIFICATION AND NAMING OF PLANTS

The wish to classify objects is a basic trait of the human intelligence. We constantly classify the things and events about us with respect to their effects upon our lives. The branch of botany known as **taxonomy** is concerned primarily with the classification and identification of plants. The plant world is composed of about 350,000 species of plants, which botanists classify into groups of varying size and relationship. Botanists and laymen alike classify plants, the former to satisfy their intellectual urge toward neat, orderly, and significant arrangement, the latter chiefly to distinguish among plants that are beautiful, ugly, weedy, poisonous, edible, etc.

The aim of a scientific classification of plants is to indicate, wherever possible, the actual relationships among the plants being classified. Such a **phylogenetic system** (or natural system) is the ultimate goal of taxonomic research. An **artificial system** of classification is one that is based upon convenience rather than upon actual relationships. Artificial systems are often employed to classify organisms whose kind and degree of relationship are not known; these are likewise used for convenience and simplicity in grouping organisms for purposes of identification. A common artificial system of plant classification is one that separates all plants into herbs, shrubs, and trees to speed identification. Obviously such an arrangement is not natural, for totally unrelated plants often have similar growth habits and external forms. Apple trees are more closely related to strawberry plants than they are to elm trees, yet, in an artificial system of classification, elms are placed closer to apple trees than are strawberry plants.

Criteria of Classification. The classification of various groups of living organisms may be based upon a number of criteria —size, color, manner of obtaining or making food, anatomy, external form, methods of reproduction, etc. The criteria considered to be most significant for purposes of classification are structural features of vegetative parts, especially with reference to vascular anatomy, the structure of reproductive parts, and the nature of reproductive processes. Reproductive criteria are especially significant as bases of classification because they are least susceptible to the molding effects of changing environmental conditions. The sizes of leaves, lengths of stems, amount of root growth, color, and other features vary widely with external factors, but the structure of flowers, fruits, seeds, and other reproductive parts is relatively constant. Often totally unrelated species of plants have almost identical gross structure. On the other hand, some members of the cactus, milkweed, and spurge families, growing in arid and semiarid regions, have barrel-shaped stems, heavy cutin layers, spines, and other morphological similarities but differ widely in the structure of their flowers and fruits. If they were classified according to the structure of their vegetative parts, they would be considered as closely related, but differences in their flower structure indicate that their relationship is actually very distant.

Units of Classification. Botanical classification involves the separation of different kinds of plants into groups of varying size and nature. Just as a continent is divided into nations, nations into states or provinces, states into counties, counties into towns and townships, towns into blocks, etc., so the plant kingdom is separated into a number of categories of varying size and rank.

The basic classificational unit in plant (and animal) taxonomy is the species. A species may be defined simply as a single *kind* of living organism—for example, silver maple is a species, red clover is a species, the coconut palm is a species. Biologists usually consider a species as the smallest unit in the classificational system whose individual members are structurally similar, have common ancestors, and maintain their characteristic features *in*

nature through innumerable generations. White oaks have always had certain characteristic features of white oaks, silver maples of silver maples, etc. Sometimes different types of organisms occur within a species; for example, all domesticated dogs belong to one species, yet there are many kinds of dogs—collies, cocker spaniels, fox terriers, etc. All of them have the specific characteristics of dogs, yet they vary. These individual types, however, *will not maintain their differences in nature*. If dogs of all kinds are left to their own devices, their progeny in a number of years will be reduced to a canine common denominator, the unifying features of each breed having vanished. Such kinds of organisms within a species are called varieties; they persist usually only when they are prevented by man's interference from breeding with other varieties.

A group of closely related species is called a genus (plural, genera). For example, all kinds of roses together constitute the rose genus, *Rosa.* The individual varieties and species of roses differ among themselves in various ways, but they all possess a common quality of "roseness" that stamps them as very closely related kinds of plants. Another example of a genus is the pine genus, *Pinus,* composed of many species of pines—white pines, sugar pines, slash pines, yellow pines, and others—that vary among themselves but that all possess a fundamental quality of "pineness."

A group of closely related genera is called a family. For example, the rose family is composed of many genera, among which are the rose genus, the apple genus, the peach genus, the strawberry genus, and others. All these genera have certain basic similarities in their floral structure, but differ among them.

selves in rather well-marked ways. The scientific names of most families end in "aceae"; thus, the technical name of the rose family is **Rosaceae,** of the pine family **Pinaceae,** etc.

A group of related families constitutes an **order,** the scientific name of which ends in "ales." Thus, the rose order **(Rosales)** is composed of the rose family **(Rosaceae),** the legume family **(Leguminosae),** the gooseberry family **(Grossulariaceae),** and others, all of which have certain common, basic features of floral structure that indicate a close relationship among them. Orders are grouped into **classes,** and a group of classes constitutes a **division.** Often, these major classificational units, such as families, orders, classes, and divisions, are split into subgroups; thus there may be subclasses, subdivisions, and subfamilies in the taxonomic system.

As illustrations of the mutual relationships of the classificational categories or **taxa** (singular, **taxon**) just described, the complete taxonomic categories of two common plants, prairie rose and corn, are presented below:

Division—Tracheophyta
 Subdivision—Pteropsida
  Class—Angiospermae
   Subclass—Dicotyledoneae
    Order—Rosales
     Family—Rosaceae
      Genus—Rosa
       Species—setigera

Division—Tracheophyta
 Subdivision—Pteropsida
  Class—Angiospermae
   Subclass—Monocotyledoneae
    Order—Graminales
     Family—Gramineae
      Genus—Zea
       Species—mays

Scientific and Common Names. Biologists refer to plants and animals by scientific names rather than by common, popular names used by laymen. Common names are often useless for scientific purposes for several reasons. They are composed of words from the native language of the country in which they are used; thus, in England, Australia, and the United States, common names consist of English words; in Mexico and Peru, they are chiefly of Spanish origin, and, in Japan, they are Japanese words. To an English or American botanist, common names in Japanese and Spanish would be meaningless; similarly, a Greek or German botanist unfamiliar with English would be puzzled by such common English names as snapdragon, milkweed, and bachelor's-buttons. Another disadvantage of common names for scientific purposes is their frequently extreme variability within the borders of a single country or even of one state. Thus, the name lady's-slipper is commonly applied to several dozen species of orchids, as well as to another plant in a family not closely related to the Orchidaceae. The name lily is given such members of the lily family as Easter lily and tiger lily; it is also used in the common names water lily, spider lily, and calla lily, none of which belongs to the lily family. Thus, one common name may be applied to several distinct species of plants, and, also, a single species of plant may be designated by several common names. Obviously, common names are often confusing and lack the standardization and precision required by scientists.

In using scientific names, biologists do not employ the complete taxonomic pedigree of living organisms, as outlined in a preceding paragraph, but use simply the names of the genus and species to which each kind of plant or animal belongs.

FIG. 18–1. Carolus Linnaeus (1707–1778), great Swedish botanist.

Thus the scientific name of the prairie rose is *Rosa setigera,* that of corn is *Zea mays.* The name of a genus begins with a capital letter, that of the species with a small letter. This system of using two words as the scientific name of a species, termed the **binomial system,** is commonly used by both botanists and zoologists. The binomial system was first used extensively by Carolus Linnaeus (1707–1778), a great Swedish botanist, who is sometimes called the father of nomenclature and classification of living organisms. Following the scientific name of each species is an initial or abbreviation, which indicates the name of the scientist who first described and named the species. For example, *Zea mays* L. was named by

Linnaeus, as were also *Pisum sativum* L. (garden pea) and *Solanum tuberosum* L. (Irish potato). *Rosa virginiana* Mill. was described and named by Philip Miller, *Rosa setigera* Michx. by Andre Michaux, and *Eriogonum harperi* Goodman by George J. Goodman.

The scientific names of living organisms are derived principally from Latin and Greek, less frequently from other languages. The advantage of scientific names over common names is that the former are governed in part by rules established by international congresses of biologists and are thus uniformly regulated and, since they are based upon two languages with which biologists are presumably somewhat familiar, they are the same in all parts of the world, constituting an international scientific language. Thus, although a German botanist might not know the meaning of the English name black walnut, he would immediately recognize the name *Juglans nigra* L.; similarly, an American botanist, ignorant of the Spanish word *cebolla,* would recognize the binomial *Allium cepa* L., the scientific name of onion or *cebolla.* Biologists invent scientific names on different bases. Sometimes a genus or species name is an ancient Greek or Latin name for a group of plants, for example, *Pinus* for pine and *Quercus* for oak. Often a name honors some distinguished scientist or public figure, as in the genera *Washingtonia* and *Linnaea;* sometimes a species name honors a person, as in *harperi* and *michauxiana.* Occasionally, scientific names refer to mythological figures, as in the genus name *Mercurialis.* Often species or genus names are descriptive of some conspicuous feature of a plant; for example, the genus name *Liriodendron* is derived from two Greek words which mean "tulip" and "tree," in reference to the tuliplike flowers of this tree; common species names are *alba* (white), *rubra* (red), *albicaulis* (white-stemmed), and *saccharinum* (sweet). Some species names indicate geographical regions or directions, for example, *canadensis* and *virginiana.* Also, species names may describe the habitats in which certain plants commonly grow, as in *Ranunculus aquaticus* (water buttercup) and *Zostera marina* (eel grass), which grows in shallow salt water of ocean bays.

REPRODUCTON IN PLANTS

Since the chief criteria of classification are based upon body structure and reproductive processes, an understanding of the basic features of reproduction is prerequisite to a study of plant classification. Reproduction is a process whereby organisms produce offspring and thus maintain their species. There are many types of reproduction in different kinds of plants. These reproductive methods are usually separated into two types: **sexual reproduction** and **asexual reproduction.** Sexual reproduction involves both **meiosis** (reduction division) and **fertilization** (fusion of **gametes** in pairs). The cell produced by the fusion of two gametes is called a **zygote.** In a few primitive plants, the gametes are alike in size and structure, though they may differ in their physiology. Such gametes are called **isogametes,** and the process of reproduction in which they participate is termed **isogamy.** The more common and more advanced type of sexual reproduction, termed **heterogamy,** involves gametes that are unlike in size and structure as well as in certain physiological characteristics. These **heterogametes** are called **eggs** (female gametes) and **sperms** (male gametes). Eggs are usually larger than sperms and are most frequently nonmotile; sperms are often equipped with protoplasmic tails (**cilia** or **flagella**) and are in such cases able to swim in a liquid medium. The fusion of an egg and a sperm in the embryo sac of an angiosperm ovule is an example of heterogamous sexual reproduction.

In asexual reproduction, neither meiosis nor fusion of gametes is involved. A portion of a plant body separates from a parent body and grows into a new individual. Among the common types of asexual reproduction in plants are **fission, budding, fragmentation, spore formation,** and **vegetative reproduction.** Fission is the method of reproduction in many primitive plants; it is the division of a single-celled organism into two new single-celled organisms. Budding is a method of asexual reproduction in which a small protuberance forms on the surface of a one-celled organism; this protuberance grows until it is almost as large as the parent cell, a wall is then formed between the parent cell and the "bud," and the two cells may separate, as in yeasts. Fragmentation is the breaking into segments of a multicellular plant body; each part is then able to grow into a complete new plant. Spores are specialized structures, usually one celled, occasionally two to several celled, that are produced by various plants; a spore separates from the parent plant and is able by repeated cell divisions to grow into a complete new plant. In some water plants (some fungi and algae) the spores possess cilia or flagella that move in undulating fashion and propel the spores through the water. Such motile spores are called **zoospores.** A structure that produces spores is called a **sporangium.** Reproduction by means of runners, cuttings, grafting, and tubers is called vegetative reproduction.

In some plants, certain algae for example, the zoospores and isogametes are almost indistinguishable in structure, differing only in size. Because of this fact, it is believed by many botanists that sexual reproduction may have originated from asexual reproduction, possibly as a result of the fusion of diminutive zoospores too small to grow singly into new individuals.

Alternation of Generations

A conspicuous feature of sexual reproduction in most plants is a phenomenon called **alternation of generations.** This means that the complete *sexual* life history (life cycle) of a plant consists of two phases or generations, one of which (the **sporophyte**) produces spores while the other (the **gametophyte**) produces gametes. Intimately associated with and characteristic of the sexual cycle are two significant processes, meiosis and fertilization, each of which must occur before the cycle can be completed. An understanding of the relationships that exist between the structures and processes mentioned above may be obtained by considering the sequence of major events in a generalized life history. Fertilization, the fusion of a female gamete (egg) with a male gamete (sperm), gives rise to a zygote. Since each gamete nucleus is haploid, that is, contains a single set of chromosomes, the zygote acquires two sets of homologous chromosomes at fertilization and is, therefore, diploid. The zygote grows into a sporophyte that likewise has the diploid chromosome number in all its cells. When the sporophyte is mature, certain of its cells (spore mother cells) undergo meiosis and produce spores. Meiosis *reduces* the chromosome complement from the diploid to the haploid condition and thereby marks the beginning of the gametophyte generation. The gametophyte into which a spore grows contains the haploid chromosome number in all its cells, including the gametes that it produces. Fertilization then re-establishes the diploid chromosome number in the zygote and marks the beginning of the sporophyte generation.

In all vascular plants, bryophytes, and some lower plants (thallophytes), both gametophytes and sporophytes are multicellular structures, usually quite unlike in relative size and appearance. In other thallophytes the zygote undergoes meiosis directly; thus a single diploid cell (the zygote) represents the sporophyte "generation." In still other thallophytes the zygote develops into a diploid vegetative phase that ultimately produces gametes by meiosis. In this type a single haploid cell (the gamete) represents the gametophyte "generation." In each of the above cases there is a cytological alternation between the haploid and diploid conditions; however, many botanists believe that alternation of generations in a morphological sense requires the alternation of multicellular haploid and diploid phases.

As you study the various plant groups you will encounter many types of plants with which you are unfamiliar. Moreover, these plants will appear to have many differences in their life histories. Remember that in all plant groups with alternation of generations, the same basic sequence of events occurs: haploid gametes fuse at fertilization to form a diploid zygote that grows into the sporophyte plant; the sporophyte produces diploid spore mother cells that undergo meiosis, giving rise to haploid spores; each spore grows into a haploid gametophyte plant that then produces gametes. If you will trace these basic similarities through all the groups having alternation of generations, the differences among them will become simple to comprehend.

ORGANIZATION OF CHAPTERS ON PLANT DIVISIONS

In your study of the various plant divisions listed in the next section of this chapter, you will encounter many new facts about these divisions. To facilitate your study, descriptions of these groups and the plants they encompass will be organized and summarized under the following headings:

1. *Growth forms and structure:* major characteristics of external and internal structure of the plants in each division.

2. *Reproduction and life cycle:* descriptions of reproductive methods and structures, and a summary of alternation of generations in each division.

3. *Physiological characteristics:* an account of the mode of nutrition (autotrophic or heterotrophic) and of other important physiological features, such as pigmentation and nature of stored foods.

4. *Habitats and distribution:* an account of the places in which members of the divisions grow—fresh water, salt water, deserts, woodland, etc.—and of their geographical distribution on the earth.

5. *Importance in nature and in human life:* importance of each group in relation to soil binding, soil fertility, sources of food for wild animals, etc., and in providing food, drugs, fibers, and other products useful in human life.

6. *Relationships with other organisms:* accounts of the known or supposed relationships with other groups of plants, with emphasis on evolutionary connections.

7. *Representative members:* description of typical orders, families, or genera of each division.

A MODERN SYSTEM OF PLANT CLASSIFICATION

The taxonomic system used in this book is a phylogenetic system based on recent results of botanical research upon the structure, reproductive methods, and apparent relationships of living and extinct plants. However, it should not be regarded as the final word in the classification of the major plant groups. There are still gaps in our knowledge of the precise relationships of some of the taxa, for example, the origin of angiosperms, and it is likely that changes will be made in this system as the future brings more information about these groups.

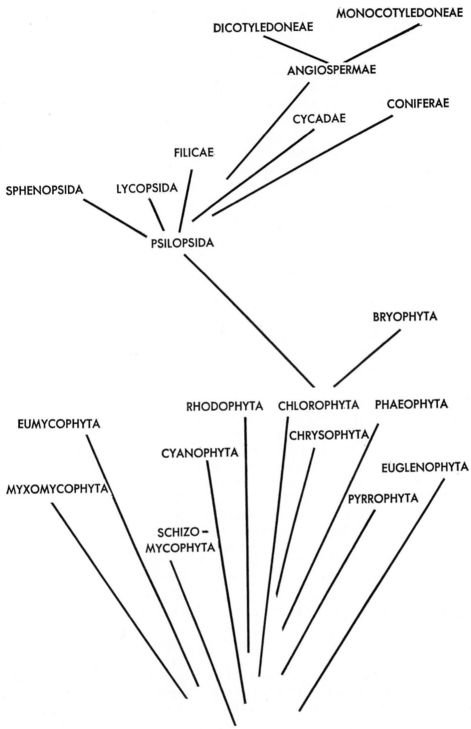

FIG. 18–2. Diagram illustrating probable relationships among the major plant groups.

As a prelude to the systematic study of the major groups of the plant kingdom, this system is presented to give orientation to students:

I. Subkingdom **THALLOPHYTA**—plants not forming embryos.
   Division 1—**Cyanophyta** (blue-green algae)
   Division 2—**Euglenophyta** (euglenophytes, etc.)
   Division 3—**Chlorophyta** (green algae)
   Division 4—**Chrysophyta** (diatoms, etc.)
   Division 5—**Phaeophyta** (brown algae)
   Division 6—**Rhodophyta** (red algae)
   Division 7—**Schizomycophyta** (bacteria)
   Division 8—**Myxomycophyta** (slime fungi)
   Division 9—**Eumycophyta** (true fungi)

II. Subkingdom **EMBRYOPHYTA**—plants forming embryos.
   Division 10—**Bryophyta,** or **Atracheata** (mosses and liverworts; plants lacking vascular tissues)
   Division 11—**Tracheophyta,** or **Tracheata** (plants having the vascular tissues xylem and phloem)
     Subdivision 1—**Psilopsida** (leafless and rootless vascular plants, almost entirely extinct)
     Subdivision 2—**Lycopsida** (club mosses and their relatives, with a simple conducting system and scalelike leaves)
     Subdivision 3—**Sphenopsida** (horsetails, with a simple conducting system, jointed stems, and scalelike leaves)
     Subdivision 4—**Pteropsida** (plants with complex conducting systems, large conspicuous leaves, other advanced features)
       Class 1—**Filicae** (ferns)
       Class 2—**Coniferae** (cone-bearing plants, often with needlelike leaves; reproductive structures borne on stem; seeds naked)
       Class 3—**Cycadae** (mostly cone-bearing plants with large, frondlike leaves; reproductive structures born on leaves; seeds naked)
       Class 4—**Angiospermae** (the flowering plants)
         Subclass 1—**Dicotyledoneae**
         Subclass 2—**Monocotyledoneae**

⫷⫷⫷ SUMMARY

1. There are approximately 350,000 species of plants living on the earth at present. Taxonomy is the branch of botany concerned with plant classification and identification.

2. The principal criteria used in classifying plants are their structure and reproduction.

3. The basic unit in the classification of living organisms is the species. A group of closely related species constitutes a genus, a group of closely related genera comprises a family, a collection of related families is an order, orders are

grouped into classes, classes constitute divisions, and divisions are grouped into subkingdoms. Various of these categories may be divided into subgroups.

4. Common names of organisms are useless for scientific purposes, for they vary from one language to another, they are often used in a loose, indefinite manner, and they are often variable within the same country or state.

5. A scientific name consists of two words, the first the name of the genus, the second the name of the species. Such a name is called a binomial. A binomial is followed by the name or initials of the biologist who described and named the species.

6. Scientific names are derived chiefly from Latin and Greek and are the same in all parts of the world, thus constituting an international system of nomenclature.

7. Two main types of reproduction in plants are sexual and asexual. Sexual reproduction involves meiosis and gametic fusion. Asexual reproduction includes all methods that do not involve these two processes.

8. Isogamy is sexual reproduction by structurally similar gametes. Heterogamy is sexual reproduction by structurally dissimilar gametes.

9. A male gamete is called a sperm, a female gamete an egg.

10. Among common types of asexual reproduction are fission, budding, spore formation, fragmentation, and vegetative reproduction.

11. Alternation of generations is a phenomenon in which the complete, sexual life cycle of a plant consists of two phases or generations: a gametophyte generation that produces gametes, and a sporophyte generation that produces spores. By means of fusion of gametes at fertilization and spore formation at meiosis, each generation in turn gives rise to the other. Alternation of generations occurs in most groups of plants.

12. The gametophyte generation has the haploid chromosome number, the sporophyte generation has the diploid number.

SUGGESTED READINGS FOR INTERESTED STUDENTS

1. Bailey, L. H., *How Plants Get Their Names.* Macmillan, New York, 1933.
2. Clute, W. N., *The Common Names of Plants and Their Meanings,* 2d ed. W. N. Clute & Co., Indianapolis, 1942.
3. Cronquist, Arthur, "The divisions and classes of plants." *The Botanical Review,* 26, 425–482, 1960.
4. Lawrence, G. H. M., *Taxonomy of Vascular Plants.* Macmillan, New York, 1951.

TOPICS AND QUESTIONS FOR STUDY

1. Define taxonomy.
2. Distinguish between artificial and phylogenetic systems of classification.
3. What are the major criteria of classification?
4. Define species, genus, family, order, class, division.
5. How may one quickly recognize the names of families? Of orders?

6. What are the objections to the use of common names of organisms for scientific study?
7. What is the binomial system?
8. What is the significance of initials or names after binomials?
9. What are the advantages of scientific names over common names?
10. Define: sexual reproduction, asexual reproduction, gamete, zygote, isogamy, heterogamy, spore, fission, budding, fragmentation, vegetative reproduction.
11. Define and describe briefly alternation of generations.
12. At what points in alternation of generations do chromosome numbers change? Explain.
13. Write out from memory the system of classification used in this book.

19

Thallophyta: The Algal Divisions

The subkingdom **Thallophyta** is a large assemblage of very diverse plants, which range from microscopic, unicellular forms to large, multicellular plants 200 or more feet in length. The plants comprising the Thallophyta are the structurally simplest and most primitive members of the plant kingdom. All members of this subkingdom have certain common characteristics: they lack true roots, stems, and leaves; they lack the vascular tissue xylem and usually lack phloem; their gametangia and sporangia (spore-producing structures) are typically one celled, or, if they are more than one celled, the gametes or spores are not surrounded by a layer of sterile, wall cells; and they do not form embryos—that is, the zygotes in those species that reproduce sexually do not produce multicellular embryos within the female gametangia or other structures. Some members of the Thallophyta have bodies that appear to be differentiated into roots, stems, and leaves; these parts are not considered to be true roots, stems and leaves, however, since they lack the characteristic tissue differentiation of these organs of higher plants.

Thallophyta have been regarded by some botanists as a group of closely related plants, but modern research indicates that they comprise several distinct divisions that are very diverse and that are not all closely related with each other. Thus, the subkingdom Thallophyta is in part, at least, an artificial group; nevertheless, for convenience, the name Thallophyta is commonly applied to this heterogeneous assemblage of plant divisions.

The divisions that constitute the Thallophyta may be separated into two groups: a group of divisions whose members contain chlorophyll and thus carry on photosynthesis, and a group of divisions whose members lack chlorophyll and therefore are incapable of photosynthesis. The chlorophyllous divisions are known collectively as **algae,** those lacking chlorophyll are the **bacteria** and **fungi.** Since most bacteria and the fungi are unable to carry on photosynthesis, they are nutritionally dependent upon externally supplied food; some species, called **parasites,** obtain their food directly from the living tissues of other organisms, called **hosts;** others, called **saprophytes,** absorb foods from dead or nonliving organic matter.

Algae are chiefly water plants that live either submerged or suspended in water or float upon the surface of water; a minority of species grows upon the surface of damp soil and upon rocks and tree bark, which are more or less continuously moist. A few species grow upon snow and ice, still others inhabit hot springs. As stated in an earlier paragraph, the algae possess chlorophyll and are thus **autotrophic,** that is, capable of manufacturing their own food (with the exception of a few heterotrophic species to be mentioned later). Some algae are green in color, while others are bluish, red, purple, brown, or of some other hue because of the presence in their cells of other pigments that mask the green color of their chlorophyll. The algae possess a great variety of methods of reproduction; some reproduce only asexually, others reproduce by both sexual and asexual methods. They play an extremely important role in nature and in human life, and it is for this reason that they deserve at least brief study in an elementary course in botany.

DIVISION CYANOPHYTA (BLUE-GREEN ALGAE)

Growth Forms and Structure

This division, with about 150 genera and 1400 species, consists of plants of simple structure. Some species are unicellular. In other species, the cells cohere to form colonies that may be **filamentous** (thread-like), ball shaped, or of some other form. Often the cells are embedded in an excreted mucilaginous sheath. The protoplasm of blue-green algae possesses less structural differentiation than the protoplasm of most other plants; it lacks organized nuclei, although granules of nuclear material are scattered in the protoplasm, and it also lacks plastids, the chlorophyll being diffused in the outer part of the protoplasm. They contain a bluish pigment **(phycocyanin)** that, with green chlorophyll, gives most members of the division their bluish-green color. In a few species, a red pigment is present. Some species are brownish green.

Reproduction and Life Cycle

Reproduction is entirely asexual, usually by fission. In some species, a filament develops special cells called **heterocysts:** a filament breaks into segments at these heterocysts, each segment growing by cell division as an independent plant. A few species form spores: certain cells enlarge, their cell walls thicken, and their food content increases; these spores separate from their parent filament and grow into new threads. No flagellated reproductive cells are formed.

Physiological Characteristics

The blue-green algae carry on photosynthesis and are thus autotrophic. Some species excrete waste materials that impart foul odors and flavors to water. Many species, as stated above, have slimy sheaths excreted by their cells. Blue-green algae store a food called cyanophycean starch, which is chemically similar to glycogen. A few species are able to incorporate atmospheric nitrogen into organic compounds, a process called **nitrogen fixation.**

Habitats and Distribution

Blue-green algae are widely distributed on the earth's surface. Most species occur in the fresh water of lakes, ponds, rivers, creeks, springs, and open tanks; a few species are marine; that is, they inhabit the salt water of oceans and seas. Some blue-green algae thrive on the surface of soil, rocks, and flower pots, especially in damp, shaded places; such algae are often troublesome pests in greenhouses. One species of Cyanophyta, which contains a red pigment, flourishes in the Red Sea and is responsible for the color of that body of water. A few species, able to withstand high temperatures, grow in hot springs, such as those of Yellowstone Park; they precipitate calcium and magnesium salts as **travertine** rock, which is sometimes brilliantly colored. Some species cause the precipitation of carbonates from water on lake bottoms. A few species are mild parasites in the intestinal tracts of man and other animals, whereas still others grow as epiphytes upon higher plants.

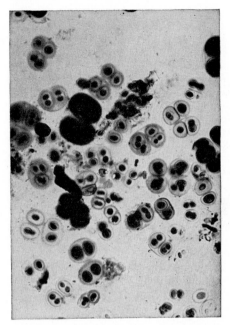

FIG. 19–1. *Gloeocapsa.* Photograph showing cells embedded in gelatinous sheath.

and other aquatic animals. Poisoning of cattle that drank water polluted by blue-green algae has been reported by veterinarians.

Importance in Nature and in Human Life

Blue-green algae are sources of food for fish and other aquatic animals, some of which provide food for man. As soil-inhabiting species grow, make food, multiply, and die, they add organic matter to soils, thus increasing their fertility and promoting the growth of bacteria and other organisms, whose activities increase soil fertility. Their extensive growth in bodies of water causes pollution of water, a condition that may render water unfit for cooking, bathing, and drinking purposes, may result in the choking of water filters and pipes in water-purifying plants, and may have a harmful effect upon fish

Relationships with Other Organisms

The exact relationships of Cyanophyta with other groups of organisms are not known. Some botanists believe that they may have evolved from an ancestral group of simpler unicellular algae. Others believe that they may be related to the red algae (Rhodophyta), partly because some blue-green algae have a red pigment chemically similar to the red pigment of the Rhodophyta. It has been suggested also that the blue-green algae may be related to bacteria, which, like the Cyanophyta, are structurally very simple. The oldest known fossil plants (about 1.6 billion years old) are algalike,

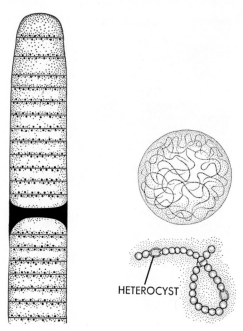

HETEROCYST

FIG. 19–2 (*left*). *Oscillatoria* filament. Black region represents soft gelatinous area that breaks filament up into hormogonia.

FIG. 19–3 (*right*). *Nostoc*. *Above:* Chains of cells embedded in a spherical, gelatinous matrix. *Below:* A portion of a filament, showing two heterocysts.

resembling most closely the blue-green algae.

Representative Members

Gloeocapsa is a genus of algae that are unicellular, with cells embedded in layers of gelatinous excretion (Figure 19–1). *Gloeocapsa* is common on wet rocks and other damp substrata, where it often forms extensive, dark-colored, slimy masses.

The genus *Oscillatoria* contains species in which the body is a filamentous colony. *Oscillatoria* grows commonly on damp soil, flower pots, and rocks; each cell is self-sufficient and may continue its existence if separated from other cells of a fila-

ment. Often the filaments exhibit a swinging or oscillating movement (hence the generic name) and sometimes glide backward or forward. Reproduction is chiefly by fission: sometimes soft gelatinous areas develop between cells, causing a filament to separate into segments (Figure 19–2) or hormogonia.

Nostoc contains forms that develop small gelatinous balls in ponds and pools. Each ball contains many filaments of somewhat globose cells, among which heterocysts often form (Figure 19–3).

DIVISION EUGLENOPHYTA (EUGLENOIDS)

Growth Forms and Structure

This division, with about 25 genera and 350 species, consists of unicellular, microscopic plants. Each plant is usually naked, that is, without a differentiated cell wall, and is usually equipped with one, two, or rarely three **flagella** inserted in a gullet. A flagellum is a slender, hairlike protoplasmic appendage, the movements of which propel the organism through the water. Each euglenoid cell has an organized nucleus and chloroplasts.

Reproduction and Life Cycle

The reproduction of most euglenoids is asexual, by longitudinal cell division. Some species form thick-walled resting cells, called **cysts,** that germinate into swimming cells. In at least one genus, sexual reproduction is known to occur.

Physiological Characteristics

The euglenoids carry on photosynthesis, but do not store starch; their reserve food is chiefly **paramylum,** a carbohydrate similar chemically to starch. Some of the pigments of the chloroplasts are similar to those of green algae (Chlorophyta) and of higher plants.

Habitats and Distribution

Euglenoids occur commonly in fresh water, especially in water rich in organic matter, in ponds, lakes, roadside puddles, and other bodies of water.

Importance in Nature and in Human Life

Euglenoids constitute an important source of food for fish and other aquatic animals, many of which supply food for human beings. *Euglena* is also used as an experimental organism in certain physiological investigations.

Relationships with Other Organisms

Zoologists often classify euglenoids among the Protozoa, the most primitive animal phylum, chiefly because some of them have gullets through which they ingest solid food particles. Botanists consider the green euglenoids to be plants, since they contain chlorophyll and carry on photosynthesis. Some euglenoidlike organisms that lack chlorophyll and that are thus regarded as animals are apparently closely related to the green euglenoids. Many biologists believe that this euglenoid group of organisms may be closely related to the primitive organisms from which both plant and animal kingdoms developed. Some biologists prefer not to separate the euglenoid organisms into green, plantlike types or nongreen, animal forms, but instead place them all in a special kingdom, the Protista, along with bacteria, slime fungi, and other organisms of uncertain relationship.

Representative Members

Members of the genus *Euglena* are elongated, tapering organisms (Figure 19–4), each with a single flagellum, a definite nucleus, numerous chloroplasts, a gullet, and a red eyespot, which is apparently a light-sensitive structure. Reproduction is by longitudinal cell division; the nucleus divides by mitosis, following which the cell divides, forming two new organisms.

DIVISION CHLOROPHYTA (GREEN ALGAE)

Growth Forms and Structure

The Chlorophyta, with 360 genera and about 5700 known species, are a group of plants of considerable diversity of structure and reproductive methods. The cells of all species have chloroplasts and nuclei, and the cell walls consist of cellulose. Some species are unicellular. In others, colonies are formed, in still others, the bodies are multicellular. Most green algae are so small that they can be seen only with a microscope or low-powered magnifying lens; a few are large enough (for example, sea-lettuce) to be readily seen by the naked eye.

Reproduction and Life Cycle

The green algae reproduce by a variety of methods. In a few species, reproduction is exclusively asexual, but in most species, isogamy or heterogamy occurs. The **gametangia** (sexual reproductive structures) are unicellular. Asexual reproduction is commonly by cell division, fragmentation, immobile spores, and swimming spores **(zoospores).** In those species that reproduce sexually, there is an alternation of haploid and diploid stages in

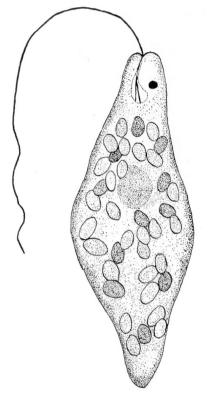

FIG. 19–4. *Euglena* with anterior flagellum, gullet, and eye-spot; central nucleus; and numerous chloroplasts.

may have been the ancestral group from which higher plants evolved. The grass-green color of these algae is similar to the green color of the leaves of most higher plants. A few species have a red pigment in addition to chlorophyll and the carotenoids. The principal storage food in most green algae is starch, as in most higher plants.

Habitats and Distribution

The Chlorophyta are among the most widely distributed of all algae. Most species inhabit bodies of fresh water, in which they often form dense green "scums" on the surface. Some species live in ocean water, and some occur on the surface of damp soil, the bark of trees, moist rock surfaces, and often upon moist shingles, bricks and fence posts. A few species grow upon ice and snow, imparting a reddish color to the substratum. Some green algae live upon or within the bodies of sponges, protozoans, and jellyfish; this relationship is thought to be one of mutual benefit, the algae supplying food for the animals and in turn receiving shelter and protection.

the life cycle: a zygote, which results from the fusion of two gametes, is diploid; reduction division usually occurs when the zygote germinates, and the cells that it produces are thus haploid. Zoospores and flagellated sex cells have flagella of equal length at their anterior end.

Physiological Characteristics

Green algae carry on photosynthesis (with the exception of a few species that parasitize higher plants). Their pigments, chlorophyll, xanthophyll, and carotene, usually occur in their plastids in the same proportions as they do in higher plants; this supports the view that green algae

Importance in Nature and in Human Life

Green algae are an important source of food for fish and other aquatic animals; thus, they play a vital role in the world's fishing industry. Some green algae are eaten directly by human beings, for example, *Ulva*, or sea-lettuce, and *Spirogyra* and *Oedogonium*, which commonly appear in the markets of India. In their photosynthesis, green algae (like other algae) release oxygen that is used by fish and other aquatic animals in their respiration; the carbon dioxide given off in respiration by these animals is used by al-

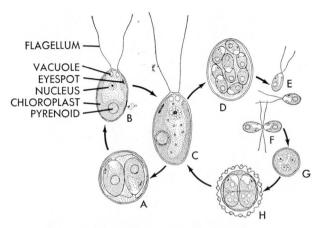

FLAGELLUM
VACUOLE
EYESPOT
NUCLEUS
CHLOROPLAST
PYRENOID

FIG. 19–5. *Chlamydomonas*. Asexual reproductive cycle at left shows mature vegetative cell (C) producing zoospores (B). In sexual cycle at right, the vegetative cell (C) produces numerous gametes (E) that unite (F) to form a zygote (G), and later, a heavy walled zygospore (H). Meiosis occurs with germination of the zygospore.

gae in their photosynthesis. The oxygen released by algae also promotes the activities of aerobic bacteria that are involved in the decomposition of organic matter in water. Soil-inhabiting green algae provide food for soil animals and increase the organic matter of soils, thus furthering soil fertility. Some marine green algae secrete calcium salts that develop into oceanic reefs. Green algae sometimes pollute water, giving it a vile odor and flavor, choking streams, and, in addition, fouling filters in water-purifying plants.

Relationships with Other Organisms

Green algae are believed to have evolved from simple, unicellular, flagellated algae. During this evolution, greater complexity of body form and of reproductive methods apparently occurred; in some green algae, only asexual reproduction occurs, in others isogamous and heterogamous sexual reproduction occurs as well. It is believed that ancient filamentous types of

green algae may have been ancestors of Bryophyta and Tracheophyta.

Representative Members

A plant of the genus *Chlamydomonas* consists of a single egg-shaped or spherical cell with a definite cell wall and protoplasm containing a single cup-shaped chloroplast, a nucleus, an eyespot, and two flagella (Figure 19–5). In asexual reproduction, the protoplasm forms 2, 4, or 8 zoospores that are liberated by dissolution of the cell wall; each zoospore swims out and becomes a new individual plant. *Chlamydomonas* may also reproduce sexually: in this process, the protoplast produces 8, 16, or 32 cells that resemble mature cells and zoospores but are smaller; these small cells are isogametes that fuse in pairs in water, forming zygotes; a zygote develops a thick wall and withstands unfavorable environmental conditions such as drought; when conditions are favorable, reduction division occurs in the zygote, resulting in the formation of 4 zoospores, which, upon their release,

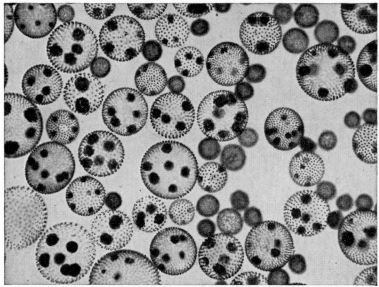

(*Copyright, General Biological Supply House, Chicago.*)

FIG. 19–6. Colonies of *Volvox,* each composed of many cells. The dark objects are daughter colonies.

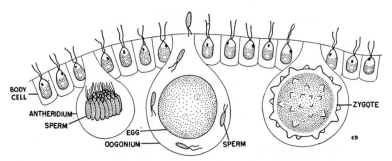

FIG. 19–7. *Volvox,* showing a portion of a section through the spherical colony. In addition to the body cells that form the outer layer of the sphere, there are shown an antheridium with numerous biflagellate sperm cells; an oogonium with an unfertilized egg; and an oogonium with a thick-walled zygote.

become mature *Chlamydomonas* plants. Sexual reproduction in plants may have first appeared in some such organism as *Chlamydomonas,* as a result of the production of small zoospores, which, unable to grow individually into new plants because of an insufficiency of stored food, pooled their food reserves by fusing in pairs. This theory is called the "hunger theory of sex."

In the genus *Volvox,* each plant is a hollow, spherical, motile colony composed of a few hundred to thousands of biflagellate cells held together by a gelatinous secretion (Figure 19–6). The individual cells are structurally similar to those of *Chlamydomonas*. Most cells of a colony do not reproduce, other cells are reproductive.

Ulothrix plants are fresh-water algae whose bodies consist of unbranched, multicellular filaments (Figure 19–8). The basal cell of the filament is a **hold-fast,** which attaches the plant to a solid object in water. Each filament cell has a single nucleus and a collar-shaped chloroplast. Asexual reproduction is by fragmentation and zoospores; certain cells become transformed into zoosporangia, each of which produces 2, 4, 8, 16, or 32 four-flagellated zoospores; after liberation, these swim about, then attach themselves to objects in water and grow into new filaments. Some cells of a filament may become gametangia, each of which produces 8, 16, 32, or 64 isogametes; these resemble zoospores in structure, except that they bear only two flagella and are smaller. The isogametes are liberated into the water, where they fuse in pairs. In this fusion, gametes from the same filament do not fuse; rather, gametes from separate filaments unite. This condition is called **heterothallic.** After a rest period, the zygote undergoes reduction division and produces four zoospores, which, upon liberation from the zygote, swim about, then become attached to objects in the water and grow into new filaments. All cells of *Ulothrix* are haploid, except the zygote, which is diploid.

Oedogonium species are fresh-water algae of common occurrence. The plant body is a multicellular, unbranched filament that is attached by a holdfast cell to some solid object in water (Figure 19–9). Each vegetative cell has a netlike chloroplast and a single nucleus. Asexual reproduction is by fragmentation and multiflagellate zoospores, which are produced singly in zoosporangia. After a pe-

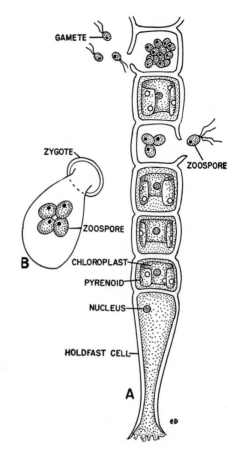

FIG. 19–8. *Ulothrix.* A. Multicellular filament with basal holdfast cell; vegetative cells, each with a single chloroplast and nucleus; zoosporangium with 4 large zoospores; and gametangium with numerous, small gametes. B. Zygote that has produced 4 zoospores.

riod of swimming, zoospores become attached to solid objects, form holdfast cells, and grow into new filaments. Sexual reproduction is heterogamous, some species being homothallic, others heterothallic. The antheridia are short cells that usually produce two sperms each; the sperms resemble zoospores, but are much smaller. Oogonia are globose cells, each with an egg; an oogonium develops a wall pore through which a fertilizing sperm en-

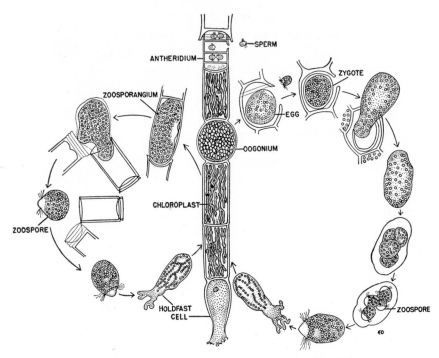

FIG. 19–9. *Oedogonium*. Life cycle in diagrammatic form; circle to left represents asexual cycle and circle to right depicts sexual phase.

ters. Fertilization occurs within an oogonium, the zygote becoming thick walled. After liberation and a period of rest, a zygote undergoes reduction division and forms four haploid zoospores that develop into new filaments. Some heterothallic species (Figure 19–10) produce dwarf male filaments that develop from special zoospores that become attached to female filaments; a dwarf male filament produces one or two antheridia, from which sperms are liberated; these fertilize the eggs in the oogonia of the larger female filament.

Protococcus is one of the most common and familiar genera of green algae. *Protococcus* plants are unicellular organisms that form the commonly encountered greenish growth upon tree bark; they also grow upon damp soil and rocks. Each cell has a single chloroplast and a nucleus (Figure 19–11). Reproduction is

exclusively asexual by fission. Often the cells cohere after fission, forming colonies of varying size and form.

Spirogyra (water silk) is a genus of unbranched, filamentous green algae that grow commonly in bodies of fresh water. Each cell has a conspicuous, beautiful, spiral chloroplast and a central nucleus (Figure 19–12). Asexual reproduction is by fragmentation; no zoospores are formed. In sexual reproduction, the cells of two filaments in contact with each other form tubes that meet and push the filaments slightly apart; an opening develops at the contact points of two tubes, and the protoplast of one cell, behaving as a gamete, moves through the **conjugation tube** and fuses with the protoplast of the opposite cell in the other filament. This protoplasmic fusion forms a zygote, which after release from the surrounding cell wall and a period of rest, undergoes reduction division, forming four nuclei, three of which disintegrate. The cell with the remaining nucleus grows into a new filament. This type of sexual reproduction, called **conjugation,** is a form of isogamy, since the gametes (protoplasts) of opposite cells are similar in size and structure. Although the gametes are structurally similar, they and the filaments in which they develop may differ physiologically, for all gametes in a filament behave in the same manner; that is, all gametes of a filament move through the conjugation tubes, or they remain in their cells receiving the protoplasts from opposite cells of the other filament. In some species of *Spirogyra,* conjugation occurs between adjacent cells of the same filament.

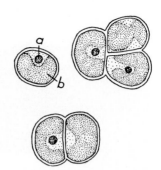

FIG. 19–11. *Protococcus.* a: nucleus; b: chloroplast.

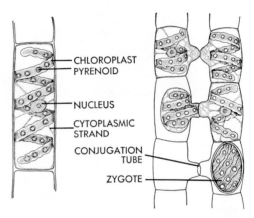

CHLOROPLAST
PYRENOID

NUCLEUS

CYTOPLASMIC
STRAND

CONJUGATION
TUBE

ZYGOTE

FIG. 19–12. *Spirogyra. Left:* A single vegetative cell. *Right:* Stages in conjugation. Beginning at the top, protuberances are shown that later fuse to form a conjugation tube. The protoplast of one cell moves through the tube to another cell, where fertilization occurs, producing a zygote.

DIVISION CHRYSOPHYTA (YELLOW-GREEN AND GOLDEN-BROWN ALGAE, AND DIATOMS)

Growth Forms and Structure

This division, with about 300 genera and 5700 species, includes algae that are chiefly unicellular, less frequently colonial or multicellular, and that are yellowish brown, greenish, or golden brown in color. Their cell walls are composed usu-

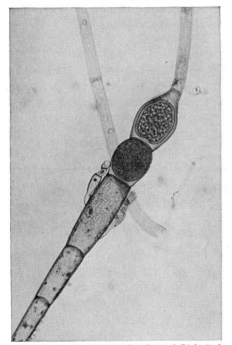

(*Copyright, General Biological Supply House, Chicago.*)

FIG. 19–10. *Oedogonium.* Two dwarf male filaments attached below two oogonia.

(*Photo by Johns-Manville Co.*)

FIG. 19–13. Diatomaceous earth deposit near Lompoc, California.

ally of two overlapping halves and usually contain silica, which gives them a hard, brittle texture. Flagella are present in some species.

Reproduction and Life Cycle

Asexual reproduction is by cell division, by zoospores, or by nonmotile spores. Flagella, when they occur, are of unequal length and bear minute branches. Sexual reproduction, which does not occur in all species, is chiefly isogamous.

Physiological Characteristics

Algae of this division contain a high percentage of yellowish and brown pigments that partly or completely mask the green color of their chlorophyll. They carry on photosynthesis. Starch is never formed; the usual storage foods are oils. Some species store **leucosin,** an albuminoid protein.

Habitats and Distribution

Most species live in water, some of them in the fresh water of lakes, ponds, springs, and streams, others in the salt water of oceans. Some species live on damp soil and stones.

Importance in Nature and in Human Life

Members of this division (especially a class called **diatoms**) are important sources of food for fish and other aquatic animals. Diatoms are especially abundant in the world's oceans; so essential are they for the nutrition of fish that they have been called the "grass of the sea." They are also abundant in fresh-water bodies; it has been estimated, for example, that as many as 35,000,000 diatoms may occur in one cubic yard of Illinois river water. The empty, siliceous walls of dead diatoms settle on the sea bottom and often accumulate in layers of great thickness; these rocklike deposits, known as **diatomaceous earth** (Figure 19–13), may be many hundreds of feet thick. In many parts of the world, these deposits occur on land above the surface of the sea as a result of geological processes of uplift; such deposits are mined and the diatomaceous earth is used in polishes for silverware, metal objects, and other products, in toothpastes and powders, in insulation of steam pipes, for refrigeration systems, and for blast furnaces, in filters for the clarification of oils, sugar syrup, and other liquids, in dynamite as an absorbent for nitroglycerin, and in concrete. Bricks for construction purposes are often cut from diatomaceous earth because of its light weight. The dome of the church of St. Sophia in Istanbul was constructed of such bricks. Some geologists believe that diatoms may have aided in the formation of petroleum deposits, since diatoms store oils and are often associated with oil-bearing sands. Some species of Chrysophyta are occasional offenders in the pollution of water.

Relationships with Other Organisms

The affinities of Chrysophyta with other groups of plants are uncertain. It has been suggested that they may be closely related to the green algae and that some of them may be relatives of the brown algae (Phaeophyta), because of a similarity in pigmentation. They are now placed together in this division chiefly because of a similarity in reserve foods and in pigmentation and because of their biparted cell walls.

Representative Members

Of the three classes of Chrysophyta, only one, the diatoms, will be considered here.

Diatoms (Figure 19–14) are unicellular algae, which occasionally form colonies. A diatom cell wall consists of two overlapping halves **(valves)** like the bottom and lid of a pill box. The cell walls are rich in silica (chief constituent of glass) and are therefore hard and brittle. The walls are ornamented with tiny dots or perforations and present a beautiful, delicately sculptured appearance. Diatom walls were at one time used to test the resolving power of microscope lenses; good lenses show a regular pattern of sharply defined, separate dots, while under inferior lenses, the dots appear to fuse and to form irregular lines. The protoplasm contains a nucleus and one or more chloroplasts, which vary from green to a golden-brown color. Diatoms occur in a great variety of sizes and forms (Figure 19–15). They often move about by a series of jerking movements, caused by cytoplasmic streaming inside the cell; this streaming creates water currents that are transmitted through a slit in the cell wall.

Reproduction of diatoms is both asexual and sexual. Asexual reproduction is by cell division; a cell divides into two cells, one remaining in the lower valve, the other in the upper valve of the parent cell. Each of these new cells secretes a new valve that fits inside the old one. As a result, one new cell is of approximately the same size as the parent cell, the other is slightly smaller. Thus, with successive divisions, some of the diatoms become successively smaller. This decrease in size is halted by the production of cells called **auxospores,** which may be formed by the protoplast escaping from valves, or as a result of a sexual process. Each of two diatom cells may form a gamete; these fuse in pairs to form zygotes that become auxospores. The auxospores then enlarge to the maximal size of the species, valves

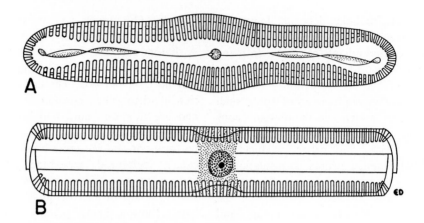

A

B

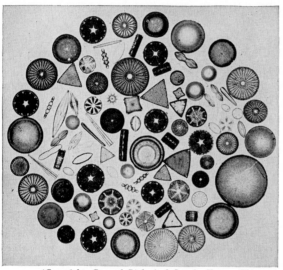

(*Copyright, General Biological Supply House, Chicago.*)

FIG. 19–14 (*above*). *Pinnularia,* a diatom. A. Top, or valve view, showing longitudinal slit, or raphe. B. Side, or girdle view, showing overlapping halves or valves.

FIG. 19–15 (*left*). Diatoms of assorted shapes and sizes.

are formed by the protoplast, and a new complete diatom is produced.

DIVISION PHAEOPHYTA (BROWN ALGAE)

Growth Forms and Structure

This division, with 190 genera and about 900 known species, is made up of chiefly marine algae that are multicellular and have great diversity of body structure. These algae are brown or greenish brown in color. In some species the plants are filamentous, in others they are branched structures frequently of considerable complexity and great size; in a few species, the plants may attain lengths of 200 or more feet. The plants are usually attached to rocks by well-developed holdfasts, which often resemble roots of higher plants. The structurally more complex brown algae are called **kelps** (Figures 19–16 and 19–17). In these, the body usually

(Photo by New York Botanical Garden.)

FIG. 19–16. *Nereocystis,* floating on the waters of Puget Sound.

possesses, in addition to a holdfast, an elongated, often branched stemlike part called a **stipe,** which bears flattened leaf-like structures, the **blades,** that sometimes attain lengths of several feet. The bodies of many brown algae also bear **bladders,** which are gas-filled enlargements of varying form; these bladders give buoyance to the kelps and enable their upper portions to float at or near the surface of the water. The kelps have a higher degree of internal differentiation than any other algae; in some, for example, there are elongated cells with perforated end walls; these cells, which apparently conduct food, resemble the sieve tube cells of the phloem of higher plants. In some species, meristematic cells resembling the cambium of higher plants are present. No xylem tissue is present in the bodies of brown algae. As in all other algal divisions except Cyanophyta, the cells of brown algae always contain chloroplasts and nuclei.

Reproduction and Life Cycle

Asexual reproduction is by fragmentation, by zoospores, and by immobile spores. Sexual reproduction in some species is isogamous, in other heterogamous. Motile reproductive cells are pear-shaped and have two lateral unequal flagella. Some species are homothallic, others heterothallic. Most brown algae have alternation of generations; in most species both gametophyte and sporophyte plants are multicellular, free-living plants, in a few species, the gametophyte (haploid) generation consists only of the gametes.

Physiological Characteristics

All brown algae carry on photosynthesis. The green color of their chlorophyll is masked wholly or partly by a brown pigment called **fucoxanthin.** Brown algae often accumulate high concentrations of magnesium, potassium, iodine, and other solutes from ocean water in their tissues. Some species of brown algae form mucilaginous substances that occur in slimy layers on their surfaces; these substances hold water very tenaciously and doubtless prevent desiccation of those plants that are exposed to the air at low tides. The most common stored food is a complex

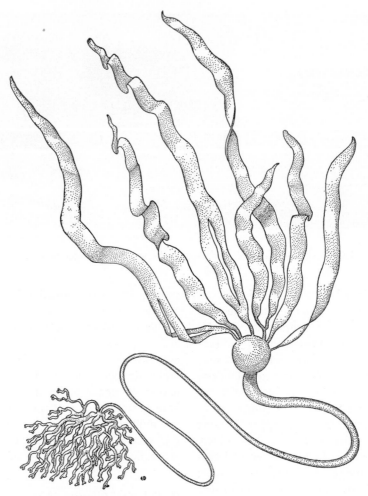

FIG. 19–17. *Nereocystis,* bull or bladder kelp, with branched hold-fast, long stipe, single bladder, and many blades.

carbohydrate that is known as **laminarin.**

Habitats and Distribution

All species of brown algae but three are marine plants. They grow most abundantly in the cooler waters of oceans; they are very abundant, for example, in the Arctic and Antarctic oceans, on the Atlantic coasts of Europe, and in ocean waters off New England and the Pacific coast of the United States. A few species thrive in warmer ocean waters of tropical regions. Brown algae usually grow attached to rocks and reefs in fairly shallow water along ocean coasts; some species grow in intertidal zones, being submerged at high tides and exposed to the air at low tides. A few species are unattached and float at or near the ocean surface. In some ocean regions, brown algae form great masses of vegetation of enormous extent; plants of a genus called *Sargassum,* for example

(Figure 19–18), occupy an area of about one-half million square miles, called the Sargasso Sea, in the Atlantic Ocean east of the West Indies.

Importance in Nature and in Human Life

Brown algae, like other groups of algae, are important sources of food for fish and other marine animals. In many coastal regions, farmers harvest brown algae (Figure 19–19) for cattle food. Many brown algae are eaten by human beings, especially in China and Japan where they are widely cultivated on bamboo stems pushed into the ocean bottom in shallow, coastal waters. Dried preparations of brown algae may be purchased in many food stores in the United States. Brown algae are rich in minerals and also have moderate quantities of carbohydrates and vitamins; thus, they constitute a good source of food for human beings. Since the total amount of photosynthesis of marine algae is believed to exceed that of land plants, biologists are turning their attention to the world's oceans as possible major sources of foods for human beings as the world's human population increases. Because of their rich mineral content, brown algae are often used as a soil fertilizer; they are sometimes spread out on fields and plowed under, or they may be dried and burned and their ash used as fertilizer. Some species of brown algae have been used as a commercial source of iodine for medicinal use. Several species become attached to ship hulls and thus cause "fouling" of ships, along with barnacles and other animals.

Relationships with Other Organisms

Because of their usually motile reproductive cells, the Phaeophyceae are thought

FIG. 19–18. *Above: Sargassum,* gulf weed. *Below: Sargassum,* gulf weed, with stemlike stipe, leaflike blades, and berrylike bladders, or floats.

to be descendants of flagellated, unicellular algae. Although the brown algae have developed highly complex and differentiated bodies, they are believed to be a terminal group that has not given rise to higher types of plants.

Representative Members

Fucus (Figure 19–20) is a genus of brown algae commonly known as rockweeds.

(Photo by San Diego Chamber of Commerce.)

FIG. 19–19. Harvesting kelp.

These plants are abundant along many seacoasts, where they grow attached to rocks in shallow water. A *Fucus* plant, which may reach a length of one foot or more, has a holdfast and a branching stipe, the terminal portions of which are flattened, ribbonlike structures with air bladders. Sexual reproduction is heterogamous. The inflated tips **(receptacles)** of the plants are covered with small, blisterlike pores that lead into cavities known as **conceptacles** (Figure 19–21). In these the gametangia are produced; in some species, the antheridia and oogonia are produced by separate plants, in others they are borne on the same plant, often within the same conceptacle. Each oogonium produces eight eggs, each antheridium numerous biflagellate sperms. Eggs and sperms are discharged from the conceptacles into sea water, where fertilization occurs. The zygotes grow into new, mature *Fucus* plants. These plants, like the zygotes, are diploid, and reduction di-

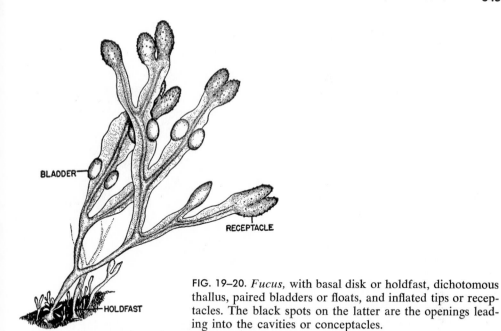

BLADDER

RECEPTACLE

HOLDFAST

FIG. 19–20. *Fucus*, with basal disk or holdfast, dichotomous thallus, paired bladders or floats, and inflated tips or receptacles. The black spots on the latter are the openings leading into the cavities or conceptacles.

vision occurs when eggs and sperms are formed. Thus, *Fucus* has no alternation of diploid and haploid plants; in *Fucus*, only the sperms and eggs are haploid.

Ectocarpus is a genus of brown algae whose bodies consist of filaments attached to rocks in ocean water. Some of the plants produce small zoosporangia (Figure 19–23) that release into the water many zoospores; these germinate in the water, producing filamentous plants that are like those just described but that produce elongated gametangia. The gametangia produce numerous isogametes, which fuse in pairs in the water, the two gametes of a pair coming from different plants. Thus, *Ectocarpus* is heterothallic. The zygote germinates, producing a new filament that produces zoospores. *Ectocarpus* thus has a definite alternation of two generations: a diploid, spore-producing plant (the sporophyte) and a haploid, gamete-producing plant (the gametophyte). The diploid chromosome number results from the fusion of isogametes and

persists in the cells of the sporophyte plant until reduction division occurs in the formation of zoospores.

DIVISION RHODOPHYTA (RED ALGAE)

Growth Forms and Structure

Plants of this division, with about 400 genera and 2500 species, are usually reddish or purplish, rarely green or brown. Red algae are multicellular plants that are simple or branched and that may be ribbonlike, fernlike, or of some other form (Figures 19–25 and 19–26). Holdfasts are usually present. Red algae rarely exceed 2 or 3 feet in length, and many are only a few inches long. As in other groups of algae, except Cyanophyta, the cells of red algae contain definite nuclei and plastids.

Reproduction and Life Cycle

A conspicuous feature of red algae is the absence of flagella on the reproductive

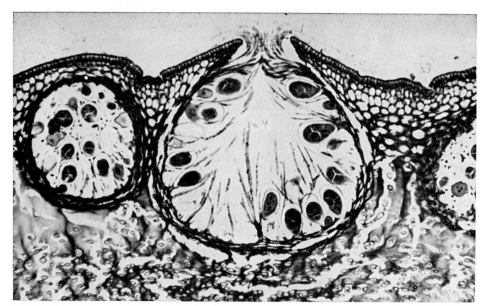

FIG. 19–21. Sectional view of *Fucus* (rockweed) female conceptacle, showing oogonia.

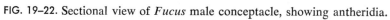

FIG. 19–22. Sectional view of *Fucus* male conceptacle, showing antheridia.

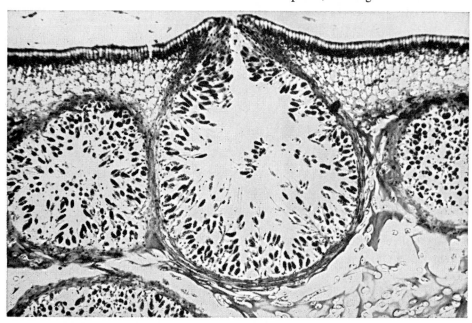

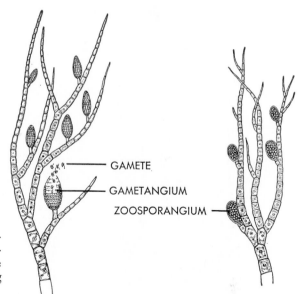

GAMETE

GAMETANGIUM

ZOOSPORANGIUM

FIG. 19–23. *Ectocarpus*, a filamentous brown alga. *Left:* One gametangium is releasing biflagellate gametes. *Right:* Filament bearing zoosporangia with zoospores.

cells, an unusual condition in plants that live submerged in water. Sexual reproduction of red algae is heterogamous. Since the sperms lack flagella, they are unable to swim and are carried passively by ocean currents to the female gametangia. Typically, a female gametangium produces an egg and develops a long, slender, hairlike protuberance called a **trichogyne.** A sperm, carried by current, adheres to a trichogyne; the sperm nucleus enters the trichogyne and migrates through it until it reaches the egg, fusing with the egg nucleus and forming a zygote. Most species of red algae have a definite alternation of generations. Asexual reproduction is by various kinds of nonflagellated spores.

Physiological Characteristics

The reddish color of most Rhodophyta is attributable to a red pigment called **phycoerythrin;** often a blue pigment, **phycocyanin,** is also present. Since red algae contain chlorophyll, they carry on photosynthesis. The reserve food is chiefly a carbohydrate called floridean starch, which is chemically related to the type of starch found in higher plants.

Habitats and Distribution

Most species of red algae are marine plants, fewer than 50 species inhabiting fresh water. Red algae are usually attached by holdfasts to rocks, although a few are free floating. They are most abundant in warm ocean waters; only a few species inhabit the colder seas. Some species grow at considerable depths in the ocean, some of them 600 feet below the surface.

Importance in Nature and in Human Life

Many red algae are eaten by fish, and some species are fed to cattle. A few species provide food for man. *Chondrus crispus,* or "Irish moss," for example, is often used in making puddings and desserts; another red alga, *Porphyra,* is used

FIG. 19–24 (*left*). *Pelagophycus,* elk kelp, from the coast of California and Alaska.

FIG. 19–25 (*below, left*). *Dasya elegans,* red alga with delicate thallus.

FIG. 19–26 (*below, right*). *Chondrus crispus,* or Irish moss.

(Photo from Smithsonian Series.)

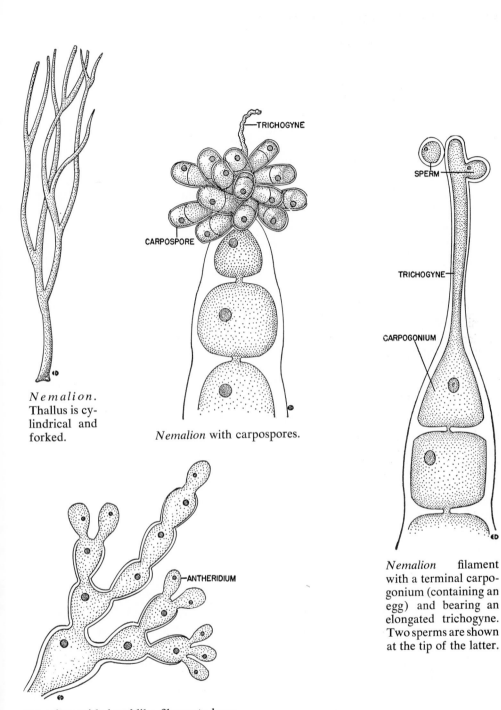

TRICHOGYNE

CARPOSPORE

Nemalion.
Thallus is cy-
lindrical and
forked.

Nemalion with carpospores.

SPERM

TRICHOGYNE

CARPOGONIUM

ANTHERIDIUM

Nemalion filament
with a terminal carpo-
gonium (containing an
egg) and bearing an
elongated trichogyne.
Two sperms are shown
at the tip of the latter.

Nemalion with brushlike filaments bearing terminal antheridia, each of which
contains one sperm.

FIG. 19–27. Structure and reproduction of *Nemalion.*

347

in parts of Europe in making soups, and is also used as food in Japan. Dulse, or sea kale, is another red alga eaten in dried form and also in soups by human beings. Several red algae, chiefly species of *Gelidium,* produce a gelatinous material called agar-agar, which has several important economic uses: as a laxative, as a sizing material for textiles, as a solidifying agent in desserts, and in culture media for bacteria and true fungi (see next chapter). Some species, called coralline algae, secrete carbonates and thus construct extensive coral reefs in tropical seas. Other red algae furnish gelatinous materials that are used in the manufacture of shoe polishes, ice cream, hair dressings, shaving creams, shampoos, and lubricating jellies. Some species cause fouling of ship hulls.

Relationships with Other Organisms

The Rhodophyceae differ from all other algal divisions, except Cyanophyta, in their lack of flagellated reproductive cells. Red algae and blue-green algae are similar also in their pigmentation; some blue-green algae contain a red pigment related chemically to phycoerythrin, and some red algae possess the blue pigment phycocyanin that is characteristic of blue-green algae. The significance of these similarities is uncertain; they probably mean that these two divisions may have had a common ancestry.

Representative Members

Nemalion is a genus of red algae that are attached to rocks of sea coasts. A *Nemalion* plant has a cylindrical, branching body (Figure 19–27), with a basal holdfast. Some branches bear short filaments whose tips produce antheridia, each with one sperm. Other branches bear the characteristic female gametangia (**carpogonia**) of red algae, each with a single egg and a trichogyne. A sperm, carried by water, reaches a trichogyne and adheres to it, the sperm nucleus passing down the trichogyne to effect union with the egg nucleus. Meiosis occurs in the zygote, and many short protuberances are formed from the trichogyne; **carpospores,** produced at the tips of these protuberances, become detached and grow into new *Nemalion* plants.

Other red algae have somewhat more complex life cycles, which will not be considered here. In many species, a definite alternation of a free-living gametophyte plant with a free-living sporophyte plant occurs.

⋘ SUMMARY

1. The subkingdom Thallophyta contains the structurally simplest and most primitive plants. Their bodies lack true roots, stems, and leaves; they lack vascular tissues (except for some brown algae that have sieve tube cells); they do not form embryos; and their gametangia are usually unicellular. The Thallophyta constitute a somewhat artificial subkingdom.

2. The name algae is applied to those divisions whose members contain chlorophyll and carry on photosynthesis. The fungi and bacteria are divisions that lack chlorophyll and obtain their food as saprophytes or parasites.

3. Algae are chiefly water plants, a minority of species living on damp soil, tree bark, moist stones, and on other land substrata.

4. Algae exhibit a great variety of colors because of the several types of pigments they contain in addition to chlorophyll.

5. Reproduction of algae is by a variety of methods. Asexual reproduction is chiefly by fission, cell division, spores, and fragmentation. In many aquatic algae, swimming zoospores are produced. Both isogamous and heterogamous sexual reproduction occur in algae. Some algae are homothallic, others heterothallic. Male gametangia are called antheridia, female gametangia oogonia (carpogonia in red algae).

6. The "hunger theory of sex" holds that isogamy, the more primitive type of sexual reproduction, may have arisen through the fusion of very small spores, which, incapable of growing individually into new plants because of their limited food reserves, pooled their resources by fusion. The resulting zygote, with double the amount of food in a single spore, was then able to develop into a new individual. The structural similarity between zoospores and isogametes in certain algae (for example, *Ulothrix*) is cited as support of this theory.

7. Many algae have a definite alternation of generations. In alternation of generations the chromosome number is doubled as a result of the union of gametes. The fertilized egg or zygote grows into a multicellular, diploid sporophyte plant that later produces haploid spores by a process involving meiosis. These spores then develop into haploid gametophytes that, in turn, produce gametes. In other algae, meiosis occurs when the zygote germinates, in which case the zygote is the only diploid phase of the life cycle.

8. The division Cyanophyta, or blue-green algae, has the following distinguishing characteristics: bodies unicellular or colonial; no organized nuclei; chromatin scattered; no chloroplasts; chlorophyll diffused in cytoplasm; a blue pigment, phycocyanin, present in addition to chlorophyll; reproduction exclusively asexual, chiefly by fission, in a few species by spores; no flagellated reproductive cells; cells often embedded in a slime sheath; reserve food cyanophycean starch; chiefly inhabitants of fresh water, a few species marine.

9. The division Euglenophyta, or euglenoids, has the following distinguishing characteristics: definite nuclei and chloroplasts in cells; grass-green color; reserve foods paramylum and fats; most species naked unicellular plants with flagella inserted in a gullet; reproduction chiefly by cell division; fresh-water plants.

10. The division Chlorophyta, or green algae, has the following distinguishing characteristics: grass color; definite nuclei and chloroplasts; cellulose cell walls; reserve food chiefly starch; motile cells with flagella of equal length at anterior ends; unicellular, colonial, or multicellular plants; reproduce asexually by cell division, fragmentation, zoospores, or immobile spores; reproduce sexually by isogamy or heterogamy; gametangia always unicellular; chiefly fresh-water plants.

11. The division Chrysophyta, or yellow-green algae, golden-brown algae, and diatoms, has the following distinguishing characteristics: considerable concentrations of yellowish and brownish pigments along with chlorophyll; definite

nuclei and plastids; food reserves chiefly oils; cell walls of two overlapping halves, often impregnated with silica; flagella present or absent; flagella when present of unequal length with minute branches; unicellular, less frequently colonial or multicellular plants; reproduction by cell division, zoospores, immobile spores, and isogamy; widely distributed in fresh and salt water and in soils.

12. The division Phaeophyta, or brown algae, has the following distinguishing characteristics: brownish in color because of masking of chlorophyll by brown pigment, fucoxanthin; definite nuclei and plastids; multicellular, often complex in structure with holdfasts, stipes, and blades; air bladders often present; motile reproductive cells pear shaped and with two lateral unequal flagella; most have alternation of generations; in some species, one generation is limited to only a few cells, while in others, both generations consist of similar plants of equal size; sieve tube cells and cambiumlike cells occur in some species; reproduction is by fragmentation, zoospores, immobile spores, isogamy, and heterogamy; almost exclusively marine plants.

13. The division Rhodophyta, or red algae, has the following distinguishing characteristics: green color of chlorophyll usually masked by a red pigment, phycoerythrin; reserve food is floridean starch; multicellular plants often ribbonlike or feathery, usually with holdfasts; rarely exceed 3 feet in length; no flagellated reproductive cells; female gametangium is carpogonium, with trichogyne; many have alternation of generations; chiefly marine plants.

14. Algae are important in nature and in human life in the following major ways: as sources of food for fish and for other aquatic animals and for soil animals; as sources of oxygen in water; as agents of water pollution; as formers of travertine and coral reefs; as human food; as food for cattle and sheep; as sources of iodine, potash, magnesium, and other substances important in medicine or in soil fertilizers; as causal agents of fouling of ships; as sources of agar-agar and other gelatinous material for bacteriological media, soups and desserts, shoe polishes, cosmetics, shaving cream, laxatives, and textile sizings. Diatoms are important ingredients in polishes for metals and other materials, in some tooth powders, in insulation of steam pipes, refrigeration systems, and blast furnaces, in dynamite, in filters for clarifying liquids, as construction materials; diatoms of past ages probably contributed to the formation of petroleum.

15. The relationships of the various algal divisions with each other are not known. It is generally thought that they are parallel series that have developed independently of each other, possibly from a common ancestral stock.

16. The Chlorophyta are regarded as the source group from which higher plants probably evolved.

⠅⠅⠅ SUGGESTED READINGS FOR INTERESTED STUDENTS

1. Bold, H. C., *Morphology of Plants*. Harper & Row, New York, 1957.
2. Smith, G. M., ed., *Manual of Phycology*. Ronald Press, New York, 1951.
3. Smith, G. M., *Cryptogamic Botany*, Vol. 1, *Algae and Fungi*. McGraw-Hill, New York, 1938.

4. Tiffany, L. H., *Algae, The Grass of Many Waters.* C. C. Thomas, Springfield, Ill., 1938.

TOPICS AND QUESTIONS FOR STUDY

1. Characterize the Thallophyta as a whole.
2. Distinguish between algae and fungi. Why are the algae considered an artificial group?
3. List the distinguishing characteristics of the following algal divisions: Cyanophyta, Chlorophyta, Euglenophyta, Chrysophyta, Phaeophyta, and Rhodophyta.
4. List and describe all asexual methods of reproduction in the algae.
5. List and describe the methods of sexual reproduction in the algae.
6. Describe briefly the "hunger theory of sex," and describe evidence in its support.
7. What is alternation of generations? State two differences between gametophyte and sporophyte generations.
8. Describe briefly the distribution and habitats of the divisions of algae.
9. Make a complete list of ways in which algae influence human life.
10. Differentiate among unicellular, colonial, and multicellular organisms.
11. Describe the structure and reproduction of *Gloeocapsa, Oscillatoria,* and *Nostoc.*
12. Describe the economic importance of the Cyanophyta.
13. Why is *Euglena* classified both as a plant and as an animal?
14. Describe the structure and reproduction of *Euglena.*
15. Contrast the Chlorophyta and the Cyanophyta.
16. Describe the structure and reproduction of *Chlamydomonas, Ulothrix, Oedogonium, Protococcus,* and *Spirogyra.*
17. Compare the reproduction of *Ulothrix* and that of *Oedogonium.*
18. List the ways in which Chlorophyta are important in human life.
19. Characterize the Chrysophyta.
20. Describe the structure and reproduction of diatoms.
21. List the economic uses of diatoms.
22. Describe the structural features of brown algae.
23. Describe the body structure and reproduction of *Ectocarpus* and *Fucus.*
24. Describe alternation of generations in the brown algae.
25. List the ways in which brown algae are important in human life.
26. Describe the habitats and distribution of brown algae.
27. Describe the habitats and distribution of red algae.
28. Describe the structure and reproductive characteristics of red algae.
29. Describe the structure and reproduction of *Nemalion.*
30. List the ways in which red algae are important to man.

20 ⫷⫷-⫷⫷-⫷⫷-⫷⫷

Thallophyta: Schizomy-cophyta (Bacteria)

Bacteria constitute a rather well-defined group of organisms that are unique in their extremely small size (they are the smallest of all known living organisms) and that are extremely simple in structure. Although they have sometimes been regarded as animals and have also been classified among the true fungi **(Eumycophyta),** they are generally placed in a distinct plant division, **Schizomycophyta,** by most biologists. Bacteria, which number about 1700 species, possess certain characteristics that stamp them as plants: some species are able to utilize carbon dioxide in the synthesis of organic compounds, as are green plants; their cell walls may have cellulose or compounds related to cellulose; and their cell structure and reproduction are similar to those of certain algae and true fungi. Bacteria lack chlorophyll and are chiefly heterotrophic, that is, unable to manufacture their own food; most bacteria are saprophytes or parasites. A few species are able to synthesize foods from inorganic matter as a result of chemosynthesis and a type of photosynthesis that involves pigments other than chlorophyll. Such auto-

trophic bacterial species constitute a minute segment of the total number of bacteria in the world today.

Growth Forms and Structure

Bacteria are typically one-celled organisms, which infrequently exceed 3 to 5 microns in length. A few species of bacteria are approximately 0.15 micron (1/165,000 inch) in diameter! Of these smaller bacteria, as many as 900, placed side by side, would just cover the printed period at the end of this sentence. Bacteria are thus visible only under considerable magnification by high-power microscopes.

There are three common forms of true bacteria: **coccus** forms, which are spherical or ovoid, **bacillus** forms, which are cylindrical or rod shaped, and **spirillum** forms, which are spiral (Figure 20–1). A fourth type of form, a filament, or thread, occurs in some species of bacteria; the number of filamentous bacterial species is small as compared with the number of rod, sphere, and spiral forms. The form of a bacterial cell is usually constant for

352

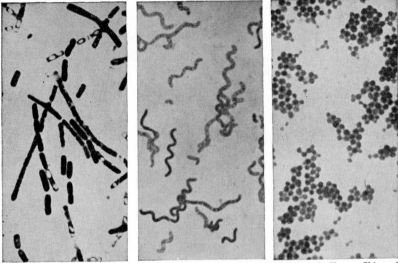

(*Copyright, General Biological Supply House, Chicago.*)

FIG. 20–1. *Left:*   *Bacillus anthrax,* the anthrax bacterium. 2300×.
   Center: *Spirillum rubrum,* a bacterium found commonly in water. 2150×.
   Right: *Staphylococcus aureus,* cause of boils and other skin infections. 2600×.

each species; the form may be altered by changes in environmental conditions, but such structural changes are usually temporary. In a few species of bacteria, however, several types of cell forms may appear in the life cycle; tiny spores develop into filaments that fragment into segments, within which spores are then produced.

A bacterial cell has a cell wall, which, in some species, contains cellulose; often the outer portion of the wall is modified into a thin slime layer, or **capsule.** Some bacteria are embedded in a gelatinous, slimy mass called a **zoogloea,** within which bacteria may develop in great numbers as they reproduce. The protoplasm of bacteria is extremely difficult to study because of the very small size of these organisms. For many years it was believed that bacterial protoplasm was relatively undifferentiated, without distinct nuclei, but recent research with the

electron microscope indicates that bacterial protoplasm is probably as complex as that of other plants; bacteria contain no plastids, but their protoplasm has membranes, vacuoles, and, at least in some species, structures that are apparently nuclei, although these nuclei are extremely minute and therefore difficult to observe.

Many kinds of bacteria are able to move about in liquids in which they live. The movements of bacteria are usually the result of the rhythmic, wavelike or screwlike motions of slender flagella. The numbers and positions of flagella vary in different species of bacteria; thus, some bacteria have only one flagellum (for example, cholera bacterium), others have a tuft of flagella at one end (for example, *Spirillum undula*) or in some cases a tuft at each end, and still others have flagella covering the entire body surface (typhoid bacillus).

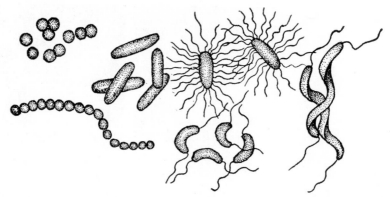

FIG. 20–2. Coccus, bacillus, and spirillum forms of bacteria. Notice the flagella.

Reproduction and Life Cycle

Inheritance studies of a few species of bacteria have shown that under certain conditions a recombination of genetic characters does occur. Many bacteriologists believe that this behavior results from a kind of sexual reproduction. Much additional information must be obtained, however, before the extent of sexual reproduction in this group can be determined.

Asexual reproduction is perhaps characteristic of all bacteria. The most common means is cell division, or fission, in which the bacterium divides into two new one-celled bacteria, the nuclear material apparently undergoing a process analogous to mitosis. In bacillus and spirillum forms, the division plane is typically transverse, that is, at right angles to the long axis of the cell (Figure 20–7); in coccus forms, there may be more than one plane. Often, after division, the newly formed cells remain together, forming colonies of varying forms and sizes. Some of these are filamentous, or threadlike, others are cubical, platelike, or of some other shape. The forms of these colonies are rather constant in some species, and

bacterial identification may thus often be aided by observing the structure of colonies. Bacteria often develop in great numbers, forming colonies held within the surrounding zoogloea. Under favorable conditions of temperature, food, and moisture supply, fission occurs as often as every 20 minutes. A cholera bacterium, reproducing at its most rapid rate, would, in 24 hours, produce *offspring numbering 4,700,000,000,000,000,000,000 and weighing about 2000 tons!* This exceedingly rapid reproduction is only theoretically possible, however, for inadequacy of food supply in any one place and the accumulation of toxic waste products of metabolism prevent such unlimited multiplication.

Some species of bacteria can form highly resistant **endospores** (Figure 20–3), thus enabling the organism to survive adverse environmental conditions that would kill cells in the vegetative state. Endospore formation is initiated as physical and/or chemical conditions for growth become progressively unfavorable, for example, through desiccation, depletion of the food substrate, and temperature change. An endospore is formed within a vegetative cell by condensation of the protoplasm into a spherical or ovoid mass that then develops a relatively thick wall. Accompanying this condensation is a loss of some water so that the resulting spore has a lower moisture content than the vegetative bacterial cell. When the endospore is mature, it is commonly liberated by the rupture or disintegration of the wall of the old vegetative cell. With the return of favorable environmental conditions, the spore germinates and will eventually grow into a vegetative cell of the type from which it was formed.

Some bacteria have special means by which they can reproduce asexually. For example, a process called **segmentation** occurs in some species; this involves the production by bacterial cells of tiny bodies called **gonidia,** which, upon encountering a suitable environment, grow into mature bacterial cells. Also, some filamentous bacteria produce small bodies called **conidia,** usually in chains at their tips.

The scientific divisional name of the bacteria Schizomycophyta refers to the fission method of reproduction. The prefix *schizo* is derived from a Greek word that means to split or cut; its use in the naming of this group of organisms refers to the characteristic splitting of bacterial cells in the fission process. The word *myco-* comes from a Greek word for fungus, and *phyta-* from the Greek word for plant. Thus, Schizomycophyta means "fungous plants that split."

FIG. 20–3. Sketch showing various types of bacterial endospores.

Physiological Characteristics

As stated earlier in this chapter, most bacteria, since they lack chlorophyll, are unable to manufacture foods from inorganic substances and thus live as saprophytes or parasites, utilizing foods manufactured originally by green plants: the growth, physiological activities, and reproduction of bacteria depend upon adequate supplies of food and moisture, upon a favorable temperature, and upon certain other environmental factors.

A minority of bacterial species is **autotrophic,** that is, capable of synthesizing organic compounds from carbon dioxide and other simple, inorganic substances. Such autotrophic species thus resemble green plants, which are also autotrophic. Autotrophic bacteria may be separated into two groups: chemosynthetic species, which obtain the energy required for their synthesis of organic compounds from the oxidation of certain chemicals such as iron compounds and hydrogen sulfide, and photosynthetic species, which utilize light energy in promoting their food-making processes. The few species of photosynthetic bacteria contain purple and greenish pigments by which they utilize light energy in the synthesis of foods. The green pigment in certain of these bacteria is not chlorophyll, but has a similar function.

Although these chemosynthetic and photosynthetic bacteria form a distinct minority of all bacterial species, they are widely distributed and their importance in nature is tremendous. Sulfur bacteria, for example, are responsible for the conversion of hydrogen sulfide, a common product of protein decay, to sulfur and then to sulfuric acid, which undergoes chemical reactions in soils to form sulfates, the principal source of sulfur for green plants. The sulfur bacteria thus play a very important role in nature, since, without their acitvity, most of the sulfur in nature might be locked up in hydrogen sulfide, and the supply of sulfates, necessary for the nutrition of higher plants, might disappear. This important activity of sulfur bacteria proceeds not only on land, but likewise in fresh water and salt water, with the result that hydrogen sulfide is constantly being transformed into sulfur compounds that both land and sea plants can utilize. Many biologists believe that the world's iron ore deposits are products of iron-oxidizing bacteria; thus, iron bacteria of past ages have been important in determining the chemical nature of portions of the earth's crust.

The photosynthetic and chemosynthetic bacteria utilize carbon dioxide as the principal source of carbon required for the synthesis of carbohydrates, fats, proteins, and other organic compounds. Parasitic and saprophytic bacteria, unable to synthesize organic substances from carbon dioxide, live at the expense of organic compounds manufactured by other organisms. Some parasites, called **obligate parasites,** can survive only when they are able to absorb foods from the tissues of a **host,** the organism that they parasitize; **facultative parasites** usually live upon the living tissues of a host, but may, under certain circumstances, derive nourishment from nonliving organic matter. Saprophytes utilize organic compounds present in nonliving matter, such as the decomposing bodies of animals, dead leaves, bark, wood, roots, and fruits, unsterilized and unrefrigerated meat, vegetables, pastries, and other foodstuffs, and animal feces.

Some bacteria are very specific in the types of organic compounds they utilize,

deriving their nourishment from certain specific substances, whereas other species can use a great variety of organic substances. Many bacteria live largely upon carbohydrates, while others utilize proteins, fats, and amino acids. In general, the common types of saprophytic bacteria that are responsible for processes of decomposition in nature are rather cosmopolitan in their nutritional requirements, obtaining nourishment from a variety of organic substances. Many parasitic, disease-producing bacteria are very specific in their food requirements and can utilize only a few types of organic compounds. Thus, certain parasitic bacteria can live only on blood, different species requiring different types of blood, or on certain specific tissues of host plants or animals.

Like other kinds of plants, bacteria manufacture enzymes, with the aid of which they digest foods, converting complex or water-insoluble foods into simpler or water-soluble foods. The enzymes of bacteria include amylase, which converts starch to malt sugar; lipases, which digest fats into fatty acids and glycerol; invertase, which transforms cane sugar into glucose and fructose; maltase, which digests maltose into glucose; and proteases, which digest proteins into amino acids. Some of the enzymes are active within bacterial cells, and are also often secreted by the bacteria into the surrounding medium, where they promote digestion.

Like all other living organisms, both plants and animals, bacteria carry on respiration, the oxidation of foods with release of energy that is necessary for growth, reproduction, and other cellular processes. Anaerobic bacteria, which thrive in the absence of free, gaseous oxygen, carry on anaerobic respiration or

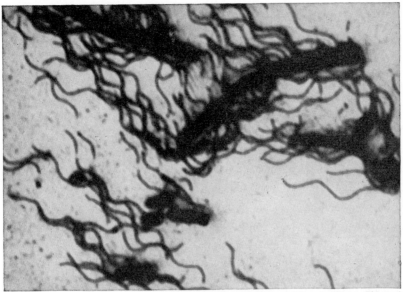

(Copyright, General Biological Supply House, Chicago.)

FIG. 20–4. Highly magnified photograph of *Eberthella typhosa*, a rod-shaped bacterium that causes typhoid fever in man. Notice the numerous, long flagella.

fermentation, in which, under the control of certain respiratory enzymes, foods are broken down, with the formation of carbon dioxide and intermediate organic compounds, such as alcohols and organic acids, and with the release of energy. Most aerobic species of bacteria, which live only in an environment containing free oxygen, complete the process of respiration through the aerobic phases, liberating carbon dioxide, water, and energy. Some facultative anaerobes, under anaerobic conditions, form carbon dioxide and organic compounds; given sufficient free oxygen, these organisms may complete the oxidation of these compounds to water and carbon dioxide.

As a result of their metabolic activities, different species of bacteria form different types of products, such as lactic, butyric, and acetic acids; gases (including carbon dioxide, methane, hydrogen sulfide, and others); red, yellow, orange, and blue pigments; and other substances. These products are often important in distinguishing among different species of bacteria.

Habitats and Distribution

As a result of their heterotrophic mode of life, most bacteria are limited to places where organic substances are readily available. According to their particular complement of enzymes, bacteria live within and upon the bodies of other living things, in soils and water, in foodstuffs, in dead bodies, and in sewage and debris of all kinds. Since most bacteria do not carry on photosynthesis, they are independent of light and can live either in light or in darkness; many species, in fact, thrive better in darkness and are injured or killed by exposure to sunlight. Bacteria

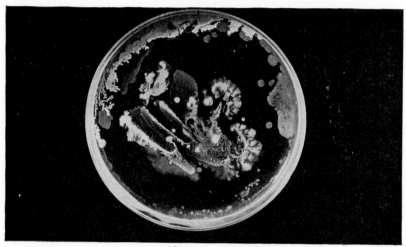

FIG. 20–5. Laboratory methods of growing bacteria. A medium, consisting of agar, a gelatinlike material, plus minerals and suitable organic compounds (sugars, blood, proteins, or others) is poured into Petri dishes, then sterilized, then inoculated with bacteria. The Petri dish culture shows several types of bacterial colonies.

require considerable amounts of moisture for their growth, and thus flourish in damp places, such as the tissues of other organisms, moist soils, manures, and foodstuffs with high water content. The occurrence of aerobic and anaerobic bacteria is conditioned by the presence or absence of free oxygen in the surrounding medium. Bacteria are probably the most widely distributed of all living organisms.

Importance in Nature and in Human Life

Harmful or Disadvantageous Activities of Bacteria. Bacteria are important to man and in nature in many ways, some harmful, some useful and beneficial. Among the harmful or wasteful results of bacterial activity are these:

1. Bacteria cause many serious diseases of man, for example, tuberculosis, meningitis, pneumonia, lockjaw, typhoid fever, cholera, diphtheria, and dysentery.

2. Bacteria cause diseases of domesticated animals, for example, tuberculosis of cattle and hogs, anthrax of sheep, chicken cholera, pneumonia, glanders in horses and sheep, and septicemia in cattle.

3. Bacteria cause many diseases of cultivated plants, for example, fire blight of pears, citrus canker, cotton root rot, potato black leg, celery, cucumber, and eggplant rot, and wilt diseases (caused chiefly by the stoppage of vascular tissues by bacteria) of tomatoes, potatoes, cucumbers, squash, and cantaloupes. These diseases cause large crop losses, the value of which reaches many millions of dollars annually.

4. Bacteria cause the spoilage of large quantities of human foodstuffs: the souring of milk, the rotting of meat, the spoilage of butter, potatoes, vetetables, and fruits, both fresh and canned. In their growth in these foodstuffs, bacteria frequently excrete waste products **(toxins)**

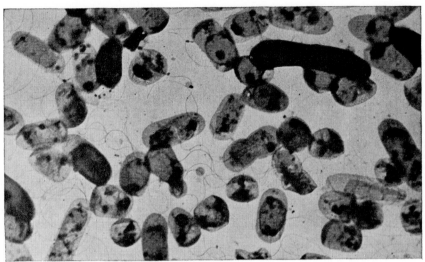

(Photo by Albert Vatter.)

FIG. 20–6. Electronmicrograph of *Pseudomonas aeruginosa,* a rod-shaped bacterium. Note flagella and cell contents.

that are toxic to human beings and frequently cause severe, even fatal, poisoning in persons who eat such bacteria-contaminated foods.

5. Denitrifying bacteria, which are especially abundant and active under anaerobic conditions in wet soils and soils with high organic matter content, break down nitrates through intermediate compounds to free nitrogen gas, which escapes into the air. Denitrifying bacteria thus reduce soil fertility by depleting the nitrogen content of soils.

An important objective of bacteriology is the control of harmful bacteria wherever they may occur. Some control techniques are designed to kill the bacteria, hence are **bactericidal;** others are **bacteriostatic,** that is, they prevent the growth of bacteria without actually killing them. The methods most commonly used include high and low temperatures, chemical treatment, drying, and irradiation. One principal type of heat treatment used in the preservation of food and in

many other processes is **sterilization.** In sterilization, all bacteria (vegetative cells and spores) are killed. Steam under pressure in an autoclave is commonly used to provide a sufficiently high temperature that is then maintained for a time determined by the nature of the material being sterilized. It should be noted that the temperature of boiling water (212°F) is sufficient to kill all vegetative cells but *not* high enough to kill all kinds of bacterial spores. Canned foods are commonly heat treated after they have been sealed in the container. Improper sterilization or sealing may result in contamination of the food, which, if eaten, could cause serious food poisoning. One of the most dangerous types of food poisoning is **botulism.** The causal agent of this disease is a toxin secreted by *Closteridium botulinum,* an anaerobic, spore-forming bacterium that occasionally contaminates food. Another method of heat treatment used in the preservation of food is **pasteurization.** In this process the temperature of the ma-

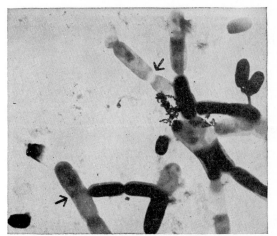

FIG. 20–7. Electronmicrograph of *Bacillus subtilis,* a rod-shaped species of common occurrence in soil, water, and milk. Arrows indicate fission.

(Photo by Albert Vatter.)

terial being treated (milk, for example) is raised for 30 minutes to approximately 145°F, as a result of which certain bacteria are destroyed, but not necessarily all species. Most types of pathogenic bacteria, including *Mycobacterium tuberculosis* (Figure 1–5), are destroyed by this treatment. Another pasteurizing process raises the temperature to about 160°F for 15 seconds. Prolonged heating at high temperatures would adversely alter the properties of the material being treated. Pasteurization is commonly applied to milk, cream, beer, and wines. Many products, such as foods and drugs, are frequently kept refrigerated since low temperatures inhibit bacterial activity. Subfreezing temperatures of food lockers are very effective in preserving foods.

Chemical agents used as food preservatives act chiefly in two ways. They may increase the osmotic concentration of the foods to a degree that bacteria in these foods are plasmolyzed and inactivated or killed as a result of plasmolysis. The effectiveness of salt in preserving meats and fish, and of sugar in preserving jellies and jams results from this plasmolytic effect. Other chemical agents added to

foods have a direct killing effect upon bacteria; among such bactericides are benzoic acid, salicylic acid, and their salts, boric acid, and borates. Caution must be used in the addition of these preservative substances to foods, since if their concentration becomes too high they may exert harmful physiological effects upon consumers.

Chemicals are widely used against bacteria in medicine, hygiene, public health, and other fields. Those chemicals that kill bacteria are called **germicides** or **disinfectants;** others inhibit or prevent the growth and activities of bacteria and are called **antiseptics.** These terms, while generally useful, require some qualification since a bactericidal compound at a sufficiently low concentration may exhibit bacteriostatic properties instead. Other factors, for example, kind and number of bacteria, temperature, and length of exposure to a particular chemical, also influence the effect of chemical (and physical) treatment. Among the best known drugs used to combat bacterial infections are the **sulfonamides** (sulfanilamide and sulfadiazine, for example) and the **antibiotics.** Antibiotics are chemical agents obtained from certain living organisms: penicillin from the mold *Penicillium;* tyrothricin, bacitracin, and polymyxins from species of *Bacillus;* and, from species of the branched, filamentous bacterium, *Streptomyces,* about fifteen commercially available kinds including aureomycin, chloromycetin, streptomycin, and terramycin. These antibiotics have been so effective in the treatment of diseases that they are popularly called "wonder drugs."

Drying, especially of foods, makes bacterial growth difficult or impossible, since bacteria require considerable amounts of water for their metabolism. Various techniques are used in drying foods for preservation, and different types of foods are dried to differing moisture contents. Thus, "dried" prunes, raisins, and apricots may contain as much as 25 percent moisture; despite this considerable moisture content, bacterial growth is virtually impossible, since the high sugar content of these fruits exerts a plasmolytic effect upon microorganisms. Other foods are dried completely for preservation purposes; for example, dehydrated vegetables, powdered eggs, powdered milk, and dried meats and fish. Some foods, such as cereals, beans, and nuts, undergo a marked decrease in moisture content as they mature, so that they naturally contain a very low moisture content by the time of harvest or shipment; thus, they are naturally protected against bacterial decomposition. Foods with high water content, such as tomatoes, beef, bananas, and fresh fish, are quickly decomposed by bacteria.

The bactericidal effect of certain kinds of radiant energy has been used with varying degrees of success for some time. Such radiations include ultraviolet rays, x-rays, gamma rays, and powerful electron beams. Ultraviolet rays are widely used for surface sterilization and air purification; moreover, they are relatively safe and inexpensive to produce. The other radiations are used in special applications requiring higher energies and greater penetrance.

Beneficial or Advantageous Activities of Bacteria. The beneficial activities of bacteria far outweigh their damaging effects upon mankind. Among the most valuable activities of bacteria are the following:

1. The metabolic processes and products of bacteria are important in many industries. The manufacture of vinegar, of butter, of certain kinds of cheese, and of sauerkraut, the tanning of leather, the curing of black tea, coffee, and cocoa beans, the removal of flax fibers from the stems of flax plants, the curing of vanilla pods, and the production of ensilage through the fermentation of fodder are examples of industrial and agricultural activities promoted by bacteria. Bacteria utilize in their metabolism various sugars, proteins, and other organic compounds, and in their metabolic activities excrete products, some of which have important commercial uses. Among these products are acetone, an ingredient used in the manufacture of explosives, photographic film, rayon, and other products; butyl alcohol, a commercial solvent especially valuable in the manufacture of synthetic lacquers; lactic acid, of special usefulness in the tanning industry; citric acid, employed as a flavoring in lemon-flavored confections, beverages, and other foodstuffs; and vitamins, useful in medicines and foods.

The manufacture of vinegar is one of oldest processes in human history that involves bacterial metabolism. Vinegar production begins with the fermentation of apple juice by yeasts, the carbohydrates

FIG. 20–8. Winter-pea plants. *Left:* Plants grown from uninoculated seeds. *Right:* Plants from seeds inoculated with proper strain of nitrogen-fixing nodule bacteria. Notice the nodules.

in the juice being converted to alcohol. In the presence of oxygen, species of the vinegar bacterium, *Acetobacter,* oxidize the alcohol to acetic acid. Other alcoholic substrates used in vinegar making are cider, wine, beerwort, and the fermented juice of sugar beets.

Ensilage is an important product of bacterial metabolism. Green plant parts, such as chopped corn stems and leaves, are packed into a silo, where they are fermented by bacteria. During this fermentation, organic acids, especially lactic acid, are produced. These acids have a preservative action that prevents the spoiling of the ensilage. Ensilage, or silage as it is sometimes called, is a nutritious food in

the diets of cattle and other domesticated animals during those seasons when fresh, green plant tissues are not available for feeding.

2. Bacteria bring about the decomposition of proteins, fats, carbohydrates, and other complex organic compounds in the bodies of plants and animals and in their waste products. Thus, they clear the earth of organic debris and return to the soil and air the simple substances necessary for the maintenance of soil fertility and for the continued food-making activities of green plants.

The bacteria involved in the decomposition of nitrogenous organic compounds are so important in the maintenance of soil fertility that they deserve somewhat detailed description. The groups of bacteria involved in nitrogen transformations in the soil are **ammonifying bacteria, nitrifying bacteria, nitrogen-fixing bacteria,** and **denitrifying bacteria.** Ammonifying bacteria transform various proteinaceous substances into ammonia (NH_3) in the soil, in a process called **ammonification.** The ammonia thus formed usually reacts with other substances in the soil to form ammonium salts, for example, ammonium sulphate. Under certain conditions some plants can obtain nitrogen from the soil in the form of the ammonium ion (NH_4^+), which is taken in through the roots. Green plants obtain most of their nitrogen by the absorption of nitrates into the roots. Certain bacteria in the soil convert ammonia to nitrites ($—NO_2$) whereas other bacteria oxidize the nitrites to nitrates ($—NO_3$); this process is called **nitrification.** Ammonifying and nitrifying bacteria are, therefore, directly concerned in the transformation of protein compounds of nonliving organic matter into nitrates and thus play a major role in the maintenance

(*Photo by Urbana Laboratories.*)

FIG. 20–9. Austrian vetch. *Left:* Plants grown from seeds inoculated with proper strain of nitrogen-fixing nodule bacteria. *Right:* Plants from un-inoculated seeds.

of soil fertility. Nitrogen-fixing bacteria contribute to soil fertility by incorporating atmospheric nitrogen (which green plants cannot utilize) into organic compounds, a process called **nitrogen fixation.** There are two types of nitrogen-fixing bacteria: saprophytic, soil-inhabiting species, and others that live in small swellings or **nodules** (Figure 20–9) on the roots of various seed plants, chiefly legumes such as alfalfa, clover, and soybeans. The saprophytic bacteria must die and be decomposed before their fixed nitrogen can be converted to nitrates as described above. The relationship between the nodule bacteria (genus *Rhizobium*) and the plants they infect is one of **symbiosis,** a state of more or less mutual benefit. The bacteria secure food from the tissues of the host plant, and the host plant obtains nitrogen that is fixed by the bacteria. It is because of this relationship

and activity that leguminous plants usually enrich the soil in which they grow. In order to ensure the development of nodule bacteria, pure cultures of various strains of such bacteria are prepared commercially in laboratories and are mixed with the proper types of seeds before planting, or are added to the soil in which the seeds are to be sown. Although these symbiotic bacteria are widely distributed in soils, they cannot fix atmospheric nitrogen unless they are associated with a suitable host plant. Inoculation of seeds or soil with the proper strain of bacteria results in a higher percentage of infections than would result from chance contact with naturally occurring soil organisms, and has the added advantage of bringing together the seeds and the particular strain of bacteria best suited to the kind of seeds planted (Figure 20–10). The three processes mentioned above directly

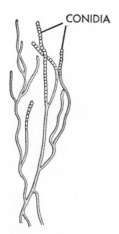

FIG. 20–10. Sketch of filamentous bacterium, *Actinomyces,* showing chains of conidia.

or indirectly increase the nitrate content in soil. In addition to vascular plants, which generally obtain their nitrogen in the form of nitrates, certain soil bacteria utilize nitrates for their metabolism and, in a sense, compete with higher plants for the available nitrate. Some of these bacteria are able to reduce nitrates to ammonia; others, the denitrifying bacteria, are able to convert nitrates to gaseous nitrogen in a process called **denitrification.** Since denitrification occurs only under anaerobic conditions, it removes only small amounts of nitrate from well-cultivated soil.

A discussion of the beneficial effects of bacteria in relation to soil fertility should also emphasize the work of **sulfur bacteria,** which, as described earlier in this chapter, convert hydrogen sulfide, a product of protein decay, through intermediate compounds into sulfuric acid, which undergoes transformation into sulfates. Still other bacteria are able to oxidize elemental sulfur to sulfates that plants can use. Sulfates are the major source of sulfur, an essential element for the metabolism of green plants. Were it not for the sulfur bacteria, the supply of sulfates

in soils would become exhausted, and the growth of green plants might become impossible.

3. Bacteria promote digestive and possibly other physiological processes in the intestinal tracts of animals. The digestion of cellulose by such herbivorous animals as horses and cattle results in part from cellulose-digesting enzymes excreted by bacteria inhabiting the intestines of these animals. Bacteria also dwell in large numbers in the human intestinal tract, particularly in the lower part of the small intestine and in the large intestine. The activity of these bacteria in the human gut and the significance of this activity are not known positively; some physiologists believe that these bacteria carry on certain digestive activities of value to the human body, while others believe that lactic acid and other metabolic products of these normally occurring bacteria inhibit the growth of putrefactive and possibly certain pathogenic bacteria. Whatever may be their specific physiological significance, it is certain that the maintenance of a normal bacterial flora in the human intestinal tract is essential to the health of the human organism and that any major disturbance in this intestinal bacterial flora results in derangements of health. It is interesting that from one fourth to one third of the dry weight of human feces consists of bodies of microorganisms, mostly bacteria. Pathogenic bacteria sometimes dwell in the human digestive tract and pass out with the feces; bacteria that cause typhoid fever and certain types of dysentery are often spread through feces. For this reason, the use of human feces as a fertilizer for soils, a practice common in many parts of the world, often contaminates carrots, potatoes, lettuce, radishes, and other vegetables and thus spreads typhoid fever and dysentery.

Relationships with Other Organisms

Nothing is known of the historical origin of bacteria upon the earth's surface and little is known positively concerning their relationships with other groups of living organisms. There is no doubt that bacteria constitute a group of great antiquity. This fact, together with their structural simplicity and small size, has led many biologists to consider them as possibly the first living organisms. Recent speculations seem to favor the view that the first living things were less complex heterotrophs than the bacteria of today. The morphological and reproductive similarities among bacteria, blue-green algae, and certain true fungi are believed by some biologists to indicate close relationship among these groups. Other biologists regard these groups as having had a more or less parallel development from some unknown common ancestral stock. Still others prefer to regard bacteria as degenerate organisms derived by evolutionary reduction from some more ancient and complex stock similar, perhaps, to the blue-green algae.

Representative Members

The classification and identification of bacteria involve certain difficulties not found in other groups of plants. These difficulties spring in part from the very small size of bacteria and the consequent difficulty of recognizing clearly their structural characteristics, and in part from the relatively restricted range of morphological differences among different species. Such morphological differences include number, length and position of flagella, body form (rods, spheres, or spirals), and size. These differences are used, of course, in distinguishing among certain groups of bacteria, but they are often inadequate taxonomically, since several bacterial species may resemble each other in their external morphology. Thus, bacteriologists must often depend upon physiological differences to identify and classify bacterial species, and must therefore investigate the types of organic compounds that bacteria utilize, the kinds of organic acids, gases, pigments, and other compounds produced in their metabolism, their growth in relation to oxygen supply, the shapes and structure of the colonies they form, and, in addition, their reactions to various biological stains.

Bacteria are presently separated into ten orders, the largest of which, the Eubacteriales, includes most of the typical coccus, bacillus, and spirillum forms. Other orders include the sulfur bacteria, iron bacteria, spirochaetes, and others. The order Actinomycetales is especially known for the production of certain antibiotic drugs by some of its members.

⫷← SUMMARY

1. Bacteria are the smallest of all living organisms, rarely exceeding 5 microns in length.
2. Most species of bacteria are saprophytes or parasites; a few species are capable of carrying on photosynthesis and chemosynthesis.
3. There are three common body forms of most bacteria: spheres, rods, and spirals.
4. A few species of bacteria have a filamentous body form.

5. Bacteria have definite cell walls, which sometimes contain cellulose. Vacuoles are present in bacteria, but plastids are absent. Nuclei appear to occur in some bacteria.

6. Many bacteria bear flagella, the rhythmic movements of which cause bacteria to move in liquids in which they may occur.

7. The common method of reproduction in bacteria is fission, or simple cell division. After successive divisions, bacterial cells often cohere to form colonies.

8. Some bacteria form resistant endospores enabling them to survive unfavorable environmental conditions that would kill cells in the vegetative state.

9. Some bacteria form reproductive bodies called gonidia and conidia.

10. There are two types of autotrophic bacteria: chemosynthetic species and photosynthetic species.

11. Chemosynthetic species oxidize various chemicals, obtaining energy from this oxidation. This energy is utilized in food synthesis. They include sulfur bacteria, iron bacteria, and nitrifying bacteria.

12. Photosynthetic species utilize light energy in food syntheses. They include purple and green bacteria.

13. Obligate parasites can live only in parasitic fashion, facultative parasites usually live parasitically, but may also live as saprophytes.

14. Heterotrophic bacteria vary greatly in the kinds of organic compounds they utilize. They also vary in the products of their metabolism.

15. Bacteria produce many types of enzymes, the functions of which are similar to those of higher plants. Bacteria carry on various types of respiration.

16. Bacteria are probably the most widely distributed of all organisms.

17. The principal growth requirements of most bacteria are: favorable temperature, abundant moisture, and a supply of organic matter. Most bacteria are independent of light; many species are injured or killed by light.

18. Aerobic bacteria thrive only in the presence of oxygen, anaerobic bacteria in the absence of oxygen.

19. Bacteria show certain structural and reproductive similarities with blue-green algae and some true fungi. The significance of these similarities is not definitely known.

20. Bacteria exert harmful or disadvantageous effects upon human life, among which are these: they cause diseases of man, of his domesticated animals, and of crop plants, they cause food spoilage, they are frequently responsible for food poisoning, and they cause a loss of nitrogen from soil.

21. Pathogenic, or disease-producing bacteria, form poisonous substances called toxins, which injure or kill host tissues.

22. Bacteria may be destroyed by exposure to sunlight and other types of radiations and by chemical agents called disinfectants or germicides. Antiseptics inhibit the growth and activity of bacteria, but do not necessarily kill them.

23. Pasteurization of foods will kill certain bacteria but not necessarily all species; heat sterilization kills all bacteria (vegetative cells and spores).

24. Cold storage and freezing of foods inhibit bacterial growth and activity.

25. Food may also be preserved through the use of chemical preservatives, such as

salt and sugar, which plasmolyze bacteria, and as benzoic acid and benzoates, which poison bacteria.

26. Dehydration of foods is an effective method of food preservation, since bacteria cannot grow in the absence of water.

27. Bacteria exert many beneficial influences upon human life. Among these are: the production of industrially important chemicals, the production of foodstuffs such as sauerkraut, cheese, vinegar, and ensilage, the curing of cocoa and other beverages, the production of vitamins, the decomposition of dead bodies of plants and animals and of their wastes, and the maintenance of soil fertility through the activities of ammonifying bacteria, nitrifying bacteria, nitrogen-fixing bacteria, and sulfur bacteria. Some bacteria are beneficial inhabitants of animal digestive tracts.

28. Physiological characteristics are very important in the classification and identification of many types of bacteria.

29. The bacteria are separated into 10 orders, of which the Eubacteriales is the largest. The order Actinomycetales contains some bacteria that produce important antibiotic drugs.

⫷ SUGGESTED READINGS FOR INTERESTED STUDENTS

1. Adler, Irving, *How Life Began.* Signet Key Book, New American Library of World Literature, New York, 1957.

2. Pelczar, M. J., and R. D. Reid, *Microbiology.* McGraw-Hill, New York, 1958.

3. Salle, A. J., *Fundamental Principles of Bacteriology,* 5th ed. McGraw-Hill, New York, 1961.

⫷ TOPICS AND QUESTIONS FOR STUDY

1. Why are bacteria regarded as more plantlike than animallike?
2. Describe the size and structure of bacteria.
3. Describe the methods of reproduction that occur in bacteria.
4. What factors favor rapid reproduction of bacteria? What factors may cause a decrease in the rate of bacterial reproduction?
5. What factors favor a high level of physiological activity in bacteria?
6. Distinguish between aerobic and anaerobic bacteria. List some of the places in which you would find these types of bacteria growing.
7. Describe briefly how bacterial movement is caused.
8. Name some common types of chemosynthetic bacteria, and briefly describe their activity.
9. What are photosynthetic bacteria? Describe their activity.
10. Why are bacteria thought to be related to blue-green algae? Why to true fungi?
11. Why do bacteriologists consider physiological differences in the classification of bacteria? Name some of the physiological activities that bacteriologists use in differentiating among bacteria.
12. List some of the harmful activities of bacteria in human life.
13. State two reasons why the drying of foods, of bedding, of freshly washed clothing is best done in sunlight.

14. Sewage contains large numbers of bacteria, and the water in streams into which sewage is poured is rich in bacteria near the point of entrance of sewage. A few miles downstream, however, the bacterial content of the water may be greatly reduced. Explain.

15. In many parts of the world, where agriculture is very intensive, it is dangerous to eat vegetables that have grown in, or have been in contact with, soils, unless the vegetables are cooked or treated with disinfectants. Explain.

16. How do salt and sugar preserve foods?

17. List some of the important chemicals produced by bacteria. What important human foods owe their flavor and other qualities to bacterial action?

18. Describe fully the importance of bacteria in the maintenance of soil fertility. Describe the work of sulfur bacteria and of the various bacteria that bring about nitrogen transformations in the soil.

19. Describe the principal methods used to preserve foods, and explain why each is effective.

20. List all the precautions that are taken in a hospital to destroy or prevent the growth of bacteria; in a food cannery; in a swimming pool; in a well-operated restaurant.

21. What methods of personal hygiene may be used to prevent the spread of bacteria?

Thallophyta: Myxomycophyta (Slime Fungi) and Eumycophyta (True Fungi)

Myxomycophyta and Eumycophyta differ from Schizomycophyta in several ways: their bodies are much larger than those of bacteria, they are chiefly many-celled, they all possess definite nuclei readily demonstrable under a microscope, their reproduction usually includes some kind of distinct sexual process, and the production and structure of their spores are usually different from those of bacteria. Like Schizomycophyta, slime fungi and true fungi lack chlorophyll and thus, like most bacteria, they are parasites or saprophytes.

DIVISION MYXOMYCOPHYTA (SLIME FUNGI, OR SLIME MOLDS)

Growth Forms and Structure

In this division of about 500 species, the vegetative body consists of a thin mass of naked protoplasm, which may be microscopic in size or may have an area of several square inches. This naked **plasmodium** is rather viscous and slimy to the touch and may be colorless or, in some species, yellow, red, violet, or some other color. Sometimes a plasmodium becomes netlike or finely branched (Figure 21–1). The plasmodium, which contains several to many nuclei, creeps, in most species, by a flowing, amoeboid movement over logs, dead leaves, or soil, often rapidly enough so that its motion may be easily seen.

Reproduction and Life Cycle

After a period of crawling movement and food intake, the plasmodium, which in the saprophytic species lives in darkness or diffuse light under logs and leaves, moves to more exposed sites and then

369

FIG. 21–1. Plasmodium of a slime fungus, *Physarum polycephalum*, growing upon agar.

(Photo by D. A. Eggert.)

produces a number of sporangia (Figure 21–2). The structure of the sporangia is constant for each species and forms the basis for classifying and identifying the slime fungi. The sporangia vary greatly in structure in different species; they are usually large enough to be visible to the naked eye and in most species do not exceed ½ inch in length, although they may reach a length of 2 or 3 inches. These sporangia, exhibiting a series of colors— white, violet, purple, orange, brown, etc. —are among the most strikingly beautiful objects in the plant kingdom. A sporangium produces a number of microscopic spores, which, after liberation, germinate on logs, dead leaves, soil, or some other substratum in the presence of moisture and favorable temperature. Each spore produces one to four naked swarm cells that move about by means of their flagella. According to the species, they may divide repeatedly, giving rise to more swarm cells that later function as gametes in sexual reproduction, or they may lose their flagella and become amoeboid **myxamoebae** that, after several divisions, also function as gametes. The zygotes thus formed may then grow directly into the creeping plasmodium, or many zygotes may fuse to form a plasmodium. The spores and myxamoebae are haploid; the diploid zygote chromosome number, beginning with sexual fusion of the swarm cells, persists through the plasmodial stage and the formation of sporangia; reduction division occurs in the formation of spores. The type of body structure just described is the type that occurs in most species. In a few slime fungi, the details of structure and reproduction vary somewhat from the features just described.

Physiological Characteristics

Most species of slime fungi are saprophytes, a few species are parasites upon cells of algae, true fungi, flowering plants, and other hosts. The plasmodia of most species ingest solid food particles, bacteria, spores, and other objects as they creep; in this respect, the plasmodia resemble animals. They require favorable temperature and abundant moisture and food for their growth, movement, and reproduction.

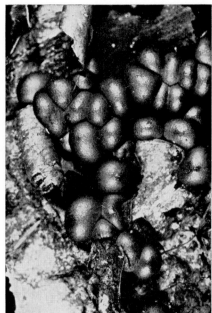

(*Photos by C. J. Alexopoulos.*)

FIG. 21–2. Sporangia of two slime fungi. *Left: Hemitrichia stipitata. Right: Lycogala epidendrum.*

Habitats and Distribution

Saprophytic slime molds occur chiefly on dead and rotting logs, leaves, and soils, as already indicated. They appear in greatest abundance following warm, rainy periods in temperate zone forests, especially in late spring, and they occur in considerable numbers in humid, tropical forests. During their vegetative activity, plasmodia usually frequent dark or dimly lighted, moist areas, moving into drier, more exposed habitats as reproduction begins. Parasitic species live within or upon the bodies of their hosts.

Importance in Nature and in Human Life

Slime molds, like many bacteria and true fungi, are involved in processes of decomposition of organic materials on and in soils. Among the economically significant species are *Plasmodiophora brassicae,* which attacks the roots of cabbage and other members of the mustard family, causing a disease called clubroot, and *Spongospora subterranea,* which causes the powdery scab disease of potato tubers.

Relationships with Other Organisms

The relationships of Myxomycophyta are not definitely known. One view holds that slime fungi are intermediate organisms between plant and animal kingdoms, since they possess both plant and animal characteristics. Adherents of this opinion usually regard slime fungi as more closely related to the animal phylum Protozoa than to any other group of organisms and classify them with the Protozoa. Some mycologists believe that Myxomycophyta are related to a primitive group of Eumycophyta that will be described in the next section.

DIVISION EUMYCOPHYTA (TRUE FUNGI)

Growth Forms and Structure

The Eumycophyta, or true fungi, comprise about 80,000 known species of plants of very diverse form, size, physiology, and reproductive methods. All species are heterotrophic; some are exclusively saprophytic, other are obligate parasites, and some are facultative parasites. The bodies of most true fungi consist of filaments called **hyphae;** in most species, a hypha is a many-celled structure, but in a minority of species, a hypha is a single, elongated, usually branched tube without cross walls. Hyphae are commonly colorless and en masse have a whitish, cottony appearance; in some species, the hyphae contain red, orange, yellow, and other types of pigments. A mass of hyphae is called a **mycelium.** In many species, the plant body consists of a loose mass of hyphae of indefinite extent, in others some hyphae become organized into reproductive bodies of definite and characteristic structure and form. A minority of species is unicellular.

Reproduction and Life Cycle

Reproduction is extremely varied in the various classes of true fungi. Asexual reproduction is by budding, zoospores, nonmotile spores, and fragmentation. The spores are microscopic in size, are usually produced in large numbers, and are widely dispersed by wind, water, insects, and other agencies. Fungous spores are commonly abundant in air, soils, and water. In most species, some form of sexual reproduction occurs. In some true fungi, there occurs a degeneration of sexual activity, culminating in a loss of sexual reproduction.

Physiological Characteristics

Since all true fungi are saprophytes or parasites, they require external sources of food. Most species are aerobic; a minority is facultatively anaerobic. Their development is best in the presence of abundant food and moisture and of favorable temperature; most species are inhibited or killed by exposure to sunlight and thus usually grow most rapidly in darkness or diffuse light. The metabolic products of true fungi, like those of bacteria, are exceedingly variable and include alcohols, organic acids, pigments, vitamins, and many other types of organic compounds, many of which have economic value.

Habitats and Distribution

Saprophytic fungi are usually able to live wherever they encounter water, warmth, oxygen, and a suitable supply of organic matter, such as that found in dead plant and animal bodies, dung, in soils, in water, in foodstuffs, leather goods, paper, cloth fabrics, and other objects of organic origin. Parasites ordinarily grow only when they are upon or within the bodies of suitable hosts. Different species of fungi vary greatly in their nutritional and environmental requirements, and their distribution is thus limited by the nature of the environment. Some species are tolerant of a wide range of conditions and are thus widely distributed, while others, particularly obligate parasites, have a more restricted distribution. In general, true fungi, along with bacteria, are probably the most nearly ubiquitous of all organisms.

Importance in Nature and in Human Life

True fungi exert profound effects upon human life and welfare. These effects will be considered only in general here, and will be discussed in greater detail in succeeding sections of this chapter. The influences of true fungi upon human life, like those of bacteria, may be classified into two groups: harmful influences and beneficial influences.

Fungi are harmful in human life in several ways: they cause serious diseases of man's important crop plants; they cause diseases of man and of his domesticated animals; they are responsible for spoilage of human foodstuffs; some species cause poisoning of man and animals when they are eaten; and they cause deterioration of wood, fibers, leather goods, fabrics, paper, and other products.

The beneficial effects of fungi are numerous: fungi, like many saprophytic bacteria, are scavengers which are responsible for the decomposition of dead bodies and of their wastes; they thus aid in returning simple substances to the air and soil and ensure continuing soil fertility; they are the sources of many valuable chemicals useful in medicine and industry; and some species are edible and constitute a savory, though not nutritious, addition to the human diet.

Representative Members

The true fungi are usually separated into 4 classes: 1. **Phycomycetes,** or algalike fungi; 2. **Ascomycetes,** or sac fungi; 3. **Basidiomycetes,** or basidium fungi; 4. **Deuteromycetes,** or imperfect fungi.

CLASS I—PHYCOMYCETES (ALGALIKE FUNGI)

General Character

The Phycomycetes include a variety of fungi that range from microscopic, single-celled organisms to those composed of hyphae and that include both saprophytic and parasitic species. The bodies of most species consist of hyphae, which are typically branched and without cross walls; a hypha of a representative member of this group is thus a **coenocyte.** Ordinarily, cross walls are formed in the hyphae only when reproductive structures are produced. The hyphae are not organized into compact bodies of definite form, but are loose, cottony masses of varying extent upon or within the substratum. The parasitic species of Phycomycetes grow upon the bodies of other fungi, of algae, seed plants, ferns, and some animals, particularly fish and insects. The saprophytic species are found in abundance in damp soils, water, foodstuffs, dead bodies, and dung. Reproduction among Phycomycetes is by both sexual and asexual methods. In some species, sexual reproduction is isogamous, in others it is heterogamous. All species reproduce asexually by spores, which are produced within sporangia of different types. In water-inhabiting species, the spores usually bear flagella; in land species, the spores usually lack flagella and depend upon air currents and animals for their dispersal.

Representatives

Members of the order **Saprolegniales** (water molds) are inhabitants of water, chiefly as saprophytes, deriving nourishment from dead leaves and twigs, dead insects and other animal bodies, and

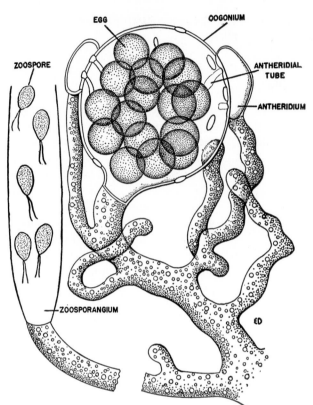

EGG

OOGONIUM

ZOOSPORE

ANTHERIDIAL TUBE

ANTHERIDIUM

ZOOSPORANGIUM

ED

FIG. 21–3. Reproduction in *Saprolegnia*, a phycomycete. *Left:* Asexual reproduction by zoospores. *Right:* Sexual reproduction by gametes produced in oogonia and antheridia.

other sources of organic matter. A few species are parasites of fish and other animals, causing diseases of these organisms. Goldfish in aquaria are often seen to be covered by cottony mycelia of water molds, which usually kill the infected fish. Asexual reproduction is chiefly by zoospores, sexual reproduction is heterogamous (Figure 21–3).

The order **Mucorales** (black molds) comprises species that are chiefly saprophytes upon bread, overripe fruit, other foodstuffs, and dung. A few species parasitize man and other animals, causing diseases of the cornea, skin, and other parts. These plants are called black molds because of the dark color of their sporangia and spores. A common representative of this order is black bread mold

(*Rhizopus nigricans*), which grows upon bread in damp places. The body of the fungus consists of an irregular whitish or grayish mycelium upon the substratum. Absorptive hyphae that penetrate the bread are called **rhizoids,** those that grow over the surface of the bread are called **stolons,** from which the spore-producing hyphae, or **sporangiophores,** arise (Figure 21–4). Each sporangiophore forms a globose sporangium at its tip; within a sporangium, numerous spores are produced. At maturity, the sporangial wall ruptures, liberating the spores, which are distributed chiefly by wind. Encountering favorable conditions for growth, a spore germinates, producing a hypha that by extensive branching forms a new mycelium. Sexual reproduction also occurs in

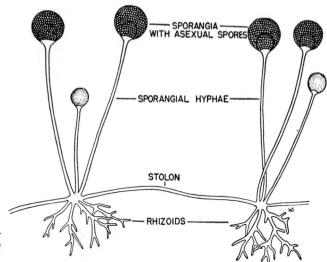

FIG. 21–4. Hyphae and sporangia of *Rhizopus nigricans* (black bread mold).

Rhizopus (Figure 21–5) as follows: short branches arise from adjacent hyphae and make contact at their tips; walls form across the tips of these hyphae, cutting off a cell (gamete) at the apex of each; the walls at the point of contact disintegrate, and the contents of the two gametes fuse in a fertilization process; the resulting zygote enlarges and develops a thick wall. After a period of rest, a zygote germinates, forming a short hypha that develops a sporangium at its apex; when the sporangial wall ruptures, the spores are liberated and germinate to form new hyphae. *Rhizopus nigricans* is **heterothallic;** that is, two physiologically distinct types of hyphae, called plus and minus hyphae, are necessary for the sexual union. In this species, two kinds of spores, which are similar in structure but different genetically and physiologically, are produced, one kind of spore growing into plus hyphae, the other kind into minus hyphae.

Members of the Mucorales are economically very important. Many species are agents in the decay of dead bodies and their wastes, and thus are important in the maintenance of soil fertility. Species of *Rhizopus* and other genera are common agents in the spoiling of fruits, bread, potatoes, and other foodstuffs. A few species are parasites of squash, cotton, and other crop plants. Some species are used industrially in the production of

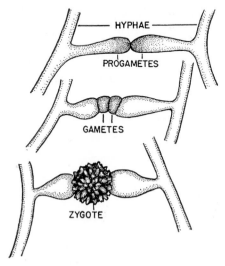

FIG. 21–5. Stages in the sexual reproduction of *Rhizopus nigricans*.

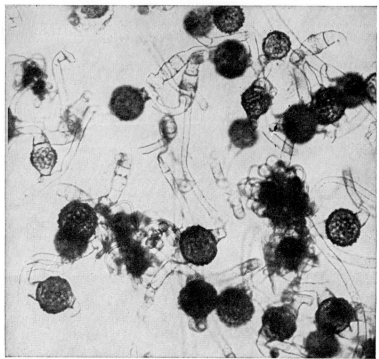

(*Photo by R. K. Benjamin.*)

FIG. 21–6. Sexual reproduction in *Cokeromyces,* a newly discovered genus of Phycomycetes. Note the hyphae and the dark zygotes, as well as various early stages in the reproductive process.

alcohols, fumaric acid (a raw material for synthetic resins), lactic acid (used in removing lime from skins before tanning, as a mordant for textile dyeing, in solvents for cellulose lacquers), and certain enzymes.

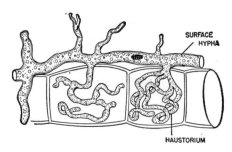

FIG. 21–7. Hyphae of a downy mildew on the surface of a leaf, with haustoria penetrating epidermal cells.

In other orders of Phycomycetes are fungi that cause the downy mildew diseases (Figure 21–7) of grapes, onions, tobacco, lettuce, sugar cane, and other crop plants. Some soil-inhabiting species of Phycomycetes attack young seedlings, causing root rots and also a disease called damping-off, which attacks stems and roots near the soil line and kills seedlings. The famous and economically important potato blight disease is caused by *Phytophthora infestans* of this class; this disease was responsible for the catastrophic potato famine in Ireland in 1845–1846, which led to widespread hunger in Ireland and was the cause of extensive migration from Ireland to the United States.

Relationships of Phycomycetes

The relationships of this class with other groups of organisms are uncertain. The structure and reproduction of some Phycomycetes are similar to certain algae, and on this basis, a theory of algal origin has been advanced. Another well-known theory, based on similarities among certain Phycomycetes and protozoans, derives these fungi from colorless flagellates.

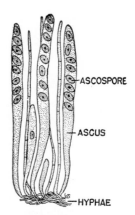

FIG. 21–8. Asci and ascospores of a sac fungus.

CLASS II—ASCOMYCETES (SAC FUNGI)

General Character

This large class of fungi includes at least 30,000 species of great diversity of structure, size, nutrition, and reproduction. Despite their diversity in these features, Ascomycetes possess a common, unifying characteristic, namely, the formation of a reproductive structure called an **ascus,** a saclike structure within which usually 8 **ascospores** are produced (Figure 21–8). An ascus usually develops as a result of a sexual process. Multinucleate gametangia develop as short, adjacent branches of the hyphae; the male organ is called the **antheridium,** the female organ the **ascogonium.** The latter produces a tubular outgrowth, a **trichogyne,** which receives the contents of the antheridium; these pass downward into the main portion of the ascogonium. The nuclei do not fuse at this stage, but group in pairs, each pair consisting of one male nucleus and one female nucleus. The ascogonium then develops a number of short hyphae, into each of which a nuclear pair migrates. From each of these hyphae a cell, containing a nuclear pair, is walled off. These discrete nuclei then divide simultaneously **(conjugate nuclear division),** one daugh-ter nucleus of each strain migrates to each pole, and a wall is formed between the two pairs, producing two similar binucleate cells. In this manner, the binucleate cells form branched filaments called **ascogenous hyphae.** At the tip of each hyphal branch is formed an ascus mother cell, within which the two nuclei fuse, giving rise to a single diploid nucleus. This fusion nucleus undergoes meiosis, producing 4 haploid nuclei; each of these usually divides mitotically, giving a total of 8 ascospore nuclei. At maturity, the asci open, releasing the spores, each of which may germinate to form a hypha and ultimately a new fungus plant. The type of reproduction just described is characteristic of many species of Ascomycetes, but not all; in some, the gametangia are morphologically alike, in others, one or the other type of gametangium is abortive, and, as a result, the development of asci is parthenogenetic.

In many species of Ascomycetes, the body consists of a loose, indefinite mat of hyphae, with asci borne separately on the hyphae. In other species, the asci are surrounded by, or are embedded in, a mass of sterile hyphae; this mass of asci and

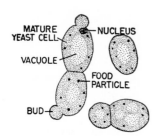

FIG. 21–9. Yeast plants, showing budding.

sterile hyphae is often very compact and
has a definite form characteristic of a species. These bodies, called **ascocarps,** are
very diverse in different species, and
their structural differences are important
in the classification and identification of
the members of this class.

In addition to their reproduction by
ascospores, many members of this class
possess other methods of reproduction,
such as budding and **conidia** formation.
Conidia are spores that are produced in
chains at the tips of certain hyphae; these
become detached from the parent hypha
and are transported by wind, insects, and
other agencies. Upon germination, a conidium forms a hypha that grows into a
new plant.

The hyphae of Ascomycetes, unlike
those of Phycomycetes, possess cross
walls. Their hyphae are thus long filaments of cells, rather than long, nonseptate tubes, as in Phycomycetes.

Ascomycetes include both saprophytic
and parasitic species. The saprophytic
species thrive in soils, on dead bodies,
dung, foodstuffs, leather goods, paper,
and many other nonliving materials rich
in organic matter. These saprophytic species play an important role in decomposing dead bodies and wastes and thus are
involved in maintaining soil fertility. A
few species occur in water. Some parasitic Ascomycetes dwell on and within the
bodies of higher plants; others are para-

sitic upon the bodies of man and other
animals. Some cause serious diseases of
crop plants and of animals. Ascomycetes
are useful to man in many ways: some
species, such as sponge-mushrooms, are
tasteful items in human diets; a few species form substances of great medicinal
value (for example, penicillin), and others produce a number of other organic
substances of commercial value.

Representatives

One order of Ascomycetes includes the
yeasts. These are one-celled fungi, which
are spherical or ovoid in shape and which
may develop short hyphae. Reproduction
is chiefly asexual by budding; in this
process, a yeast cell produces a small protuberance that grows for a time, then is
delimited from the parent cell by a wall
(Figure 21–9). The cells may then separate or may cohere, each continuing to
bud until chainlike colonies are formed.
Infrequently yeasts form asci, each usually with four ascospores. Yeasts are
among the economically most important
fungi. Some yeasts respire sugars, by
means of an enzyme system called **zymase,** to alcohol, and are the principal
source of alcoholic beverages and industrial alcohol. In dough, the bubbles of
carbon dioxide they release in respiration
cause the dough to "raise." Yeasts also
manufacture vitamins, and one species
has been found that synthesizes proteins
from molasses and ammonia; this activity may become very important in the
production of protein foods. A few yeasts
are parasites of higher plants, causing diseases of tomato fruits and garden beans.
Several yeast species of the genus *Torula*
are pathogenic in man, causing several
serious diseases, best known of which is
blastomycosis, which attacks the skin and

central nervous system and often ends fatally.

The order **Aspergillales** contains fungi whose bodies consist chiefly of loose masses of hyphae of indefinite extent that grow in and upon the substratum. To this order belong the various bluish, greenish, and yellowish molds, chiefly of the genera *Penicillium* and *Aspergillus,* which grow commonly on foodstuffs, leather, and other organic materials in damp places. Reproduction of these fungi is most often by conidia produced in chains at the tips of certain hyphae (Figure 21–10); these conidia are variously colored, and the colors of these fungi en masse are due chiefly to their conidial masses. The conidia are microscopic and are produced in enormous numbers; they are almost always present in air and dust, and when they encounter organic material and moisture, they quickly germinate. Thus, old shoes in a damp cellar or a stale lemon in a moist place soon show a growth of *Aspergillus* or *Penicillium.* The genera *Aspergillus* and *Penicillium* are of great importance in human life, both as enemies and benefactors of man. Species of *Aspergillus* cause rots of fruits, decay of tobaccos and cigars, the spoilage of bread, nuts, and other foodstuffs, and the deterioration of leather goods and fabrics, and are responsible for several diseases of human beings, such as ear and lung infections, and of animals. *Aspergillus* species are used in the manufacture of alcohol from rice starch and in the production of citric and other organic acids. Species of *Penicillium* are responsible for the spoilage of tremendous quantities of foods, including apples, pears, grapes, citrus fruits, and bread, and for the discoloration and deterioration of paper, books, lumber, fabrics, leather, and other products. *Penicillium roqueforti* and *P. camemberti* im-

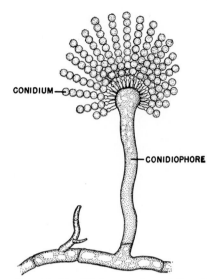

CONIDIUM

CONIDIOPHORE

FIG. 21–10. Hyphae and conidia of *Aspergillus.*

part the characteristic odors and flavors to well-known types of cheese as a result of their metabolic activities in the butterfat and proteins of milk; the bluish-green splotches in these cheeses are masses of conidia of these fungi. *Penicillium notatum* and *P. crysogenum* are widely used in the commercial preparation of **penicillin,** a drug that exerts a strong inhibitory effect on the growth of certain bacteria (bacteriostasis) and, to a lesser extent, acts as a bactericidal agent (Figure 21–11). The best known of all "wonder drugs," penicillin is used effectively in the treatment of gas gangrene, gonorrhea, meningitis, pneumonia, and certain other diseases caused by pathogenic bacteria. Penicillin belongs to a group of organic substances called **antibiotics,** or substances that are synthesized by one kind of organism and that inhibit or destroy other kinds of organisms. Antibiosis often appears when two species of fungi grow in the same culture dish; one often inhibits the growth of the other, or both may exert mutual inhibition (Figure 21–12).

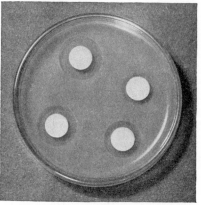
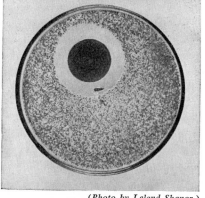

(Photo by Eli Lilly Co.)   *(Photo by Leland Shanor.)*

FIG. 21–11 (*left*). Action of penicillin on bacteria. White filter-paper disks containing penicillin solution are placed on agar culture of bacteria; penicillin diffusing from the disks destroys bacteria, leaving clear zones in the agar. The clouded portions of the agar have not been reached by the penicillin and still contain living bacteria.

FIG. 21–12 (*right*). Antibiosis between two species of *Penicillium*. The clear area on the agar medium is a zone of mutual antagonism, resulting from the secretion of antibiotic substances by these fungi.

The order **Erysiphales** of the Ascomycetes includes the powdery mildews, which are parasites chiefly on leaves of higher plants. The hyphae on leaf surfaces form asci enclosed by small, usually dark-colored ascocarps that are just large enough to be visible to the naked eye. These ascocarps are often of delicate beauty (Figure 21–13). Powdery mildews may be found commonly on leaves of clovers, roses, lilacs, apples, dandelions, grapes, and many other flowering plants. They are usually mild parasites, causing slight damage to host plants; a few species sometimes cause severe crop losses in grapes, cherries, cucumbers, and other cultivated plants.

The order **Pezizales** (cup and sponge fungi) is composed of saprophytic fungi with fleshy ascocarps of definite form and constant structure in each species. They are found commonly in soils and upon dead trunks, branches, and stumps of trees, the tissues of which are penetrated by the hyphae, from which the visible reproductive bodies develop. These ascocarps are composed of tightly packed hyphae, are typically fleshy, and vary in size from barely visible cup-shaped struc-

LEAF
EPIDERMIS

HAUSTORIUM

FIG. 21–13. Hyphae and cleistothecium of a powdery mildew on the surface of a host leaf.

FIG. 21–14. Cup fungi (*Peziza*) on rotting wood.

tures to large cups or spongelike bodies several inches in length (Figure 21–14). The ascocarps are often brightly colored, especially in shades of red and orange, and are conspicuous, particularly on rotting logs. In the cup fungi, the ascocarps are cup shaped, with the asci borne in the concavities of the cup. The sponge fungi, or morels, have stalked spongelike or saddle-shaped ascocarps on which the asci are produced. Species of the genus *Morchella* (Figure 21–15) are highly prized edible fungi.

Other orders of Ascomycetes include many fungi of great biological or economic interest; among these are the parasites that cause such well-known plant diseases as Dutch elm disease, apple scab, apple canker, chestnut blight, and peach leaf curl. An ascomycetous fungus called ergot causes a serious disease of rye and other cereals. The ergot disease transforms rye grains into enlarged purplish bodies filled with hyphae; these bodies contain a toxic substance, ergotinine, that poisons and kills animals, including man, that eat the grains or rye flour in which ground ergot bodies are present. Ergot is a valuable drug, often used at

childbirth, since it checks hemorrhages and other uterine disturbances. Also in the Ascomycetes are the truffles, subterranean edible fungi, which are frequently

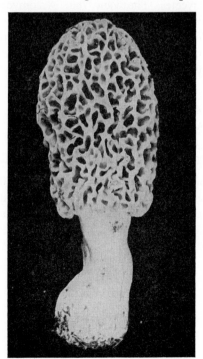

(*Photo by C. F. Hottes.*)

FIG. 21–15. *Morchella esculenta* (morel), a fleshy, edible sac fungus.

hunted by dogs or hogs trained to locate them by scent; truffles are popular edible fungi in Europe.

Relationships of the Ascomycetes

According to one view, Ascomycetes may be closely related to red algae, since there are certain similarities in reproduction in the two groups. Another interpretation holds that Ascomycetes are probable descendants of Phycomycetes; this view is based upon similarities in the development of asci and in zygote germination in Phycomycetes to form a sporangium, the appearance in a few Phycomycetes of one-spored sporangia (similar to Ascomycete conidia), the coenocytic hyphae of a few Ascomycetes, and similarity between ascogonia and the oogonia of Phycomycetes. The view that Ascomycetes are more closely related to Phycomycetes than to any other possible ancestral group is the more popular one among present-day mycologists.

CLASS III—BASIDIOMYCETES (BASIDIUM FUNGI)

General Character

This large class comprises some 25,000 species of great variety of form, structure, and physiology. The unifying character

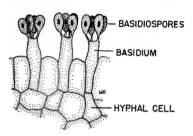

FIG. 21–16. Basidia and basidio-spores of a club fungus.

common to all members of this class is their possession of a special reproductive structure, the **basidium** (Figure 21–16). A basidium is usually an enlarged, terminal, club-shaped cell of a hypha; a basidium develops four spores (rarely two) called **basidiospores,** which at maturity are situated singly at the tips of minute stalks. In a minority of species, a basidium is four celled, each cell producing a basidiospore.

A basidium typically develops from a two-nucleate terminal cell of a hypha; as the cell enlarges, the two haploid nuclei fuse to form a single diploid nucleus that then divides meiotically, producing four haploid nuclei. The growing basidium produces four protuberances, into each of which one nucleus passes; when a nucleus reaches the apex of the protuberance, the tip of the latter becomes walled off to form a basidiospore with one nucleus. At maturity, the basidiospores fall, or are ejected, from their stalks **(sterigmata),** and are dispersed by winds, insects, or other agencies. Encountering favorable conditions of temperature, moisture, and food supply, a spore germinates, forming a **primary hypha** of uninucleate cells. After a period of growth, the cells of these primary hyphae become binucleate by the fusion of protoplasts of cells from different hyphae (in heterothallic species) or from the same hypha (in homothallic species). The binucleate condition persists throughout the growth of these hyphae **(secondary hyphae),** the nuclei duplicating by conjugate division as new cells are formed. The cytogenetic condition of these cells is designated as $n + n,$ because each nucleus is haploid. At the time of basidium formation, the two nuclei in a terminal cell fuse, producing a single diploid nucleus as described earlier. The nuclear fusion that precedes the maturation of the basidium is regarded as a sexual process.

Representatives

Members of the order **Ustilaginales** are known commonly as smuts because of the sooty color of their spore masses. Smuts are obligate parasites chiefly of grasses, such as corn, oats, wheat, and barley. The bodies of smuts consist of irregular masses of hyphae in host tissues. The hyphae develop smut spores, especially in the ovary tissues of the hosts, so that the growing grains are usually transformed into sooty, ill-smelling masses of spores (Figure 21–17). The smut spores may infect other plants, or may remain dormant until spring, when they germinate, forming hyphae that produce basidiospores; these then infect host plants. Smut fungi cause tremendous crop losses in grains.

The rust fungi (order **Uredinales**) are obligate parasites of certain seed plants and ferns. They are called rusts because of the reddish-brown color of some of their spores, which are produced chiefly upon the surfaces of host leaves and stems. A remarkable feature of the rusts is the fact that many of them must parasitize two different hosts in order to complete their sexual reproductive cycle, a condition known as **heteroecism.** One of the most destructive and most extensively studied rusts is *Puccinia graminis* var. *tritici,* the wheat rust fungus. The hyphae of this fungus live in stem and leaf tissues of wheat plants in spring and summer; during the summer, they produce in surface pustules called **uredia** (Figure 21–18), many one-celled, reddish-brown spores **(urediospores)** that are carried by wind to other wheat plants where infection occurs. The spread of infection by urediospores is an asexual reproductive

(Photo by Benjamin Koehler.)

FIG. 21–17. Corn smut caused by *Ustilago zeae* on ear of corn.

process sometimes called the "repeater stage" because new uredia (hence new urediospores and new infections) are produced at approximately two-week intervals through much of the summer. At about the time the wheat grains begin to mature, the uredia begin forming black **teliospores** in addition to urediospores. The proportion of teliospores in new pustules increases until they alone are produced. Pustules containing only teliospores are called **telia** (Figure 21–21A). Many of these two-celled, resistant spores remain on wheat stubble throughout the

(*By permission of the Canada Dept. of Agriculture Research Station, Winnipeg, Canada.*)

(*By permission of the Canada Dept. of Agriculture Research Station, Winnipeg, Canada.*)

FIG. 21–18 (*left*). Uredial stage of stem rust (*Puccinia graminis* var. *tritici*) on wheat.

FIG. 21–19 (*right*). Aecial stage of stem rust (*Puccinia graminis* var. *tritici*) on barberry.

winter. Teliospores germinate in the spring and produce basidia and basidiospores. Basidiospores are then carried by the wind to the common barberry, which becomes parasitized. The hyphae produced after spore germination consist of uninuclear cells that grow in the internal leaf tissues, forming flask-shaped structures called **pycnia** (Figure 21–21B) that open onto the upper leaf surface and from which are produced small **pycniospores** and **receptive hyphae.** The same mycelium produces small masses of cells **(aecial primordia)** close to the lower leaf surface. When a pycniospore of one physiological strain comes in contact with a receptive hypha of the opposite physiological strain, its nucleus migrates through a pore into the hyphal cell, where it divides. The wall separating adjacent hyphal cells has a small central perforation, through which one of the daughter nuclei migrates. Again the nucleus divides and again one of the daughter nuclei migrates to the next cell. This process **(dikaryotization)** is repeated until virtually all of the hyphal cells have become binucleate. Cells of the aecial primordia then begin to divide, forming both binucleate **aeciospores** and an outer, cellular jacket, collectively referred to as an **aecium.** The enlarging aecium ruptures the lower leaf epidermis, the cellular jacket splits open, and the aeciospores are released (Figures 21–19, 21–21B). The sexual cycle is completed when the aeciospores are carried to wheat plants in the spring. The essential cytological details of the wheat rust life cycle are shown in Figure 21–20.

Wheat rust is an extremely virulent

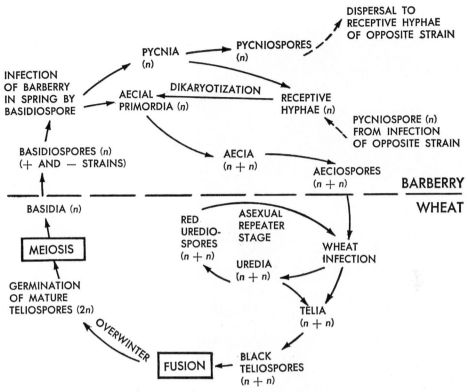

FIG. 21–20. Life cycle of wheat rust. Explanation in text.

parasite, frequently causing extensive crop damage. Eradication of the barberry host has long been practiced as a means of control, especially in cooler regions of the temperate zone. The fungus is then unable to complete its sexual life cycle, for the urediospores ("summer spores") cannot survive cold winters and the teliospores ("winter spores") and basidiospores cannot infect wheat plants. However, urediospores can survive the mild winters of the southern temperate regions and infect wheat plants in the spring. The summer spores are then carried northward by the wind. Most of the new races of rust fungus originate through hybridization, which is prevented by the destruction of barberry. However, the complete elimination of this alternate host would

not permanently wipe out the disease, since new races also originate through mutation. A second feasible approach to the problem of control is found in the disease resistance of certain wheat varieties. Extensive breeding programs are maintained to develop additional resistant varieties in an attempt to "keep ahead" of the disease.

Another common rust is cedar-apple rust, which lives for a part of the year on cedars, another portion of the year on apples, hawthorns, and related plants. The white pine blister rust alternates between white pine trees and wild gooseberries and currants; it causes serious damage to white pines, and may be in part controlled by the eradication of the alternate hosts, the wild gooseberries and cur-

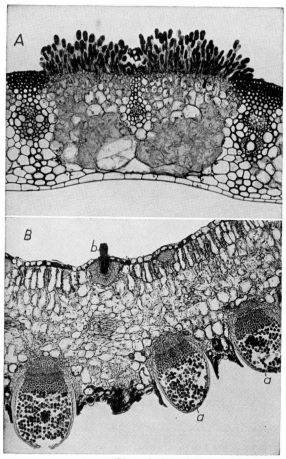

FIG. 21–21. Wheat rust.

A: Teliospores breaking through epidermis of wheat leaf.

B: Aeciospores forming in cups (a) on barberry leaf. A pycnium (b) may be seen beneath upper epidermis of leaf.

(Photos by Triarch Botanical Products.)

rants. Other species of rusts cause diseases of rye, oats, corn, pears, peaches, cherries, plums, firs, hemlocks, figs, coffee, asparagus, carnations, and snapdragons.

The order **Agaricales** includes a large number of saprophytic species, which derive their nourishment from decomposing organic matter in soils, dead leaves, dung, and dead or dying bark and wood, and a small number of species parasitic on seed plants. The vegetative body consists of a loose and extensive growth of hyphae that penetrate the soil, bark, or other substratum; when temperature and moisture

conditions are favorable and the hyphae have absorbed sufficient food, they form fruiting bodies, or **sporophores** (Figure 21–22), which grow upward or outward into the air and which bear basidia and basidiospores. The spores are often produced in enormous numbers; a common field mushroom (*Psalliota campestris*) produces about 1,800,000,000 spores, and a single shaggy-mane mushroom releases about 100,000,000 spores per hour for several hours. The sporophores, which are commonly fleshy, less frequently woody, are composed of compactly grouped hyphae and are of definite form

FIG. 21–22. Sporophores of *Psalliota campestris,* the commonly cultivated edible mushroom, growing in a mushroom cellar.

and structure in each species; one may thus distinguish among the species of this order by observing the structure, size, and coloration of the sporophores. The color of the basidiospores is also important in the identification of these fungi. Members of this order, like many other species of fungi, are important in the cycles of nature in that they aid in the decomposition of dead bodies and their wastes, and thus restore simple substances to the air and soil.

The largest family of Agaricales is the gill fungus, or mushroom family. In the mushrooms (or toadstools as they are often called), the fleshy sporophore consists typically of a stalk **(stipe),** surmounted by a broad, umbrella-shaped cap, the **pileus.** On the undersurface of the cap are **gills,** thin, radiating hyphal plates, which bear basidia and basidiospores (Figure 21–23). After the basidiospores are shed, they germinate to form hyphae. These absorb food and grow for

a time, ultimately form sporophores, and thus complete the life cycle. It should be emphasized that a mushroom is only one part of the body of a mushroom fungus; the remainder of the body consists of an extensive mass of food-absorbing hyphae that grow hidden in the soil, rotting logs, or other substrata. Many species of mushrooms produce toxic organic compounds that poison human beings or animals that eat them; often this poisoning results only in illness, but it sometimes causes death. Other species of mushrooms are edible, and are prized for their delicate aromas and flavors. Some edible species are extensively cultivated, especially *Psalliota campestris.* Mushroom culture is generally carried on in cellars or dark sheds; the principal growth requirements of these fungi are an abundance of organic matter (usually in the form of dung), a suitable supply of moisture, and a moderate temperature. Some edible species are harvested from fields and forests;

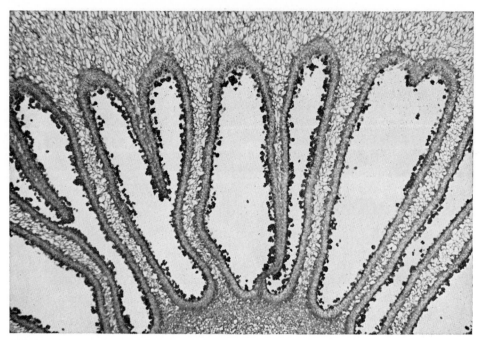

FIG. 21–23. Transverse section of *Coprinus pileus* (inky cap fungus), showing gills. Small, black objects are basidiospores.

(Photo by E. D. Burkhart.)

FIG. 21–24. A mushroom (*Pleurotus*) growing from hickory trunk. Notice the gills.

this is a dangerous practice, for poisonous species are often confused by amateurs with the edible ones. Careful study and observation are necessary to distinguish among edible and poisonous species, and only persons who are thoroughly familiar with mushrooms should eat wild species.

Another family of Agaricales is that of the pore fungi, whose sporophores often resemble those of mushrooms but differ from them in that the underside of the sporophore contains hundreds of tiny tubes, which appear as pores on the lower surface of the cap. The cap hyphae surrounding these tubes produce basidia and basidiospores; the latter escape through the pores and are dispersed by wind and insects. Some pore fungi grow in soils, others are parasites or saprophytes on trees and stumps. The hyphae of the tree-inhabiting species secrete enzymes that

FIG. 21–25. Shelflike sporophores of a pore fungus (*Fomes*) growing on a tree stump.

digest the hard tissues of bark and wood, and absorb organic compounds from these tissues. After a period of vegetative activity, these hyphae form sporophores that, in many species, grow horizontally like shelves from the surface of the tree trunk or post upon which they grow. Such fungi, which are often tough and woody, are called shelf fungi or bracket fungi (Figure 21–25). These fungi are common and active agents of wood decomposition, and the parasitic species damage and kill trees. Among the important wood-rotting pore fungi is *Merulius lacrymans,* which causes a type of wood decomposition known as dry rot; this fungus is a common destructive agent of wood in buildings. Few species of pore fungi are poisonous, but most species are so tough that they cannot be eaten.

The order **Lycoperdales** includes the puffballs and related fungi, which are very similar to the Agaricales in many respects; they are chiefly saprophytes, obtaining their food from dead leaves, animal wastes, and decomposing bark and wood; their vegetative hyphae grow extensively through the soil or other substratum; and their sporophores, at least when young, are fleshy. The principal difference between members of the Lycoperdales and those of Agaricales is in the structure of their sporophores; in the puffballs, the sporophore is very often globose, pear shaped, or ovoid (Figure 21–26) with a conspicuous surface layer. The basidia and basidiospores develop on hyphae within this layer, which, at maturity, ruptures or opens by a pore, liberating the spores. The sporophores of puffballs vary greatly in size, color, form, and texture in different species. The sporophores of some species are very small, while others may attain diameters of 4 feet. No poisonous species of puffballs are known, and the young fleshy sporophores of many species are edible. Puffball "steaks" may be cut from the sporophores of vari-

(Photo by C. F. Hottes.)

FIG. 21–26. Puffballs on rotting wood. Notice the rhizomorphs (compact strands of hyphae) penetrating the wood.

ous giant puffballs; these are a culinary delicacy when they are fried in butter or cooked with beefsteak. As puffballs mature, however, they become dry and leathery or powdery and are no longer palatable. A sharp blow with a stick upon a matured puffball causes a great cloud of spores to burst forth; a single large puffball may produce as many as 7,000,-000,000,000 spores, a number about 40,-000 times the population of the United States!

Other orders of Basidiomycetes include the bird's-nest fungi, in which the sporophores are cup shaped with enclosed ovoid basidia-producing bodies, and the stinkhorns, which have stalked sporophores with spongelike structures at the apices of their stalks (Figure 21–27 shows examples). These spongelike caps bear the basidia and basidiospores and are covered by a slimy material that is green-ish or brownish in color and has a vile stench attractive to insects; these crawl over the slimy caps and aid in the dispersal of spores. Closely related to the stinkhorns are the net fungi; in the latter, the basidia and spores are borne on the conspicuous and beautiful net.

Relationships of the Basidiomycetes

Most mycologists regard the Basidiomycetes as a group of fungi that have evolved from Ascomycetes, since the Basidiomycetes resemble Ascomycetes more closely than any other class of fungi. Their hyphal structure is similar, and the development of asci and of basidia is very similar in the two groups. In both groups of fungi, fusion of protoplasts from two cells occurs, but nuclear fusion is delayed for some time, each fusion cell containing two nuclei. Most mycologists believe that

(*Photos by Leland Shanor.*)

FIG. 21–27. *Left:* Sporophore of a stinkhorn fungus (*Ithyphallus impudicus*), a member of the order Phallales of the Basidiomycetes. *Right:* Sporophore of a net fungus, *Dictyophora phalloidea*, of the order Phallales.

a basidium is an evolutionary development from an ascus. The fact that some Ascomycetes produce asci with only four spores is considered further evidence of close relationship between these two classes of fungi.

CLASS IV—DEUTEROMYCETES (IMPERFECT FUNGI)

The Deuteromycetes is a heterogeneous, rag-bag group of many types of fungi, which have been observed to reproduce only asexually, usually by conidia. In the absence of sexual stages (also called perfect stages), these species cannot be assigned to the other classes of fungi that have already been described. Some species of fungi are not known to have sexual stages, but are placed in classes other than the Deuteromycetes because of their obvious structural similarities with species with known perfect stages. Thus, some fungi that lack sexual reproduction but have coenocytic hyphae are placed in the Phycomycetes. Also, some fungi that produce rust-colored spores but lack sexual stages are placed in the rusts of the Basidiomycetes. Mycologists generally believe that most imperfect fungi are Ascomycetes in which sexual reproduction has not been found, or in which sexual stages never occur.

Some imperfect fungi are very important in human life. A number of species are parasitic on higher plants, causing serious diseases of apples, cabbage, corn, tomato, tobacco, celery, wheat, oats, citrus fruits, cowpeas, strawberries, flax, lettuce, peaches, garden beans, and many other crop plants. The imperfect fungi include also species that are parasites of man, causing a number of diseases, many of them very serious. The genus *Candida* (*Monilia*) includes species that cause a throat and mouth disease called thrush, pulmonary infections, diseases of the nails and the mucous membranes of the genital organs, various types of skin diseases, and sprue, a widespread intestinal disease of the tropics. The imperfect fungi also include a group called Trichophytoneae, or ringworm fungi, which parasitize man and other animals, causing diseases of the hair follicles, hair, skin, nails, feathers, and horns. Many of the skin diseases caused by these fungi are known by such popular names as ringworm, barber's itch, athlete's foot, and dhobie itch. These diseases are widespread and, although they infrequently become serious, they are unsightly and irritating. Sanitary safeguards in barber shops, gymnasiums, shower rooms, and swimming pools, plus personal cleanliness, are effective in limiting their dissemination.

MYCORRHIZAE

One of the most interesting relationships between fungi and higher plants is that found in **mycorrhizae**. A mycorrhiza is an intimate morphological and physiological combination of a fungus and a root of some species of higher plant. Mycorrhizae occur in many species of trees, shrubs, and herbs in all parts of the world; most species of woody plants appear to have them.

The fungi of mycorrhizae belong to the various classes of fungi already described, especially to Ascomycetes and Basidiomycetes. Mycorrhizal roots differ in certain structural features from uninfected roots; they are often short and thick, commonly lack root caps and root hairs, and they sometimes do not branch.

The physiological and biological significance of mycorrhizae is not thoroughly understood and therefore is the cause of some disagreement among biologists in interpreting these structures. Some botanists regard mycorrhizal fungi as parasites upon the roots they inhabit and thus consider mycorrhizae as purely pathological structures. Other botanists believe that the relationship between these fungi and the roots they inhabit is more complex than direct parasitism and that both fungi and roots benefit from their close association. According to this latter view, the fungi receive food from root tissues, and in turn facilitate certain physiological activities of roots; some investigators believe that these fungi may increase water absorption by roots, others that mycorrhizal fungi promote the absorption of certain organic nitrogenous substances from the soil, or that they carry on nitrogen fixation in much the same manner as nitrogen-fixing bacteria.

The view that the fungi may have some beneficial effect upon roots is supported by a number of observations and experiments. In some species of plants, particularly certain species of trees, shrubs, and orchids, the mycorrhizal association is seemingly universal; that is, it occurs in all individuals of the species. The invariability of this occurrence may be interpreted as indicating a condition of mutual benefit. Also, controlled experiments have indicated that some species of higher plants derive benefit from the mycorrhizal relationship; if seedlings of certain species of pine trees, for example, are grown in sterile soils, or in soils that do not contain suitable species of mycorrhizal fungi, the growth of the seedlings is slow and weak; if the soil is inoculated with these fungi and if the fungi then infect the roots, the growth of the seedlings quickly and conspicuously improves.

LICHENS

Lichens, of which there are estimated to be about 15,000 species, are associations of certain algae and fungi that live together in an intimate relationship, often described as symbiosis. Symbiosis means simply a state in which two organisms live together in close structural and physiological combination; in the broad meaning of the word, the relationship between a parasite and its host may be termed symbiosis; some biologists use the term in a more restricted sense to refer to any association in which there appears to be mutual benefit accruing to both partners from their proximity. The fungi in lichens are mildly parasitic upon the algal cells, which they surround (Figure 21–28) and from which they obtain food; the algal cells may receive some benefit from the fungi, which are believed to aid the algae in the absorption and retention of water. It has been demonstrated experimentally that the algae of lichens can be grown without the fungi with which they are associated in lichens, but that the fungi cannot survive without the algae. Thus, it appears that the benefits of the association are heavily in favor of the fungi. The algal components of lichens are chiefly members of the Cyanophyta (blue-green algae) and Chlorophyta (green algae); the fungi are chiefly Ascomycetes, infrequently Basidiomycetes. The fungi and algae of lichens may reproduce independently, or by **soredia,** disc-shaped or cup-shaped structures that contain hyphae and some algal cells. Lichens vary greatly

FIG. 21–28. Cross section of a lichen, showing the small algal cells enmeshed in fungous hyphae. The cup-shaped reproductive body bears asci with ascospores.

in color; some are grayish green, others are white, orange, yellow, yellowish-green, brown, or black.

Lichens are common on rocks, tree bark (Figure 21–29), certain types of soils, shingles, fence posts, and other wooden objects. Some lichens are able to withstand low temperatures and long periods of drought. Such species are abundant on high mountain elevations, in the arctic tundras, in desert regions, and in many other environments where conditions are unfavorable for the growth of other types of plants.

Although they do not usually form a conspicuous part of the vegetation, except in such habitats as those mentioned in the preceding paragraph, lichens play important roles in nature and in human life. Tundra lichens are valuable sources of food for reindeer, caribou, musk ox, and other wild animals. Lichens are also important in nature in that they excrete organic acids that disintegrate rocks, thus forming soil and preparing substrata in which other kinds of plants can subsequently become established.

In Lapland, Iceland, and other subarctic regions, as well as in India, Japan, and other parts of the Orient, lichens are harvested and dried to be used as human

(Photo by R. V. Drexler.)

FIG. 21-29. Crustose lichens on a tree trunk.

"moss" produces a mucilaginous substance that has some value as a laxative. It is also an ingredient in salves, puddings, and culture media for bacteria, as well as in sizings for paper and calicoes and in isinglass. Some lichens produce dyes that have been used for centuries in coloring fabrics and paints; among these dyes are orchil, a beautiful blue dye, used since pre-Christian times, cudbear, another blue dye, and various brown and yellow dyes. The dye known as litmus, used in chemical work as an indicator of acidity and alkalinity, is obtained from certain lichens. Some lichens contain tannins and are used for tanning animal hides in France and other European countries.

PLANT DISEASES

Plants, like animals, suffer from diseases, which are responsible for structural and physiological derangements and often the death of the diseased plants. Diseases of man's cultivated plants are responsible for tremendous economic waste, since they result in food crop reductions and losses (for example, in 1953 the U. S. Department of Agriculture estimated that plant diseases in the United States cause an annual loss of about 3 billion dollars), the injury and death of ornamental plants, and the blemishing of fruits and other plant products that are thus rendered unsalable. Most diseases of higher plants are caused by true fungi (Figure 21–34), some plant diseases may be traced to slime fungi, bacteria, parasitic flowering plants, such as dodders (Figure 21–31) and mistletoes (Figure 21–32), animals (such as insects and roundworms), viruses and physiological derangements resulting from unfavorable storage temperatures, inadequate oxygen

food and sometimes as food for cattle, swine, and horses. It is generally believed that the manna of the Bible was a lichen, *Lecanora esculenta,* which is still eaten by desert tribes of Asia Minor. Fragments of lichens found with foodstuffs in Egyptian tombs indicate that lichens were used as human foodstuffs in ancient Egypt. Assorted medicinal benefits have been ascribed since pre-Christian times to various lichens; they have been used in the treatment of jaundice, diarrhea, fevers, epilepsy, and skin diseases. Most of these supposed medicinal benefits are now known to be without scientific foundation; however, a lichen known as Iceland

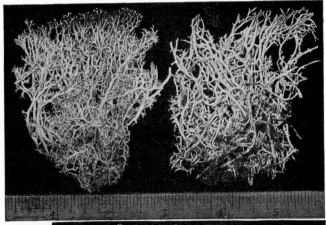

FIG. 21–30. *Above:* Reindeer "moss," *Cladonia rangiferina*, a fruticose lichen. *Below:* A foliose lichen, *Parmelia*. Notice the cup-shaped reproductive bodies.

(*Photos by Missouri Botanical Garden.*)

FIG. 21–31 (*left*). Dodder, a flowering-plant parasite, growing on *Vernonia*.

FIG. 21–32 (*right*). Mistletoe growing on an Osage orange tree.

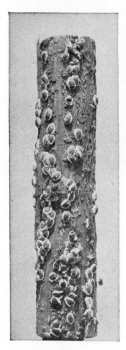

FIG. 21–33. *Above:* Elm bark lice are serious pests on elm trees. *Right:* Mealy bugs attacking a plant stem.

(Photos by Missouri Botanical Garden.)

supplies, and deficiencies of essential nutrients in soils.

The **pathogens,** that is, the fungi, bacteria, roundworms, and other parasites responsible for plant diseases, affect their host plants in several ways. They rob host tissues of foods, thus weakening the host plants and reducing their growth and yield, they may inhibit or reduce flower formation and seed production, they often produce toxic excretions which kill host tissues, and they may plug up the vascular tissues of the host, thus interfering with the conduction of water, essential nutrient elements, and foods. Some parasites (for example, many powdery mildews) do not ordinarily kill their hosts, but may continue to live in host tissues for long periods without produc-

ing serious injury; others, such as the fungi responsible for the chestnut blight disease and for Dutch elm disease, kill their hosts very quickly.

Plant diseases are usually manifested in various symptoms, commonly visible to the naked eye. These overt indications of disease are of many types: chlorotic areas in leaves, scabs and blotches on fruit surfaces, brownish spots of dead tissues in leaves, rotting, ill-smelling masses of host tissues, blisters resulting from the rupture of host epidermis by hyphae and spore masses, discolorations of host tissues, wilting of leaves and stems, whitish or grayish masses of hyphae on surfaces of host organs, etc. The identification of plant diseases is made in part through these externally visible symptoms, in part by microscopic and physiological studies of the pathogens.

Since plant diseases are responsible annually for billions of dollars in crop losses, the eradication or control of these diseases is obviously an important field of plant science, one that is carried on by scientists in universities, agricultural experiment stations, forestry schools, food-producing companies, and companies that manufacture agricultural chemicals. Among the methods used to check or eradicate plant diseases are these: the treatment of crop seeds with chemicals that destroy bacteria and fungous spores adhering to seed coats; the application of chemical sprays and dusts that kill pathogenic organisms to plant organs that are diseased or are liable to disease infection; the removal or destruction of diseased plants to prevent the spread of disease to healthy plants; the destruction, through sprays and dusts, of insects that carry fungous spores and bacteria from plant to plant; the regulation, through governmental quarantines, of movement of plants and plant products from one country to another or from one state to another. The development of disease-resistant varieties of crop plants through genetic breeding and selection is an important method of disease control, since it results in the production of new varieties of plants that are resistant to specific diseases.

Plant pathology, the study of plant diseases and their control, is a very active and important field of plant science, one that offers excellent professional opportunities in university teaching and research, state and federal governmental agricultural and forestry agencies, and private industry to young men and women interested in practical applications of plant science.

(Photo by Benjamin Koehler.)

A   B   C

FIG. 21–34. Smut diseases of barley. A: healthy barley spike; B: covered smut of barley (caused by *Ustilago hordei*); C: loose smut of barley (caused by *Ustilago nuda*).

≪← SUMMARY

1. Members of the Myxomycophyta and Eumycophyta are larger than bacteria. They are more complex in structure, their cells have conspicuous nuclei, and most reproduce sexually.

2. The Myxomycophyta possess both plantlike and animallike characteristics. Their sporangia and spores resemble those of other fungi. Their life cycle includes naked bodies with amoeboid movement and with ability to ingest solid food particles.

3. Myxomycophyta are chiefly saprophytes on dead trees and leaves, occasionally parasites on higher plants. The life cycle of a typical member of this order follows: the vegetative body consists chiefly of a naked, multinucleate plasmodium that produces sporangia, within which spores are formed. The spores germinate, producing microscopic myxamoebae that creep for a time, then fuse in pairs to form zygotes. A zygote grows into a new plasmodium, or several zygotes may fuse to form a plasmodium. After a period of vegetative activity, the plasmodium forms sporangia. No hyphae are present.

4. Eumycophyta comprise groups of fungi, in which the body consists typically of fungous filaments, or hyphae, and in which no true plasmodia are formed, as in Myxomycophyta.

5. Eumycophyta are usually separated into four classes: Phycomycetes, Ascomycetes, Basidiomycetes, and Deuteromycetes.

6. Eumycophyta include many species of saprophytes, which typically require moisture, favorable temperature, and an abundance of organic matter for their growth. Most species are aerobic, a few are facultative anaerobes. Many species grow better in darkness or diffuse light than in bright light. Eumycophyta also include many parasites. Most Eumycophyta are multicellular.

7. Eumycophyta are important in nature and to man in these ways:
   a. Some species are eaten by man and other animals. Some produce food products, such as cheese, that are used as human food.
   b. Some species cause diseases of man, of other animals, and of plants, including valuable crop plants.
   c. Some species are poisonous and may injure or kill animals that eat them.
   d. Some species cause food spoilage.
   e. Some species cause rotting of wood products, paper, leather, fabrics, and other materials containing organic matter.
   f. Some species produce enzymes, drugs, alcohols, organic acids, vitamins, and other substances useful in industry.
   g. Most species cause decay of dead bodies and of animal dung, thus ridding the earth's surface of organic debris and contributing to the maintenance of soil fertility by returning simple substances to soil and air.

8. Phycomycetes range from one-celled plants to those with bodies composed of many hyphae. The hyphae are nonseptate and are coenocytic; they do not combine to form definite bodies, but extend through or over the substratum

in mats of varying extent. Reproduction is asexual by zoospores and other types of spores, and sexual by isogamy or heterogamy.

9. Phycomycetes include water molds, black molds, downy mildews, and damping-off fungi.

10. Ascomycetes range from one-celled fungi to those in which the body consists of hyphae and in which the reproductive structure (ascocarp) may be 5 inches or more in length. In some species, the hyphae form no definite ascocarps, in others ascocarps of definite, constant form are developed. The hyphae have cross walls. Asexual reproduction is most commonly by conidia, in some species by budding. The unifying character of the group is the presence of an ascus, which usually results from a process of sexual fusion (or may develop parthenogenetically) and which typically forms 8 spores.

11. Ascomycetes include yeasts, blue and green molds, powdery mildews, cup and sponge fungi, and truffles.

12. Ascomycetes are believed to have evolved from Phycomycete-like ancestors.

13. Basidiomycetes are many-celled fungi, in which the hyphae have cross walls. The distinguishing characteristic of the group is the basidium, a reproductive structure that develops following a process of nuclear fusion and that bears usually 4 basidiospores externally on stalks; conidia and related types of spores are produced in some species; in some, the hyphae form no definite sporophores, in others sporophores of definite, constant structure are produced.

14. Basidiomycetes include rusts, smuts, mushrooms, pore fungi, puffballs, and related fungi.

15. Basidiomycetes are usually considered to have evolved from Ascomycetes. A basidium is interpreted as a derivative of an ascus.

16. Deuteromycetes, or imperfect fungi, are a miscellaneous group of species in which sexual or perfect stages do not occur, or have not been found; most species are believed to be Ascomycetes in which sexual fusion and ascus formation have disappeared.

17. Mycorrhizae are symbiotic associations of certain fungi with roots of higher plants. Some mycorrhizae are apparently pathological structures, in which the fungi are strictly parasitic upon host roots; others are believed to be mutually beneficial associations, in which the fungi obtain food from the roots and may promote the absorption of water or organic nitrogen compounds or may fix nitrogen.

18. Lichens are symbiotic associations of certain algae and fungi. In some lichens, the relationships may be mutually beneficial, the fungi deriving food from the algae and aiding the algae in water absorption and conservation, or promoting the absorption of nitrogenous compounds. In other lichens, the fungi are parasitic upon the algae, which derive no benefit from the fungi. Lichens are sometimes used as human food, and as sources of tannins, dyes, and gelatinlike substances. In nature, they often disintegrate rock surfaces and are eaten by wild animals.

19. Plant diseases are caused by bacteria, slime fungi, true fungi, viruses, animals,

and nutrient deficiencies. These diseases are manifested by stunted growth, discolored tissues of the host, visible hyphae, tissue rotting, chlorotic tissues, etc. Plant diseases are of great economic value because of the crop losses they cause. Plant diseases are controlled by chemical treatment of seeds, spraying plants with dusts and liquids containing compounds toxic to pathogens, quarantines, and breeding of resistant varieties of crop plants.

⫷ SUGGESTED READINGS FOR INTERESTED STUDENTS

1. Alexopoulos, Constantine J., *Introductory Mycology.* Wiley, New York, 1952.
2. Bold, Harold C., *Morphology of Plants.* Harper & Row, New York, 1957.
3. Christensen, Clyde M., *Common Fleshy Fungi,* rev. ed. Burgess Publishing Co., Minneapolis, 1955.
4. Gray, William D., *The Relation of Fungi to Human Affairs.* Holt, Rinehart and Winston, New York, 1959.
5. *Plant Diseases.* The Yearbook of Agriculture, U. S. Government Printing Office, 1953.
6. Ramsbottom, John, *Mushrooms and Toadstools.* Collins, London, 1953.
7. Rayner, M. C., *Trees and Toadstools.* Rodale Press, Emmaus, Pa., 1947.
8. Smith, Alexander H., *The Mushroom Hunter's Field Guide.* University of Michigan Press, Ann Arbor, 1958.
9. Stevens, Neil E., and R. B. Stevens, *Disease in Plants.* Ronald Press, New York, 1952.
10. Walker, John C., *Plant Pathology,* 2d ed. McGraw-Hill, New York, 1957.

⫷ TOPICS AND QUESTIONS FOR STUDY

1. List the principal differences between bacteria and true fungi.
2. List the distinguishing characteristics of Myxomycophyta.
3. Why do some biologists regard Myxomycophyta as animals? As plants?
4. Describe the life history of a typical slime fungus.
5. How are slime fungi important in human life?
6. List the differences between Eumycophyta and Myxomycophyta.
7. Comment upon the distribution of Eumycophyta in nature. What environmental conditions are essential to their growth?
8. Define the following terms: saprophyte, parasite, autotrophic, heterotrophic, obligate parasite, facultative parasite, hypha, mycelium.
9. Shoes, suitcases, and other leather objects can be protected from fungi if they are occasionally exposed to sunlight. Explain.
10. Since the beginning of World War II, U. S. government agencies have conducted extensive investigations on fungous growth in the tropics. How might such fungi affect the operations of a military force?
11. List all the major ways in which fungi influence human life.
12. How are fungi important in nature?

13. Comment upon this statement: In one major respect, fungi are more like animals than they are like plants.

14. How does the exchange of gases between fungi and the atmosphere differ from that between green plants and the atmosphere?

15. Describe briefly the structure and reproduction of Phycomycetes.

16. Name the principal groups of fungi that belong to the Phycomycetes and distinguish among them.

17. Describe the life cycle of *Rhizopus nigricans*. Why are the gametes of this fungus not called eggs and sperms?

18. A loaf of bread as it comes from a hot oven is sterile. Within a few hours after cooling, however, bread mold may begin to grow upon it. From where does the fungus come?

19. Name some Phycomycetes that are important in human life.

20. State the ideas concerning the evolutionary origin of Phycomycetes.

21. Characterize briefly the Ascomycetes.

22. Describe briefly the development and structure of an ascus.

23. It has been said that many Ascomycetes are losing their ability to reproduce sexually. Explain.

24. List and describe briefly the common asexual reproductive methods of Ascomycetes.

25. Name some of the principal orders of Ascomycetes and distinguish among them.

26. Make a complete list of the ways in which Ascomycetes influence human life.

27. Describe briefly a *Penicillium* fungus and describe how species of this genus are important to man.

28. State the present ideas concerning the relationships of Ascomycetes.

29. Describe briefly the development and structure of a basidium. How does a basidium differ from an ascus?

30. Name the principal orders of Basidiomycetes and characterize them briefly.

31. Describe the structure, nutrition, and reproduction of a typical mushroom; of a pore fungus.

32. Describe the structure, nutrition, and reproduction of puffballs.

33. What is the generally accepted idea concerning the evolutionary origin of Basidiomycetes?

34. Characterize the Deuteromycetes. Why is this class sometimes called the "fungal wastebasket"?

35. How do members of the Deuteromycetes affect human life?

36. Describe the structure of mycorrhizae and summarize the ideas concerning the physiology of mycorrhizae.

37. Contrast symbiosis and antibiosis.

38. Describe the structure and reproduction of lichens. What are the physiological relationships between the algal and fungal components of lichens?

39. Describe briefly the importance of lichens in nature and in human life.

40. List as many similarities as you can between algae and fungi. Name some

algal and fungal species (or orders) that strikingly resemble each other.

41. Most of the hyphae of a mushroom are subterranean, but the sporophores grow upward into the air before their spores mature. Of what advantage is this behavior?

42. How would you proceed to grow mushrooms commercially?

43. The hyphae of fungi are slender, soft, delicate structures, yet they are able to penetrate with ease such hard materials as wood. Explain.

44. List the major causes of plant diseases.

45. List several methods of plant disease control.

22

Embryophyta: Bryophyta (Mosses and Liverworts)

EMBRYOPHYTA AS A WHOLE

The plant divisions that remain to be studied are members of the **Embryophyta,** the second of the two plant subkingdoms. Plants of the Embryophyta have the following characteristics in common:

1. The gametangia of the Embryophyta are always multicellular. Male gametangia are called **antheridia,** as in the thallophytes; female gametangia are termed **archegonia.** Each of these reproductive structures possesses an outer wall of sterile cells that provides nutrients and protection for the gametes, zygote, or developing embryo within. In contrast, thallophyte gametangia are unicellular, or, if multicellular, lack sterile walls. The absence of gametangia in many embryophytes is thought to have resulted from evolutionary reduction of an ancestral stock that had multicellular gametangia.

2. All members, following fertilization, produce multicellular embryos in their female gametangia, or, when archegonia are lacking, in other parts of the female gametophyte. During the period of retention, the embryo is nourished and protected against desiccation and mechanical injury by the surrounding gametophyte tissue. The retention of the embryo with its concomitant advantages is in striking contrast with the condition in algae, in which the zygote, soon after fertilization, is usually found in the surrounding medium as a free cell containing a small supply of stored food within its single protective wall. The development of the embryonic condition is believed to be related to the establishment of a land existence of plants. Botanists believe that the earth's first plants were water plants and that land plants evolved from these primitive water plants.

3. All members of the Embryophyta have heterogamous sexual reproduction.

4. All members of the Embryophyta have alternation of generations, in which reduction of the diploid chromosome number to the haploid number occurs in the formation of spores and in which the change from the haploid chromosome number to the diploid number occurs at the fertilization of an egg by a sperm.

5. All members have multicellular sporangia, with sterile wall layers.

In addition to these features found in

403

all members of the Embryophyta, *most* members of this subkingdom have certain other characteristics in common, among which are:

1. They are chiefly land plants, with few species living in water.

2. They possess the vascular tissues xylem and phloem and thus have true roots, stems, and leaves. (The Bryophyta lack vascular tissues.)

3. They have a cuticle on most aerial parts. The cuticle is exceedingly important in land plants, since it conserves moisture and thus reduces chances of desiccation of leaves and other organs exposed to air.

4. They possess chloroplasts, in which the pigments are the same as those of green algae.

5. The sporophyte in most species is the larger, more complex generation.

DIVISION BRYOPHYTA (MOSSES AND ALLIES)

Growth Forms and Structure

This division, with about 840 genera and 23,000 species, is made up of small plants that rarely exceed 8 inches in height or length, lack xylem and phloem, and have no true roots, stems, or leaves. Nevertheless, many species have hairlike absorptive and anchoring structures called **rhizoids,** which penetrate the substratum and absorb water and minerals from it. Many species have also short, slender, stemlike, erect structures that bear tiny, green, leaflike scales; these structures are not called stems and leaves, because they lack vascular tissues. It is believed that the lack of xylem and phloem has been responsible for the small sizes of Bryophyta, for the absence of these tissues results in inadequate conduction of materials and in insufficient strength for greater growth and size.

Reproduction and Life Cycle

The gametophyte generation is larger and structurally more complex than the sporophyte generation. A single gametophyte may produce both archegonia and antheridia (monoecious species), or archegonia and antheridia may be borne on separate female and male gametophytes (dioecious species). An antheridium forms numerous sperms, an archegonium one egg. An antheridium is typically ovoid or cylindrical, an archegonium is usually shaped like a tenpin, with a somewhat enlarged hollow base **(venter),** within which the egg is produced, and a long slender **neck** (Figure 22–5). When an archegonium is mature, its neck develops a central canal, which opens at the apex of the neck. Sperms, which can reach the archegonia only by swimming through water or by being carried to the archegonia by splashing water, swim through the neck canal to the venter, where a single sperm fertilizes the egg. The zygote then undergoes cell division and begins to grow into the embryo sporophyte *within the archegonium.* During its growth, the embryo develops a basal structure called a **foot,** which becomes embedded in the gametophyte tissue, from which it absorbs food and water. The upper part of the young embryo ultimately becomes the major part of the sporophyte, which commonly consists of a stalk **(seta)** and, at the apex of the stalk, a **capsule,** within which reduction division occurs and spores are formed. In some species, the sporophyte consists only of a capsule. At maturity, the capsule opens, liberating the spores that, when deposited in a suitable environment, germinate. As a result of growth, the germinating spores form gametophyte plants, which then reproduce in the manner described above, completing the life cycle. In Bryophyta, the sporophyte remains attached to the gametophyte and depends upon the gametophyte for its nourishment; the gametophyte is always larger and structurally more complex than the sporophyte.

Physiological Characteristics

All Bryophyta contain chlorophyll and hence carry on photosynthesis. Plants of most species experience rapid water loss from their aerial parts and thus are subject to desiccation in dry habitats.

Habitats and Distribution

Bryophyta thrive in moist, shaded habitats. They grow upon damp soil and rocks and upon the moist bark of trees in diffuse light. Thus, they may be found in greatest abundance in forests and in deep, shaded ravines. They are widely distributed over the earth's surface, from arctic regions through the temperate zones to equatorial forests. In tropical regions, mosses often form dense epiphytic growths upon the trunks and branches of trees, upon posts, and upon the roofs of buildings. Mosses often grow in dense mats, which may attain areas of many square yards or acres, especially on the damp soil of northern forests and in bogs and swamps. A few species are aquatic.

Importance in Nature and in Human Life

Bryophyta play important, though inconspicuous, roles in the cycles of nature. Some of them provide food for herbivorous mammals, birds, and other animals. Water-inhabiting mosses contribute to the filling in of ponds and lakes and thus to the building of soil. Extensive mats of bryophytes, because of their dense growth, diminish the force of falling rain and absorb large amounts of moisture, thus preventing soil erosion. Some bryophytes that inhabit dry places often appear, along with lichens, as colonizers of rock surfaces and exert a disintegrative action upon rocks, thus contributing to the formation of soil from rock and providing a substratum in which higher plants may grow. The direct uses of bryophytes by man are relatively few. Plants of the genus *Sphagnum,* called peat mosses, are used in a number of ways and are the most important economically of all bryophytes. Peat mosses are used as a packing material in the shipment of china and other fragile objects; as a stuffing in upholstery; as bedding for domesticated animals; as a source of organic matter to loosen tight, clayey soils; as an absorbent substitute for cotton in surgical bandages; and as packing for cut flowers, grafting scions, and other plant materials that must be protected against drying during shipment. *Sphagnum* "leaves" contain many large, empty, dead cells that absorb and hold water in large quantities; thus, peat mosses increase the water-holding capacity of soils with which they are mixed and keep flowers packed in them fresh and moist. Dried, compressed peat, dug up from peat beds in many parts of the world, is widely used as a fuel.

Relationships with Other Organisms

Botanists are generally agreed that the Bryophyta have evolved from algal ancestors, probably from green algae. Evidence in support of this idea is derived from several similarities between bryophytes and green algae. For example, early stages in the gametophytes of most

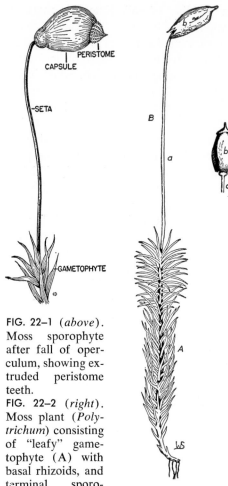

FIG. 22–1 (*above*). Moss sporophyte after fall of operculum, showing extruded peristome teeth.

FIG. 22–2 (*right*). Moss plant (*Polytrichum*) consisting of "leafy" gametophyte (A) with basal rhizoids, and terminal sporophyte (B) made up of foot, long stalk or seta (a), and terminal capsule (b), the latter with lid or operculum (c).

Bryophyta are branching, green filaments that strikingly resemble various branching, filamentous green algae. Also, the bodies of Bryophyta are essentially thalli, since they lack vascular tissues and are thus not much more complex structurally than most algae. Further, the chloroplast pigments of bryophytes are virtually identical with those of green algae. An older view was that Bryophyta were an intermediate group of plants that arose from algal ancestors and then gave rise to the higher, vascular plants. At present, botanists acknowledge the probable algal ancestry of bryophytes, but they do not regard them as a group from which vascular plants have evolved. Rather, they favor the idea that the bryophytes constitute a group that has not given rise to higher plants and that they may thus be regarded as a terminal group of plants that originated from algae and migrated to land but failed to undergo further development.

Representative Members

Bryophyta are separated into three classes, two of which, Musci (mosses) with about 14,000 species and Hepaticae (liverworts) with about 8500 species, will be described.

CLASS I—MUSCI (TRUE MOSSES)

General Character

Mosses are small plants with usually erect stemlike axes, which are anchored in the soil at their bases by rhizoids and which bear small, green, leaflike scales on their aerial portions (Figure 22–2). This "leafy shoot" or "moss plant" is the principal portion of the gametophyte generation of a moss species. The "leafy shoot" bears antheridia or archegonia, or both, at its apex; in some species of mosses, both antheridia and archegonia are produced on the same gametophyte, in other species, they are borne on separate male and female gametophytes. When the gametangia (Figure 22–5) are mature and are covered by a layer of water or are struck by falling rain, the antheridia discharge their biflagellate sperms, which swim to the archegonia and enter their neck canals, a single sperm reaching and fertiliz-

FIG. 22–3 (*left*). Moss (*Polytrichum*) sporophytes. Terminal capsules covered with hairy caps or calyptras.

FIG. 22–4 (*right*). Capsule of a moss (*Polytrichum*). *Left:* Calyptra covering capsule. *Right:* Cross sections of capsule, showing spore masses.

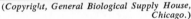

ing an egg. The zygote grows into the sporophyte, which is attached by its **foot** to the gametophyte from which it absorbs food and water. A moss sporophyte has a slender stalk **(seta)** that rises from the apex of the gametophyte and that bears a spore-producing capsule at its tip. The capsule is often covered by a caplike structure, the **calyptra,** or remnant of the archegonial neck and upper part of the venter, which is carried upward by the growth of the sporophyte. The calyptra usually falls off or disintegrates as the capsule matures, exposing the capsule lid, or **operculum.** Beneath this lid is a ring of teeth, the **peristome;** these teeth open outward into dry air and bend downward into the capsule in humid air. These movements result in a dispersal of the spores, which are formed within the capsule. The sporophytes of mosses usually contain small amounts of chlorophyll, so that they are able to synthesize some food; however, they depend chiefly upon the gametophytes to which they are attached for their nourishment and water.

An immature capsule contains **spore mother cells,** each of which undergoes meiosis, forming four haploid spores. A germinating spore produces a branched, green, algalike filament, the **protonema,** upon which buds develop (Figure 22–6). Each bud grows into a new "leafy shoot," or mature gametophyte, which then produces gametes as described. In alternation of generations in mosses, the gametophyte begins with the spores and includes the protonema, leafy shoot, gametangia, and gametes; the sporophyte begins with the zygote and includes the foot, seta, capsule and its parts, and spore mother cells. All gametophyte structures are hap-

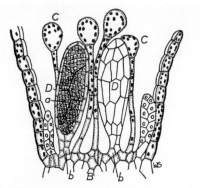

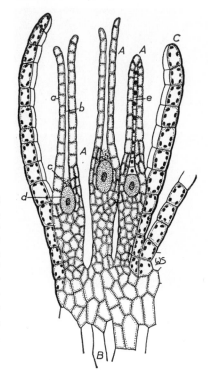

FIG. 22–5. *Above:* Longitudinal section through the tip of a male gametophyte of a moss, showing multicellular male gametangia or antheridia (D) and paraphyses or sterile hairs (C). Each antheridium (D) consists of a short stalk (b), sterile wall or jacket layer, and many sperms (a). *Right:* Longitudinal section through the tip of a female gametophyte of a moss, showing multicellular female gametangia or archegonia (A) and paraphyses or sterile hairs (C). Each archegonium consists of a stalk, long neck (a) with canal (b), and venter (c) with egg (d).

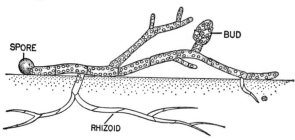

FIG. 22–6. Moss spore and protonema—the latter a prostrate, branching, green filament with chloroplasts, bud, and underground rhizoids with oblique cross walls.

loid, all sporophyte structures diploid. The life cycle of a typical moss is represented by Figure 22–7. Mosses may reproduce by fragmentation; a portion of a leafy shoot may break away from other portions of a plant, form rhizoids, and become a new individual.

Representatives

Common and well-known genera of mosses are *Polytrichum* (hairy cap moss) and *Sphagnum* (peat moss). Species of *Poly-*trichum are dioecious; that is, they have two kinds of gametophytes, male and female, which produce antheridia and archegonia, respectively. In such mosses, two types of spores are formed by the sporophyte, one kind producing male gametophytes, the other female gametophytes. These two kinds of spores are identical in size and structure, different in their genetic constitution. Various features of *Polytrichum* and its life cycle are shown in the illustrations of this chapter. In *Sphagnum*, antheridia and archegonia

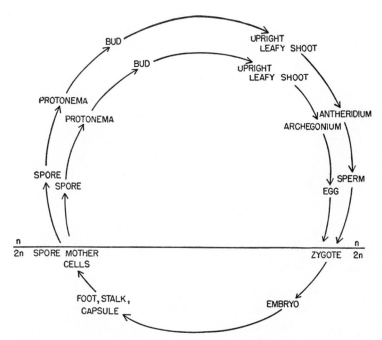

FIG. 22–7. Diagram of the life cycle of a moss, showing points where chromosome changes occur.

may be borne on separate gametophytes, or they may be borne on the same "leafy shoot."

Relationships of the Musci

The modern interpretation of the relationships of mosses holds that these plants are probably the most primitive bryophytes and that the liverworts, to be described in subsequent paragraphs, have evolved from mosslike ancestors through reduction or simplification of structure. According to this view, mosses are more similar to the supposed algal ancestors of Bryophyta than are the liverworts.

CLASS II—HEPATICAE (LIVERWORTS)

General Character

Liverworts differ from mosses in that their habit of growth is usually horizon-

tal rather than erect and their sporophytes are usually smaller and less conspicuous than those of mosses. In some liverworts, the body is a flat, ribbonlike, forked thallus that grows closely appressed to the substratum (these plants are called liverworts because of their resemblance to the lobed livers of higher animals). Rhizoids grow from the under surface of the thallus, anchoring it to the soil and absorbing water and nutrients. The upper surfaces of many liverwort thalli have conspicuous, rhomboidal areas, each with a pore that opens into an air chamber beneath it; through these pores exchange of gases between the external atmosphere and the internal portions of the thallus occurs. Many liverworts bear on their upper surfaces **gemmae cups** (Figure 22–10), within which are produced small, flattened, elliptical structures called **gemmae**. When sepa-

FIG. 22–8. Bed of peat moss (*Sphagnum*) growing in a bog. The small black structures are sporophytes.

rated from the parent plant, the gemmae grow directly into new thalli. Reproduction by gemmae is vegetative and may be compared with reproduction by rhizomes, runners, and similar structures in flowering plants. Many other species of liverworts have leaflike scales growing from a central stemlike axis and thus resemble true mosses, except for their prostrate habit of growth. These "leafy" liverworts are thought to be the most primitive liverworts and to be more closely related to mosses than are other liverworts. The liverwort plants just described are gametophytes, some species of which bear their antheridia and archegonia on separate thalli while other species produce both kinds of gametangia on the same thallus.

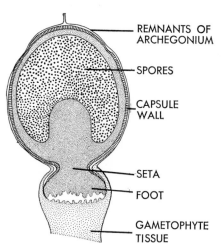

REMNANTS OF ARCHEGONIUM

SPORES

CAPSULE WALL

SETA

FOOT

GAMETOPHYTE TISSUE

FIG. 22–9. *Sphagnum* sporophyte with basal foot embedded in gametophytic tissue, short stalk or seta, and large capsule containing many spores.

FIG. 22–10. A liverwort (*Lunularia*), showing gemmae cups with gemmae.

The gametangia, similar in structure to those of mosses, may be embedded in the thallus, opening at maturity onto the upper thallus surface, or may be borne on specialized stalks that rise from the upper surface of the thallus. As in mosses, liverwort sperms can reach the archegonia only by swimming through water; thus

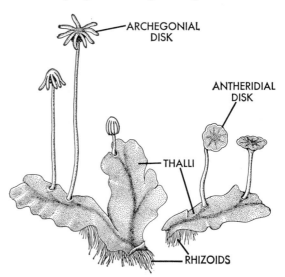

FIG. 22–11. *Marchantia* gametophytes. *Left:* Archegonial plant showing lobed disc borne on stalk (archegoniophore). *Right:* Antheridial plant with disc borne on stalk (antheridiophore).

ARCHEGONIAL DISK

ANTHERIDIAL DISK

THALLI

RHIZOIDS

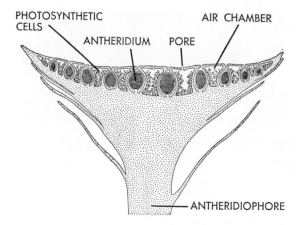

FIG. 22–12. *Marchantia* antheridial disc in longitudinal section, showing air chambers, pores, and antheridia in sunken cavities.

the plants must be wet before fertilization can occur. An egg is fertilized in an archegonium, and the zygote develops into the sporophyte as in mosses, with the young sporophyte embedded in the gametophyte and enclosed by the archegonial wall. A liverwort sporophyte, in addition to its foot, usually has a very short seta and a capsule, within which spore mother cells, after meiosis, form spores. The sporophyte of a liverwort usually has traces of chlorophyll and thus can manufacture a small amount of food, but it depends chiefly upon the gametophyte for its nourishment. When the sporophyte is mature, the capsule opens, liberating the spores; these, encountering favorable conditions, germinate and grow into new thalli, which then reproduce as described earlier. In liverworts, as in mosses, the gametophyte generation is larger and more complex structurally than the sporophyte.

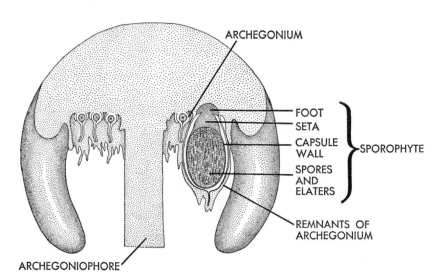

FIG. 22–13. *Marchantia* archegonial disc in longitudinal section, showing archegonia and a sporophyte.

Representatives

In *Marchantia* plants (Figure 22–11), which are dioecious, the gametangia are borne upon short stalks that grow upward from the upper surfaces of the thalli. Antheridia are embedded in disc-shaped structures surmounting the stalks of the male thalli (Figure 22–12); the antheridia open onto the upper surfaces of these discs. The female plants produce stalks with smaller discs, which bear marginal rays like the ribs of an umbrella; the archegonia develop on the undersides of the discs (Figure 22–13). Sperms reach the archegonia by swimming through water when the plants are wet or are pelted by rain drops, and fertilization of an egg occurs within an archegonium. The small sporophyte is attached by its foot to the disc tissue of the female stalk, from which it absorbs food and water.

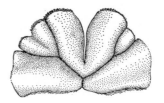

FIG. 22–14. Habit sketch of dichotomously lobed gameto- phyte of *Riccia*.

The mature sporophytes, which are barely visible to the naked eye, occupy a pendulous position under the ribs (Figure 22–13). Among the spores, within a capsule, are slender, threadlike **elaters,** which undergo movements with changes in atmospheric humidity; these movements aid in pushing the spores from the capsule. The spores fall to the substratum, where they germinate, growing into new thalli. As in dioecious mosses, two

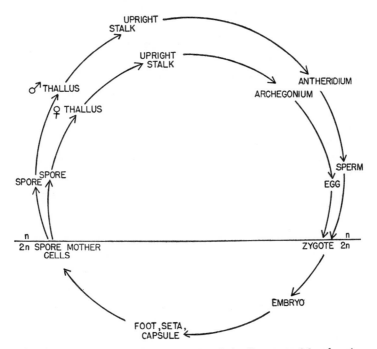

FIG. 22–15. Diagram of the life cycle of the liverwort *Marchantia,* indicating the stages at which chromosome changes occur.

types of genetically different but morphologically similar spores are formed, one kind producing male thalli, the other growing into female thalli; the two types of thalli are morphologically similar except for their differing gametangia and the stalks upon which these gametangia are borne. The life cycle of *Marchantia* is represented by Figure 22–15.

In the genus *Riccia,* the thalli (Figure 22–14) resemble those of *Marchantia* and have a similar internal structure. The archegonia and antheridia are borne on the same thallus and are embedded in the thallus, onto the upper surface of which they open at maturity. The sporophyte of *Riccia* is very simple, consisting of only a layer of wall cells that surround the mass of spores; foot and seta are absent.

Relationships of Hepaticae

Available evidence suggests a fairly close relationship between the true liverworts and the mosses. The present view is that liverworts are more advanced in evolution than mosses; that they appear to be less complex structurally than mosses is supposedly the result of structural simplification during their evolution.

⪻ SUMMARY

1. Plants of the subkingdom Embryophyta have the following common characteristics:
   a. Gametangia, both male (antheridia) and female (archegonia), are multicellular and have sterile wall cells. An antheridium produces numerous sperms, an archegonium contains a single egg. Embryophytes lacking gametangia are thought to be derived by reduction from ancestral forms that had multicellular gametangia.
   b. Multicellular embryos are produced in the archegonia or, when lacking, in other parts of the gametophyte. In this way, the embryo receives nourishment and protection from the surrounding tissues. Retention of the embryo is thought to be associated with the transition from an aquatic to a land habitat of plants.
   c. They have heterogamous sexual reproduction.
   d. They have alternation of generations.
2. *Most* members of the Embryophyta have these additional features:
   a. They are chiefly land plants.
   b. They have the vascular tissues xylem and phloem and thus have true roots, stems, and leaves. Bryophyta lack vascular tissues.
   c. They possess a cuticle.
   d. They have chloroplasts that contain pigments similar to those of green algae.
   e. Their sporophytes are dominant, except in Bryophyta.
3. Members of the Bryophyta have the following common characteristics:
   a. They are small in stature, rarely in excess of 5 inches.
   b. They have no vascular tissues.
   c. They have no true roots, stems, or leaves.
   d. Water is necessary for fertilization.
   e. The gametophyte is larger and more complex than the sporophyte and

nutritionally independent; the sporophyte is attached to the gametophyte and wholly or largely dependent upon it for food.

    f. Sperms have flagella.

4. The sporophyte of bryophytes consists typically of a foot, seta, and spore-producing capsule. In some species, the sporophyte consists only of a capsule.

5. Bryophyta grow chiefly in moist, shaded habitats; a few species inhabit dry places, such as bare rock surfaces. Bryophyta are widely distributed on the earth's surface.

6. Bryophyta are important in nature and in human life in these ways: they furnish food for some animals; some species colonize rock surfaces and promote the formation of soil from rocks; they reduce soil erosion; peat mosses are important for fuel, for packing material, and for the addition of organic matter to soils.

7. Bryophyta are believed to have evolved from green algae. They are regarded as a terminal group that has not given rise to higher types of plants.

8. Bryophyta are separated into two major classes: Musci (mosses) and Heptaicae (liverworts).

9. A true moss plant (leafy shoot) consists of a stemlike axis, bearing rhizoids and leaflike green scales. Antheridia and archegonia are borne at the tips of the shoots, on the same plant or on different plants. Sperms swim to the archegonia in water, a single sperm fertilizing the egg within the archegonium. The zygote develops within the archegonium into the embryo sporophyte, which grows upward from the archegonium. The upper portion of the archegonium may form a hood (calyptra) over the capsule. The sporophyte consists of a foot, seta, and capsule. The capsule produces and liberates spores. Spores germinate on a suitable substratum, a spore forming a branched, green, filamentous protonema; buds borne on the protonema develop into leafy shoots, which then produce antheridia and archegonia. Reduction division occurs within the capsule when spores are formed from spore mother cells. Spores, protonema, leafy shoot, gametangia, and gametes are haploid and constitute the gametophyte generation; the zygote is the first stage of the sporophyte, all cells of which are diploid.

10. Liverworts grow appressed to the substratum (or float on water) and are usually branched, ribbonlike thalli. A majority of species are "leafy," bearing a superficial resemblance to mosses. The sporophytes of liverworts are smaller and usually simpler in structure than those of mosses. Gametangia of liverworts are embedded in the thalli, or are borne on short stalks arising from the thalli. Sperms swim from antheridia to archegonia through water, one sperm fertilizing the single egg in the archegonium. The zygote develops into the sporophyte within the archegonium, the growing sporophyte rupturing the archegonial wall as it enlarges. In many species, elaters occur among the spores and, through their movements, push spores from the capsule. A liverwort sporophyte may consist of foot, stalk, and capsule, or it may consist only of a capsule. As in mosses, the gametophyte is the larger, independent generation, the sporo-

phyte is smaller, less complex morphologically, and wholly or largely dependent upon the gametophyte for its food and water.

11. Many botanists believe that the division Bryophyta has evolved probably from green algae, that mosses are probably the more primitive bryophytes, and that liverworts have probably been derived from some mosslike ancestral stock.

⫷ SUGGESTED READINGS FOR INTERESTED STUDENTS

1. Bold, H. C., *Morphology of Plants.* Harper & Row, New York, 1957.
2. Conard, H. S., *How to Know the Mosses.* H. E. Jaques, Mt. Pleasant, Iowa, 1944.
3. Grout, A. J., *Mosses with a Hand Lens,* 3d. ed. Publ. by author, Newfane, Vermont, 1924.
4. Smith, G. M., *Cryptogamic Botany,* Vol. II: Bryophytes and Pteridophytes. McGraw-Hill, New York, 1938.

⫷ TOPICS AND QUESTIONS FOR STUDY

1. List the characteristic features of Embryophyta, Bryophyta, Musci, and Hepaticae.
2. Describe briefly the distribution of Bryophyta.
3. List the ways in which Bryophyta are important in nature and in human life.
4. Describe the structure and life history of a typical moss.
5. Describe alternation of generations in Bryophyta.
6. How might you explain the fact that Bryophyta are small plants?
7. How would you explain the fact that Bryophyta are usually limited to moist habitats?
8. Describe the structure and life history of a liverwort. How do liverworts resemble mosses? How do they differ from mosses?
9. Describe the similarities between bryophytes and thallophytes; the differences between them.
10. Why are rhizoids, axes, and leaflike scales of mosses not considered to be true roots, stems, and leaves?
11. What is the advantage of multicellular gametangia and sporangia over unicellular gametangia and sporangia?
12. What are the advantages of the retention of the embryo sporophyte within the archegonium?
13. Describe briefly the modern interpretation of the origin and evolution of Bryophyta.
14. How are mosses effective in preventing or reducing soil erosion?

23

Tracheophyta: Psilopsida

The division **Tracheophyta,** which embraces about 260,000 known species of plants, is the second of the two divisions of the subkingdom Embryophyta. In addition to their possession of the characteristics listed for the Embryophyta as a whole in the last chapter, they have the following common characteristics:

1. Their bodies possess the vascular tissues xylem and phloem (hence the name of the division, which is derived from the Greek words *tracheia*—windpipe, and *phyton*—plant). These vascular tissues ordinarily occur only in the sporophyte generation.

2. The sporophyte generation is larger and more complex structurally than the gametophyte generation and, except for a very short embryonic period, is nutritionally independent of the gametophyte. Familiar tracheophyte plants such as ferns, pine trees, apple trees, rose bushes, and corn plants are sporophytes; the gametophytes of such plants are small, inconspicuous structures that are usually less than 1 inch in length and that, in most tracheophytes, are so small that they can be seen only with magnifying lenses. In a minority of tracheophyte species, the gametophytes possess chlorophyll and are nutritionally independent; in most species, however, the gametophytes lack chlorophyll and depend upon sporophyte tissues for their nourishment. The relationship between the two generations of tracheophytes is thus the reverse of that in bryophytes, in which the gametophyte is the larger, nutritionally independent generation, the sporophyte the smaller, nutritionally dependent generation.

The division Tracheophyta is divided into four subdivisions: **Psilopsida, Lycopsida, Sphenopsida,** and **Pteropsida.** The Psilopsida (Greek *psilo*—slender, *phyton*—plant) are the most primitive of these; they are chiefly extinct and are known principally from fossils; only two genera of Psilopsida contain species of plants that still live upon the earth; these are only rarely seen and constitute a negligible part of the earth's living flora, but their evolutionary implications are so important that they therefore deserve brief discussion.

417

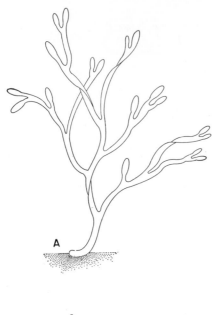

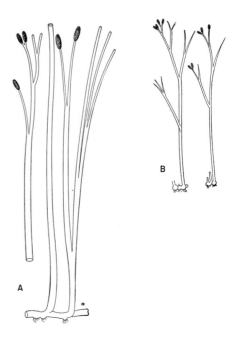

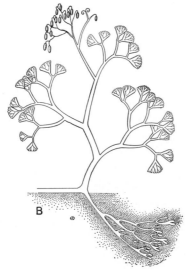

FIG. 23–1 (*left*). Diagram illustrating a widely accepted theory of the origin of land plants. A: Dichotomously branched thallus of a green alga from which land plants may have originated. B: Hypothetical primitive land plant, resembling Psilopsida, with dichotomous branches, one entering the soil to become a root, others forming leaves and sporangia.

FIG. 23–2 (*above*). Two psilophytes. A: *Rhynia,* with creeping rhizome bearing rhizoids, and dichotomously branched stems bearing sporangia. B: *Horneophyton,* with tuberous rhizomes.

SUBDIVISION PSILOPSIDA

Growth Forms and Structure

The bodies of Psilopsida are relatively undifferentiated (Figures 23–2 and 23–3). They lack true roots and leaves, although in a few species, leaflike scales are present. They have cylindrical, elongated stems with **dichotomous** branching (forking repeatedly into two branches); these aerial stems grow upward from underground rhizomes that may have rhizoids. The vascular tissues are very primitive in structure and arrangement, and the stems lack cambium.

Reproduction and Life Cycle

The plants described above are sporophytes, the aerial portions of which bear
small, scalelike appendages and three-
lobed sporangia (Figure 23–3). Each
sporangium is borne terminally on a minute lateral branch in the axil of a pair of
scales. A sporophyte produces one kind
of sporangium in which, following meiosis, a single type of spore is formed. The
spores germinate in the soil, each giving
rise to a small, branching, nongreen
gametophyte (Figure 23–4) that, unlike
the gametophytes of other vascular
plants, sometimes contains a small
amount of vascular tissue. Nutrition of
these heterotrophic gametophytes is probably facilitated by closely associated fungi. Both antheridia and archegonia are
produced on the same gametophyte and
are similar to those of bryophytes. Sperms
swim to the archegonia through water, a
single sperm fertilizes the egg in an
archegonium, and, as in bryophytes, a
zygote begins its growth within the archegonium, ultimately developing into a mature sporophyte. Early in the development of a sporophyte, the gametophyte,
from which the sporophyte grows, disintegrates. Gametophytes of the extinct species have not been found; they were probably like those of living species.

Physiological Characteristics

Living species of Psilopsida contain chlorophyll and thus carry on photosynthesis.
The extinct species were probably autotrophic.

Habitats and Distribution

Extinct species of this subdivision were
widely distributed on the earth's surface

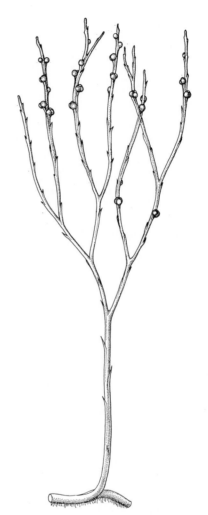

FIG. 23–3. *Psilotum* with dichotomous aerial stem arising from a
rhizome. Scales are borne at intervals on the stem; some of the
scales have 3-lobed sporangia in
their axils.

about 350,000,000 to 380,000,000 years
ago. The living species are tropical and
subtropical plants, occurring in such
places as Florida, Bermuda, Hawaii,
Australia, New Zealand, New Caledonia,
and the Philippine Islands. Some species
are occasionally cultivated in greenhouses
as botanical curiosities.

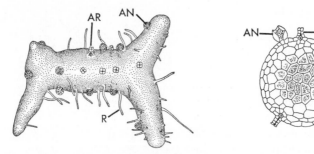

FIG. 23–4. *Psilotum* gametophyte with rhizoids (R), archegonia (AR), and antheridia (AN). *Left:* Habit sketch enlarged. *Right:* Transverse section. (After Lawson.)

Importance in Nature and in Human Life

Psilopsida have no economic value in human life.

Relationships with Other Organisms

As stated in the last chapter, botanists believe that land plants, that is, Bryophyta and Tracheophyta, originated from water plants, probably the Chlorophyta, or green algae. According to one interpretation, the Bryophyta evolved from algal ancestors and in turn gave rise to vascular plants; supporters of this view believe that bryophytes with fairly complex sporophytes may have been the ancestors of the Tracheophyta. An opposing interpretation holds that the Bryophyta are a terminal group that has not given rise to vascular plants. Adherents to this second theory, which is receiving increasingly wide acceptance, believe that at least two major groups of land plants arose from algal ancestors: the terminal, nonvascular Bryophyta, and a group of primitive vascular plants from which higher types of vascular plants developed. The results of paleobotanical research (the study of plant remains and impressions in the layers of the earth's crust) indicate that this group of primitive vascular plants,

which seems to have evolved from algae and from which higher plants appear to have arisen, had psilopsid characteristics.

Information concerning the supposed origin of vascular plants from water plants is meager, and any account of the changes that occurred when plants left the water for a land existence is necessarily in large part speculative. It has been suggested that some dichotomously branched green algae may have given rise to a land plant in this way: one of the branches of the algal thallus may have penetrated the soil at or above the water line and may have become a primitive root or rhizome; other branches of the thallus may have formed the main axis stem system, portions of which later became flattened into leaves (Figure 23–1). During these hypothetical changes, this primitive land plant developed a cuticle, and its internal organization experienced increasing morphological specialization, which led to the origin of primitive vascular tissues.

Certain extinct Psilopsida approach remarkably this hypothetical, primitive land plant. Their bodies were very simple, with rhizomes and a simple stem system, with usually dichotomous branches and no leaves, and their vascular tissues were simple in structure and arrangement. Some fossils of Psilopsida are scarcely distinguishable in their superficial appearance from the dichotomous thalli of certain algae. That the most primitive Psilopsida were apparently inhabitants of swamps and possibly seaside marshes may be regarded as evidence indicating the origin of these plants from water plants.

The discovery of fossils of extinct Psilopsida chiefly in rocks of the Silurian and Devonian periods supports the theory that primitive vascular plants arose directly from algae, for the earliest known fossils of Bryophyta occur in rock layers formed many millions of years *after* the rocks in which the first fossils of vascular plants appear. In other words, the fossil record seems to show that vascular plants lived *before* bryophytes appeared on the earth. The paleobotanical evidence, together with certain morphological evidence, thus indicates that plants with psilopsid characteristics may be the "missing links" between Thallophyta and the higher land plants.

Representative Members

Among the most primitive fossil genera of Psilopsida are *Rhynia* and *Horneophyton* (Figure 23–2). Plants of these

FIG. 23–5. A living *Psilotum* plant. These plants are sometimes grown in botanical gardens as "living fossils."

genera apparently did not exceed 2 feet in height, with stems about ¼ inch or slightly greater in diameter. A few fossil members of this division reached heights of 9 feet and were somewhat fernlike in appearance. Better known of the two living genera is *Psilotum* (Figure 23–5).

⫷⫷ SUMMARY

1. The distinguishing characteristics of the division Tracheophyta (in addition to those of Embryophyta as a whole) are:
   a. The presence of the vascular tissues xylem and phloem, which in most species occur only in the sporophyte generation.
   b. The greater size and complexity of the sporophyte generation as compared with the gametophyte, and the nutritional independence of the sporophyte (except for a short period early in the development of the sporophyte).
2. The Tracheophyta are divided into four subdivisions: Psilopsida, Lycopsida, Sphenopsida, and Pteropsida.
3. The division Psilopsida is known chiefly through fossils of extinct plants and includes only two genera of living plants.

4. The bodies of Psilopsida are simple in structure. Their sporophytes lack true roots and leaves, have rhizomes with erect, usually dichotomous, slender, cylindrical stems, which bear terminal sporangia. All sporangia are of the same type, and one kind of spore is produced. The gametophytes of living species are small, heterotrophic structures that bear archegonia and antheridia and sometimes contain vascular tissue.

5. The living species contain chlorophyll and are autotrophic, as were apparently the extinct species.

6. Extinct species were widely distributed in the Silurian and Devonian periods. The living species have a scattered distribution in tropical and subtropical regions.

7. Botanists agree that land plants arose from water plants, probably green algae.

8. One theory of the origin of vascular plants holds that they possibly evolved from Bryophytes.

9. An opposing theory holds that the bryophytes are a terminal group of plants that arose from algae and gave rise to no other plant groups and that primitive vascular plants evolved directly from algae. Supporters of this theory believe that these vascular plants had psilopsid characteristics.

10. The occurrence of Psilopsida fossils in rock layers formed earlier than those in which the first bryophyte fossils appear supports the second theory.

11. Among the best known fossil genera of Psilopsida are *Rhynia* and *Horneophyton*. Better known of the two living genera is *Psilotum*.

SUGGESTED READINGS FOR INTERESTED STUDENTS

1. Andrews, H. N., *Ancient Plants and the World They Lived In*. Comstock Publishing Co., Ithaca, N. Y., 1947.
2. Arnold, C. A., *An Introduction to Paleobotany*. McGraw-Hill, New York, 1947.
3. Eames, A. J., *Morphology of Vascular Plants*. McGraw-Hill, New York, 1936.
4. Foster, A. S., and E. M. Gifford, Jr., *Comparative Morphology of Vascular Plants*. Freeman, San Francisco, 1959.

TOPICS AND QUESTIONS FOR STUDY

1. Characterize Tracheophyta as a whole.
2. Name the subdivisions of Tracheophyta.
3. Characterize the Psilopsida as a whole.
4. Describe briefly reproduction and alternation of generations in Psilopsida.
5. What is the present distribution of living Psilopsida?
6. Describe two theories concerning the origin of vascular plants.
7. Which of these theories is more generally accepted at present? What are the evidences in support of this theory?
8. Contrast algae and vascular plants with respect to: (a) environmental conditions; (b) adaptations that help the plants survive under these conditions.

Tracheophyta: Lycopsida (Club Mosses)

The subdivision **Lycopsida,** like the Psilopsida, is a group of plants that reached their greatest development in past geological periods and that are apparently on the road to extinction, since only 4 genera with 900 species survive in the earth's living flora. During the Carboniferous and associated periods, great forests of giant Lycopsida were widely distributed on the earth's surface; these arboreal species have long been extinct, and only herbaceous species have survived to the present time. Some of these extinct tree club mosses are shown in Figure 24–9.

Growth Forms and Structure

The sporophytes of Lycopsida (commonly called club mosses and their allies) have true roots, stems, and leaves (Figure 24–2). The leaves are usually spirally arranged and are very small, rarely exceeding ½ inch in length in the living species. Each leaf typically has a single, unbranched vascular bundle. The leaves are apparently **enations,** that is, outgrowths from the surface tissues of the stems. The

vascular bundle that enters a lycopsid leaf does not leave a leaf gap in the vascular tissues of the stem, a condition very different from that in Pteropsida, in which a leaf gap occurs in the vascular tissues of the stem at the base of each leaf (Figure 24–1). The stems and roots of Lycopsida usually branch dichotomously. All living species are herbaceous; their stems rarely exceed 10 inches in height, although in a few species, creeping, or climbing stems may reach lengths of several feet. Many extinct species, known only through fossils, were trees that reached heights over 100 feet, with trunks 5 or 6 feet in diameter.

Reproduction and Life Cycle

The lycopsid plant just described is part of the sporophyte generation and produces spores. These are produced in sporangia that are borne singly on the upper surfaces of specialized leaves called **sporophylls,** which are located in most species in cylindrical clusters (Figure 24–3) at the apices of stems; these club-

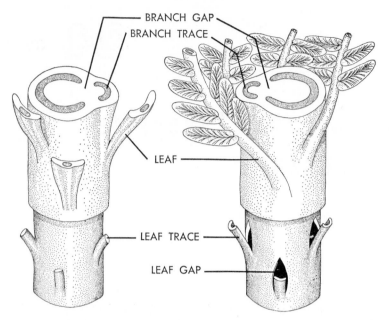

FIG. 24–1. Nodal structure of the Lycopsida and the Pteropsida. *Left:* Lycopsida. Note absence of leaf gaps. *Right:* Pteropsida. Branch gaps and leaf gaps present.

like clusters, called **strobili,** or **cones,** are responsible for the common name "club mosses" applied to living members of this subdivision. The multicellular sporangia produce spore mother cells, which, as a result of meiosis, form haploid spores. The spores may fall to earth, where they germinate, forming small gametophytes, or they may germinate to form gametophytes *within* the spore walls. In some species, one type of spore is produced, which develops into a single gametophyte with archegonia and antheridia; such species are called **homosporous.** In other species, two types of spores are produced: extremely small spores **(microspores),** and larger spores **(megaspores),** which develop respectively into male gametophytes **(microgametophytes)** with antheridia, and female gametophytes **(megagametophytes)** with archegonia; such species are termed **het-**

erosporous. In both homosporous and heterosporous species, the sperms, which are usually biflagellate, swim through water from the antheridia to the archegonia, which they enter, a single sperm fertilizing an egg. The zygote begins its growth within the archegonium, forming an embryo that ultimately becomes the mature sporophyte. As in all other plants with alternation of generations, there are two points in the life cycle at which changes in chromosome numbers occur: at spore formation, when the diploid chromosome number of the sporophyte generation is reduced to the haploid number, and at fertilization, when the union of a haploid sperm with a haploid egg produces a diploid zygote. As in Psilopsida, the sporophyte generation is larger and structurally more complex than the gametophyte. The sporophyte is well equipped with chloroplasts and is thus

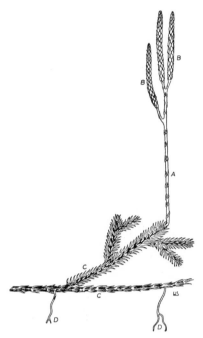

FIG. 24–2. *Lycopodium*, or club moss, showing prostrate stem with many small leaves (C), upright stem (A) bearing cones or strobili (B), and roots (D) arising from rhizome.

ics. A few species live partly or wholly submerged in water, and another small group of species is semixerophytic, growing on bark, dry rock surfaces, and in desert regions. The resurrection plant (*Selaginella lepidophylla*) is a club moss that inhabits dry regions from Texas to Peru; it becomes a tight, brown ball under arid conditions, quickly unrolls into a graceful, green plant when moisture is available. The dependence of club mosses upon water for the transportation of sperms to eggs is a major factor limiting most species to moist habitats.

Importance in Nature and in Human Life

The economic significance of living species of Lycopsida is very slight. Several species of "ground pines," chiefly *Lycopodium obscurum*, are widely used in Christmas decorations. A few species, especially of the genus *Selaginella*, are sometimes used as ornamentals in greenhouses and gardens. Some club mosses are eaten by deer and other wild, herbivorous animals. Lycopodium powder, sometimes used by druggists in the compounding of pills, consists of the spores of *Lycopodium clavatum*. *Lycopodium* spores are occasionally used in dusting powders for the skin, and extracts of *Lycopodium* have been used as kidney stimulants. The underground stems of *Isoetes* are eaten by muskrats, ducks, beavers, and other water animals.

The extinct species of Lycopsida, which reached their greatest development during the Carboniferous period, were of greater economic importance than their living relatives. The dead, partly decomposed bodies of these long-extinct plants formed a large part of earth's coal deposits.

nutritionally independent. The gametophyte depends upon sporophyte tissues for its food, or it may develop a small amount of chlorophyll and thus manufacture a portion of its food.

Physiological Characteristics

All living species of Lycopsida have an abundance of chlorophyll in their sporophytes and thus are autotrophic. The chloroplast pigments of these species are like those of green algae, Psilopsida, and the other subdivisions of Tracheophyta.

Habitats and Distribution

Most living species are plants of moist, shaded woodlands, especially in the trop-

FIG. 24–3. *Lycopodium clavatum*, a common club moss in eastern North America. Note the dichotomous reproductive stems with strobili.

Relationships with Other Organisms

The Lycopsida are believed to have evolved from the Psilopsida, some members of which resembled lycopods in their dichotomous branching, their small leaves, and their primitive stem anatomy. The Lycopsida apparently gave rise to no more advanced group of plants and are apparently far along the road to extinction, all arboreal forms having disappeared from the earth's flora and only a small group of herbaceous species having survived to the present time.

Representative Members

Lycopodium is a genus of plants known commonly as club mosses or ground pines. A *Lycopodium* plant has a creep-

ing rhizome, adventitious roots that grow from the rhizome, anchoring the plant and absorbing water and nutrients from the soil, and erect, dichotomous branches bearing small, spirally arranged leaves (Figure 24–2). The leaves resemble superficially the leaflike scales of true mosses and give *Lycopodium* plants their mosslike appearance. The vascular system of *Lycopodium* is primitive, and all tissues are primary, since there is no cambium. Certain leaves, the sporophylls, bear sporangia on their upper surfaces, one sporangium developing on each sporophyll. In most species of *Lycopodium*, the sporophylls occur in tightly packed, clublike terminal strobili that may reach lengths of several inches. A sporangium produces many spores, all of the same type (*Lycopodium* is homosporous). Reduction division occurs in the formation of spores from spore mother cells, and the spores are thus haploid. The sporangial walls open at maturity, and the microscopic spores are dispersed by wind. Reaching a favorable soil habitat, a spore germinates and grows, producing a small gametophyte (Figure 24–5) that rarely exceeds ¾ inch in length and is wholly or partly embedded in the soil. The gametophyte of most species becomes infected by a fungus, thus creating a relationship thought to be symbiotic. Portions of a gametophyte that protrude above the soil develop chlorophyll and carry on photosynthesis. The lower portion of a *Lycopodium* gametophyte bears rhizoids, the upper portion archegonia and antheridia, which resemble those of mosses. At maturity and in the presence of water, the antheridia liberate sperms, which swim to and enter the archegonia. A single sperm fertilizes the egg in an archegonium, and the zygote develops into a small embryo within the archegonium. This embryo is nutritionally dependent upon the gametophyte for a brief period, until it has grown sufficiently to develop its own green leaves. The embryo also forms a rhizome and roots, and the young sporophyte then begins an independent existence, as the gametophyte from which it developed decays and disappears. At maturity, the sporophyte produces spores in the manner described.

Selaginella is a genus whose members are commonly called spike mosses. *Selaginella* plants are very similar in general structure and appearance to *Lycopodium* plants but differ from the latter in their smaller size and more delicate form, in their heterosporous reproduction, and in several other features. Plants of *Selaginella* are chiefly creepers upon the soil, although a few species grow erect and one

(*Copyright, General Biological Supply House, Chicago.*)

FIG. 24–4. Portion of stem of *Lycopodium selago*, in which the sporophylls are not clustered in terminal strobili but occur in groups along the stem, interrupted by ordinary, vegetative leaves. Note the sporangia near the bottom of the photograph.

is a vine. Their stems branch dichotomously and bear tiny leaves that are usually arranged in four longitudinal rows. Roots are produced on special leafless branches that penetrate the soil. The small sporophylls are clustered in terminal cones (Figure 24–6). The uppermost sporophylls in a cone bear small sporangia **(microsporangia)**, which produce numerous tiny spores **(microspores).** The lower sporophylls of a cone bear larger sporangia **(megasporangia)**, each of which contains four large spores **(megaspores).** The two types of sporophylls are called **microsporophylls** and **megasporophylls,** respectively. Reduction division

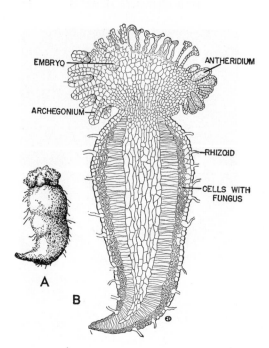

EMBRYO

ANTHERIDIUM

ARCHEGONIUM

RHIZOID

CELLS WITH FUNGUS

A

B

FIG. 24–5. *Lycopodium* gametophyte or prothallus. (After Bruchmann.) A: External view of lumpy, subterranean gametophyte. B: Longitudinal section of gametophyte, showing archegonia and antheridia embedded in the top portion, rhizoids arising at the surface, and cells containing a fungus (dark cells).

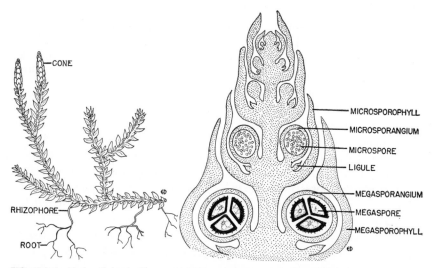

CONE

MICROSPOROPHYLL

MICROSPORANGIUM

MICROSPORE

LIGULE

MEGASPORANGIUM

MEGASPORE

RHIZOPHORE

MEGASPOROPHYLL

ROOT

FIG. 24–6. *Left: Selaginella,* or small club moss, with creeping, dichotomous stems bearing numerous, tiny leaves and leafless branches, or rhizophores, that produce roots at their tips. Cones are located at the ends of the leafy branches. *Right:* Diagram of a longitudinal section through a *Selaginella* cone, showing upper microsporophylls with microsporangia containing many small microspores, and lower megasporophylls with megasporangia containing 4 large megaspores. (After Lyon.)

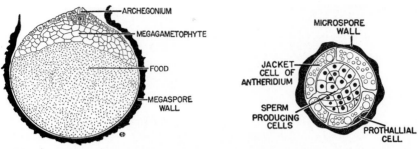

FIG. 24–7. *Left:* Section through a *Selaginella* megaspore, showing the internal female gametophyte or megagametophyte cells with an archegonium at the top and stored food below. (After Lyon.) *Right:* Section through a *Selaginella* microspore, showing thick microspore wall enclosing a single prothallial cell and one antheridium—the latter with a layer of jacket cells surrounding the sperm-producing cells. (After Lyon.)

occurs within these sporangia, each spore mother cell producing four haploid spores; a megasporangium has only one spore mother cell, which gives rise to four megaspores. While still in the surrounding microsporangium, each microspore germinates, forming a male gametophyte (**microgametophyte**), a tiny structure (Figure 24–7) consisting of a single **prothallial** cell and an antheridium that develops several sperms; none of the cells of a microgametophyte has chlorophyll, and thus the entire structure is dependent upon adjacent sporophyte tissue for its food. Like a microspore, a megaspore germinates within its sporangium, forming a female gametophyte (**megagametophyte**), which consists of a mass of food-storing cells and several archegonia; some of these cells may contain chlorophyll and thus may carry on photosynthesis. As a megagametophyte grows, it exerts pressure that ruptures the megaspore wall, exposing a portion of the gametophyte (Figure 24–7). When the microsporangial walls are mature, they rupture, liberate the microspores with their enclosed, growing microgametophytes; the microspores fall, or are carried by wind, and

some of them land on or near the megasporangia, which by this time contain mature megagametophytes. In the presence of water, the microspore wall opens and the enclosed antheridium liberates sperms that swim to the megagametophytes. Sperms swim into the archegonia, a single sperm fertilizing an egg. The zygote begins to divide, producing a tiny embryo, which is attached to the female gameto-

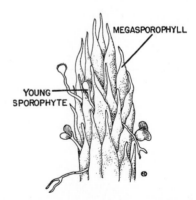

FIG. 24–8. Portion of a cone of *Selaginella* with young sporophytes growing out from the megagametophytes in the megaspores, which are, in turn, in the megasporangia borne in the axils of the megasporophylls. (After Lyon.)

FIG. 24–9. Restoration of a Carboniferous coal swamp. The massive trunks at the left are lepidodendrids (Lycopsida) whose grasslike leaves and large cones are in the upper left-hand corner. Also at the left are seed ferns, fernlike plants bearing seeds. To the right, the trees with whorled branches are calamites (Sphenopsida). The small plants in the foreground are sphenophylls.

phyte, which in turn is partly enclosed by the megasporangial wall. Since the young embryo sporophyte lacks chlorophyll, it derives its food from the female gametophyte, which in turn obtains some or all of its food from the sporophyte tissues from which it grew. The embryo produces a root, a stem, and two cotyledons; this young sporophyte (Figure 24–8) then develops chlorophyll and begins an independent existence, ultimately becoming a mature sporophyte of the type already-described.

Selaginella has several noteworthy features: 1. It is heterosporous. 2. It possesses two kinds of sporophylls, sporangia, spores, and gametophytes. 3. Its gametophytes are small and are wholly or partly dependent upon sporophyte tissues for food. 4. Both gametophytes develop inside the enclosing sporangial walls. In the development of the female gametophyte and of the young embryo within the megasporangium, *Selaginella* resembles the seed plants, in which similar behavior, to be described later, occurs. The megasporangium of *Selaginella,* with its enclosed gametophyte and young embryo developed within the gametophyte tissue, may be regarded as a primitive type of seed. In angiosperms, the 8-nucleate embryo sac is a megagametophyte that is within a megasporangial wall (nucellus). Fertilization of the egg by a sperm occurs within the embryo sac, a condition similar to that in *Selaginella.*

⫷ SUMMARY

1. The subdivision Lycopsida of the division Tracheophyta reached its greatest development during past geological periods and is represented in the earth's present flora by only 4 genera with 900 species.
2. The Lycopsida have the following characteristics:
   a. they possess the vascular tissues xylem and phloem.
   b. They have true roots, stems, and leaves.
   c. Their leaves are chiefly spirally arranged and are very small. Each leaf has a single vascular bundle.
   d. The vascular tissues of the stems have branch gaps but no leaf gaps.
   e. Their roots and stems usually branch dichotomously.
   f. Sporangia are borne singly on the upper surfaces of sporophylls.
   g. The sporophylls are usually borne in terminal, elongated, club-shaped cones (strobili).
3. A lycopsid plant with its roots, stems, leaves, and sporophylls is a sporophyte.
4. The life cycle of a homosporous lycopsid plant (for example, *Lycopodium*) is as follows:
   The sporophyte bears sporangia on the upper surfaces of its sporophylls. Reduction division occurs in the sporangia, as a result of which haploid spores of one type are produced. A spore germinates, usually on the soil, forming a small gametophyte that bears both archegonia and antheridia. At maturity, sperms swim through water from the antheridia to the archegonia, one sperm fertilizing the single egg in the archegonium. The zygote, which is diploid, begins its development into an embryo within the archegonium; the growing embryo soon pushes its way out of the archegonium and the gametophyte,

forming ultimately a mature, green, independent sporophyte that then produces spores in the manner already described.

5. The life cycle of a heterosporous lycopsid plant (for example, *Selaginella*) is as follows:

   The sporophyte bears cones with microsporophylls and megasporophylls upon which microsporangia and megasporangia are borne. A microsporangium produces numerous microspores, each of which gives rise to a microgametophyte; a megasporangium produces four megaspores, one of which develops into a megagametophyte. A microgametophyte bears one antheridium, which forms several sperms, a megagametophyte bears several archegonia, each with a single egg. A sperm swims through water from a microgametophyte to a megagametophyte, fertilizing an egg in an archegonium; after a short time, the embryo grows into a new mature sporophyte, the attached gametophyte disintegrating. The mature sporophyte then produces microsporophylls and megasporophylls, as described above.

6. The sporophytes of all Lycopsida possess chlorophyll and are thus autotrophic. The gametophytes, which rarely exceed ¾ inch in length, have no chlorophyll or only small amounts of chlorophyll, and are thus completely or largely dependent for their nourishment upon food supplied by sporophyte tissues. The sporophyte of lycopsids, like that of Psilopsida, is the dominant, more complex generation; the gametophyte is very small and relatively simple in structure.

7. Most living species of Lycopsida inhabit moist, shaded forests. They are especially numerous in humid, tropical forests. A few species are aquatic and desert plants.

8. Living species of Lycopsida are of little economic significance. Some species are used as ornamental plants. Lycopodium spores have been used by pharmacists in the preparation of pills. Some species are eaten by wild animals. Extinct species, which formed extensive forests during the Carboniferous period, contributed to coal deposits.

9. Lycopsida are believed to have evolved from Psilopsida, which they resemble in their dichotomous branching, their small leaves, their primitive stem anatomy, and in other features. The Lycopsida seem not to have given rise to more advanced groups of plants and are apparently on the road to extinction. All arboreal species of lycopsids have disappeared from the earth's flora, and only a small group of herbaceous species has survived to the present time.

10. Various members of the Lycopsida have a number of advanced characteristics: the aggregation of sporophylls into strobili, heterospory, the production of male and female gametophytes, and the development of seedlike structures resulting from the retention of the female gametophyte and young embryo sporophyte within the megasporangium.

⫷ SUGGESTED READINGS FOR INTERESTED STUDENTS

1. Andrews, H. N., *Ancient Plants and the World They Lived In*. Comstock Publishing Co., Ithaca, N. Y., 1947.

2. Arnold, C. A., *An Introduction to Paleobotany*. McGraw-Hill, New York, 1947.
3. Foster, A. S., and E. M. Gifford, Jr., *Comparative Morphology of Vascular Plants*. Freeman, San Francisco, 1959.

TOPICS AND QUESTIONS FOR STUDY

1. List the distinguishing characteristics of the Embryophyta, Tracheophyta, and Lycopsida.
2. List the differences and similarities between Lycopsida and Psilopsida.
3. What is the structural nature of the leaves of Lycopsida?
4. Describe the structure of a *Lycopodium* sporophyte; of a *Lycopodium* gametophyte.
5. Describe the life cycle of *Lycopodium*.
6. Describe the sporophyte generation of *Selaginella;* the gametophyte generation.
7. Describe the life cycle of *Selaginella*.
8. Describe the differences between *Lycopodium* and *Selaginella*.
9. Describe the resemblances between *Selaginella* and the seed plants.
10. Describe briefly the economic importance of Lycopsida.
11. From what other groups of plants are the Lycopsida believed to have evolved?
12. Describe the distribution on the earth's surface of living species of Lycopsida.
13. List three ways in which you might distinguish between true mosses and club mosses.
14. List the advanced characteristics of the Lycopsida.

Tracheophyta: Sphenopsida (Horsetails)

The subdivision **Sphenopsida,** like the Lycopsida, is a group of plants that reached its zenith in past geological ages and is traveling the road to extinction. The Sphenopsida, or horsetails, attained their greatest development about 250,-000,000 years ago. During this time, shrubby and tree species of Sphenopsida flourished in many parts of the earth; one genus, *Equisetum,* with about 30 species, is the only genus of this subdivision that has survived in earth's present flora.

Growth Forms and Structure

In Sphenopsida, the sporophyte, which is the dominant generation, has true roots, stems, and leaves, with xylem and phloem. The vascular tissue of the stems, like that of Lycopsida, has branch gaps but not leaf gaps. The leaves of Sphenopsida are small, but, unlike those of Lycopsida, they appear to be derived from flattened, small branches rather than from emergences. The stems of Sphenopsida are distinctly jointed and are hollow, usually with conspicuous, longitudinal ribs

and with leaves occurring in whorls at the nodes (Figure 25–1). The leaves of living species are greatly reduced to small scales. The tissues of living sphenopsids

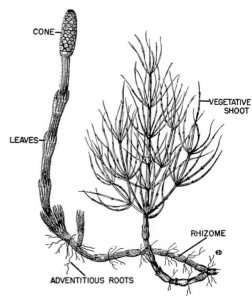

FIG. 25–1. *Equisetum,* or horsetail, with rhizome producing adventitious roots, bushy vegetative shoot, and fertile axis with terminal strobilus. Note small, whorled leaves at nodes.

434

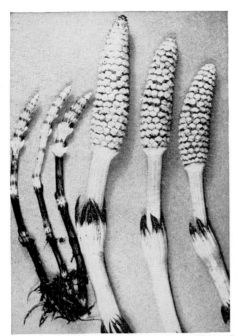

FIG. 25–2. Plants of *Equisetum arvense,* showing ribbed stems, whorled leaves, and strobili (cones).

FIG. 25–3. Close up of portion of strobilus of *Equisetum arvense,* showing individual sporangiophores.

are impregnated with silica and as a consequence are rough and harsh to the touch; the bodies of the extinct species appear to have been similarly impregnated.

Reproduction and Life Cycle

The sporophyte described above produces sporangia on stalked, umbrellalike **sporangiophores,** which are borne in cylindrical or ovoid cones (Figures 25–2, 25–3, 25–4). Reduction division occurs in the sporangia, and the haploid spores, shed from the sporangia, germinate on the soil and produce small gametophytes (Figure 25–5). These are green, and in homosporous species (all living species are homosporous) bear archegonia and antheridia. The sperms swim through

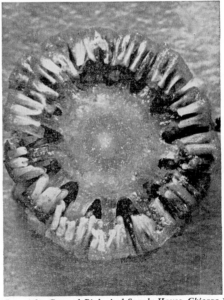

FIG. 25–4. Section of *Equisetum* strobilus, showing sporangiophores with sporangia.

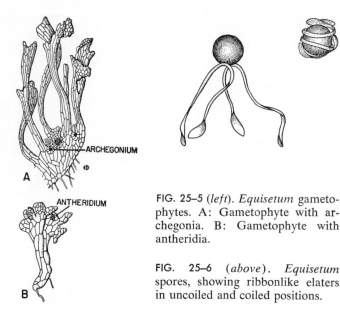

FIG. 25–5 (*left*). *Equisetum* gameto-phytes. A: Gametophyte with archegonia. B: Gametophyte with antheridia.

FIG. 25–6 (*above*). *Equisetum* spores, showing ribbonlike elaters in uncoiled and coiled positions.

water to the archegonia, one sperm fertilizing the single egg in an archegonium. A zygote begins to develop into an embryo within the archegonium; the embryo pushes its way out of the archegonium and ultimately grows into a mature sporophyte, which then produces sporangia on sporangiophores in the manner described.

Physiological Characteristics

The sporophytes of Sphenopsida are green and thus carry on photosynthesis. The gametophytes of living species are also green and autotrophic.

Habitats and Distribution

In the Devonian and Carboniferous periods, Sphenopsida were widely distributed in the warmer, humid regions of the earth, forming forests of large trees. The living species of *Equisetum* are distributed from tropics to the cool areas of temperate zones. Most species of *Equise-*

tum thrive in moist habitats, such as creek banks, river bottoms, and humid forests, but a few species grow in such dry sites as railroad embankments. The dependence of these plants upon water for the swimming of sperms from antheridia to archegonia is in part responsible for their more frequent growth in moist environments.

Importance in Nature and in Human Life

Living species of horsetails have virtually no economic value in human life. Because of their rough texture, horsetail stems have been used as an abrasive material for scouring cooking pots, pans, and floors; this use has almost disappeared, except in remote rural areas. The bodies of some Sphenopsida of the Carboniferous period contributed to the formation of coal beds.

Relationships with Other Organisms

Modern botanical opinion holds that the Sphenopsida, like the Lycopsida, arose from Psilopsida. Certain fossils of Sphenopsida resemble strikingly some Psilopsida in the structure of their sporophytes. The Sphenopsida are considered to be a parallel group with the Lycopsida; both subdivisions apparently originated during the Silurian period, reached their greatest development during the Carboniferous, and had become a relatively inconspicuous part of the flora by the end of the Paleozoic era (225,000,000 years ago). The Sphenopsida have apparently given rise to no more advanced groups of plants.

Representative Members

The only living sphenopsid genus, *Equisetum,* derives its name from the fact that the stems of some species resemble superficially the tails of horses (Latin *equus*—horse, *seta*—bristle). *Equisetum* plants have creeping rhizomes with numerous adventitious roots and erect stems with scalelike leaves borne in whorls. In most species, these stems are herbaceous and rarely exceed 4 feet in height; a few species are shrubby, and one South American species is a vine that may reach a length of more than 30 feet. In most species, two types of stems occur: vegetative stems, which are green and branched, and reproductive stems, which usually lack chlorophyll, are unbranched, and bear strobili at their tips. A cone consists of a number of sporangiophores, each with 5 to 10 sporangia, within which spores are produced. A spore wall produces 4 ribbonlike **elaters,** which coil and uncoil with changes in humidity and which aid, through these movements, the discharge of spores from the sporangia (Figure 25–6). The spores germinate on moist soil, forming gametophytes, which are usually irregular, ribbonlike struc-

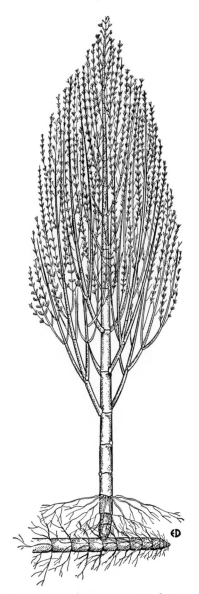

FIG. 25–7. *Calamites,* or tree horsetail, showing underground rhizome bearing adventitious roots and a huge, erect shoot. (After Hirmer.)

tures less than 1 inch in length (Figure 25–5). A gametophyte bears a few rhizoids and usually both antheridia and archegonia. Sperms swim through water to the archegonia, which they enter, a sin-

FIG. 25–8. *Left: Sphenophyllum,* with sessile, wedge-shaped leaves occurring in whorls. One strobilus is also shown. *Right:* A calamite fossil embedded in rock. Note the whorls of long, linear leaves.

gle sperm fertilizing an egg. The zygote begins its development within the archegonium and the embryo ultimately produces a mature horsetail sporophyte.

A fossil genus, *Calamites,* included large trees (Figures 25–7 and 25–8) that reached heights of 60 to 90 feet. *Calamites* plants resembled gigantic *Equisetum* plants. Some extinct horsetails are shown in Figure 24–9, page 430.

⫷ SUMMARY

1. The subdivision Sphenopsida (horsetails) has the following characteristics:
   a. Sporophytes have true roots, stems and leaves, with vascular tissues.
   b. The vascular tissue of the stems has branch gaps but no leaf gaps.
   c. The leaves are small and are borne in whorls.
   d. The stems have a jointed appearance, with enlarged nodes, are hollow, are commonly impregnated with silica, and often have longitudinal ribs or ridges.

e. The sporangia are borne on sporangiophores that form cylindrical or ovoid cones.

2. The sporophyte of Sphenopsida is the dominant generation and is autotrophic. The sporophyte produces spores, which germinate on soil, forming small, often branched gametophytes that are autotrophic and that bear archegonia and antheridia. Sperms swim through water to archegonia, which they enter, one sperm fertilizing an egg. The zygote forms an embryo that is dependent briefly upon the gametophyte for food; the embryo grows into a mature sporophyte.

3. Living species are homosporus; some extinct species were heterosporous.

4. Living horsetails are widely distributed on the earth's surface, principally in moist habitats. Some of the extinct species were also widely distributed.

5. Living horsetails have negligible economic value; they are occasionally used as abrasives for scouring purposes. Horsetails of the Carboniferous period contributed to the formation of coal.

6. The Sphenopsida are believed to have arisen from Psilopsida, with which they have certain common structural features, and apparently gave rise to no more advanced groups of plants. The Sphenopsida reached their greatest development during the Devonian and Carboniferous periods and are nearly extinct, only about 25 species having survived to the present time.

7. The only living genus of Sphenopsida is *Equisetum,* species of which are chiefly herbaceous, a few shrubby. *Equisetum* plants, which rarely exceed 4 feet in height, have erect stems that arise from underground rhizomes. These stems are usually of two types: vegetative stems, which are green and branched, and reproductive stems, which are usually not green or branched and which bear strobili.

8. Members of fossil genus *Calamites* were woody plants, some of them large trees.

SUGGESTED READINGS FOR INTERESTED STUDENTS

1. Arnold, C. A., *An Introduction to Paleobotany.* McGraw-Hill, New York, 1947.
2. Foster, A. S., and E. M. Gifford, Jr., *Comparative Morphology of Vascular Plants.* Freeman, San Francisco, 1959.

TOPICS AND QUESTIONS FOR STUDY

1. List the distinguishing characteristics of the Sphenopsida. What similarities exist between Sphenopsida and Lycopsida? What differences?
2. In what geological periods of earth's history did Sphenopsida reach their greatest development?
3. What is the present status of Sphenopsida in the earth's flora?
4. Describe the structure of *Equisetum* sporophytes and gametophytes.
5. Describe the life history of *Equisetum*. Where in the life cycle does the haploid chromosome number change to the diploid number? The diploid number to the haploid number?
6. Discuss briefly the supposed origin of the Sphenopsida.

Tracheophyta: Pteropsida-Filicae (Ferns)

The subdivision **Pteropsida** comprises four great classes of plants:

Class I—**Filicae**—ferns

Class II—**Coniferae**—conifers and their relatives

Class III—**Cycadae**—cycads

Class IV—**Angiospermae**—flowering plants

Members of the Pteropsida have the following common features (in addition to those of the Embryophyta as a whole):

1. True roots, stems, and leaves, with vascular tissues.

2. Larger, more complex leaves than those of Lycopsida and Sphenopsida.

3. Leaves apparently evolved from the flattening of branch systems, rather than from emergences, as in Lycopsida.

4. Leaf gaps and branch gaps present.

5. Through most of their existence sporophytes are independent and are larger and more complex than the gametophytes, which, in most species, lack chlorophyll and are parasitic upon the sporophytes.

6. Sporangia are borne on the lower surfaces of sporophylls, or on the margins of sporophylls.

FILICAE

This class comprises about 260 living genera and 9300 living species of ferns and related plants and a number of gen-

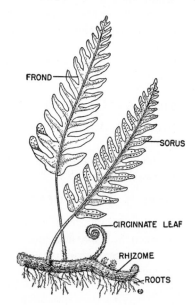

FIG. 26–1. *Polypodium,* or polypody fern, with horizontal rhizome bearing adventitious roots and large leaves with sori on the lower surfaces.

FIG. 26–2. Young tree ferns, Jamaica.

era and species that flourished in past geological ages and are now extinct.

Growth Form and Structure

The sporophytes of members of this class usually have conspicuous and often rather large leaves, a stem that in most species is a subterranean rhizome, and roots that grow from the stem and function as anchoring and absorbing organs. A few species, the tree ferns, have upright stems (Figure 26–2). In most species, a cambium and secondary tissues are lacking.

Reproduction and Life Cycle

The dominant sporophyte produces sporangia, usually on the lower surfaces or margins of leaves. Reduction division occurs in the formation of spores from spore mother cells within the sporangia, and the spores are thus haploid. Most species are homosporous, producing one type of spore. At maturity, the sporangia open, liberating the spores, which germinate on a suitable substratum, usually rich, moist, shaded soil. A germinating spore produces a small, green, nutritionally independent gametophyte that rarely exceeds ¼ inch in diameter and that is anchored to the soil by rhizoids. In homosporous species, a gametophyte produces both archegonia and antheridia, which form eggs (one per archegonium) and numerous sperms, respectively. The sperms swim through water to the arche-

FIG. 26–3 (*left*). Sori on lower surface of leaf of *Athyrium filixfoemina*. Note the sporangia and indusia.

FIG. 26–4 (*right*). Highly magnified view of the underside of a fern leaf (*Cibotium splendens*), showing sori.

gonia, which they enter, a sperm fertilizing an egg and thus producing a diploid zygote. The zygote begins its development into a young embryo sporophyte within the archegonium; the embryo soon forces its way out of the archegonium, forms chlorophyll, and develops into a familiar fern plant (sporophyte). A few species of this class are heterosporous. No seeds or seedlike structures are produced by members of this class.

Physiological Characteristics

Both gametophytes and sporophytes of members of this class contain chlorophyll and are thus autotrophic. The young sporophytes are nutritionally dependent for a brief time upon the gametophytes from which they grow, but they soon develop chlorophyll and then begin to manufacture their own food.

Habitats and Distribution

Plants of this class are widely distributed on the earth's surface, especially in the warmer parts of the temperate zones and in humid tropical regions. Most species cannot withstand drought, and thus usually grow in habitats that are at least periodically moist. The dependence of ferns upon water for transporting sperms to eggs is a factor that limits most ferns to moist locations. Intense sunlight, partly because of its drying effects upon leaves, is unfavorable to the growth of many ferns that are thus limited to shaded habi-

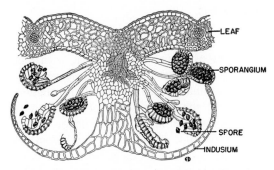

FIG. 26–5. Cross section of a fern leaf and a sorus. The sporangia are covered by the indusium. (After Kny.)

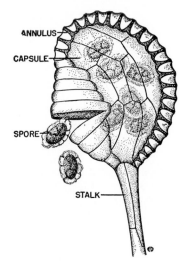

FIG. 26–6. Fern sporangium with stalk, capsule, spores, and the thick-walled annulus.

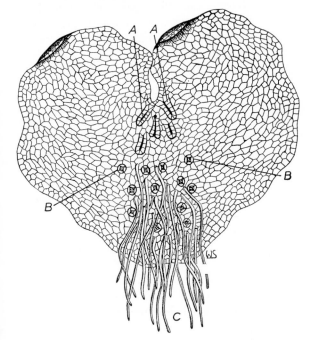

FIG. 26–7. Fern prothallus with A, archegonia, B, antheridia, and C, rhizoids.

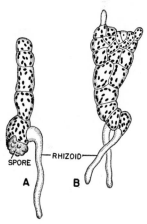

FIG. 26–8. Germinating fern spore. A: Fern spore has produced a filament of green cells. B: Filament has widened into a plate of cells.

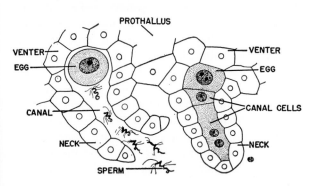

FIG. 26–9. Archegonia of a fern. *Left:* Mature archegonium, showing sperms entering neck canal to reach the egg in the venter of the archegonium. *Right:* An immature archegonium.

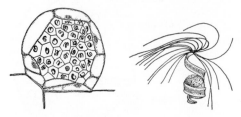

FIG. 26–10. *Left:* Mature antheridium of *Sticherus.* Coiled structures are sperms. (After Stokey.) *Right:* Multiflagellate male gamete of a fern.

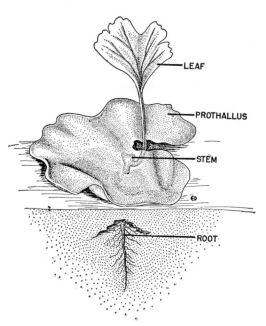

FIG. 26-11. Young fern sporophyte, with root, leaf, and short stem attached to gametophyte (prothallus).

tats on forest floors and in deep ravines. Many tropical species are epiphytes, growing upon the branches of trees.

Importance in Nature and in Human Life

The importance of ferns in nature and in man's economy is relatively slight. Some ferns are eaten by wild animals. Many species of ferns, because of the graceful and delicate beauty of their leaves, are cultivated as ornamental plants. In the tropics, fern leaves are occasionally used as thatch for buildings, and the tough stems of tree ferns find some use in the construction of small buildings. Epidermal hairs from some ferns have sometimes been used as stuffing in pillows and upholstery. A drug derived from the rhizomes of the "male fern" is used to expel tapeworms, liver flukes, and other parasitic worms from animal bodies. The ferns of the Carboniferous period contributed to the formation of coal.

Relationships with Other Organisms

Modern botanical opinion holds that the Filicae evolved from Psilopsida, since certain ancient, extinct ferns strikingly resembled Psilopsida in structure and reproduction. In some of these ferns, sporangia were borne at the stem tips, leaves were not well differentiated from stems, and dichotomous branching of stems occurred, features that are like those of most Psilopsida. Many species of ferns, now extinct, formed an important part of the flora of the Carboniferous period, sometimes called the Age of Ferns.

Representative Members

The Filicae are usually separated into four orders, of which only the largest order, the Filicales, or true ferns, will be described in this book. A typical fern plant (Figure 26–1) consists of a stem, commonly a rhizome, large leaves **(fronds)** that unroll in a "fiddlelike" or **circinate** fashion, and adventitious roots growing from the stem. Xylem and phloem are present in these organs; no cambium is present in true ferns, and sec-

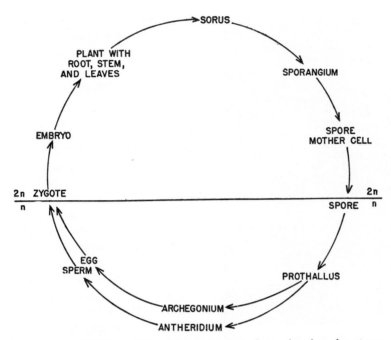

FIG. 26–12. Diagram of the life cycle of a fern, showing the stages where chromosome changes occur. Sporophyte generation is above the line, gametophyte generation below.

ondary xylem and phloem are thus absent. The sporangia of true ferns are borne usually in small clusters called **sori** on the lower surfaces or margins of the leaves. The arrangement, structure, sizes, forms, and colors of these sori (Figures 26–3 and 26–4) are important characters used to distinguish among various fern genera and species. In some ferns, each sorus is covered by a membranous structure, the **indusium** (Figure 26–5). Sori are commonly brownish in color, less frequently golden yellow, silvery, or of some other hue. A single sporangium (Figure 26–6) consists typically of a short stalk, a capsule with thin walls, and an **annulus,** a ring of cells with thickened inner and lateral walls and thin outer walls. An annulus extends over about two thirds of the circumference of the capsule and, at its free end, joins a small group of thin-

walled cells. As the cell walls of the annulus dry out unequally, strains develop that cause the annulus to rupture the thin-walled cells at its end, breaking the sporangial wall and flinging out spores; then the annulus may experience further movements with subsequent changes in atmospheric moisture, dispersing the remaining spores.

On reaching a suitable substratum such as rich, moist, shaded soil, a spore germinates, forming a filament of green cells that soon grow into a heart-shaped gametophyte (Figure 26–7) usually not more than ¼ inch across. This **prothallus** is green and is anchored to the soil by rhizoids that grow from its lower surface and that absorb water and minerals. A prothallus bears both archegonia (Figure 26–9) and antheridia (Figure 26–10), the archegonia in the region of the notch,

FIG. 26–13. Walking fern (*Asplenium rhizophyllum*). Note new plants developing from tips of leaves that have touched the soil.

the antheridia scattered among the bases of the rhizoids. These gametangia open out onto the lower surface of the prothallus, and, when a film of water covers the prothalli, sperms swim from the mature antheridia to the archegonia, whose neck canals they enter, one sperm fertilizing the single egg in the base (venter) of an archegonium. Since the archegonia and antheridia on a single prothallus usually mature at different times, sperms from one prothallus usually fertilize eggs on another prothallus. The fertilized egg, or zygote, begins to develop

within the archegonium, forming an embryo, which is nourished by the prothallus for a brief period through a foot, formed from certain basal cells of the embryo. Other cells of the growing embryo form a primary root, others form the first green leaf, and another group forms the stem. When the embryo sporophyte (Figure 26–11) emerges from the prothallus, it begins to carry on photosynthesis and to lead an independent existence, as the prothallus dies. After a period of growth, the young sporophyte reaches maturity, producing spores as described above.

As in other groups studied, the gametophyte generation of ferns begins with the haploid spores and includes the prothallus and its parts and the eggs and sperms. The sporophyte generation begins with the zygote, with its diploid chromosome number, and includes the roots, stems, leaves, sporangia, and spore mother cells of the mature fern plant. Meiosis occurs in the formation of spores from the spore mother cells within the sporangia (Figure 26–12).

Segments of fern rhizomes, separated by the death of intervening cells, may grow vegetatively into new fern sporophytes. Another type of vegetative reproduction occurs in the "walking fern" (Figure 26–13), the leaf tips of which produce new fern plants where they touch the soil.

In some members of the Filicae, such as the sensitive fern, the sporangia are not produced by the ordinary leaves, but are borne on specialized reproductive leaves.

⫷ SUMMARY

1. The subdivision Pteropsida comprises three important classes of plants:
   a. Filicae—ferns
   b. Coniferae—conifers and their relatives

    c. Cycadae—cycads

    d. Angiospermae—flowering plants

2. Common features of Pteropsida are:

    a. True roots, stems, and leaves, with vascular tissues.

    b. Leaves larger and more complex in structure than those of Lycopsida and Sphenopsida.

    c. Leaf gaps and branch gaps present.

    d. Leaves evolved through flattening of branch systems.

    e. Sporophyte nutritionally independent, except for a brief early period when embryo is dependent upon gametophyte, and more complex structurally than gametophyte.

    f. Sporangia borne on lower surfaces or margins of sporophylls.

3. The principal characteristics of Filicae are:

    a. Leaves usually large.

    b. Water necessary for swimming of sperms to eggs.

    c. Gametophytes autotrophic and free living, sporophyte autotrophic for most of its life.

    d. Cambium absent from most species and thus secondary tissues usually absent.

    e. No seeds produced.

    f. Most species homosporous.

4. Most ferns do not thrive under dry conditions or in bright sunlight and thus usually grow in moist, shaded habitats. They are most abundant in the warmer parts of the temperate zones and in humid, tropical regions.

5. Ferns are relatively unimportant in human life and in nature. They are often used as ornamental plants and as a source of fibers for stuffing. Carboniferous ferns contributed to coal formation.

6. Filicae are believed to have evolved from Psilopsida, which some ferns resemble.

7. Most species of Filicae belong to the order Filicales, or true ferns. A true fern plant is a sporophyte that produces spores in sporangia borne in clusters (sori) usually on the under surfaces of leaves. Spores liberated from the sporangia germinate on the soil, forming small, heart-shaped gametophytes (prothalli) that bear archegonia and antheridia. Sperms swim from the antheridia to archegonia through water, and fertilization occurs within the archegonia. A zygote forms an embryo that soon grows out of the enclosing archegonium and becomes the conspicuous sporophyte plant.

8. In a few ferns, sporangia are borne on specialized leaves or branches.

9. Meiosis occurs in fern sporangia, and the spores are haploid. The diploid chromosome number begins with the zygote at fertilization.

10. Vegetative reproduction occurs in some ferns by segmentation of rhizomes. In the "walking fern," leaf tips in contact with the soil form new plants.

11. Although most ferns do not exceed a few feet in height, tropical tree ferns may reach heights of 50 feet.

⋘ SUGGESTED READINGS FOR INTERESTED STUDENTS

1. Bower, F. O., *The Ferns* (*Filicales*), 3 vols. Cambridge, 1923, 1928.
2. Foster, A. S., and E. M. Gifford, Jr., *Comparative Morphology of Vascular Plants*. Freeman, San Francisco, 1959.
3. Wherry, E. T., *Guide to Eastern Ferns*, 2d ed. Science Press, Lancaster, Pa., 1942.

⋘ TOPICS AND QUESTIONS FOR STUDY

1. List the distinguishing features of Embryophyta, Tracheophyta, Pteropsida, and Filicae.
2. What is the supposed evolutionary origin of fern leaves?
3. Describe the structure of a typical fern plant.
4. Describe the life cycle of a fern, indicating the points at which chromosome numbers change.
5. Describe the habitats and distribution of ferns.
6. Describe the structure of a fern prothallus.
7. Describe the structure of a fern sporangium and the action of the annulus in spore dispersal.
8. What are sori?
9. Describe briefly how ferns may reproduce vegetatively.
10. List the economic uses of ferns.
11. What is the supposed evolutionary origin of the Filicae? What is the evidence in support of this view?
12. With what structure or structures in a moss plant is a fern prothallus comparable?
13. With what structure or structures in a moss plant is a fern sporophyte comparable?
14. Compare the life cycle of a fern with the life cycles of a moss, of *Lycopodium*, and of *Equisetum*.

27

Tracheophyta: Pteropsida- Coniferae and Cycadae (Gymnosperms)

The so-called gymnosperms or naked-seeded plants are grouped into two distinct classes: the **Coniferae,** which includes such familiar forms as pine and spruce, and the **Cycadae,** a much smaller group of less familiar, tropical plants. There are approximately 70 genera and 725 species of living gymnosperms.

In addition to the general characteristics of the Embryophyta as a whole and of the Tracheophyta and Pteropsida, the gymnosperms have the following features:

1. They are heterosporous, producing microspores and megaspores that develop into microgametophytes and megagametophytes, respectively.

2. They have true seeds; that is, the megagametophyte develops within the megasporangium, which is surrounded by a seed coat (integument) and within which fertilization occurs and the embryo develops. Immature seeds are called ovules.

3. They are all woody plants, chiefly trees.

4. Most species are evergreen.

5. They have active cambial layers, which produce usually abundant secondary xylem and secondary phloem tissues.

6. Their sporophytes are large, autotrophic, and more complex than the gametophytes, which are very small and which are nutritionally dependent upon the sporophytes.

7. Water is not essential for the transportation of the sperms to the eggs. This transportation is achieved by wind pollination and the growth of pollen tubes into the ovules, which contain the eggs.

8. Their seeds are naked; that is, they are not enclosed by fruits, but develop usually in an exposed position, in most species on the surfaces of cone scales. (The word gymnosperm is derived from two Greek words that mean "naked seed.")

9. The wood of most species lacks vessels and consists chiefly of tracheids.

10. Sieve cells, the conducting elements in gymnosperm phloem, are structurally less specialized than sieve tube members and characteristically lack companion cells.

449

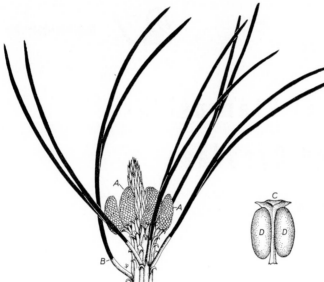

FIG. 27–1. Pine twig with leaves (B) and male cones (A). To the right is shown a single microsporophyll (C) with its stalk and two microsporangia (D).

11. Their female gametophytes bear eggs in very small archegonia. Since a single female gametophyte usually bears several archegonia, each with an egg, fertilization may occur in several archegonia, and several embryos may begin to develop in an ovule. Only one embryo, however, usually matures in a seed.

The Coniferae, comprising four orders (one of them a group of extinct plants) are typically large, much-branched plants with simple, commonly needlelike leaves, small pith, scanty cortex, well-developed wood, and with the reproductive structures borne on stems. The Cycadae include three orders, two of which are extinct. Cycads are smaller, sparingly branched plants with large, frondlike, compound leaves, large pith, thick cortex, scanty wood, and with reproductive structures borne on leaves. In this book, only the largest order of gymnosperms, the Coniferales, will be described in any detail. This order contains about 50 living genera and approximately 540 living species.

CONIFERALES

Growth Forms and Structure

Most species of conifers (Latin *conus*—cone, *fero*—bear) are trees, a few are shrubs. These woody plants have well-developed root systems, extensively branching stems, which often reach great sizes, as in California redwoods and Big Trees, and simple, usually needlelike or scalelike leaves that ordinarily do not exceed 6 inches in length. In most species, secondary xylem is extensively developed, sometimes to the extent that trunk diameters may exceed 15 feet.

Reproduction and Life Cycle (Pine)

The reproductive processes and life cycle of a pine tree are representative of most species of this order and class. Pine trees produce two kinds of cones: **pollen cones,** which are usually rather small and somewhat soft in texture, and **seed cones,** which are larger than pollen cones (some-

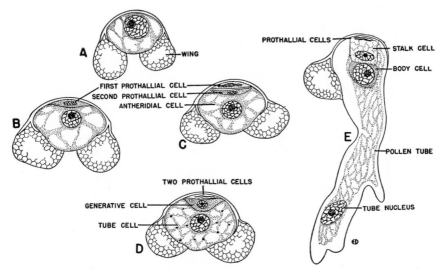

FIG. 27–2. Stages in development of pine microgametophyte. A: Microspore. B, C: Stages in development of pollen grain from a microspore. D: Pollen grain. E: Nearly mature microgametophyte with body cell that later divides to form two sperms.

times reaching a length of nearly 2 feet) and which are typically hard and tough. Pine trees are monoecious; that is, a single tree bears both types of cones. A pollen cone consists of a slender axis that bears many spirally arranged microsporophylls (Figure 27–1), each consisting of a short stalk and two microsporangia, within which numerous pollen grains develop, following reduction division of microspore mother cells. A seed cone (Figure 27–3) bears many spirally arranged, usually tough **ovuliferous scales** (seed cone scales) on a central axis. These scales, each of which bears two ovules on its upper surface, represent reduced branch systems; therefore, they are *not* homologous to megasporophylls. A young ovule (Figure 27–4) consists of a single integument with a pore or micropyle, and a megasporangium **(nucellus)** within which a single megaspore mother cell is borne. This mother cell, as a result of meiosis, forms four megaspores, one of

which develops into the female gametophyte within the nucellus, the other three disintegrating. A mature female (mega) gametophyte consists of a mass of storage tissue and usually two or three archegonia.

When the pollen cones are mature, pollen grains are shed from the microsporangia and are carried by wind (Figure 27–5). Each pollen grain (Figure 27–2) has a pair of wings that give it buoyancy in the air. Some of the pollen grains lodge near the ovules, the micropyles of which exude a sticky liquid. As this liquid dries, the pollen grains are drawn into the micropyles until they reach the nucellus. Each pollen grain forms a pollen tube, which, through internal cell division, develops five cells; the pollen grain and its tube constitute a mature microgametophyte. One of the nuclei in a pollen tube divides, forming two male gametes (sperm nuclei). In fertilization, which occurs about a year after pollination, a

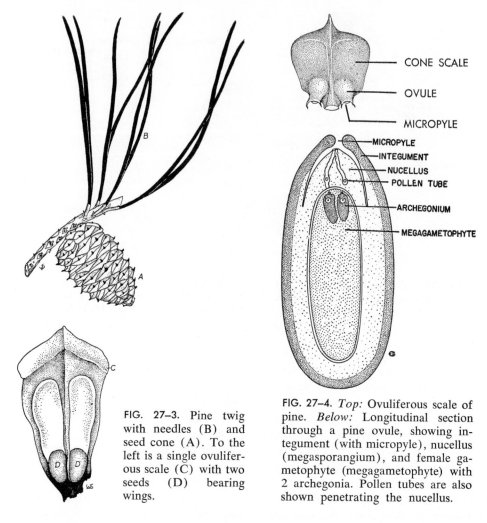

FIG. 27–3. Pine twig with needles (B) and seed cone (A). To the left is a single ovuliferous scale (C) with two seeds (D) bearing wings.

FIG. 27–4. *Top:* Ovuliferous scale of pine. *Below:* Longitudinal section through a pine ovule, showing integument (with micropyle), nucellus (megasporangium), and female gametophyte (megagametophyte) with 2 archegonia. Pollen tubes are also shown penetrating the nucellus.

sperm fuses with the egg in an archegonium, forming a zygote, which develops into an embryo. The other sperm nucleus disintegrates. Since two or more archegonia occur in a megagametophyte and since each archegonium contains an egg, two or more eggs may be fertilized. Each zygote thus formed may begin to develop into an embryo, although usually only one embryo survives and hence a mature pine seed ordinarily contains only one embryo (young sporophyte). A mature embryo (Figure 27–6) consists of a hy-

pocotyl, several cotyledons, and a shoot apex. In a mature seed, the embryo is embedded in the storage tissue of the gametophyte, which is surrounded by a rather tough seed coat developed from the integument of the ovule. A wing develops in a pine seed, and this possibly facilitates dispersal by wind. When the seeds are mature, the cone scales shrink and separate, and the seeds fall from the cones. After germination, the embryo grows into a seedling that ultimately becomes a pine tree, or mature sporophyte.

(Photo by C. F. Hottes.)

FIG. 27–5. Pine tree shedding pollen. The tree is being shaken to scatter a sufficient amount of pollen to be photographed.

The life cycle of a pine tree (Figure 27–7) has several conspicuous features that deserve special emphasis:

a. The gametophytes are very small, lack chlorophyll, and are nutritionally dependent upon the sporophyte.

b. Pine is wind pollinated. Sperm is carried to the egg by the growth of a portion (pollen tube) of the male gametophyte into the female gametophyte. Thus, water is not necessary for fertilization.

c. The female gametophyte remains within the megasporangium, within which fertilization and embryo development occur. The megasporangium, the enclosed megagametophyte and embryo, and the surrounding, matured integument or seed coat constitute a pine seed.

d. The storage tissue of a pine seed is a part of the megagametophyte, *not* the re-

sult of a triple nuclear fusion, as in flowering plants.

Reproduction in other conifers is essentially similar to that of pines, although minor differences occur in some genera. Thus, in the genus *Juniperus* (cedars), the seed cone has only three to six scales, which become somewhat fleshy, superficially resembling a berry. In *Abies* (firs), *Picea* (spruces), and some other genera, the seed cones mature their seeds in the first year, instead of the second year, as in pines.

Physiological Characteristics

The sporophytes of all coniferous species contain chlorophyll and are thus autotrophic. Many species produce aromatic oils and resins that give their leaves and

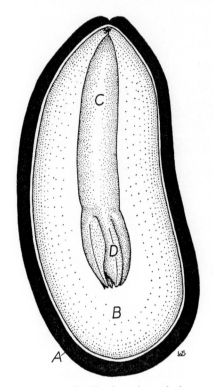

FIG. 27–6. Longitudinal section of pine seed.
A. Seed Coat.   C. Hypocotyl.
B. Storage tissue.   D. Cotyledons.

often their wood characteristic, pungent odors. The leaves of most species are evergreen, remaining on the stem for several years. A few conifers, such as bald cypresses and tamaracks, are deciduous, dropping their leaves at the end of a growing season and producing a new crop of leaves in the following spring.

Habitats and Distribution

Most species of conifers thrive in the cooler regions of the temperate zones, or at higher elevations in the tropics. Thus, in the Americas, most coniferous forests occur in such regions as the Rocky Mountains of the United States and Canada, in the northeastern United States, in north-ern Wisconsin, Michigan, and Minnesota, and in the Pacific coast states and Alaska. The oldest known living thing, bristlecone pine (*Pinus aristata*), grows in Inyo National Forest, California, at an altitude of 10,000 feet. A study of its growth rings has shown it to be 4600 years old! In tropical America, coniferous forests are much less extensive and are limited to higher mountains. Some conifers inhabit warmer regions of the earth, such as islands of the South Pacific, the Gulf states of the United States, and portions of southern Asia.

Importance in Nature and in Human Life

The conifers are exceedingly important in nature and in man's economy. Vast forests of coniferous trees in many parts of the world are effective in checking soil erosion and are important in providing shelter and edible seeds for many wild animals. The world's important softwoods, such as pine, cedar, redwood, spruce, fir, and Douglas fir, are products of coniferous species. These woods are especially valuable in construction work and in the manufacture of paper pulp. When these woods are distilled, they give off vapors from which are derived wood gas, wood tar, wood alcohol, and other industrially valuable products. Aromatic compounds, such as oil of cedar and oil of pine (turpentine), are important ingredients in medicines, paints, incense, and perfumes. Resins from conifers are particularly valuable in varnishes and paints. Amber, used in jewelry and pipe stems, is the fossilized resin of an extinct Baltic pine. Hemlock bark is an important source of tannins used in the tanning of hides to form leather and in the manufacture of some kinds of ink. The seeds of some pines, such as the piñon pine of the

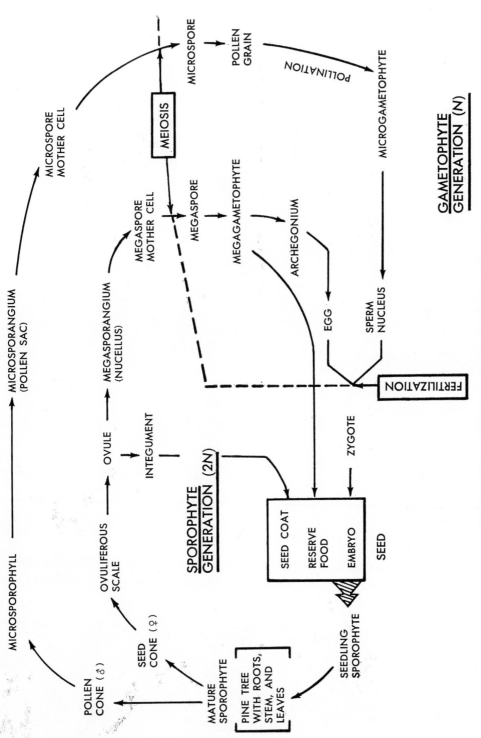

FIG. 27-7. Diagrammatic representation of pine life cycle.

FIG. 27–8. *Dioon,* a cycad, with thick trunk and crown of pinnate leaves.

southwestern United States, are eaten by human beings. Many species of conifers are widely used in ornamental plantings in gardens and parks.

Relationships with Other Organisms

The Coniferales are believed to have evolved from a primitive group of gymnosperms, the Cordaitales, which lived in the Paleozoic era. The origin of the Cordaitales is unknown; however, it seems probable that this group evolved from an ancestral stock that had some psilophytic and some seed fern-like characteristics.

Representative Members

The Coniferales include many well-known genera, some of which have been mentioned in preceding paragraphs: *Pinus* (pines), *Juniperus* (cedars), *Sequoia* (California redwood), *Sequoiadendron* (California Big Tree), *Abies* (firs), *Picea* (spruces), *Taxus* (yews), *Larix* (larches or tamaracks), *Taxodium* (bald cypresses), *Tsuga* (hemlock), *Pseudotsuga* (Douglas fir), *Cupressus* (cypresses), *Thuja* (arborvitae), *Libocedrus* (incense cedar), and numerous other familiar genera.

OTHER GYMNOSPERMS

Class Cycadae

This class includes the true cycads (order Cycadales), extinct, cycadlike plants (order Cycadeoidales), and the seed ferns (order Pteridospermales), a primitive group of plants from which the cycads and cycadeoids evolved. There are only 9 genera of living cycads; all other Cycadae are known from fossils. The oldest group is the seed ferns, which reached

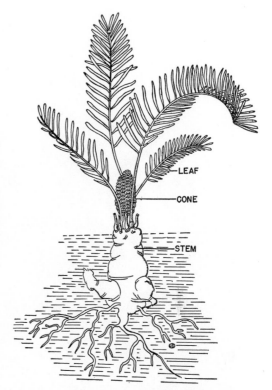

FIG. 27–9. *Zamia,* cycad, showing short, tuberous stem; basal roots; crown of leaves; and a seed cone.

their greatest development in the Carboniferous period. They coexisted with the Cordaitales and probably arose from ancient ancestors that had both psilophytic and fernlike characteristics.

The true cycads (Cycadales) number about 100 species of tropical and subtropical regions, such as Mexico, the West Indies, South Africa, and Australia. In the Mesozoic they were widely distributed on the earth and included many species now extinct. Cycads have usually unbranched stems, which rarely exceed 20 feet in height and which bear a crown of palmlike leaves (Figures 27–8 and 27–9); some species resemble large pineapples. The sporophylls of cycads are borne in

FIG. 27–10. Maidenhair tree (*Ginkgo biloba*).

cones of two types, pollen cones and seed cones, which develop on separate individuals; that is, cycads are dioecious. Reproduction in cycads is generally similar to that of conifers. Cycad sperms bear cilia, although they are carried to the female gametophyte in pollen tubes; the presence of cilia is regarded as an ancestral trait retained long after use for it has disappeared. Cycads are of relatively little economic value; arrowroot starch is obtained from the tubers of cycads known as "sago palms." Some species of cycads are cultivated as ornamental plants in tropical gardens.

Class Coniferae

This class contains, in addition to Cordaitales (extinct) and Coniferales, the ginkgo or maidenhair tree (Figure 27–10), the only living species of the order Ginkgoales. This handsome tree, *Ginkgo biloba,* a native of China, is widely

FIG. 27–11. Pollen "cones" and leaves of maidenhair tree (*Ginkgo biloba*).

planted as an ornamental tree. Washington, D. C., for example, is noted for its numerous fine ginkgo trees. This order contains many genera and species that lived in past geological ages and that are now extinct. Because it alone of this group has survived to the present time, the ginkgo tree is sometimes called a "living fossil." Ginkgo trees have branching stems, which bear fan-shaped, often notched leaves (Figures 27–11 and 27–12). The species is dioecious, some individuals producing pollen cones, others the seed "cones." A seed "cone" consists of a stalk bearing two ovules; usually one of these develops into a mature seed, the outer wall of which becomes fleshy and ill-smelling at maturity. As in cycads and conifers, pollination is by wind, and details of reproduction in ginkgo resemble those of other gymnosperms.

FIG. 27–12. Seed "cones" and leaves of *Ginkgo*.

⫷⫷ **SUMMARY**

1. The gymnosperms of the subdivision Pteropsida contain about 70 living genera and 725 species.
2. In addition to the characteristics of Embryophyta, Tracheophyta, and Pteropsida, gymnosperms have the following features:
   a. They are heterosporous.
   b. They have true seeds.
   c. They are woody.
   d. They are chiefly evergreen.
   e. They have active cambial layers and usually abundant secondary tissue.
   f. Their sporophytes are large and autotrophic, their gametophytes usually very small and dependent upon the sporophytes for food.
   g. Water is not necessary to transport sperms to eggs.
   h. Pollination is by wind.
   i. Their seeds are naked, that is, not enclosed by fruits.
   j. Woods of most species lacks vessels.
   k. The conducting elements of phloem are sieve cells; companion cells are lacking.
   l. The female gametophyte bears eggs in archegonia.
3. Gymnosperms are separated into two classes:
   a. Coniferae: trees or shrubs with simple leaves, branching stems, small pith and cortex, abundant wood.
   b. Cycadae: smaller trees with compound leaves, usually unbranched stems, large pith and cortex, and scanty wood.
4. The life cycle of the Coniferae may be illustrated by the life cycle of pine:
   a. Pine trees bear pollen cones and seed cones.
   b. Pollen cones are composed of an axis with microsporophylls, which bear microsporangia, in which pollen grains develop.
   c. Seed cone has an axis with ovuliferous scales, each with two ovules on upper surface.
   d. Ovule at time of pollination has an integument and enclosed megasporangium (nucellus) within which the megagametophyte occurs. The latter consists of food storage tissue and usually two or three archegonia, each with one egg.
   e. Pollen grains are carried to seed cones by wind, some reaching a drop of liquid on micropyle. Pollen grains are drawn into micropyle by shrinkage of this liquid.
   f. Pollen grain forms a tube that penetrates archegonium, a sperm from pollen tube fertilizing the egg. Pollen grain plus sperm nuclei and tube constitute mature male gametophyte.
   g. Zygotes in the archegonia begin to develop into embryos, one embryo reaching maturity in a seed.
   h. Mature embryo is embedded in food storage tissue and consists of a hypocotyl, an epicotyl, and several cotyledons. Food storage tissue of mature

seed is part of female gametophyte and is surrounded by a seed coat, developed from integument of seed.

   i. Cone scales shrink and separate, and seeds, each with a wing, fall from cone.

5. Reproduction of pine is fundamentally similar to that of other gymnosperms, although details of reproduction vary somewhat in different orders and genera.

6. All gymnosperms have chlorophyll (in their sporophytes) and are thus autotrophic. Most species of conifers produce characteristic odoriferous "oils" and resins.

7. Conifers are widely distributed in the cooler parts of temperate and in subarctic regions, less widely in the tropics, where they grow principally at high, cool elevations. Some species inhabit warm regions.

8. Importance of conifers: check soil erosion, provide shelter and edible seeds for wild animals, furnish softwood lumber, aromatic "oils," resins, and tannins, produce seed for human food, and serve as ornamental plants.

9. Conifers are believed to have evolved from primitive, extinct gymnosperms (Cordaitales), which apparently arose from ancient, extinct plants that had characteristics of psilophytes and seed ferns.

10. Coniferales include pines, cedars, firs, spruces, yews, tamaracks, cypresses, redwoods, and other familiar plants.

11. The Cycadae includes the extinct seed ferns (Pteridospermales), extinct, cycadlike plants (Cycadeoidales), and the true cycads (Cycadales), small palmlike, dioecious trees that generally resemble conifers in their reproduction. Sperms in cycads bear cilia, which are functionless, since the sperms do not swim through water.

12. The class Coniferae, in addition to Cordaitales and Coniferales, includes the order Ginkgoales, with only one living species, the maidenhair tree (*Ginkgo biloba*). Reproduction of the ginkgo tree is similar to that of conifers, but the seed "cone" consists only of a stalk with two ovules, usually one of which becomes a mature seed with a fleshy coat.

⫷ SUGGESTED READINGS FOR INTERESTED STUDENTS

1. "Ancient seed plants: the cycads." *Missouri Botanical Garden Bulletin,* Vol. 43, pp. 65–80, 1955.

2. Arnold, C. A., "Classification of gymnosperms from the viewpoint of paleobotany." *The Botanical Gazette,* Vol. 110, pp. 2–12, 1948.

3. Chamberlain, C. J., *Gymnosperms, Structure and Evolution.* University of Chicago Press, Chicago, 1935.

4. Foster, A. S., and E. M. Gifford, Jr., *Comparative Morphology of Vascular Plants.* Freeman, San Francisco, 1959.

⫷ TOPICS AND QUESTIONS FOR STUDY

1. List and describe briefly the characteristic features of Tracheophyta, Pteropsida, gymnosperms, Coniferae, and Cycadae.

2. Describe the structure of a pine tree.

3. Describe the geographical distribution of the gymnosperms.
4. Describe the economic value of the Coniferales.
5. Describe the reproduction and life cycle of a pine tree.
6. Compare the life cycle of a pine tree with that of a fern; with that of a moss; with that of *Selaginella*.
7. What is the supposed evolutionary origin of Coniferales?
8. Name several plants, in addition to pines, that belong to the gymnosperms.
9. Describe briefly the structure and distribution of cycads.
10. Describe the structure and reproduction of a ginkgo tree.
11. What is the oldest known living organism?

28

Tracheophyta: Pteropsida-Angiospermae (Flowering Plants)

The fourth and last class of the subdivision Pteropsida, the Angiospermae or flowering plants, which number about 250,000 species, has been described in detail in earlier chapters. Thus, this chapter presents only a summary of the salient features of the angiosperms and a comparison of certain of these features with those of other classes of Pteropsida. The word angiosperm is derived from two Greek words that mean "covered seed."

The major characteristics of the angiosperms (in addition to the general characteristics of the Embryophyta as a whole and of the Tracheophyta and Pteropsida) are these:

1. Angiosperms produce flowers and seeds. The seeds develop within fruits.

2. They are heterosporous; that is, they produce two kinds of spores and two kinds of gametophytes.

3. Their sporophytes are autotrophic (except in a few parasitic and saprophytic species) and are dominant, their gametophytes lack chlorophyll, are nutritionally dependent upon the sporophytes, and are microscopic in size.

4. The transportation of their sperms to eggs is accomplished by the processes of pollination and pollen tube growth (as in gymnosperms), and they thus do not require water for fertilization.

5. Archegonia and antheridia are lacking.

This list demonstrates that angiosperms have some of the same fundamental features as gymnosperms. They differ from gymnosperms, however, in the following major respects:

1. The reproductive structures of angiosperms are flowers, those of gymnosperms are cones.

2. In angiosperms, seeds are enclosed by carpels (modified megasporophylls); a mature carpel or group of carpels is a fruit. In gymnosperms, seeds are not enclosed, but are borne on surfaces of cone scales.

3. Angiosperms have double fertilization: the fusion of one sperm with an egg in an embryo sac, and the fusion of a second sperm with the polar nuclei to form the endosperm nucleus, which develops into the endosperm of a seed. In gymno-

sperms, only single fertilization occurs; that is, sperms fuse only with eggs.

4. The endosperm of angiosperms is triploid, since it originates in the fusion of one sperm nucleus with two polar nuclei, all of which are haploid. This tissue is used for food by the developing embryo. In gymnosperm seeds, the embryo utilizes haploid megagametophyte tissue for food.

5. In gymnosperms, pollen grains land directly upon the exposed ovules. In angiosperms, since the ovules are enclosed by the carpels (a pistil is composed of one or more carpels), pollen grains do not reach the ovules directly, but land upon the apex of the pistil, the stigma. The pollen tubes then grow downward through the tissues of the stigma, style, and a portion of the ovary before they reach the ovules.

6. The xylem of most angiosperms has vessels; the xylem of most gymnosperms lacks vessels.

7. Sieve tube members and companion cells are usually found in angiosperm phloem. Sieve cells, the conducting elements in gymnosperm phloem, are structurally less specialized than sieve tube members and characteristically lack companion cells.

8. In gymnosperms, pollination is exclusively by wind, whereas in angiosperms, pollination in most species is by insects, in a minority of species by wind. In some species of angiosperms, pollination may be by birds or water.

9. Angiosperms lack archegonia and antheridia, gymnosperms have archegonia but no antheridia (or an antheridium consisting of one cell).

LIFE CYCLE OF AN ANGIOSPERM

Since the details of reproduction of angiosperms are described in Chapter 15,

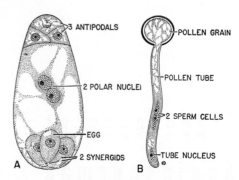

FIG. 28–1. The gametophyte generation of angiosperms. A: Female gametophyte with egg, 2 synergids, 2 polar nuclei, and 3 antipodals; B: Male gametophyte consisting of pollen grain and pollen tube with sperm nuclei and tube nucleus.

this chapter will merely relate these details of reproduction to alternation of generations.

An angiosperm "plant," such as a rose bush, apple tree, or corn plant, is the sporophyte of the life cycle. The cells of such a plant are diploid, and the plant produces two types of spores, microspores and megaspores. The microspores are produced in the anthers, as a result of reduction division of microspore mother cells. The stamens, of which the anthers are parts, are interpreted as microsporophylls, the pollen sacs of the anthers as microsporangia. Megaspores are produced within the ovules, which are enclosed by the carpels (megasporophylls). Each ovule bears a megasporangium (nucellus), within which a megaspore mother cell develops; this cell, as a result of meiosis, produces four megaspores, three of which disintegrate, the fourth of which develops into the megagametophyte (embryo sac). The microgametophyte (pollen grain with its tube) and megagametophyte (embryo sac) constitute the haploid generation, the microgametophyte producing sperms, the meg-

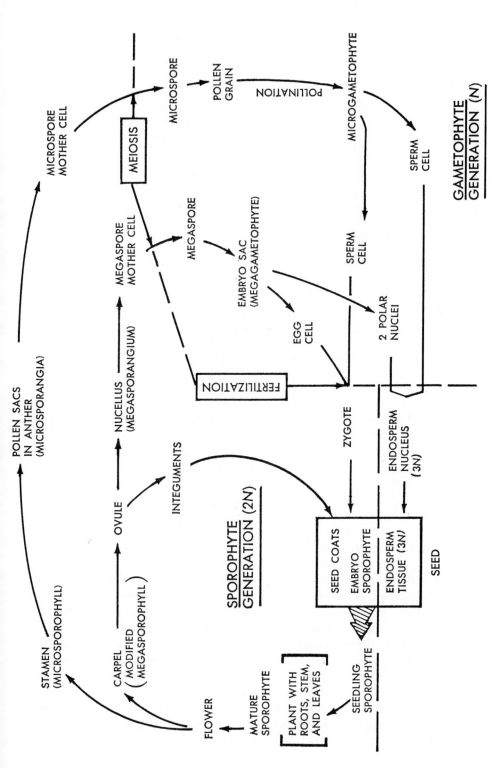

FIG. 28–2. Diagrammatic representation of the life cycle of an angiosperm. Note that endosperm belongs to neither gametophyte nor sporophyte generation.

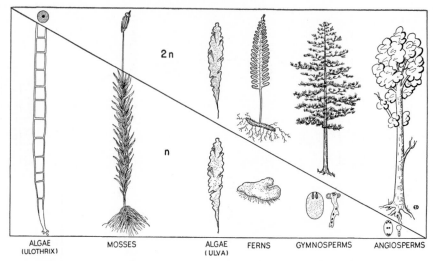

FIG. 28–3. Evolution of alternation of generations in plants, illustrating the increasing size and complexity of the sporophyte and the diminishing size and complexity of the gametophyte. All structures above the diagonal line are sporophytes ($2n$), those below are gametophytes (n). In many algae the sporophyte is represented by a zygote; in some others it may be over 100 feet long. Vascular plant sporophytes, however, are always dominant.

agametophyte eggs. Thus, the gametophyte generation (Figure 28–1) consists of two very small structures, which ordinarily can be seen only with magnification. The gametophytes of angiosperms lack antheridia and archegonia. The female gametophyte of an angiosperm typically has 8 nuclei, although in a few species, other numbers occur. As described in Chapter 15, only three of these nuclei are actually involved in reproduction: the egg, or female gamete, and the two polar nuclei. The remaining nuclei are believed to be vestigial structures, or "evolutionary holdovers." Both gametophytes lack chlorophyll, both obtain their food from the surrounding tissues of the sporophyte. Further, the gametophytes never reach the soil in their reproductive activity. A pollen tube penetrates an embryo sac through the micropyle of an ovule, one sperm fertilizing the egg, the other fusing with the polar nuclei. The fertilized egg,

or zygote, constitutes the first stage in the sporophyte generation; the zygote, which is diploid, grows into the embryo of the seed.

The life cycle of a typical angiosperm is shown in Figure 28–2.

EVOLUTION OF ALTERNATION OF GENERATIONS

Review of the reproduction and life cycles of the various plant groups indicates that a pronounced evolutionary change in the relative development of sporophyte and gametophyte generations has occurred in the plant kingdom. Figure 28–3 represents this change diagrammatically. In lower plant groups, such as most algae, mosses, and liverworts, the gametophyte generation is the larger, more complex, dominant, nutritionally independent generation, the sporophyte is smaller, less complex, and wholly or partially dependent upon the gametophyte generation for its food. In some algae, both generations are independent and are similar in size and structure. In higher groups of plants, such as club mosses, ferns, gymnosperms, and angiosperms, the relative development of the two generations is the reverse of that in the lower groups. Thus, in the higher plants, the sporophyte is nutritionally independent and more complex in its structure, the gametophyte is smaller and of diminishing complexity. The culmination of this expansion of the sporophyte and the reduction of the gametophyte occurs in the angiosperms, in which the gametophytes are tiny, microscopic structures lacking chlorophyll and completely dependent upon sporophyte tissues for their food. Another conspicuous feature of these generations in plants is the presence of vascular tissues *only* in sporophytes. The sole exception is *Psilotum,* the gametophytes of which have been shown occasionally to contain a few vascular elements.

ORIGIN OF ANGIOSPERMS

The ancestors of our modern flowering plants are unknown, although certain similarities between living angiosperms and extinct fossil plants have led botanists to speculate concerning their origin. One theory of the origin of angiosperms regards an extinct group of gymnosperms, the Cycadeoidales, as the probable ancestors of flowering plants. The first fossils of true flowering plants occur in rocks of the Cretaceous period, about 125,000,-000 years old. Among these angiosperm fossils are magnolias, sassafras, tulip trees, elms, maples, sycamore, poplar, and many other familiar flowering plants.

CLASSIFICATION OF ANGIOSPERMS

As indicated in earlier chapters, the class Angiospermae is subdivided into two subclasses: Monocotyledoneae and Dicotyledoneae. Monocotyledons have a single cotyledon in their embryos, have flower parts typically in threes, usually lack cambium and thus secondary tissues, have scattered vascular bundles, and commonly possess rather narrow, elongated leaves with parallel main veins. The dicotyledons have two cotyledons in their embryos, have flower parts most commonly in fives or fours, usually have cambium, have cylinders of vascular tissues or vascular bundles in a circle, and commonly have broad leaves with net venation. The monocotyledons, which embrace about 3000 genera and 50,000 species, include cattails, grasses, sedges, palms, lilies, irises, amaryllises, tulips, bananas, cannas, orchids, and many other familiar kinds of plants. The dicotyledons, which number about 9500 genera and 200,000 known species, include willows, oaks, walnuts, elms, maples, magnolias, buttercups, carnations, apples, roses, legumes, mints, tomatoes and their relatives, phloxes, geraniums, poppies, sunflowers and other composites, and thousands of other common plants.

≪← SUMMARY

1. The Angiospermae constitute the third class of Pteropsida and number about 250,000 species.
2. The major characteristics of angiosperms are:
    a. Flowers, seeds, and fruits.
    b. Heterospory.

    c. True roots, stems, and leaves.

    d. Sporophytes dominant, autotrophic; gametophytes very small, dependent upon sporophytes for food.

    e. Sperms reach eggs as result of pollination and pollen tube growth.

    f. Archegonia and antheridia absent.

3. Angiosperms differ from gymnosperms in these major ways:

    a. Angiosperms have flowers, gymnosperms have cones.

    b. Angiosperm seeds enclosed by carpels, gymnosperm seeds borne exposed on cone scales.

    c. Angiosperms have double fertilization, gymnosperms do not.

    d. Endosperm of angiosperms is triploid. Stored food in gymnosperm seeds is haploid.

    e. In gymnosperms, pollen grains land on ovules; in angiosperms, pollen lands on stigma, pollen tubes grow through tissues of stigma, style, and ovary to reach ovules.

    f. Angiosperm xylem usually has vessels, gymnosperm xylem usually does not.

    g. Angiosperm phloem usually includes sieve tube members and companion cells; these two cell types are not found in gymnosperms.

    h. Gymnosperm pollination is by wind, angiosperm pollination by insects, wind, birds, water.

    i. Angiosperms lack antheridia and archegonia; gymnosperms have archegonia but no antheridia.

4. An angiosperm "plant" is a sporophyte.

5. The common names of some significant structures involved in angiosperm reproduction and their more meaningful, morphologically equivalent names are:

stamen—microsporophyll

pollen sac—microsporangium

pollen grain—immature microgametophyte

pollen grain and tube—microgametophyte

carpel—modified megasporophyll

nucellus—megasporangium

megaspore—megaspore

embryo sac—megagametophyte

6. The gametophytes of angiosperms are tiny, have no chlorophyll, do not come in contact with the soil.

7. The five extra nuclei in an angiosperm embryo sac are thought to be vestiges of an archegonium and prothallus.

8. In evolution of alternation of generations in plants, there has occurred an increasing complexity and size of the sporophyte, decreasing complexity and size of the gametophyte. Also, sporophytes in higher plants are autotrophic, gametophytes are heterotrophic.

9. Vascular tissues occur only in sporophyte generation.

10. The evolutionary origin of angiosperms is not known but these plants are believed to have evolved from primitive gymnosperms, possibly the seed ferns.

11. The earliest angiosperm fossils have been found in Cretaceous rocks about 125,000,000 years old.
12. The class Angiospermae is separated into two subclasses: Monocotyledoneae and Dicotyledoneae.

⋘ SUGGESTED READINGS FOR INTERESTED STUDENTS

1. Eames, A. J., *Morphology of the Angiosperms.* McGraw-Hill, New York, 1961.
2. Benson, L., *Plant Classification.* Heath, Boston, 1957.
3. Foster, A. S., and E. M. Gifford, Jr., *Comparative Morphology of Vascular Plants.* Freeman, San Francisco, 1959.
4. Porter, C. L., *Taxonomy of Flowering Plants.* Freeman, San Francisco, 1959.

⋘ TOPICS AND QUESTIONS FOR STUDY

1. List the major characteristics of: Tracheophyta, Pteropsida, Coniferae, Angiospermae, Monocotyledoneae, Dicotyledoneae.
2. List major differences among Lycopsida, Sphenopsida, and Pteropsida.
3. Describe briefly the distribution of angiosperms on the earth.
4. How do angiosperms compare with other plant groups in number of species?
5. Are there any habitats on the earth in which the angiosperms are not the dominant plants? Name such habitats, and indicate which are their dominant plants.
6. Diagram an angiosperm life cycle.
7. With what structures in the life cycle of a moss is a corn plant comparable (from the standpoint of alternation of generations)?
8. With what structures in angiosperms is a liverwort thallus comparable?
9. With what structures in an angiosperm is a fern prothallus comparable?
10. Compare the sporophyte generation of an angiosperm with the gametophyte of an angiosperm.
11. List the major differences between angiosperms and gymnosperms.
12. In what geological period are found the oldest angiosperm fossils?
13. Compare the origin of stored food in an angiosperm seed with that of a gymnosperm seed.
14. What is thought to be the evolutionary origin of angiosperms?
15. Describe the evolution of sporophyte and gametophyte generations in plants.
16. What features of gymnosperms and angiosperms fit them for a successful land existence?

The Evolution of Plants

29

The earth and the living organisms of earth have not always been as they are now. The earth has cooled, the oceans were formed, land masses have arisen from the waters and have sunk beneath them, mountain ranges have been thrust up from the earth's surface and mountain ranges have been worn down by glaciers and the erosive action of water and wind, volcanoes have sprung into fiery activity and have lapsed into inactivity. Living organisms have slowly changed in the long period of their existence and have given rise to new kinds of living things. All such changes are called **evolution.** **Inorganic evolution** embraces all those transformations that nonliving entities—rocks, oceans, soil—have experienced; **organic evolution** includes the whole continuous series of changes associated with the genetic adaptation of organisms to their environments. The concept of organic evolution has influenced all fields of biological science and is today a point of departure, a working blueprint, in many phases of biological investigation. This concept holds that the first living organisms on the earth were very simple in structure; that all plants and animals that have appeared on the earth are descendants of these simple, primordial organisms; and that during the main course of evolutionary change there has occurred, in general, an ever-increasing structural complexity and diversification. In some groups of plants and animals, processes of simplification have occurred, resulting in the evolution of structurally simple organisms from more complex ancestors. Reputable biologists agree generally upon the fact of organic evolution. That living plants and animals arise only from pre-existing plants and animals, that living organisms usually produce descendants somewhat different from the parents, and that different kinds of plants and animals have inhabited the earth at different phases of its history are undisputed facts that have been proved again and again by careful observations and by actual experiments.

EVIDENCES OF ORGANIC EVOLUTION

The evidences that have led biologists to accept evolution as a demonstrated fact

(Photo by W. N. Stewart.)

FIG. 29–1. Fossilized leaf of a fern, showing sporangia on leaf margins.

are many, and have been derived from studies of many aspects of plants and animals. The most significant evidences have been gathered from the study of fossils, from observations on the comparative morphology of living organisms, from investigations of geographical distribution, and from genetic and biochemical studies.

Evidence from Plant Fossils. When plants die, their bodies are ordinarily decomposed by heterotrophic organisms. Decomposition usually results in the eradication of all traces of dead plant tissue. Sometimes, however, dead plants or plant parts are deposited in places where the process of decomposition is greatly retarded, for example, at the bottom of a lake or pond of mineral-charged, acid water. Under these conditions, the dead remains may be rapidly covered with sediments that later become rocks. Such preserved parts or their impressions are called **fossils** (Figures 29–1 and 29–2).

The study of plant fossils **(paleobotany)** shows that different kinds of fossils occur in the various layers of rock that constitute the earth's crust. This observation leads to the conclusion that the earth's vegetation has not been constant and unchanging, but that different types of plants have inhabited the earth's surface at different periods during its history. Investigations have demonstrated that the kinds of fossils found in each rock stratum are generally not sharply distinguished from fossils found in adjacent strata, but that structural similarities can frequently be traced from the fossils of one layer to those of other layers formed before and later. The presence of such morphological resemblances in plants of different geologic ages indicates that close relationship exists among them and that the plants of various periods have developed from plants of earlier times. The changes that have appeared in the earth's vegeta-

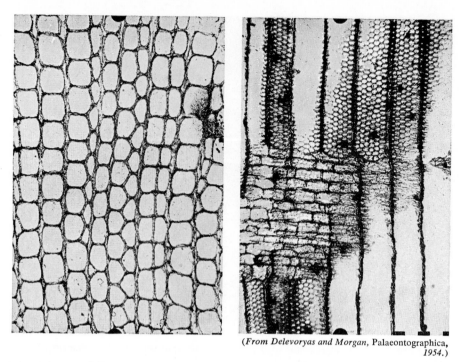

(*From Delevoryas and Morgan,* Palaeontographica, *1954.*)

FIG. 29–2. Petrified wood of an ancient seed fern, *Callistophyton poroxyloides. Left:* Transverse section showing tracheids. *Right:* Radial section showing pits in tracheid walls, and a portion of a vascular ray.

tion in successive geological periods are believed to have occurred partly as a result of gradual alterations in the earth's climatic and topographic features. A study of many kinds of plant fossils shows that there has been an increasing complexity in the structure of plants from the fossils of the oldest (lowermost) rock layers to the plants of the present time.

Evidence from Comparative Morphology of Living Organisms. Marked structural similarities among organisms are usually interpreted as an indication of close affinities, and pronounced structural dissimilarities usually suggest more distant relationships. For example, on the basis of morphological resemblances we recognize that beans, clovers, and peas are closely related, and that grasses, sunflowers, and magnolias are much less closely related,

though they are all flowering plants. There is virtually no doubt among botanists that all plants are related to each other to a greater or lesser degree. We may conclude, then, that close relationships in a given group of plants indicate common ancestry of the members of that group. The morphological evidences for evolution of plants have been marshaled from a number of sources—from studies of floral morphology, seed structure, wood anatomy, embryology, etc. Everywhere the same principles hold: morphological similarity usually indicates close relationship, and close relationship denotes common ancestry.

Genetic Evidence. That living plants have a potentiality for change may be readily demonstrated by simple experiments in hybridization. Both natural and artificial cross-breeding of plant species frequently result in the production of new types—hybrids that may or may not persist in succeeding generations. In some genera (for example, in asters, oaks, willows, and hawthorns), natural populations of intergrading plants are produced by interspecific hybridization and repeated backcrossing. Such hybrid populations may include the parental types and numerous transitional forms representing various degrees of intermediacy between the parents. If all species were specially created, immutable entities, such intergrading plants could not reasonably be expected to exist. Genetic evidence of evolution is also found in mutation, an important means by which plants may undergo heritable change. Numerous mutations have appeared in many groups of plants; moreover, it seems likely that these spontaneous changes occur in all groups. In the domestication of plants, man has wrought many changes through hybridization and selection and has also taken advantage of conspicuous mutations in the development of new varieties. Some plants have been so completely altered during the many centuries through which they have been under cultivation that they cannot at present be found in a wild state; that is, they have been changed to such an extent that they no longer show enough similarity to wild plants to be referred to them.

Evidence from Geographical Distribution. Many types of plants are widely distributed on the earth's surface, but other species tend to be restricted in their ranges. The fact that different species of plants are frequently found growing under similar climatic conditions in widely separated parts of the world indicates that climatic differences alone cannot explain such distribution. The desert regions of the southwestern United States and of western Africa are similar climatically, but the species of plants growing in these regions are very different. Common in the American deserts and lacking in the African are numerous species of cacti, while spurges (*Euphorbia*) abound in the African deserts and are rare in the deserts of the United States. Ordinarily, similar species of plants occupy the various areas of a general region. If these areas are separated by barriers, such as high mountains or large bodies of water over which plants cannot pass, the plants in these isolated areas tend to develop along divergent lines and to become quite distinct. In general, the longer the period of isolation of one region from another, the greater is the degree of difference among the plants of the two regions, as a result of differences in the course of evolution in the separated regions. This explanation accounts, in part, for the great differences among plants growing under similar conditions but in widely separated and long-isolated parts of the earth. Regions that have been separated from other land areas for a very great period of time usually have floras peculiar to them, floras consisting largely of plants found in no other parts of the world. Such regions became isolated early in the history of life on the earth, and the course of evolution under such prolonged isolation has produced floras different from those of other areas. Examples of long-isolated lands with very characteristic and limited floras are the Hawaiian, the Fiji, and other oceanic islands.

Evidence from Comparative Biochemistry. Chemical similarities and differences among plants furnish important information regarding relationships and ancestry. Perhaps the widest use of chemical criteria has been at the higher taxonomic levels. For example, the types of pigments and stored foods are major diagnostic characteristics used in determining divisional affinities among the algae. The presence of volatile, essential oils is an indication of close relationship among the members of the mint family; the presence of resinous substances is a similar indication in the pine family, etc. Chemical investigations have shown marked differences among different groups of plants in terms of the presence of certain proteins as characteristic protoplasmic constituents; the closer the relationship among plants, the more nearly alike chemically are their proteins. An entire system of plant classification has actually been proposed upon the basis of the protein characteristics of various plant groups.

CAUSES OF EVOLUTION

The Theory of Darwin. The theory of organic evolution proposed by Charles Darwin in 1859 and termed the Theory of Natural Selection is so well known that the word Darwinism is frequently (and erroneously) used as a synonym for evolution. The concept of evolution in human thought may be traced as far back as the philosophers of ancient Greece and thus is not a theory or idea invented by Darwin. Darwin's name is more intimately connected with the concept of evolution than that of any other man because his researches upon the evolution of living organisms have been more extensive and more critically described than those of any other investigator in the history of the evolutionary concept.

Darwin's theory is based upon the following principles:

1. *Overproduction.* Organisms are prodigal in their reproduction and produce far more offspring than can possibly survive. This principle in Darwin's theory is recognized as fact by all biologists. A single orchid flower may produce over 1,000,000 seeds, a single plant of pigweed (*Amaranthus*) may form 2,000,000 seeds, one mushroom may scatter into the breeze as many as 2,000,000,000 spores. Obviously neither the room nor the food materials necessary for the growth of these enormous numbers of reproductive structures is available—that is, too many offspring are produced to survive.

2. *Competition.* Because of the limitations of space and of food, all these offspring cannot survive, and they compete with each other for space in which to grow and for nutrition. Thus, there develops a "struggle for existence," not only among organisms of different species, but also among individuals of the same species. However, only a small percentage of the offspring is able to survive and achieve growth to maturity. This competition acts as a natural check upon the numbers of individuals that attain maturity in different species and results in an equilibrium among the species growing in a particular region, so long as factors tending to disturb this equilibrium do not arise.

3. *Variation.* That individual organisms of the same species are not exactly alike but vary in different degree from other individuals in the species is a long-recognized biological fact. According to Darwin, under a given set of environmental conditions certain individuals of a species possess variations tending to adjust them very advantageously to these external conditions, whereas other individuals of the same species possess less favorable variations and thus are at a disadvantage in relation to the same environmental factors. Individuals with the

more favorable variations, thought Darwin, would be the survivors in the competition for space and nutrients, while those with less favorable variations would perish. Those individuals with the favorable variations tend to transmit these variations to their offspring; among the offspring variation again occurs, some individuals surviving, others dying in the "struggle for existence"; the former then in turn pass on their variations to their offspring, and thus the process continues generation after generation. Darwin considered this "survival of the fittest" a type of selection which he termed **natural selection.** This process, continuing through many generations, supposedly results in a slow but increasing modification of the species toward characters better suited for survival in the environment. Since only the individuals with favorable variations in the direction of better adaptation to their environment survive and the individuals with less advantageous variations disappear, in time many new forms of life come into existence, according to the Darwinian theory.

The Darwinian theory of evolution has excited more discussion and disputation than any other evolutionary theory. Many biologists have supported the theory in its entirety, others have accepted some portions and rejected other parts of it. Certainly Darwin's basic assumptions are true—namely, overproduction, competition, variation, and the survival of those individuals with the most favorable variations for a particular environment. The most controversial points in Darwin's theory are those of the inheritance of variations and of the degree to which natural selection can lead to significant changes in organisms. It should be emphasized that Darwin himself realized that his theory contained weaknesses

and that he believed that natural selection was but *one* factor among several factors operative in evolution.

One objection that has been leveled at Darwin's theory is its failure to account for nonadaptive characters. There is no doubt that natural selection has accounted for many types of adaptation of organisms to their environments. Successful adaptation to an environment implies, of course, the development and intensification of useful characters for the particular complex of environmental conditions. In addition to such valuable traits, most organisms possess numerous characters that have little or no apparent adaptive significance; in fact, the principal differences that distinguish many species of plants and animals are trifling, nonadaptive characters seemingly of little moment with respect to adjustment or survival. Darwin's theory accounts for the evolution of adaptive characters but ignores the nonadaptive traits that often constitute the major differences among species.

Another criticism of Darwin's theory has been directed at his failure to distinguish between heritable and nonheritable variations and his assumption that nearly all variations are heritable. Ordinarily, only those variations that are carried by the chromosomes in gametes can be transmitted from parent to offspring; many variations are merely direct environmental modifications of somatic or body cells and are not related to hereditary determiners; such variations are not transmitted from generation to generation. Thus, selection based upon somatic or body-cell variations cannot induce changes in the nature of organisms and of course cannot be significant in evolution.

One more criticism of Darwin's theory has been made—namely, that it has failed in many instances to distinguish between variations of small magnitude, which do not exceed the limits of normal variability within a species, and variations that are so large as to mark the individuals in which they occur as distinctly new types of organisms. The proponents of this criticism find it difficult to see how appreciable evolutionary changes could be wrought by small, more or less continuous variations, and they emphasize the importance of larger, discontinuous variations in evolutionary processes.

The Mutation Theory. Hugo de Vries, a Dutch botanist, proposed in 1901 a theory to explain the phenomenon of evolution in living organisms. He observed that among plants of a species of evening primrose (*Oenothera lamarckiana*) new types of individuals occasionally developed that were genetically pure, that is, that continued to produce offspring of exactly the same kind through successive generations. Some of these new kinds of evening primroses were sufficiently distinct from the parent type to be considered new species and have accordingly been named as new species. The sudden distinct changes that produced these new kinds of plants de Vries called mutations. Impressed by the mutants (organisms that arise by mutation) in his evening primroses, de Vries formulated his Mutation Theory of Evolution, the essential point of which is that new species of organisms are formed by sudden unexplained changes of considerable magnitude (mutations) and that these newly formed species are distinct from the very instant of their origin. Mutations are sometimes called **discontinuous variations** because they are not connected by series of intermediate forms. In contrast, Darwin's theory emphasized the importance of **continuous variations** that form an unbroken, gradually merging series.

De Vries believed that during the "struggle for existence" of newly arisen mutants, natural selection results in the elimination of some and the survival of those better adapted to the environments in which they occur. Thus, de Vries offered what is essentially a modification of Darwin's theory of Natural Selection; he altered Darwin's theory on one point— namely, on the nature of variations. Whereas Darwin regarded variations as continuous and intergrading, de Vries considered them discontinuous and distinct.

That mutations are to be regarded as outward expressions of alterations in the chromosomal material in nuclei is supported by the discovery of numerous gene mutations and chromosome aberrations associated with externally visible changes in living organisms. In some plants, Jimson weed (*Datura*), for example, cell division sometimes fails after the chromosomes have separated in mitosis. The result is development of a cell with a chromosome number double the normal number. If this happens during reduction division, diploid gametes are formed. If such a gamete fuses with a normal haploid gamete, a **triploid** zygote results; a diploid gamete fusing with another diploid gamete forms a **tetraploid** zygote. If such zygotes develop into mature plants, triploid and tetraploid individuals result. Associated with increased numbers of chromosome sets **(polyploidy)** and other chromosomal aberrations are various externally visible or experimentally demonstrable modifications, such as increased size and growth rate of polyploid plants, unusually large flowers, varying degrees of sterility, and, occasionally, slower growth.

Certain objections have been voiced against the Mutation Theory. Chief among these is the fact that mutations, though they arise frequently in certain genera of living organisms, such as *Oenothera* and Boston ferns, are generally rather uncommon and, in certain groups of plants and animals, have never been found. Critics of the Mutation Theory argued that, if mutation were a fundamental cause of species formation, it might be expected to be a much more general phenomenon than it seems to be among living organisms. This objection might be in part refuted by pointing out that the development of new species is also a rather infrequent occurrence and that, although it is infrequent during the span of an investigator's life, it is not an infrequent phenomenon when regarded against the background of geological time. That mutation is a mode of species origin in certain groups of organisms is a proven fact, despite the objections that have been offered against de Vries' theory.

The Modern Interpretation. During the past fifty years, biologists have learned much about the physical basis of inheritance and about variation and its transmission. This information has expanded greatly our understanding of the "mechanics" of **speciation**—that is, the means by which new species are formed—and has contributed much to a working concept regarding the causes of evolution. As presently viewed, evolution is a composite of four basic processes: mutation, recombination, natural selection, and reproductive isolation.

1. *Mutations* have been called the raw materials of evolution, for it is through them that new kinds of genes are introduced into the **gene pool,** which is the term for all the genes of an interbreeding population. Mutations are produced through spontaneous alterations of genetic material ranging from single genes to whole sets of chromosomes. These unpredictable changes arise infrequently and without environmental direction; that is, a particular type of environment does not determine a particular kind or kinds of mutations. Those mutations that produce small effects (micromutations) generally have greater evolutionary significance than those producing large effects (macromutations). In a well-adapted population of green plants, a macromutation producing chlorophyll deficiency would have little chance of becoming incorporated into the gene pool, for the species would not long survive; however, a micromutation that increases the number of epidermal hairs per square millimeter from 10 to 12 would involve no loss of fitness. It is largely through the gradual accumulation of numerous small mutations that intervarietal and interspecific differences arise.

2. *Recombination* is a major source of variation among the individuals of an interbreeding population. Although this process does not add new genes to the gene pool, it does "reshuffle" them in various combinations and thus gives added importance to mutation. Most gene recombinations are brought about through the mechanisms of sexual reproduction, including independent assortment, crossing over, and random fertilization. Hybridization between varieties and between species greatly enhances variation, provided, of course, that the hybrids are fertile. Actually, hybrid sterility is common; in such cases, the degree of sterility reflects the degree of genetic incompatibility between the parents. When sufficient differences exist between the sets of parental chromosomes in the hybrid, these chromosomes pair improperly (if at all) at meiosis. The result of

such behavior is the production of aberrant, inviable spores. On rare occasions, such a hybrid undergoes spontaneous doubling of the chromosome number, after which identical chromosomes may pair. This plant then produces polyploid spores capable of further development. The union of two diploid gametes is followed by the development of a fertile tetraploid individual. Plants with this type of polyploid origin differ considerably from the parents and are sometimes classified as new species.

3. *Natural selection* is viewed today as a creative evolutionary process that results in the establishment of favorable variations in the population, or, put differently, favorable gene combinations in the gene pool. The basis for this interpretation lies in differential reproduction. Within any interbreeding population, certain individuals produce more offspring than others. Therefore, those with the most progeny contribute more to the gene pool than those with fewer offspring. Continued through succeeding generations, the increased reproduction of individuals with certain combinations of genetic characteristics results in an increase in frequency of their genes in the population. Those individuals that produce no progeny, regardless of the reason, contribute nothing to the gene pool; in an evolutionary sense, their genes are lost. Thus, reproductive fitness of the individual has more evolutionary significance than has survival. It is through differential reproduction that natural selection results in the adaptation of plants (and animals) to their environments. Every species possesses myriad adaptations, for the very existence of a plant in a particular environment implies an adjustment between the plant and that environment. In many plants, adaptive changes have led to rather extreme types of specialization; for example, xeromorphism in cacti and other plants, and elaborate pollinating mechanisms.

4. *Reproductive isolation* is a process of great evolutionary significance, for it reduces or stops interbreeding and thus prevents effective gene exchange. This restriction to interbreeding results in the gradual accumulation of genetic differences among the isolated population units, and in the concomitant divergence of these groups. The various kinds of genetically controlled isolating mechanisms also are believed to arise gradually by gene accumulation, usually after a period of spatial isolation. Spatial isolation may involve a geographical barrier that completely prevents interbreeding among the individuals thus separated, or it may involve a greatly reduced gene exchange among widely separated members of a relatively large population. However, spatial isolation per se does not produce divergence among the separated populations; such divergence is fostered by the many genetically controlled mechanisms, such as hybrid sterility, different moisture or other environmental requirements, structural differences making pollination impossible, different times for flowering, etc. It is in this manner that species, varieties, and races are formed. The evolution of higher taxonomic categories is essentially the same as for species, except that intermediates become extinct.

THE ORIGIN AND EVOLUTION OF PLANTS

Since the earliest recognizable plant fossils are those of morphologically simple algae and bacteria and since the fossils from later periods in the earth's history give ample evidence of increasing structural complexity, it is reasonable to suppose that the earliest plants were at least as simple in their structure as the most primitive living thallophytes, if not simpler. Most algae and bacteria decompose rapidly after death and are not ordinarily preserved. Thus fossil records of such organisms are rare and no unmistakable evidence concerning the first living plants has been derived from the record of the rocks.

Recent speculations about the origin of living things suggest that the first organisms were aquatic heterotrophs living in a world devoid of free atmospheric oxygen. These organisms probably obtained their energy from some kind of anaerobic respiration, as a result of which carbon dioxide was released. The gradual accumulation of carbon dioxide in the water and in the air set the stage for the next major evolutionary event—the appearance of photosynthetic organisms. Oxygen, released by autotrophs, was accumulated slowly in the environment and led to the evolution of aerobic respiration. The earliest green plants were probably algae, the oldest green plants in the fossil record and, morphologically, the simplest of green plants. The blue-greens may have been among the first to appear, for fossils of what seem to be blue-green algae have been found in very ancient rocks (about 1.6 billion years old). Further, blue-green algae are very similar to many bacteria in their structure. Coincident with, or following the appearance of blue-green algae, there may have developed primitive types of animals, probably microscopic and unicellular, like the bacteria and blue-green algae themselves, and later, other more complex types of algae. The appearance of green plants was the beginning of a great forward movement in the plant world, for it established a

mode of nutrition that was to become dominant among plants and initiated lines of development destined to lead through the ages to the infinitely varied flora of modern times.

The various sedimentary rock strata that form a major portion of the earth's crust have been deposited in the order of the time of their formation, with more recently formed layers deposited upon successively older ones. Thus, the oldest rock strata are those now found at the bottom of any given sequence of layers and the more recently formed ones occur above these in order. Geologists have been able to estimate in a rather general fashion the age of the earth and the ages of the various rock strata by use of certain chemical and physical techniques. A comparison of the rock layers in different places and of the fossils contained in them enables geologists to piece together a sequence of strata from oldest to youngest.

Studies of plant fossils have enabled botanists to reach several conclusions concerning the history of plants on the earth. Investigations of the earth's oldest rock layers, at least 3,000,000,000 years old, show no evidence of plant remains, whereas in rock layers of more recent time, many types of plant fossils have been found. Rocks of the Paleozoic era, which extended from 230 million to 600 million years ago, have yielded fossilized algae, fungi, bryophytes, psilophytes, club mosses, horsetails, and ferns. During the Carboniferous periods of the Paleozoic era, great beds of coal were formed by the partial decomposition and burial of the bodies of ferns, horsetails, and their relatives. In the closing years of the Paleozoic, seed plants somewhat similar to some of our present gymnosperms appeared in the earth's flora. In the Mesozoic era, which extended from 60 million to 230 million years ago, there occurred a rapid development and diversification of gymnosperms and a decline of giant ferns, horsetails, and club mosses. Late in the Mesozoic era, the first true angiosperms, or flowering plants, appeared, as is shown by the discovery of fossils of magnolias, willows, tulip trees, palms, and oaks in late Mesozoic rocks. As the Mesozoic era drew toward its close, the gymnosperms were in marked decline, and the angiosperms experienced the beginning of their ascendancy. In the Cenozoic era, which began about 60,000,000 years ago and which extends down to the present time, rapid and diverse evolution of angiosperms occurred, leading to the dominance of these plants in our modern flora. The Cenozoic era is sometimes called the Age of Angiosperms. Thus, the record of the rocks shows us that plant life on the earth has not always been as it is now, that various plant groups have arisen, expanded, and disappeared from the earth's surface, and that there has been an ever-increasing complexity in plants through the ages.

The Family Tree of the Plant Kingdom. As a result of numerous investigations principally of the structure and reproduction of fossil and of living plants, botanists have reached tentative conclusions concerning the probable path of evolution in the plant kingdom. These conclusions are presented in generalized form in Figure 18–2 (p. 321). This family tree of the plant world should be regarded as an expression of opinion concerning plant evolution, an opinion based upon the facts of plant relationships as they are now known. Numerous other phylogenetic arrangements have been made in the past and have been altered as new facts about plants have been unearthed; so it is with the present arrangement, which doubtless

will in the future undergo changes, as have earlier representations of plant evolution.

Certain generalizations may be derived from a study of the phylogenetic tree. Most striking of these perhaps is the fact that the course of evolution cannot be represented by a straight line along which various groups of plants may be placed, but that it is adequately shown only by a branching system of lines, similar in their positional relationships to the branches of a tree; hence the popular designation of "family tree" for a scheme of phylogeny. Many of the branches of a family tree represent terminal groups, some of which have become extinct, others of which are living groups that are seemingly static—that is, which have not given rise to other types of plants. Another feature of evolution clearly illustrated by a phylogenetic tree is the fact that not all the groups of plants that have appeared in succession along a main evolutionary line have survived to the present time; some of these organisms (for example, the euglenoids) have lived through a large section of geological time, others (for example, some seed ferns) arose from earlier groups, led to the development of later and more complex types of plants, and then became extinct.

Evolutionary Changes in the Plant Kingdom. Our brief survey of living and extinct plant groups has indicated that numerous, striking evolutionary changes have occurred in plants during their long residence upon the earth. The more obvious and more significant of these evolutionary transformations have been discussed in earlier chapters, but are presented again at this point for emphasis and summary, as follows:

1. The transformation of unicellular plants into colonial and multicellular

(Photo by Missouri Botanical Garden.)

A   B   C   D

FIG. 29–3. Convergent evolution illustrated by A: *Dyckia altissima* (pineapple family). B: *Agave decipiens* (amaryllis family). C: *Haworthia margartifera* (lily family). D: *Aloe humilis* (lily family).

plants, with increase in size and complexity of external and internal structure.

2. The transition from simple, undifferentiated protoplasts to highly specialized protoplasts with nuclei, plastids, and other organized bodies.

3. The origin and evolution of sexual reproduction, possibly from some type of asexual reproduction.

4. The evolution of a terrestrial from an aquatic mode of life.

5. The differentiation of vascular, strengthening, storage, and other types of tissues that have made possible successful adaptation to land conditions.

6. The progressive differentiation of plant organs into distinctly vegetative and distinctly reproductive structures termed cones and flowers.

7. The development of seeds as a result of the retention of gametophytes and young sporophytes within sporangial walls.

8. The decrease in size and complexity of the gametophyte generation and the corresponding rise of the sporophyte.

9. The release from dependence upon water for fertilization through the development of pollen tubes in the seed plants.

As stated earlier in this chapter, the most conspicuous tendency in the evolution of plants has been an increase in structural complexity and specialization. This **progressive evolution** has likewise been the principal evolutionary trend in the animal kingdom. Although the course of evolution in both plants and animals has thus been primarily upward, evolutionary changes have not been exclusively progressive, nor have they proceeded at a constant rate. There are many examples among both plants and animals of evolutionary transformations leading toward decreased complexity and simplification from structurally more complex ancestors. Examples of such **retrogressive evolution** are common in the plant kingdom: the development of structurally simplified types of flowers from more elaborate, more complex flowers (for example, the evolution of grass flowers from lilylike ancestors), the reduc-

A   B

FIG. 29–4. Convergent evolution illustrated by A: *Euphorbia cereiformis,* a spurge. B: *Cereus euphorbioides,* a cactus.

tion of sexual structures and activity in certain fungi, the morphological degeneracy accompanying a transition from an autotrophic to a parasitic mode of life in such flowering plants as beechdrops and dodder. Although evolutionary changes of a retrogressive nature have been rather common in certain groups of plants, such changes have been merely sidetracks along the trunk line of progressive evolution and have not appreciably altered the direction of evolutionary advances in the plant kingdom as a whole. In the evolution of different groups of plants, changes frequently occur that follow a common pattern and culminate in similar morphological organization, although the plants that travel such similar paths may be genetically only very distantly related. Such parallelism in evolutionary changes is apparent in numerous groups of plants and may occur in both progressive and retrogressive transformations. Among ex-

amples of this **parallel evolution** in plants is the morphological reduction that occurs in the transition from an autotrophic to a parasitic or saprophytic mode of life; dodders, beechdrops, and pinedrops are heterotrophic angiosperms that are only distantly related but that have experienced similar modifications in their evolution from autotrophic ancestors —reduction and modification of roots into haustoria that penetrate host tissues, reduction of leaves, and complete disappearance of or marked diminution of chlorophyll.

When parallel evolution proceeds in different plant groups in almost exactly the same manner and under nearly identical conditions, the ultimate products of such evolution may be so similar morphologically as to be distinguished only with great difficulty. This striking condition is sometimes called **convergence,** and the type of parallel evolution that produced it, **convergent evolution.** A conspicuous example of convergent evolution is the development of similar, often nearly identical, xeromorphic characters in very distantly related families of angiosperms (Figure 29–3). In most species of the cactus family (Figure 29–4), and in certain desert-inhabiting members of the spurge, lily, milkweed, stonecrop, and amaryllis families, the formation of heavy layers of cutin, the extensive development of water storage tissues, the reduction or complete disappearance of leaves, and the production of numerous spines or surface hairs are so nearly alike that one is frequently unable to distinguish among the members of these families on the basis of their vegetative structure.

⋘ SUMMARY

1. The earth and the earth's living organisms have undergone changes that are known collectively as evolution.
2. Evidences in support of evolution are derived from studies of fossils, comparative morphology of living organisms, genetics, geographical distribution, and comparative biochemistry.
3. The following are prominent theories that have attempted to explain the facts of evolution:
   a. The Theory of Darwin (Natural Selection) is based upon the facts of overproduction, of limited food, of competition, of variation, and of the elimination of organisms with unfavorable variations in the struggle for existence. According to Darwin, organisms with favorable variations pass these variations on to their offspring. This process, continuing through many generations, supposedly results in the modification of species.
   b. The Mutation Theory of de Vries holds that evolution occurs as a result of the appearance of sudden, distinct changes, called mutations. These develop as a result of changes in the genes, or hereditary determiners in living organisms. Mutations are heritable, and if they are of sufficient magnitude, they result in the formation of new species.
4. Evolution is presently viewed as a composite of four processes: mutation, recombination, natural selection, and reproductive isolation. Variations resulting from mutation and recombination are distributed in the gene pool by natural selection, the basis of which lies in differential reproduction. Reproductive isolation prevents effective gene exchange and promotes the divergence of isolated population units.
5. The first organisms were probably anaerobic heterotrophs; these were followed by photosynthetic organisms. Blue-green algae may have been among the first green plants to appear.
6. The Paleozoic club mosses, horsetails, ferns, and seed ferns constituted the major portion of the earth's vegetation during the Carboniferous period of the Paleozoic era; their death and transformation led to the formation of coal.
7. Toward the end of the Paleozoic era, there grew extensive forests of primitive gymnosperms, some of which were the ancestors of our living gymnosperms.
8. During the early years of the Mesozoic era, there occurred a rapid evolution

of gymnosperms and the disappearance of most ancient ferns. The gymnosperms of the Mesozoic era included species very similar to our modern conifers, cycads, and ginkgos. These gymnosperms constituted the major part of the earth's vegetation during most of the Mesozoic era. During the latter part of the Mesozoic era, the first true angiosperms appeared.

9. The Cenozoic era, which includes the present time, may be termed the "Age of Angiosperms," for these plants have reached their greatest development and have become dominant in this era.

10. The principal evolutionary changes that have occurred in the plant kingdom are summarized in this chapter.

11. Progressive evolution is evolution toward greater structural complexity and specialization. Retrogressive evolution is evolution leading toward decreased complexity and simplification from structurally more complex ancestors. Parallel evolution is evolution that follows a similar sequence of events in distantly related groups of organisms; parallel evolution occurs in both retrogressive and progressive changes. Convergent evolution is an extreme type of parallel evolution that results in the development, in different groups of organisms, of individuals that are morphologically almost indistinguishable.

⋘ SUGGESTED READINGS FOR INTERESTED STUDENTS

1. Adler, Irving, *How Life Began.* Signet Key Book, New American Library, New York, 1957.
2. Merrell, David J., *Evolution and Genetics.* Holt, Rinehart and Winston, New York, 1962.
3. Ross, Herbert H., *A Synthesis of Evolutionary Theory.* Prentice-Hall, Englewood Cliffs, N. J., 1962.
4. Delevoryas, Theodore, *Morphology and Evolution of Fossil Plants.* Holt, Rinehart and Winston, New York, 1962.
5. Tax, Sol, ed., *Evolution after Darwin,* Vol. I, *The Evolution of Life.* University of Chicago Press, Chicago, 1960.
6. Wald, George, "The Origin of Life." *Scientific American,* Vol. 191, No. 2, pp. 44–53, August 1954.
7. Wallace, Bruce, and A. M. Srb. *Adaptation.* Prentice-Hall, Englewood Cliffs, N. J., 1961.

⋘ TOPICS AND QUESTIONS FOR STUDY

1. Distinguish between inorganic evolution and organic evolution.
2. Describe the early steps in the evolution of plants.
3. Describe the types of plants that appeared during the various geological eras and periods.
4. Is organic evolution a theory or a fact?
5. Describe the evidences in support of organic evolution. Can you cite any evidence that might disprove evolution?
6. Summarize the major evolutionary changes that have taken place in the plant kingdom.

7. Distinguish among progressive, retrogressive, parallel, and convergent evolution. Give an example of each.
8. Summarize and evaluate the several theories that attempt to explain the causes of evolution.
9. What is the modern view concerning the causes of evolution?
10. Construct a phylogenetic tree of the plant kingdom. On it indicate the points where important advances have taken place.
11. Many plants that inhabit desert regions have reduced leaves, heavy layers of cutin on their leaves and stems, and extensive development of water storage tissue. How would Darwin explain the evolution of these plants? How would de Vries?

30

Ecology and
Distribution of Plants

Plants are dynamic organisms that, like animals, possess the fundamental protoplasmic property of irritability and that are, therefore, affected in many ways by the continually shifting factors of their surroundings. The study of living organisms in relation to their environment is called **ecology.** Although the following discussion deals primarily with plants, it should be kept in mind that animal populations form integral parts of biotic associations. **Plant ecology** is a branch of botany that endeavors to determine the effects of environmental influences upon such things as the form and activities of individual plants and plant parts, the migration and distribution of plant species, and the formation and distribution of plant communities.

Ecology aims also, through application of its body of knowledge, to give practical aid to the science of conservation of natural resources and thus contributes to the control of soil erosion, reforestation, restoration of wild animal life as well as of grassland vegetation, and flood control, all of which are fundamentally ecological problems.

Ecology is one of the most expansive and intricate fields of biology: it involves the consideration of exceedingly complex factors and relationships, and its searching and discriminating study requires extensive field experience and a formidable background in taxonomy, plant physiology, chemistry, geography, geology, meteorology, and soil science.

According to many ecologists, the basic vegetational unit is the **community,** a group of plants living together in a particular environment or habitat. Communities vary greatly in area; for example, a grassland or forest community may cover thousands of acres whereas a lichen or moss growing on a rock may form a community that covers less than a square inch. Within a community, the organisms have mutual relationships among themselves and their environment. The characteristics of a community are influenced to a considerable degree by three intracommunity relationships: **competition** for various factors such as light, water, and nutrients, which are usually in limited supply; **stratification,** the layering that results from differences in the size of mature plants, for example, the trees, shrubs, and herbs of a forest community; and **dependence** of some species upon the community structure for their survival as illustrated by herbs that grow only in dense shade and by epiphytes that grow on tree trunks and branches.

One of the most striking features of plant life is the fact that different kinds of plants grow in different places under different kinds of environmental conditions. Black willows, for example, grow principally along the banks of streams and the margins of lakes; cattails thrive only in swamps or in the marshy borders of lakes or in moist ditches; sunflowers are plants of open, sunny, moderately dry regions; and cacti are typically inhabitants of arid and semiarid areas. Each species and its distribution pattern represent an intricate adjustment among genetically controlled morphological and physiological tolerance limits and the selective forces of the environment. A species is eliminated from a particular habitat if any one of the environmental factors exceeds the physiological tolerance limits to which that species is genetically adapted.

Some species grow and reproduce in only a few areas where the environmental factors comprising each habitat are quite similar; these species, such as California redwood, some ferns, and many herbs, have narrow tolerance ranges while other species are much more widely distributed and thus grow in a diversity of habitats. Widely distributed species such as big bluestem grass, ponderosa pine, and quaking aspen are commonly spoken of as species having wide tolerance to variations in factors such as light intensity, soil moisture, soil acidity, and temperature. Experimental data show that the individuals of a given widespread species are often grouped into genetically distinct populations that are physiologically adapted to particular habitats. Such populations are called **ecotypes.** The recognition of ecotypes and ecotypic variation is an important part of ecology for it helps explain how the populations of a species can grow and reproduce in quite different habitats. In certain species, ecotypes are known to occur in response to differences in soils, photoperiod, and temperature.

THE FACTORS THAT INFLUENCE PLANT DISTRIBUTION

The factors that have been, or are, important in determining the distribution of different kinds of plants may be classified into two major categories:

Factors of the Past. As described in the chapter on evolution, the distribution of plants on the earth is in part a result of major geological transformations in the earth's history. The fact that long-isolated islands, such as those of Hawaii, have floras that are very different from floras in other parts of the world; the great similarities between the plants of the more southerly islands of the West Indies and those of northern South America; the occurrence in the climatically similar desert regions of the southwestern United States and of South Africa of entirely different species of plants; and the fact that certain species that grow in the high New England mountains also grow in the far north of Canada and Greenland but not in central and southern Canada—these are a few examples of features of plant distribution that can be explained only upon the basis of long-term climatic and geological phenomena of past ages. Among the important geological events that have influenced the distribution of plants have been the upthrust of high mountain ranges, the emergence and subsidence of land masses beneath the surfaces of seas, and the advance and retreat of glaciers. Geological phenomena, together with associated changes in climate, have resulted in the formation of **barriers** and **highways** that have restricted or facilitated the dispersal of various species of plants, and they have frequently brought about changes that have resulted in the extinction of many species in certain regions. In the study of plant distribution, particularly over rather large areas, a knowledge of the geological and climatic history of these areas is prerequisite to an interpretation of the observed facts of distribution.

Contemporary Factors. These factors, which at the present time are affecting the daily growth, reactions, and distribution of living plants, may be separated into four groups:

a. *Climatic factors*—those that act upon plants through the atmosphere: temperature, precipitation, light, wind, and humidity.

b. *Edaphic factors*—those that act upon plants through soils: soil moisture, soil air, soil temperature, soil reaction, soil nutrients, etc.

c. *Biotic factors*—those that involve relations with other kinds of plants and with animals.

d. *Fire*

In this discussion of factors influencing plant distribution, emphasis will be placed upon the contemporary ecological factors.

Climatic Factors

Temperature. The climatic factors that are most influential in affecting the distribution of plants are temperature and moisture. Different species grow best and reproduce within different ranges of temperatures. Thus, many temperate zone trees and shrubs are commonly able to endure high summer and low winter temperatures, while woody plants from the tropics are killed when the temperatures to which they are exposed approach the freezing point of water. In most plants, the minimum and maximum temperatures through which active physiological processes continue are in the vicinity of 35°F to 110°F, respectively. Certain algae grow and reproduce in snowbanks at temperatures lower than 35°F, while certain other algae live in 170°F water in hot springs. Temperature variations influence the rates of all physiological processes and may even affect them qualitatively. The production of flowers and the formation of seeds in many species of plants are likewise directly influenced by temperature conditions of the environment. Thus, temperature may be a factor in determining survival or extinction of plants within a given area, in part through direct effects upon vegetative processes, in part through its effects upon reproduction. For example, in Illinois, mistletoe, which is sensitive to low temperatures, grows only in the extreme southern part of the state. Following very mild winters, mistletoe plants may extend their range northward. Severe winters kill the plants that have begun to grow in more northerly districts after mild winters, and thus fix the northern limit of the mistletoe at the extreme southern end of the state.

Precipitation. Precipitation is the moisture that falls to earth in the form of rain, snow, sleet, and hail. Only a portion of this moisture enters soils and becomes available to plants; the rest runs off the surface into streams and is evaporated, or it enters the soil and moves down to the water table. The distribution of plants is greatly affected by the amount of available soil moisture, some species surviving in regions of 4 to 6 inches of annual precipitation while others grow only where 60 to 80 inches occur. Seasonal distribution of precipitation is frequently more important than the total amount. The vegetation will be more luxuriant in an area where much of the total precipitation occurs in summer than in another area where much of an even higher total precipitation occurs in winter and the summer has one or more dry spells. The ecological importance of soil moisture will be discussed in greater detail in the section on edaphic factors.

Light. Light influences the growth and distribution of plants through its effects upon photosynthesis, transpiration, enzyme action, the production of flowers, soil temperatures, rate of water absorption, and numerous other processes. Light is ordinarily less important than temperature and moisture in influencing the distribution of plants over wide regions, but within limited areas, as for example, on a hillside, a forest floor, or in a deep ravine, it is an exceedingly important factor. Just as various species of plants are physiologically adapted to different ranges of temperature and soil moisture, so are they adapted to different ranges of light intensity and duration. Many plants thrive in diffuse light that has only 5 to 25 percent of the intensity of full sunlight; these plants include many species of ferns, mosses, and late spring- and summer-blooming woodland wildflowers, such as lady-slipper orchids, hydrophyllums, geraniums, and the seedlings of numerous forest tree species. Other species grow best and produce abundant seed only in open areas such as grasslands, pasture, and cut-over forest land; prominent among them are big bluestem grass, Indian grass, many composites such as sunflowers, rosin weeds, asters, and many species of the milkweed, spurge, and legume families. Shade tolerance or intolerance of a species results largely from its relative efficiency of photosynthesis at low light levels.

Light exerts an important effect upon plant distribution through its influence upon flowering. Some plants are adjusted to a long-day photoperiod and will flower only in high latitudes (for example, northern Alaska, Canada, southern Argentina) where the days are very long in summer. Other species are short-day plants and will flower only under the short-day conditions of low latitudes or in the spring or fall seasons of mid-latitudes. A third group of plants is day-neutral, flowering in response to factors other than day length. Short-day plants are seldom able to flower when grown in high latitudes; conversely, long-day plants of high latitudes usually do not flower when they grow under the short-day conditions of lower latitudes. Thus, light duration exerts great influence upon the reproduction and distribution of many plants. Photoperiod also influences leaf fall and the seasonal activity of cambium in many tree species.

Wind. At high mountain elevations and similar exposed positions, strong winds may exert marked mechanical effects upon plants, bending and twisting them grotesquely. High wind velocity, coupled with low winter temperatures and consequent difficulty of water absorption, is a factor that sets the upper limit (timber line) at which trees are able to grow, and is thus important ecologically. The major physiological effect of wind upon plants is to increase their rates of transpiration.

Plants are able to grow successfully only so long as they can balance their water income with water outgo; if transpiration exceeds absorption for a prolonged period, wilting and death are inevitable. Plants vary greatly in the degree to which they can maintain this balance; those species that are most sensitive to the drying effects of winds and that are unable to increase their rate of water absorption are less likely to survive than species that are less susceptible to wind action and that are able to absorb water more effectively. Winds may also influence the distribution of plants through their effects upon the soil in which plants are growing. High winds cause shifting of light soils and thus prevent many kinds of plants from becoming established in such substrata. Ordinarily, only perennials with deep, much-branched roots and with well-developed underground rhizomes, or stolons, grow successfully upon sand dunes and other types of shifting soils.

Winds are important along sea coasts, where they not only affect transpiration rates but also produce salt spray from the ocean. Species have different salt spray tolerance limits and thus there are zones of vegetation along coastal areas; grasses are frequently found nearest the shore, followed by shrub and finally forest communities.

Humidity. The amount of water vapor in the air has a profound effect upon the rates both of evaporation from the soil and of transpiration. The combination of high temperatures, winds, low precipitation, and low humidity results in very sparse vegetation in some desert areas, while regions that have higher precipitation and higher humidity support much more luxuriant vegetation.

The presentation thus far would indicate that these factors act independently of each other when, in reality, they usually operate together. **Factor interaction** can best be illustrated in such physiological processes as transpiration and photosynthesis, the rates of which depend in part upon available soil moisture, air temperature, humidity, wind, and light intensity.

Edaphic Factors

Soil Moisture. Edaphic factors are those that act upon plants through the soil; of these, soil moisture is of prime importance. Available soil moisture is influenced by many conditions; for example, size and nature of soil particles, rate at which water infiltrates the soil, internal drainage characteristics, amount and distribution of precipitation, and the kinds of plants occupying the site. Water-holding capacity of a soil is largely dependent upon soil particle size. Soils with high sand content hold much less water than do soils high in silt and clay, because the total surface area and interparticle space is greater in a silt or clay soil. Organic content also increases water-holding capacity of soils. This helps to explain why sandy soils even in regions of adequate precipitation often support desertlike vegetation. Not all the water held within a soil is available to plants; the available water is only that portion between **field capacity,** which is the maximum amount of water the soil can hold against the force of gravity, and **permanent wilting percentage,** which is the water left in the soil at the time plants become permanently wilted. This available water is held in the capillary pore spaces in the soil and is frequently called **capillary water.** For most temperate region plants, permanent wilting percentage occurs at about 15 atmospheres; that is, the plants can remove water in sufficient quantities to replace transpirational losses until the water is held with forces equal to 15 atmospheres. Some of the remaining water may be absorbed by roots, but not rapidly enough to prevent permanent wilting. Desert plants, however, and those plants that grow in soils with high soluble salt content can remove water until forces in excess of 100 atmospheres are developed. This is an important adaptation mechanism that permits these plants to grow in habitats where soil water is held by forces that are beyond the water-absorbing limit of most plants.

The combination of temperature, precipitation, and available soil moisture plays the major role in determining the broad features of plant distribution upon the earth's surface. Thus, the most luxuriant vegetation occurs in those regions in which temperatures and available soil moisture are high throughout the year, as in the tropical forests of southeastern Asia, central Africa, and South America. If temperatures are high but soil moisture is not readily available, vegetation is sparse, as in the desert areas of Mexico, southwestern United States, and northern Africa. In northern Alaska, northern Canada, and Greenland, precipitation is adequate but temperatures are low. These conditions limit the vegetation to lichens and mosses, short grasses, sedges, and dwarf shrubs. Within a rather small area having topographic relief, considerable differences can be found in temperature, humidity, soil moisture, and soil drainage so that exposed ridges with thin soils support only scrub forests of oak, while moist ravine slopes that are cooler and soils that hold more water support a more luxuriant forest. This again shows the importance of factor interaction. The relationships between plant growth and the available-water content of soils are so striking that plants may be grouped into four categories, already described in an earlier chapter, namely, **xerophytes** (Figure 30–11), which survive and live under conditions of scanty available soil moisture (examples: cacti, agaves); **hydrophytes** (Figure 30–1), which live partly or wholly in water (example: water lilies); **mesophytes** (Figure 30–9), which grow in soils with moderate supplies of available moisture (examples: elms, corn, wheat, petunias, maples); and **halophytes,** which grow in soils that may contain abundant water but that have high concentrations of soluble salts (examples: greasewood, shadscale).

Soil Air. The air content of soils is of great importance, particularly in root growth and seed germination. Actively growing roots require oxygen in considerable quantities for their respiration and usually become stunted or otherwise abnormal when the oxygen content of the soil is reduced. The roots of most mesophytes and xerophytes are especially sensitive to oxygen deficiencies in soils, whereas the roots of most species of hydrophytes are able to grow in apparently normal fashion even when the oxygen supply of the substratum is very low. The oxygen content of soils is also an important factor in seed germination, for germinating seeds respire rapidly and ordinarily require large amounts of oxygen. Again, hydrophytes are somewhat of an exception to this generalization, for many of them (for example, water lilies, cattails) have seeds that are able to germinate in very low oxygen concentrations, which would inhibit the sprouting of seeds of most other plants. The oxygen content of the soil air is important also in the activities of bacteria, fungi, worms, and

(Photo by Missouri Botanical Garden.)

FIG. 30–1. Water-lilies (*Victoria* and *Nymphaea*), true hydrophytes.

other soil organisms that require oxygen for their respiration. Carbon dioxide content in some soils may attain levels that are toxic to plants. This is especially true of soils that remain flooded for periods of time.

Soil Temperature. Soil temperatures are an edaphic factor of importance in the ecological relationships of plants, particularly when temperatures are low, for low temperatures reduce the rate of absorption of water and solutes and growth of roots. One of the reasons why many kinds of evergreen trees cannot be successfully grown in those parts of the middle latitudes with only moderately cold winters is the fact that air temperatures on winter days are frequently high enough to promote rather rapid transpiration, while soil temperatures are sufficiently low to retard water absorption. In such circumstances, evergreen trees frequently grow very slowly or die as a result of an excess of water outgo over water income. Soil temperatures are affected

by air temperatures, the intensity of sunlight, the angle at which sunlight strikes the soil, the daily duration of sunlight, the amount of moisture in the soil, and by other factors.

Soil Reaction. Another edaphic factor that influences the growth and distribution of plants is the reaction of the soil, that is, its degree of acidity or alkalinity. The principal importance of this factor probably lies in its effect upon the solubility and, therefore, the availability of various soil nutrients.

Soil Nutrients. The nature and availability of the soil solutes is fundamentally important from the standpoint of plant nutrition. Only when all the essential elements are present can green plants grow in normal fashion. Although all green plants apparently require approximately the same ions for their normal development, different species require them in varying quantities; thus, certain soils support the growth of some species of plants better than they do other species.

Biotic Factors

The growth and development of all living organisms are influenced by the activities of other living organisms, as well as by climatic and edaphic factors. These biotic relationships are the most complex in the myriad ecological phenomena of living organisms. Not only do various species of plants affect the development of other species, but there are also intimate inter-relations between plants and animals. Thus, any ecological investigation that concentrates upon plants and neglects the relations of those plants with animals can present only an incomplete analysis. Similarly, an animal ecologist who fails to consider plants in his studies can see only a limited portion of nature's canvas.

Competition. Individual plants of the same species and plants of different species compete for soil moisture, soil nutrients, light, and space for shoot and root development so long as the supply does not meet or exceed the requirements of the individuals. Usually, competition for one or several of these factors is most pronounced between individuals of the same species. One of the reasons why **weeds** are undesirable is that they absorb considerable quantities of water and thus rob the soil of moisture that might be absorbed by the cultivated plants with which weeds compete. Weeds compete with cultivated plants also for soil nutrients, for space, and for light. Morphological features, such as depth of root systems, number of root branches, and development of water storage tissues, and physiological characteristics, such as rate of transpiration, rate of water absorption and rate of growth, are factors that determine what species of plants will survive under a given set of environmental conditions and what species will succumb. The natural competition among different species and among individuals of the same species is an important factor in checking the growth of populations; Charles Darwin recognized this significant feature of competition and incorporated it into his Natural Selection Theory of evolution.

Parasitism. Parasitism is a biotic relationship that influences strikingly the development and distribution of plants. Serious infections by virulent fungous parasites interfere with photosynthetic activity and thus indirectly reduce the numbers and impair the quality of seeds produced, a result that in turn retards the efficiency with which the infected plants propagate themselves. Especially serious parasites, such as the chestnut blight fungus and the Dutch elm disease fungus, have changed the community composition of numerous forests in the eastern United States by destroying all their host plants. Moreover, it seems probable that such parasitically induced changes in biotic communities have been of regular occurrence over a long period of geologic time.

Symbiosis. Akin to parasitic relationships are symbiotic relationships. The term **symbiosis** merely means "living together" and in this broad sense may be applied to all intimate relations among living organisms, including parasitism. Symbiosis is commonly used in a more restricted sense, however, to refer to a biotic relation in which the organisms live together more commonly than they live apart and in which this relationship seems to be mutually beneficial. Symbiotic relationships are numerous; lichens, for example, are regarded as symbiotic associations of algae and fungi, in which the fungi receive food from the algae and the algae possibly receive water, mineral nutrients, and protection from the surrounding hyphae. The nitrogen-fixing bacteria

(*Photo by C. F. Hottes.*)

FIG. 30–2. *Tillandsia* (Spanish moss), an epiphyte growing on the branches of trees. *Tillandsia* is a member of the pineapple family.

that inhabit nodules of leguminous roots live apparently in a symbiotic relationship of mutual benefit with their hosts; these bacteria convert nitrogen of the air into nitrogenous compounds in the soil, which ultimately become a source of nitrate for higher plants, and, in turn, the bacteria receive food from the roots in which they live.

Epiphytes. Another interesting biotic relationship is seen in the growth of **epiphytes** (Figure 30–2) upon other plants. Epiphytes are hitchhikers of the plant world; they grow upon the limbs of trees and other plants, upon wires and wire poles, and roofs of buildings, particularly in warm, humid regions. Most epiphytes are chlorophyllous and manufacture their own food, and thus do not rob the plants upon which they grow of food. They obtain carbon dioxide and some moisture from the humid air, and their roots absorb some moisture and nutrients from the wind-borne debris that collects about them and in the crevices of the bark over which they grow. Many species of orchids, mosses, ferns, lichens, and members of the pineapple family are epiphytes. Though most epiphytes do not take food from the bodies of the plants upon which they grow, they may constitute a source of injury, for they shade the leaves of their supporting plants and frequently, because of their weight, cause limbs to break and fall.

Interrelationships of Plants and Animals. The broadest and most inclusive of the various approaches in ecology is that which treats the community and its environment as an interacting, functional unit or **ecosystem.** Many studies at this level are concerned with the mutual relationships and exchange of materials within an ecological system. The principal

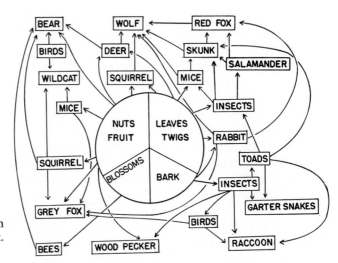

FIG. 30–3. Food chain in an Illinois deciduous forest. (After Shelford.)

components of an ecosystem may be conveniently classified as follows: (1) **abiotic components,** which include the physical and chemical factors of the nonliving environment, (2) **producers,** or autotrophic organisms, (3) **consumers,** chiefly animals that ingest other organisms, and (4) **decomposers,** those heterotrophic organisms such as bacteria and fungi that utilize organic compounds, eventually releasing simpler substances that can be used by producers and thus be recycled. Autotrophic plants, the producers, form the base within the ecosystem, since all animals depend directly or indirectly upon green plants for food. Animals, the consumers, may be divided into primary consumers or **herbivores,** such as cows, horses, rabbits, and mice, each of which derives nourishment (energy) directly from plants, and **carnivores,** such as weasels, foxes, and wolves, each of which obtains its food wholly or largely from herbivores. The nutritional relationships among plants and animals are often extremely complex and constitute an important field of ecological research. Ecosystem studies may emphasize the investiga-

tion of energy transfer from one food level **(trophic level)** to one or more higher levels, for example, from producers to herbivores to carnivores. Other ecosystem studies may focus upon the growth of organisms in each trophic level and attempt to relate growth rates to various biotic and abiotic factors. In general, the number of organisms decreases while the average size of the individuals increases at successively higher trophic levels. The intricate nutritional relationships among organisms within an ecosystem are sometimes called **food chains.** Food chains may be traced wherever animals and plants live: in rivers, lakes, oceans, deserts, grasslands, deciduous forests (Figure 30–3) and all other aggregations of plants and animals. Man is, of course, the terminal link in many food chains, for he directly consumes various plant products, and he eats also the flesh of cattle, hogs, birds, fish, crabs, oysters, deer, and other animals, which in turn obtained their nourishment and built up their tissues at the expense of plants or smaller animals, or both.

The complexity of biotic relationships

that exist within the food chain of a forest ecosystem and the tremendous imbalance that can occur within such an ecosystem can be illustrated with the following example. In a spruce forest, as a result of severe windstorms, most of the woodpeckers normally resident there disappeared. The disappearance of the woodpeckers, which feed upon bark beetles, removed a natural check upon these insects, so that they multiplied rapidly and attacked the spruce trees. The dead trees, killed by the beetle infestation, then burned as a result of a lightning stroke. The destruction of the forest by this fire exposed the soil to the erosive effects of heavy rains with these results: the top soil was washed away, streams down the valley were silted, and floods inundated rich farm lands and towns hundreds of miles away.

Another example of complex biotic relationships may be found in the overgrazing of considerable areas by deer on the north rim of the Grand Canyon in Arizona. At various times, government hunters, in order to protect livestock herds, killed many of the mountain lions in this forest, and sportsmen on occasion have been permitted to hunt these lions in the forest. As a result, many lions, which prey upon deer, were killed, and the removal of this natural check upon deer resulted in enormous increases in the deer population in this area. This population increase taxed the natural feeding resources of the forest beyond their limits to provide feed, and thousands of deer starved. Further, the excessive grazing by the increased deer population killed many plants and led to widespread soil erosion. The study of food chains is intriguing scientifically and valuable economically, since the restoration and maintenance of wild life depends

upon a knowledge of the feeding habits and nutritional relationships among animals and plants.

The decomposers (saprobes and saprophytes), which attack the complex substances that constitute the bodies of plants and animals and their wastes, form an integral part of the ecosystem, for the decay process releases water, carbon dioxide, ammonia, nitrates, and other substances. The carbon dioxide is used again in photosynthesis while other end products of decomposition are the source of essential elements absorbed by green plants. The complex transformations involved in the cycling of carbon and nitrogen are presented in graphic form in Figure 30–4. The amounts of nutrients and the time required for their cycling are important aspects of some ecosystem studies.

Animals are important biotically as carries of many kinds of seeds, as has been pointed out in an earlier chapter. Birds eat many types of fruits and seeds; some of the seeds pass through their digestive tracts and are distributed with their feces. Many mammals also eat fruits and seeds and thus aid in seed dissemination. Animals with furry coats frequently carry the spiny or barbed seeds and fruits of cocklebur, beggar-ticks, and other kinds of plants for great distances and thus unwittingly (sometimes probably wittingly if they brush against seeds with large, sharp spines!) distribute plants over considerable areas.

The presence or absence of flower-pollinating insects is an important biotic factor influencing the distribution of plants, for most species of angiosperms are insect pollinated and are therefore dependent upon pollinating insects for their production of seeds. Fluctuations of insect populations thus affect the seed crop of many

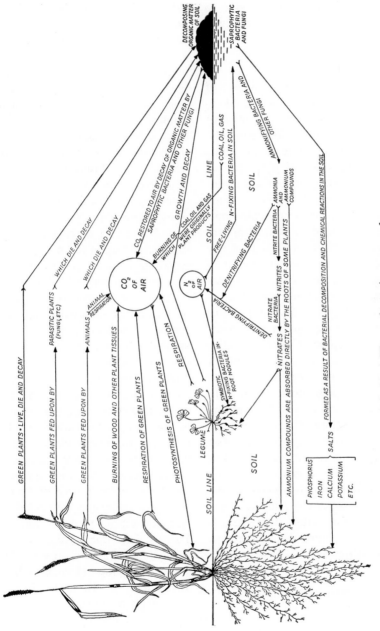

FIG. 30–4. The carbon-nitrogen cycle.

plants and thus influence the degree to which plants may propagate themselves.

Fire

Whether it is the result of lightning, of volcanic activity, or of human carelessness, fire destroys thousands of acres of forest and shrub vegetation annually, kills wild animals of these areas, alters the chemical and physical properties of soils, and thus exerts profound and extensive ecological effects. Fire is one of the major factors that destroys stable communities and thus leads to ecological succession (see the following section of this chapter). Fire is an important factor in maintaining particular kinds of vegetation such as the low evergreen shrub communities (chaparral) that cover lower slopes of many mountains in California. Fire is also an important factor in maintaining the general boundary between forest and grassland in regions of Illinois, Wisconsin, Iowa, and other states. With the elimination of most fires, open groves of trees become closed forest communities. Moreover, forest species are then able to invade more or less unbroken grassland. Carefully controlled burning is used to maintain pine forests in the coastal plain of the south Atlantic states where the economic return from pines is greater and more rapid than the return from deciduous forests.

PLANT SUCCESSION AND CLIMAX VEGETATION

Plant communities are constantly changing. At times these changes are great, one community type replacing another community type on the same site; such sequential changes are termed **succession.** Plant succession is frequently a slow proc-

ess and thus cannot be readily observed unless one visits frequently the same area over a period of years. Succession is very evident in abandoned pasture and cultivated lands (Figure 30–5) and in burned or lumbered forests. Such conditions as these exemplify **secondary succession,** since the dominant, established species of the community have been extinguished and are being replaced by different species. **Primary succession,** on the other hand, involves the establishment of plants upon substrata that had not previously supported vegetation, for example, upon bare rocks, upon newly formed river islands, and upon the new substrata provided by volcanic activity, glacial recession, and the natural filling in of lakes.

High in importance among the numerous causes of succession are the modifications of a habitat by the plant community, thereby making that habitat more suitable for another, dissimilar community. One such modification is increased amount of shade. The succession of communities from grasses and other herbaceous plants to coniferous forests to forests of deciduous trees is strongly influenced by the shade tolerance of different species. As was mentioned earlier, the shade tolerance of many species is closely associated with relative photosynthetic efficiency under reduced light. This efficiency largely determines whether seedlings of a given species will survive in shaded conditions such as those on a forest floor or elsewhere. Thus, knowledge of photosynthetic efficiency for certain species during the course of succession contributes much to our understanding of why certain species replace other species. Another community-induced modification is the accumulation of plant debris on and in the soil. Incorporation of plant debris produces sig-

(*Photo by L. C. Bliss.*)

FIG. 30–5. Loblolly pine becoming established in a field of broom-sedge grass, an early stage of secondary succession on abandoned farm land in the Piedmont of North Carolina.

nificant changes in the soil's organic content, nutrient content, reaction, and water-holding capacity. Other causes of succession include climatic changes, changes in land surface by erosion, and changes resulting from different life cycle patterns, for example, increasing dominance of perennial plants in areas where chiefly annual plants have become established. Similar habitats within a region frequently support similar plant communities and, in turn, have similar patterns of succession whereas communities and successional patterns in different habitats are usually different.

In general, there is a tendency for succession to proceed toward a type of community that is somewhat more mesic (adapted to medium amounts of available moisture) than the earlier successional stages; for example, succession on bare, dry rocks and on the margins of

lakes leads toward communities that have more intermediate moisture requirements than either extreme. In most undisturbed areas, succession continues until ultimately a relatively stable community, the **climax community,** becomes established. It will maintain itself with little change so long as there are no major biotic or abiotic alterations in the immediate environment. When a major environmental change occurs that destroys the climax vegetation or throws it out of equilibrium with the factors of the environment, the climax community may be replaced by another type of climax community that may maintain itself under the changed environmental conditions, or the original climax type may become re-established if the original environmental conditions are restored. The destruction of a climax forest by lumbering or by burning usually sets back the succession of communities a number of stages; succession must proceed again before the climax vegetation is re-established. The climax community is characterized largely by the ability of its species to reproduce within the community and to utilize the resources of the environment to the maximum degree.

While directional community changes or succession are quite universal in occurrence, they are not always clear-cut or operative in the same relative proportions. Certainly many of our forest management practices are based upon a knowledge that succession occurs and that sometimes forest types within the successional sequence are of greater economic value than are the climax forest types, especially where time is an important factor. In the southeastern United States, pines can be harvested for pulp every 15 to 30 years, whereas it would take much longer for deciduous forest trees to reach a comparable size.

Man has been a major factor in bringing about environmental changes of such magnitude that some climax associations have been largely or completely destroyed. Forest fires that often result from human carelessness, overgrazing by domesticated animals, wasteful lumbering methods, and unrestricted hunting are examples of the destructive forces loosed by man upon plant communities. Much of the grassland vegetation of the Great Plains has been destroyed by overgrazing and unsuited agricultural methods; the harvest is appalling soil erosion, lost grazing land, dust storms, and unprofitable agriculture. Much of the so-called "sagebrush desert" of the western United States was originally grassland; the climax grasses have now largely disappeared, and only sound scientific management of such lands will ensure the succession that will lead to the restoration of the climax grass associations. The descriptions of the large, natural assemblages of plants **(plant formations)** that follow are essentially descriptions of these formations as they existed 50 to 100 years ago; man's greed and wastefulness have destroyed many of the original features. Bison no longer roam the rolling grassland of the Great Plains, the antelope has virtually disappeared from this grassland formation, mountain goats and mountain sheep are extinct in many parts of the coniferous forest formation, the northern white pine is gone from many of the areas in which it was originally a dominant species, and the redwoods of California might now be approaching extinction, were it not for the valiant efforts of government conservation agencies and private organizations dedicated to the cause of conserving our dwindling natural biological resources.

PLANT FORMATIONS

The constantly changing panorama of vegetation is one of the most striking features seen in traveling across the continent. If one travels from California to Maine, he passes through the scrubby chaparral of the California coast ranges to the pines and fir of the Sierra Nevada, through the sagebrush and shadscale of the cold desert of the Great Basin to the coniferous forests of the Rocky Mountains, across eastern Colorado where the forests give way to grassland that extends as far as Missouri and Illinois, to the broadleaf forests of Indiana and Ohio, to the Maine forests of pine, hemlock, birch, and maple. Accompanying these differing vegetational types are characteristic and distinct animal inhabitants: jack rabbits, prairie dogs, and ground-nesting birds of the Great Plains; bears, deer, and timber wolves of the forested areas; and lizards, desert coyote, and kangaroo rats of desert areas.

These plant formations are the largest vegetational units; when considered with their characteristic faunas, they are termed **biomes.** The concept of the biome emphasizes the interrelations of plants and animals and thus forms a sound basis for the study of ecological problems.

The general nature and extent of formations are determined by many factors, some of which were described earlier in this chapter: temperature, precipitation, available soil moisture and other soil factors, barriers, biotic factors, and past geologic and climatic history. While plant formations have a similar appearance throughout, there are usually floristic variations in different parts of the formation resulting in part from climatic, geologic, and topographic differences; therefore, major subdivisions or **associations** can be recognized. For example, we can recognize oak-hickory, beech-maple, and mixed mesophytic associations within the eastern deciduous forest. The Rocky Mountain coniferous forests may be similarly subdivided into spruce-fir, ponderosa pine and Douglas fir associations.

It should be emphasized that plant formations and their constituent plant associations are usually not sharply delimited, but merge gradually into each other. These transition zones between overlapping communities are termed **ecotones.** Studies of ecotones usually show that there are environmental gradients that coincide with the vegetational gradients, and that the ecotone contains vegetational as well as environmental characteristics of both communities. Ecotones are prominent in Wisconsin, Illinois, and Missouri where grassland and deciduous forest meet, in Northern Canada between

arctic tundra and coniferous forest, and in Colorado and Wyoming where grassland comes in contact with coniferous forests of the mountains. Ecotones can also be seen in the zonation of communities along a river, bog, or lake margin, and numerous other locations.

MAJOR PLANT FORMATIONS OF NORTH AMERICA

1. Tundra. Plant ecologists recognize at least two types of tundra: **arctic tundra,** which begins at the tree limit and extends northward to the permanent ice of arctic regions, and **alpine tundra,** which occurs above the tree line in high mountains of lower latitudes. Arctic tundra is found in northern Alaska and Canada and is characterized by short, cool summers during which the soil may thaw to a depth of only a few feet or less; by summers with very long days or continuous light; and by vegetation composed of grasses, sedges, dwarf shrubs (for example, rhododendron, blueberry, and willow), and many lichens and mosses. Most shrubs over one foot in height are restricted to areas of winter snow cover.

Alpine tundra (Figure 30–7), such as that found in the Rocky Mountains, Sierra Nevada, and a few of the higher New England mountains, differs from arctic tundra by having warmer soil temperatures in summer, a different photoperiodic regime throughout the year, and, frequently, more wind and snow.

2. Coniferous Forest. While the predominant trees of this formation are gymnosperms, they are frequently associated with deciduous, hardwood species. The northern or boreal forests, which form a wide belt extending from Alaska to New England, consist principally of spruce, fir, and birch (Figure 30–8). Boreal forest is

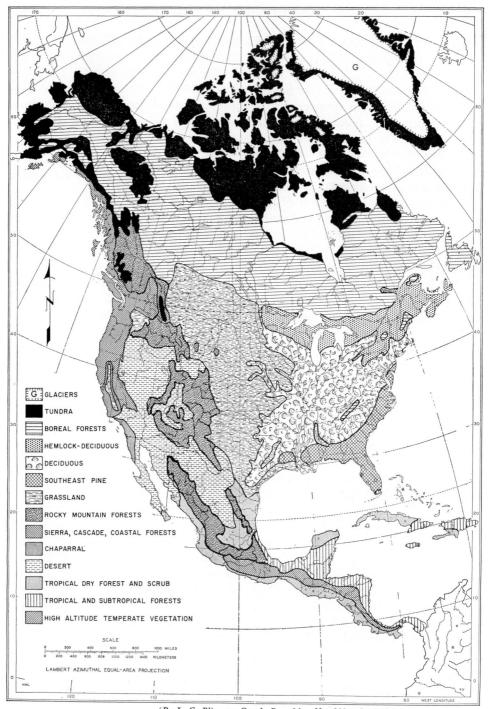

GLACIERS

TUNDRA

BOREAL FORESTS

HEMLOCK-DECIDUOUS

DECIDUOUS

SOUTHEAST PINE

GRASSLAND

ROCKY MOUNTAIN FORESTS

SIERRA, CASCADE, COASTAL FORESTS

CHAPARRAL

DESERT

TROPICAL DRY FOREST AND SCRUB

TROPICAL AND SUBTROPICAL FORESTS

HIGH ALTITUDE TEMPERATE VEGETATION

SCALE

LAMBERT AZIMUTHAL EQUAL-AREA PROJECTION

(*By L. C. Bliss, on Goode Base Map No. 202 published by the Department of Geography, University of Chicago. Copyright by the University of Chicago.*)

FIG. 30–6. Map of the vegetation regions of North America; regions based on information from Braun, Oosting, Porsild, Rowe, and Shantz and Zon.

FIG. 30–7. Alpine tundra at 12,000 feet elevation in Rocky Mountain National Park, Colorado. Most of the plants are less than 6 inches high.

FIG. 30–8. Coniferous forest of spruce and fir at 10,300 feet elevation in the Medicine Bow Mountains, Wyoming.

(Photo by L. C. Bliss.)

FIG. 30–9. Mixed mesophytic forest in the Great Smoky Mountains. Dominant species include basswood, buckeye, hemlock, and sugar maple.

also characterized by short, cool summers and long, cold winters with much snow. Coniferous forests of spruce, fir (*Abies*), Douglas fir (*Pseudotsuga*), and pine also predominate as climax and subclimax vegetation in the mountains of western North America. Because of the low light levels and acid soils within these forests, relatively few herbs and shrubs become established. Pine is one of the dominant species of the extensive subclimax forests in the Gulf states and coastal plain of the southeastern United States. Coniferous forests also occur in the mountains of tropical America.

3. **Decidous Forest.** This formation covers much of the United States east of the Mississippi River. Forest composition is quite variable as would be expected in such a large geographic area with considerable ranges in temperature, precipitation, soils, and topography. The major plant associations within the formation are usually named according to the predominant tree species comprising the various associations; for example, the oak-hickory associations in the drier, western areas and the beech-maple associations on glacial soils in the Great Lakes region. On the moist but well-drained slopes of the Allegheny, Cumberland, and Great Smoky mountains are found mixed mesophytic associations that include basswood (*Tilia*), buckeye (*Aesculus*), hemlock, magnolia, maple, oak, and others (Figure 30–9). **Stratification,** the development of tree, shrub, and herb layers, is usually quite evident in deciduous forest. This formation is also characterized by rather spectacular seasonal changes in the vegetation as a result of the annual loss of leaves.

4. **Grassland.** Grassland is characterized by the dominance of grasses and broad-leaved herbs (Figure 30–10). It extends north from Texas and New Mex-

(*Photo by H. L. Andrews.*)

FIG. 30–10. Manitoba grassland.

ico into southern Canada and from the Rocky Mountains to the deciduous forests in the east; its continuity is broken only by forests along rivers and streams. Near the Rocky Mountains where precipitation is lower, short and medium grasses such as buffalo grass, grama grasses, and western wheat grass predominate, while in Oklahoma, eastern Kansas and Nebraska, Iowa, and Illinois, tall grasses such as big bluestem, Indian grass, slough grass, and little bluestem predominate. Herbs belonging to the legume and composite families are also of common occurrence. The soils that develop in relation to grassland vegetation in a climate of rather limited precipitation produce the richest soils from the standpoint of nutrient and organic content and are today our most valuable agricultural lands. This has resulted in the near elimination of grassland communities in Illinois, Iowa, and westward to the areas of Kansas, Nebraska, and the Dakotas where grazing lands replace cultivated crops.

5. Desert. This formation occurs in central and western regions of northern Mexico and in parts of Arizona, New Mexico, southern California, and adjacent states. Deserts in North America, as in other continents, are confined to areas of low precipitation and high evaporation; consequently, plant cover is frequently sparse. Following the usually brief periods of rain, short-lived, colorful annual plants spring into bloom, produce seeds, and die. The dominant shrubby plants of warm, southern desert include cacti, yuccas, agaves, creosote bush, and mesquite (Figure 30–11). Northern desert areas, such as those in Utah and Nevada, have low winter temperatures—much lower than in southern desert. The dominant shrubs of this so-called cold desert include sagebrush, shadscale, and greasewood. Numerous structural modifications help protect desert plants from excessive water loss, for example, reduction in leaf size and number, loss of leaves during the dry season, complete absence of leaves in some species, sunken sto-

(*Photo by C. F. Hottes.*)

FIG. 30–11. Joshua trees (*Yucca brevifolia*) and other desert plants in the Mojave desert of California.

mata, thick cuticles, and extensive root systems.

6. **Tropical Rain Forest.** In North America, tropical rain forest is limited to continuously warm and moist regions of southern Mexico and Central America and to areas within the West Indies. This formation typically includes a large number of broad-leaved evergreen tree species representing numerous families of flowering plants. These trees grow rapidly and attain great heights; many have broad supporting buttresses extending from their bases. Epiphytic plants and climbing vines are also common in tropical rain forest (Figure 30–12). Stratification within the forest is pronounced and, because of the optimal conditions for growth, plant succession is rapid.

ECOLOGY AND CONSERVATION

The conservation of natural resources in an effective manner may be regarded as a practical application of ecological facts and principles. Conservation programs, which are carried on by various agencies of the United States government and of state governments, by private commercial firms, such as lumber companies, by trade associations, by professional scientific organizations, and by civic groups, are usually planned and executed by trained ecologists. These programs have several objectives: the restoration of grassland in areas in which the grass associations have been destroyed, the reduction and prevention of soil erosion, the increase of populations of deer, mountain sheep, antelope, wild birds, fish, and other animals, the reforestation of lands from which trees have been removed or burned, in order to ensure a continuing supply of lumber, the control of diseases of forest trees, the regulation of water resources to prevent destructive floods and to conserve water for irrigation and the generation of water power, the control of weeds, and

FIG. 30–12. Tropical rainforest in Java. Notice the numerous epiphytes.

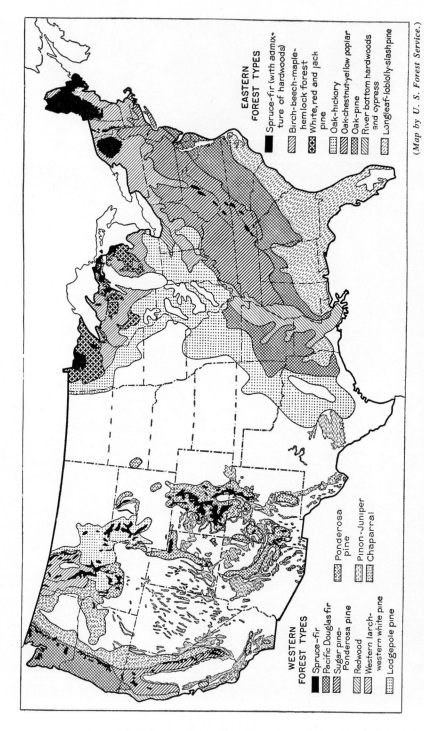

WESTERN
FOREST TYPES

Spruce-fir
Pacific Douglas-fir
Sugar pine-
Ponderosa pine
Redwood
Western larch-
western white pine
Lodgepole pine

Ponderosa
pine
Pinon-Juniper
Chaparral

EASTERN
FOREST TYPES

Spruce-fir (with admix-
ture of hardwoods)
Birch-beech-maple-
hemlock forest
White, red and jack
pine
Oak-hickory
Oak-chestnut-yellow poplar
Oak-pine
River bottom hardwoods
and cypress
Longleaf-loblolly-slashpine

(*Map by U. S. Forest Service.*)

FIG. 30-13. Forest associations of the United States. Note that the forests of the western states are primarily coniferous, evergreen forests, while those of the eastern states are chiefly broad-leaf, deciduous forests.

the improvement and maintenance of recreational areas for the citizens of our country. A knowledge of the growth habits, reproduction, water and nutrient requirements, light and temperature relations, and other features of grasses is essential for a conservationist whose job is to restore grasses in their original environments and to ensure their continued growth and productivity; the soil conservationist must also have a knowledge of the chemical and physical properties of soils and of such meteorological phenomena as rainfall, snowfall, wind action, and annual temperature variations. A forester, who is essentially a tree ecologist, must possess information concerning the identification of trees, their growth habits, their moisture, nutrient, light, and temperature requirements, their insect and fungous parasites, their reproductive peculiarities, their susceptibility to fire, the structure and physiology of their seeds, and their potential yield of economically valuable lumber. A wild-life ecologist must possess knowledge gained by years of study of the habits of wild animals and of the relations between animals and plants; he must be familiar with the feeding habits of, and food sources for, animals, with their reproductive cycles and behavior, their migrations, diseases, and enemies. Farm advisers and agronomists also are ecologists in a sense, and must have information pertaining to crop ecology if their work is to be effective.

Thus, ecology, in addition to its purely scientific value, possesses immeasurable practical significance. As public awareness of the need for conservation practices increases, the demand for thoroughly trained ecologists grows. The future will doubtless bring about an expansion in ecological investigations and applications, and young men who are interested in outdoor life and work will have increasing opportunities to enter upon careers in applied ecology.

⫷⫷⫷ SUMMARY

1. Ecology is the study of the relations of plants and animals with their environments.
2. Plants are grouped together into units called communities.
3. A widespread species may consist of several ecotypes, that is, populations of individual plants physiologically adapted to different habitats within the range of the species. Ecotypic variation is important in understanding the distribution patterns of many species.
4. The distribution of species into various habitats results from the interaction of their genetically controlled physiological tolerance limits and natural selective forces represented by the environment.
5. The contemporary factors of plant distribution may be divided into four categories: climatic factors, edaphic factors, biotic factors, and fire.
6. Climatic factors are those operative through the atmosphere: precipitation, temperature, light, wind, and humidity.
7. The combination of precipitation and temperature is fundamentally important in determining the distribution of the general vegetation of the earth.
8. Different species of plants are variously affected by differences in temperature, moisture, and light.

9. Temperature affects the rate of physiological processes, reproduction, and the survival or death of plants.

10. Moisture availability to plants is determined by the annual amount of precipitation, the monthly distribution of precipitation, and various soil factors.

11. Light affects photosynthesis, transpiration, flowering, and other activities of plants.

12. Winds exert mechanical effects on plants and influence transpiration.

13. Edaphic factors of distribution are those operative through the soil: soil moisture, soil nutrients, soil reaction, soil temperature, soil air, and soil structure.

14. On the basis of availability of moisture in the soils in which they grow, plants may be classified into four types: xerophytes, hydrophytes, mesophytes, and halophytes.

15. Normal plant growth requires readily available moisture and the essential nutrient elements from soils.

16. Soil temperatures influence the rate of absorption by roots and the rate of root growth.

17. Oxygen in the soil air is essential for the normal respiration of roots and of many soil organisms and for the germination of seeds.

18. Ecosystem studies attempt to determine the nature and extent of materials and energy exchange among the component trophic levels, that is, producers, consumers, and decomposers.

19. Plant community changes that are relatively rapid and directional are termed succession. Both primary and secondary succession are recognized.

20. Succession usually proceeds toward a relatively stable climax community that is in equilibrium with its environment.

21. The largest spatial communities are called plant formations; each is characterized by a given growth form, that is, tree, shrub, or herb. Formations are subdivided into associations.

22. Plant formations and their characteristic faunas are collectively termed biomes.

23. The major plant formations of North America are: arctic and alpine tundra, coniferous forest, deciduous forest, grassland, desert, and tropical rain forest.

24. Overgrazing, destructive lumbering, agricultural operations, and fires may destroy climax associations. Man has thus been a major factor in altering the biomes and their associations.

25. The objectives of conservation agencies are the protection of natural resources and their restoration, wherever they have been destroyed. Sound conservation practices are based upon ecological facts and principles.

⫷⫷⫷ SUGGESTED READINGS FOR INTERESTED STUDENTS

1. Daubenmire, R. F., *Plants and Environment,* 2d ed. Wiley, New York, 1959.
2. Odum, Eugene P., *Fundamentals of Ecology,* 2d ed. Saunders, Philadelphia, 1959.
3. Oosting, Henry J., *The Study of Plant Communities,* 2d ed. Freeman, San Francisco, 1956.

4. Sears, Paul B., *Deserts on the March*. University of Oklahoma Press, Norman, 1935.

TOPICS AND QUESTIONS FOR STUDY

1. Define ecology and describe its scope.
2. What subjects should be studied by persons planning careers in ecological work?
3. What is a plant community and what are some of its characteristics?
4. What is the importance of ecotypic variation in understanding the distribution of some species?
5. Name the major climatic factors that influence the distribution of plants, and describe their effects upon plants.
6. Describe the effects of soil factors upon plant growth and distribution.
7. Explain how geographical and geological factors influence plant distribution.
8. Distinguish among hydrophytes, mesophytes, xerophytes, and halophytes, and name some specific plants as examples of each.
9. What is competition? What is its importance in plant distribution? Name some familiar plants in your area that are successful competitors.
10. What is the importance of competition in evolution?
11. What is a weed? Why are weeds undesirable?
12. May a species of plant be regarded as weedy in one area and as a desirable plant in another region? Explain and cite specific examples.
13. Name some parasites that belong to the angiosperms.
14. How have parasites affected the distribution of plants?
15. Define symbiosis, and describe some examples of this phenomenon.
16. Distinguish among producers, consumers, and decomposers.
17. What is a food chain? Trace out some familiar food chains.
18. What is the position of man in food chains? Does man ever form a basal link in a food chain? Explain.
19. Why is the study of food chains important in a practical way?
20. Describe the ways in which animals influence plants.
21. Distinguish among parasites, saprophytes, and epiphytes.
22. What is meant by plant succession? Climax community?
23. What is the difference between primary and secondary succession?
24. What is a plant formation? A biome?
25. What is the relation of an association to a formation?
26. Name the plant formations of North America. What are some of their characteristics? Their important plants?
27. How would you account for the fact that plant formations are not uniform throughout?
28. Describe some of the changes that man has produced in North American biomes.
29. What steps would you take to reverse these changes and to restore these biomes?

30. Name as many specific organizations as you can that are engaged in conservation work.
31. Name and describe briefly the objectives of conservation practices and agencies.
32. Using specific examples, explain how ecological facts and principles are essential to the work of conservationists.

Plants and Man

Throughout this book, emphasis has been placed upon the relations of plants to human life as sources of food, of oxygen, of wood, and of other products. For the most part, these relationships have been mentioned secondarily and incidentally to the discussion of the structure, physiology, and reproduction of various plant groups, and, thus far, no organized account of the principles underlying the effects of plants upon human life has been presented. In the treatment of various lower groups, such as bacteria, fungi, and algae, emphasis was upon the influences of these plants upon human existence; in this chapter, the major emphasis will be upon the significance of seed plants in contemporary life.

The study of the effects of plants upon human life is called **economic botany,** a phase of plant study that crosses into such other fields of human knowledge as history, geography, sociology, chemistry, archeology, economics, and anthropology. Some botanists argue against the use of the term economic botany, since, they aver, all plants have significance in human life. Thus, some of the oxygen you are breathing in as you read this sentence may have been put into the air as a result of the photosynthesis of some moss or liverwort or fern with no direct economic use, and some of the food you have eaten today owes its synthesis in part to the activities of soil bacteria involved in maintaining soil fertility. Accordingly, one may regard all plants as having some economic significance; however, when we speak of economic botany, we usually refer to the study of the more readily apparent and more direct involvements of plants in our lives.

The effects that seed plants exert upon human life may be separated into two categories: **harmful effects** and **beneficial effects.**

HARMFUL EFFECTS OF SEED PLANTS UPON HUMAN LIFE

Certain species of seed plants have harmful or disadvantageous effects upon human life. The benefits that seed plants exert in behalf of man far outweigh their harmful effects; nevertheless, these harmful relations to our lives are sufficiently important to deserve emphasis. Seed plants influence man disadvantageously chiefly in these ways:

1. **Weeds.** As indicated in earlier chapters, many seed plants are weeds that compete with man's field, garden, and orchard crops for space, light, water, and soil nutrients and that, if their growth is not checked, contribute to a reduction in yield or even to the death of man's cultivated crop plants.

2. **Poisonous Plants.** Some species of seed plants elaborate and store in their tissues substances that are poisonous to man and to his domesticated animals. Such plants as deadly nightshade, poison ivy, loco weed, henbane, Jimson weed, death camas, and poison hemlock are responsible for various types of poisoning in man and in his useful animals. The poisoning may be a superficial but nevertheless irritating effect, as in ivy poisoning of the human skin, or, if the plant tissue is eaten, it may produce serious illness or death of human beings, of swine, sheep, cattle, and horses.

3. **Allergenic Plants.** Some wind-pollinated flowers, such as those of ragweeds, some grasses, and various trees, liberate into the air large quantities of wind-borne pollen grains that, in contact with the human respiratory system, induce the physiological reactions known as "hay fever." Although hay fever is rarely fatal, it produces symptoms that bring discomfort and lowered efficiency to persons who are susceptible to these pollens. Other types of allergies in man result from eating certain plant foods.

4. **Narcotic Plants.** Some plants, such as opium poppy, common hemp or marijuana, and the coca plant, store in their tissues organic substances that, when eaten or smoked by human beings, induce physiological and mental aberrations that commonly lead to physical, intellectual, and moral degeneracy and thus produce grave social problems in human life. An interesting feature of certain narcotics is that, in minute and carefully controlled quantities, they may have beneficial medicinal effects in relieving pain, inducing local anaesthesia, and quieting hysteria.

5. **Plants with Harmful Mechanical Effects.** Some species of plants produce fruits with hard, spiny bristles or other types of outgrowths that may cause injury or death in domesticated animals that eat them or come in contact with them (Figure 31–1). Thus, cattle and sheep sometimes eat the bristly fruits of porcupine grass or may, as they browse upon range grasses, inadvertently eat fruits of the buffalo bur; the hard spines of these fruits may puncture the intestines of these animals and thus may lead to infections that cause death. The tough, spiny fruits of the unicorn plant sometimes become embedded in the noses or mouths of grazing animals and may result in the establishment of fatal infections in these wounds.

6. **Parasitic Seed Plants.** As indicated in Chapter 21, mistletoes and dodders parasitize many species of autotrophic seed plants, robbing them of food, decreasing their growth, and often resulting in their death.

BENEFICIAL EFFECTS OF SEED PLANTS UPON HUMAN LIFE

The beneficial effects of seed plants in human life may be subdivided into two categories: **indirect effects** and **direct effects.** The indirect effects involve the growth habits or general physiological behavior of seed plants; they include such

FIG. 31–1. Fruits harmful to grazing animals. *Left:* Unicorn plant. *Right:* Buffalo bur.

phenomena as the prevention or reduction of soil erosion by vegetation, the provision of food and shelter for wild animals, the maintenance of the atmospheric oxygen supply through photosynthesis, and the effects of masses of plants in breaking the force of winds and in influencing atmospheric humidity and temperature. The direct effects involve the products that are formed by seed plants and that are immediately useful to man. In this chapter, only these directly beneficial effects will be considered, for many of the indirectly beneficial effects have been previously described.

The major groups of seed plant products that are directly useful to man are the following:

1. **Foods.** The complete dependence of human beings and of all other animals upon the food synthesized by green plants has received such emphasis in earlier chapters that little additional comment is required. Our cereals (corn, wheat, rice, barley, oats, and rye) are man's basic food plants. They, together with legumes, vegetables, fruits, and nuts, are all products of flowering plants. The edible flesh of cattle, swine, poultry, fish, molluscs, and other groups of animals is produced at the expense of cereal grains, grasses, legumes, algae, and other plants upon which these animals feed.

2. **Fibers.** Fibers are elongated cells, or tightly cohering groups of cells, that are used principally in the weaving of cloth fabrics and in the manufacture of rope, string, thread, nets, and bags. Some fibers, after physical and chemical alteration, are used in the production of rayon, paper, cellulose lacquers, and cellophane. The most valuable plant fibers are cotton, linen (flax), jute, Indian hemp, Manila hemp, sisal hemp, and ramie.

3. Wood and Wood Derivatives. The major direct uses of wood have been described in Chapter 11 and are sufficiently familiar that they require no further discussion. In addition to the common structural and decorative uses of wood, there are many economically valuable products derived from woods that have been subjected to various physical and chemical treatments, such as wood distillation: charcoal, wood alcohol, wood gas, acetate of lime, acetic acid, wood tars and resins, rayon, paper, cardboard, and tannins.

4. Drugs. Although many of the plant drugs used by mankind in earlier periods of history have been supplanted by synthetic drugs produced by organic chemists, and although many plant drugs formerly thought to possess curative properties have been proved worthless, nevertheless there are still many kinds of medicinal substances of plant origin that are extremely valuable in modern medicine. Among these are quinine, used in the treatment of malaria; digitalis, a valuable drug in certain types of heart disease; ephedrine, an important ingredient in nasal sprays; cascara and senna, laxatives; morphine, effective in easing pain; cocaine, used in local anaesthesia; and balsams, soothing and healing agents.

5. Beverages. The study of the history of beverage plants indicates that the human civilizations that arose in different parts of the world developed their own characteristic beverages. Thus, tea was the beverage of eastern Asia, cocoa (or cacao) of the civilizations of Mexico and Central America, and coffee of northeastern Africa and Arabia. These beverages are used by man, partly because they contain mildly stimulating alkaloids, such as caffeine, partly because of their pleasing flavors and aromas. Only one of the world's important beverages has any appreciable food value, namely cocoa, which is also used in the form of chocolate as a nutritious food.

6. Gums and Related Substances. These substances are natural derivatives of cellulose and other carbohydrates and are mucilaginous or sticky when they are wet. Gums swell and dissolve in water, forming viscous liquids used in the manufacture of mucilages and other adhesives, and are used also as binders in medicinal pills, as stabilizing agents that keep solid particles in suspension in liquids, as soothing agents for inflamed mucous membranes (many cough drops and syrups contain plant gums), and as stiffening agents in ice creams, meringues, candies, and other confections.

7. Essential "Oils." Essential "oils" are odoriferous substances that are generally regarded as waste products of metabolism and that occur widely in plant tissues. They are not true oils, but they commonly have an oily texture, and, unlike the true oils, they evaporate rapidly when they are exposed to air. Essential oils are extracted from the tissues in which they develop, and are used by man in many ways. Essential oils from flowers of jasmine, carnation, lavender, roses, and many other plants give pleasing odors to perfumes, soaps, and other cosmetics. Oil of camphor is used in medicinal preparations, in cosmetics, and in the manufacture of celluloid. Oil of citronella is a common ingredient in insect repellents and in cheap soaps and perfumes. The characteristic odors and flavors of such spices as cinnamon, nutmeg, anise, ginger, and cloves, used in flavoring foods and beverages, are attributable to essential oils. Oil of turpentine, from pine wood, is important as a paint solvent, and many other essential oils are employed in deodorants and incense.

8. Resins. Resins are substances that develop in some plants as a result of the partial or complete oxidation of essential oils. Some resins are sticky, viscous liquids, while others are hard, brittle solids. Resins of some species are nearly colorless, others range from pale yellow through shades of orange, red, and brown to black. Some are clear, while others are turbid. Resins frequently resemble gums superficially, but differ from them in their origin and chemical nature and also their solubility; resins are insoluble in water but dissolve readily in alcohol and other organic solvents, while gums dissolve in water and are insoluble in alcohol. Resins dissolved in organic solvents are called varnishes; when the solution is spread out in a thin film, the solvent evaporates, leaving a hard, protective layer of resin. Many resins, such as Canada balsam, balsam of Peru, and benzoin, have valuable medicinal properties and are used in soothing ointments, in cough medicines, and for the relief of nasal congestion. Some resins are used as perfume fixatives, which retard the rate of evaporation of the essential oils responsible for perfume odors and thus prolong perfume fragrance, and others are ingredients of incense and tobacco flavorings. Rosin, a distillation residue of turpentine resin, is used in the manufacture of linoleum, oil cloth, printer's ink, roofing compounds, and paper sizing.

9. Tannins. These are organic compounds of bitter taste that occur in many plant tissues and are usually regarded as metabolic waste products, since they tend to accumulate in dead or physiologically inactive tissues, such as heartwood, cork, and old leaves. Tannins are extracted commercially from bark (mangrove, hemlock, chestnut oak), from wood (quebracho), from leaves (sumac), and from other plant parts. Tannins react with proteins of animal skins in such manner that the skins become and remain soft and pliable (leather); in the absence of this tanning treatment, skins soon become hard, brittle, and unsuited to the manufacture of shoes, bags, belts, and other leather objects. Tannins are used in the manufacture of certain inks, forming blue-black or green-black substances in the presence of soluble iron compounds.

10. Cork. Cork, from the outer bark of a Mediterranean oak, in addition to its familiar use in bottle stoppers, is employed for various other purposes: insulation against sound and against temperature changes, cigarette tips, motor gaskets, flooring, insoles of shoes, etc.

11. Dyes. Dyes extracted from the tissues of seed plants have been used for thousands of years for the coloring of fabrics and skins and for personal adornment. Within the past 80 years, many natural dyes have been supplanted by synthetic dyes prepared by organic chemists, so that the economic importance of plant dyes has been diminishing. Nevertheless, a few plant dyes have persisted as important commodities in world trade, largely because they possess certain qualities not supplied by synthetic dyes. For example, the best and most nearly permanent black dye available is logwood, derived from a tropical American tree, and used in dyeing fine fabrics and in the staining of biological tissues. Indigo, a deep blue dye from plants, is unrivaled in the permanency of its color and is thus still an important natural dye. Fustic, from a tropical American tree, furnishes important yellow, olive, and brown colors still widely used in the dyeing industry. Several plant dyes are commercially valuable in the coloring of foods and beverages, since they are odorless, tasteless,

FIG. 31–2. Trunk of Pará rubber tree, showing tapping cuts and flowing latex.

and without adverse physiological effects upon human beings. Dyes of this type are saffron, a yellow dye used in coloring foods and medicines; annato, a yellowish-orange dye utilized in coloring butter, cheese, and other food products; and chlorophyll, the abundant green pigment of plants, used in coloring foods and beverages.

12. Fatty Oils and Related Substances. These are true oils and fats, synthesized by plants and commonly stored in seeds, fruits, and other parts as reserve foods. Many of these oils, for example, olive oil, soybean oil, corn oil, and cottonseed oil, are important foods in human diets; they are used as cooking oils, in the manufacture of oleomargarine, salad oils, and vegetable shortenings, and in the tinning of fish and meats. Some fatty oils, such as linseed oil and tung oil, dry rapidly upon exposure to air, hardening to form durable films; such drying oils are widely used in the manufacture of paints, linoleum, and printer's ink. Coconut oil, olive

oil, and African palm oil are used in the manufacture of soaps. Oil cloth, artificial leather, putty, glycerine, nitroglycerin, and lubricants are other important products of fatty oils.

Plant fats, which are chemically related to oils but which differ from them in their solidity at room temperatures, include cocoa butter, an important ingredient of cosmetics, confections, and medicinal ointments, and nutmeg butter, used in medicines and candies.

Plant waxes are chemically related to fats and are harvested chiefly from leaves and fruits, on the epidermal layers of which they sometimes occur in considerable quantities. Most valuable of the plant waxes is carnauba wax, from the leaves of a Brazilian palm. This wax is widely employed in the manufacture of candles, wax varnishes and polishes, and phonograph records. A wax that is well known in the United States, though of minor commercial value, is bayberry wax, derived from the fruits of a small shrub native to the northeastern states; bayberry wax is used in the manufacture of candles.

13. Latex Products. Latex, a viscous, milky juice of unknown physiological significance, occurs in several hundred species of flowering plants. The latex of some species contains organic substances that harden upon exposure to air or chemical treatment and that form pliable or elastic solids. Most familiar and most valuable of these is rubber, which, because of its elasticity, pliability, and resilience, is used in hundreds of products of great economic importance: tires, inner tubes, hose, mattresses, shock absorbers, drug and surgical appliances, and many others. Most of the world's natural rubber is a product of the Pará or Brazil rubber tree (Figure 31–2), which is a native of the

Amazon basin and which is widely cultivated in the East Indies, Malaya, and Africa. Another latex product of economic value is gutta-percha, from several species of Asiatic trees; gutta-percha differs from rubber in that it is only slightly elastic; it is resilient and pliable, however, and finds important uses in the insulation of marine and other kinds of cables, in the manufacture of golf balls, telephone mouthpieces and receiver cases, surgical splints and apparatus, and in dentistry for temporary fillings, dentures, and molds. Similar to gutta-percha is balata, a product of a tree native in northern South America; balata is used as a substitute for gutta-percha, and is a common ingredient of machine belting. Another latex product, chicle, chiefly from southern Mexico, Central America, and Venezuela, is the basis of chewing gum.

14. Miscellaneous Products. Among other economically valuable plant products are substances that are smoked and chewed by man for their stimulatory action or their fancied production of relief from nervous tension. Tobacco, of course, is the principal plant product smoked; a native of tropical America, tobacco has reached all areas of the earth inhabited by man, and its cultivation and processing are major industries. Chicle, described in the preceding section, is the major ingredient of chewing gum, one of the world's favorite masticatories. Chewing gum possesses no food value; its use supposedly relaxes nervous tension, stimulates the flow of saliva, and may partially clean the teeth; its use is innocuous, except for its violation of auditory and visual sensibilities. The peoples of the Orient chew betel nuts, the seeds of a palm native to Ceylon and Malaya. The chewing of betel nuts provides a mild physiological stimulation and a feeling of mental well-being, and its effects are no more harmful than those of tobacco; the principal objection to its use is the brownish or maroon discoloration that it imparts to the teeth of the user. In many parts of tropical Africa, the natives chew cola nuts, since they contain caffeine and produce a stimulation comparable with that of coffee.

THE ORIGINS OF CULTIVATED PLANTS

Man obtains many useful products from plants growing in their wild state; among such products are chicle, most resins and gums, balata, most woods, many tannins, and some drugs. Most of man's valuable plant products, however, are derived from plants cultivated in gardens, vineyards, fields, and orchards. Obviously these cultivated plants have had their origins in wild plants that have been domesticated through the centuries of their use by mankind.

Botanists have found the study of the origins of these cultivated plants an extremely interesting one, which has shed much light on purely botanical questions and which has had ramifications in the study of human migrations, of archeology, of anthropology, and of other fields of knowledge. In their investigations of the origin of cultivated plants, botanists have attempted to answer two basic questions: how long has man cultivated various species of economic plants, and where on the earth's surface have these useful plants originated?

The answers to these questions have come from several types of studies and various kinds of evidence, among which these have been especially important:

1. Archeological Evidence. This refers to the evidence derived from the study of past civilizations, such as the Egyptian, the Babylonian, the Aztec, the Mayan,

and the Incan. The excavation of ancient cities, the study of ancient sculptures, mosaics, and paintings, and the opening of tombs of long-defunct royal personages have provided much information about the plants cultivated by these civilizations and about their agricultural practices. The study of such archeological remains and of seeds and plant fragments found in them have contributed to our knowledge of the origins of cultivated plants, from the geographical and time viewpoints.

2. Manuscripts. The translation of manuscripts from various periods of human history has revealed much information about the agricultural practices and the kinds of plants cultivated by ancient and medieval peoples. Ship's logs, diaries, and travel records written by various explorers of the fifteenth and sixteenth centuries contain descriptions of the economic plants and agricultural practices of the Americas; these native American plants were unknown to Europeans before the discovery of America. Similarly, written records of fifteenth and sixteenth century explorations of Asia and the islands adjacent to southeastern Asia revealed much about the native cultivated plants of the Orient.

3. Origins of Plant Names. The names of many cultivated plants are sources of information about the time and places of origin of these plants. Thus, the word avocado is derivative of an Aztec word, maize of a Caribbean Indian word, mango of a Malayan word, sugar of a Sanskrit word, and alfalfa of an Arabic word. These philological evidences are useful in reaching conclusions about plant origins.

4. Distribution of Cultivated Plants. Most species of plants appear to be of relatively limited distribution on the earth's surface.

Thus, when we find a plant cultivated over a wide geographical area, we may reasonably conclude that this plant has been cultivated for a long time by man and that it has been carried by human migrations through the long period of its cultivation. Corn, for example, was cultivated from Argentina to the St. Lawrence river valley shortly after (and probably before) the discovery of America, and, by the beginning of the Christian era, wheat was cultivated from Europe and North Africa across Asia Minor as far east as India. Thus, both corn and wheat are apparently of great antiquity of cultivation.

5. Wild Ancestors. Some of our valuable cultivated plants have never been found in a wild state, some bear no resemblance to any known wild plant species. The absence of a wild ancestor is interpreted as indicating a very ancient history of cultivation; presumably, during many centuries of its cultivation, a cultivated species may have become so changed that it no longer resembles a wild ancestral plant species, or the wild ancestor may have died out. Thus, the absence of wild ancestors of corn and of sugar cane is regarded as evidence of the great antiquity of their cultivation.

6. Radioactive Carbon Studies. Carbon-14, an unstable, radioactive form of carbon, occurs in the earth's atmosphere as a result of the bombardment of nitrogen-14 by cosmic rays. These carbon-14 atoms combine with oxygen to form radioactive carbon dioxide, which becomes mixed in the atmosphere with ordinary carbon dioxide in a constant proportion. In their photosynthesis, green plants utilize some carbon-14 in building carbohydrates and thus all green plant bodies have a fixed proportion of organic compounds containing this radioactive carbon; about 1/trillionth of a gram of carbon-14 occurs with each gram of ordinary, nonradioactive carbon in living plants. When a plant dies, it is no longer utilizing carbon dioxide and thus no longer incorporates carbon-14 into its tissues. Since carbon-14 is unstable, it loses its radioactivity slowly and becomes transformed into nonradioactive carbon. As plant remains (for example, corn cobs and old seeds) age, their proportion of carbon-14 accordingly decreases; the older the plant remains, the lower is the proportion of carbon-14 in them. Thus, physicists, knowing the proportion of carbon-14 in living plant tissues and knowing the rate of carbon-14 disappearance in dead tissues, can estimate the approximate age of any plant fragment, up to about 40,000 years, by determining the amount of carbon-14 in its tissues. This new method of dating plant remains from ancient tombs and city sites is furnishing valuable evidence of the age of certain cultivated plants.

The Origins of Specific Cultivated Plants. Utilizing the above-described evidences, botanists have reached some conclusions concerning the general geographical areas of origin of important cultivated plants and their relative ages of cultivation. These conclusions are summarized in the tables on page 523. There the term Old World refers to Asia, Europe, and Africa; the term New World refers to the Americas (Figures 31–3 and 31–4).

These lists, which are not complete but which include man's most important cultivated plants, indicate three major conclusions concerning the origin of cultivated plants:

1. The number of important cultivated plant species of Old World origin is appreciably larger than the number of cultivated species of New World origin. This may be explained by man's longer residence in the Old World; the human species originated in the Old World, and there carried on agriculture for many centuries before some of its members migrated to the New World. Thus, mankind has had a much longer period of time in the Old World in which to domesticate native plant species of that portion of the earth.

2. Man's most important cultivated plants (for example, wheat, corn, barley, date, kidney bean, soybean, and rice) are his most ancient cultivated plants; those plants that have come into cultivation since the beginning of the Christian era, both in the Old and New Worlds, are for the most part secondary in importance.

3. There is not a single species of important cultivated plant that is common both to the Old World and the New World. This indicates that the first human beings who migrated from the Old World to the New must have been wandering, nomadic hunters, rather than cultivators of plants, for we know that whenever an agricultural people migrates, it always takes with it the seeds of its most important crops. Had these first migrants to the New World cultivated plants, they would inevitably have carried seeds of their cultivated plants with them, and thus we might have expected to find some cultivated species common to both the Old World and the New. There are some genera of cultivated plants common to both Old World and New, for example, grape, cotton, strawberry, and chestnut; but the *species* of these genera are different in the Old and New Worlds.

THE FUTURE OF PLANT EXPLOITATION

Although the study of economic botany indicates that the dependence of man

FIG. 31–3. Important food plants of Old World origin.

FIG. 31–4. Important food plants of New World origin.

Plants of Old World Origin

A. Plants cultivated for at least 4000 years, possibly longer:

almond	fig	peach
apple	flax	pear
apricot	grape (some types)	rice
banana	hemp	sorghum
barley	mango	soybean
cabbage	millet	watermelon
date	olive	wheat
eggplant	onion	

B. Plants cultivated for at least 2000 years, probably longer:

alfalfa	chestnut	pepper (black)
asparagus	citrus fruits	plum
beet	cotton (some types)	poppy
breadfruit	lettuce	radish
carrot	nutmeg	rye
celery	oats	sugar cane
cherry	pea	tea
		English walnut

C. Plants cultivated for less than 2000 years:

artichoke	gooseberry	parsnip
buckwheat	muskmelon	raspberry
coffee	okra	rhubarb
currant	parsley	strawberry (some types)

Plants of New World Origin

A. Plants of unknown antiquity of cultivation, certainly over 2000 years and probably more than 4000 years:

cacao (cocoa)	kidney bean	sweet potato
corn	maté	tobacco

B. Plants of more recent cultivation, some since the beginning of Christian era, others before the Christian era:

avocado	pineapple	rubber
cassava	potato	squash
cotton (some types)	pumpkin	tomato
peanut	red peppers	vanilla

upon plants increases as his civilization becomes more complex, the basic dependence of modern man upon plants is the same as the basic dependence of primitive man, namely, upon plants as the source of his foods. The major prob- lem that now faces man in many parts of the world, in Japan, China, and India, for example, is the basic problem of securing enough food. The advances of medical science in the past century have greatly reduced infant mortality and have significantly lengthened the human life span, so that the world's human population is now increasing at a more rapid rate than at any other time in human history. Within the next century or two, the world's agriculture, as it is now carried on, will probably be inadequate to provide enough food for the human race. Thus, man, if he is to survive, must greatly increase food production by plants. Already economists, botanists, statesmen, biochemists, horticulturists, agronomists, and others are giving consideration to possible methods of increasing the world's food supply. The experiments, observations, and plans of these men indicate that increasing the world's food will involve many different approaches: more effective means of increasing and maintaining soil fertility; more effective methods of soil conservation; increasing the productivity of crop plants by breeding and selection to develop new and better plant varieties; the extension of irrigation projects to bring into agricultural use millions of acres of desert land that now receive insufficient water for crop culture; the breeding of improved types of forage plants and of superior types of meat-producing animals; and increased utilization of food products of the sea, not only of fish and other marine animals, but also the direct use of marine algae as sources of human food. It has been estimated that the total amount of photosynthesis carried on by marine algae may be ten times greater than the total photosynthetic activity of all land plants. If this is true, then man may well look to the plants of the sea as a rich, abundant, relatively untapped source of foodstuffs. In some parts of the world, for example, Japan and China, algae of the sea have for many years been important items in the human diet. These various methods of increasing the world's food supply will require the efforts of many kinds of plant scientists and thus will offer numerous opportunities in research and in production to young men and women in the plant sciences.

⋘ SUMMARY

1. Economic botany is the study of the effects of plants upon human life.
2. Some seed plants exert harmful effects upon human life; among seed plants that exert such effects are weeds, poisonous plants, allergenic plants, narcotic plants, parasitic plants, and plants that cause physical injuries to domesticated animals.
3. Indirect beneficial effects of seed plants upon human life include the prevention of soil erosion, the provision of food and shelter for wild animals, maintenance of atmospheric oxygen supply, and the influencing of atmospheric humidity and temperature.
4. Direct beneficial effects of seed plants upon human life are found in their products that are useful to man: fibers, wood, drugs, beverages, gums, resins, cork, essential "oils," tannins, dyes, fats, latex products, and tobacco.
5. Man's most valuable plants are cultivated plants, which have been derived from wild plants.
6. Evidences used to determine the place of origin and length of cultivation of plants are derived from the study of archeology, of manuscripts, of plant

names, of the distribution of cultivated plants, of the presence or absence of wild ancestors, and of radioactive carbon content of plant tissues.

7. The number of important cultivated plants of Old World origin is larger than the number of cultivated plants of New World origin.

8. Man's most important cultivated plants have been under cultivation for at least 4000 years.

9. There is not a single species of important cultivated plant common in origin to both Old and New Worlds.

10. An exceedingly important problem of man in the next century or two will be the need to increase the world's food supply.

SUGGESTED READINGS FOR INTERESTED STUDENTS

1. Anderson, Edgar, *Plants, Man, and Life*. Little, Brown, Boston, 1952.
2. Dorrance, Anne, *Green Cargoes*. Doubleday, New York, 1945.
3. Hill, A. F., *Economic Botany*, 2d ed. McGraw-Hill, New York, 1952.
4. Schery, Robert W., *Plants for Man*. Prentice-Hall, Englewood Cliffs, N. J., 1952.
5. Wilson, C. M., *et al.*, *New Crops for the New World*. Macmillan, New York, 1945.

TOPICS AND QUESTIONS FOR STUDY

1. Assume that all plant products except foods, fibers, and wood, were withdrawn from human use. What changes in our twentieth century civilization would immediately follow? Would appear more slowly?

2. Make lists of the kinds of plant products that you believe were used by:
   a. Europeans during the tenth century A.D.
   b. American Indians, before the discovery of America by Columbus.
   c. Americans of the thirteen colonies in 1775.
   d. Americans in the year 1850.
   Compare these with a list of plant products which Americans use now.

3. Make a list of plant products that are less extensively used now than they were 100 years ago, and account for the decline in their use.

4. List as many ways as you can in which plant taxonomy may be regarded as "economic botany." Do the same for plant physiology, plant morphology, plant genetics, plant ecology.

5. Name the principal groups of plant products, and economic uses.

6. Make a list of economically valuable plants that are native to the Old World (Europe, Asia, and Africa).

7. How would you account for the fact that most of our economic plants are natives of the Old World?

8. List the economically valuable plants that are native to the Americas.

9. List and describe the evidences used to determine the geographical origin and length of cultivation of economic plants.

10. Assume that you and a small group of your friends are to be transported to an uninhabited island in the South Pacific to live and that you will be permitted to

take seeds of 12 species of plants with you. State which ones you would select and your reasons for your selection.

11. The world's most important rubber-producing plant, the Pará rubber tree, is a native of Brazil, but most of the world's supply of Pará rubber comes from plantations in Sumatra and Malaya. What factors are responsible for this situation?

12. Although certain countries of the American tropics possess vast forests of hardwood trees, they import softwood lumber in considerable quantities from the United States. How would you explain this?

13. Describe the economic and social differences among people engaged in exploiting these differing types of plant resources in the United States: grasslands, forest, orchards, truck gardens, grain cultivation.

Glossary

Important technical terms, such as names of structures and processes, used in the text are included in this glossary. Excluded are names of individual plants and of plant groups. The source languages for the technical terms are indicated by the following abbreviations:

Ar.—Arabic
AS.—Anglo-Saxon
F. —French

G. —German
Gr. —Greek
L. —Latin
ME.—Middle English

OF.—Old French
San.—Sanskrit
Sw. —Swedish

Abscission (L. *abscissus*—cut off): separation of leaves and other plant parts by the dissolution or separation of the cells of an abscission layer.

Abscission layer (L. *abscissus*—cut off): layer of cells that disintegrates and thus separates a leaf or other structure from the plant; separation layer.

Accessory fruit (L. *accedere*—approach): a structure consisting of a true fruit (ripened ovary) plus other parts, such as calyx or receptacle.

Achene (Gr. *achaines*—with a single prong): a simple, dry, one-seeded, indehiscent fruit, with unfused seed coat and fruit wall.

Active transport: absorption of ions as a result of expenditure of energy by living protoplasm and usually against a concentration gradient; ion accumulation.

Active water absorption: the osmotic uptake of water by living cells whose osmotic concentration has been raised by ion accumulation; process responsible for guttation and root pressure.

Adaptation (L. *ad*—to; *aptere*—fit): adjustment to environmental conditions; a structural or functional development that causes such adjustment.

Adenine: one of the nitrogenous bases found in DNA and RNA.

Adsorption (L. *ad*—to; *sorbere*—suck): the adhesion in very thin layers of a substance to the surface of a solid particle with which it is in contact; the particles that adsorb other materials are chiefly colloidal.

Adventitious bud: a bud that develops in some place other than the axil of a leaf or the tip of a stem.

Adventitious roots: roots that do not arise from a hypocotyl, primary root, or one of its branches, but that arise from stems, leaves, etc.

Aeciospores (Gr. *aikia*—injury; *spora*—spore): binucleate spores produced in cup-shaped aecia of some rust fungi.

Aerobe (Gr. *aer*—air, mist): an organism that lives in air containing oxygen.

Aerobic respiration (Gr. *aer*—air, mist; L. *re*—again; L. *spirare*—breathe): respiration in the presence of free, gaseous oxygen.

Aggregate fruit (L. *aggregare*—collect): a cluster of fruits developed from the ovaries of a single flower.

Aleurone grains: particles of protein found in the seeds of some plants.

Alkaloid (Ar. *al-qili*—ashes of salt-wort plant): a nitrogenous organic substance of alkaline (basic) reaction, and usually bitter in taste and poisonous to animals.

Alternate (L. *alternus*—by turns): describing the condition in which a single leaf or bud occurs at a node.

Alternation of generations (L. *alternus*—by turns; *generare*—bring to life): the alternation of a spore-producing phase and a gamete-producing phase in the sexual life cycle of a plant.

Amino acids (L. *Ammon*—referring to the

527

discovery of sal ammoniac in camel's dung near the temple of Jupiter Ammon; *acidus*—sour): organic, nitrogenous acids from which protein molecules are constructed.

Ammonification (L. *Ammon*—see Amino acids; *facere*—make): formation of ammonia following the decomposition of proteinaceous substances by ammonifying bacteria.

Amylase (Gr. *amylon*—starch): an enzyme that hydrolyzes starch to maltose.

Anaerobe (Gr. *an*—not; *aer*—air, mist): an organism that lives in the absence of gaseous oxygen.

Anaerobic respiration (see Aerobic respiration): respiration in the absence of free oxygen, or in the presence of reduced concentrations of free oxygen.

Anaphase (Gr. *ana*—up; *phasis*—appearance): a stage in mitosis in which the newly separated chromatids (daughter chromosomes) move toward opposite ends of the spindle.

Annual (L. *annus*—year): a plant that completes its life cycle and dies within one year.

Annulus (L. *annulus*—ring): a row of specialized cells in the wall of a fern sporangium; contraction of the annulus causes rupture of the sporangium and dispersal of spores.

Anther (Gr. *anthos*—flower): pollen-bearing part of a stamen.

Antheridium (Gr. *anthos*—flower; *idion*—diminutive ending): a structure that produces sperms.

Anthocyanins (Gr. *anthos*—flower; *kyanos*—dark blue): blue, red, and purple pigments of plants; water soluble, as contrasted with plastid pigments.

Antibiosis (Gr. *anti*—against; *bios*—life): physiological antagonism of one organism toward another; used chiefly in reference to such antagonism among fungi.

Antibiotics (see Antibiosis): drugs that are obtained from living organisms (chiefly bacteria and true fungi) and that destroy pathogenic organisms, chiefly bacteria.

Antipodals: three small ephemeral cells within the embryo sac in an ovule.

Antiseptic (Gr. *anti*—against; *sepo*—rot): a substance that inhibits growth and activities of bacteria and other microorganisms.

Apical dominance (L. *apex*—summit; *dominor*—rule): the inhibitory influence of terminal buds upon lateral buds.

Apical growth (L. *apex*—summit): growth occurring at the tip or apex of an organ.

Archegonium (Gr. *archaios*—primitive; *gonos*—offspring): a multicellular egg-producing gametangium.

Ascocarp (Gr. *askos*—bag; *karpos*—fruit): in sac fungi, a structure that produces asci.

Ascogonium (Gr. *askos*—bag; *gonos*—reproduction): the female gametangium of sac fungi.

Ascospore (Gr. *askos*—bag; *spora*—spore, seed): a spore produced by sac fungi in asci.

Ascus (Gr. *askos*—bag): a saclike structure within which ascospores are formed.

Asexual (L. *ab*—away; *sexus*—sex): referring to any type of reproduction that is independent of sexual processes.

Assimilation (L. *assimilare*—make like): the transformation of foods into living protoplasm.

Association (L. *associare*—join): an assemblage of plants, usually dominated by a few species and representing a major subdivision of a plant formation.

Autotrophic (Gr. *autos*—self; *trophe*—food): referring to a plant that is able to manufacture its own food.

Auxins (Gr. *auxe*—grow): a class of growth-regulating compounds.

Avena test: a test for auxin activity, based on the response of living oat (*Avena*) coleoptiles to the growth-regulating compound.

Axil (L. *axilla*—armpit): the upper angle between a twig or leaf stalk and the axis from which it grows.

Axillary bud (L. *axilla*—armpit; ME. *budde*—bud): a bud borne in the axil of a leaf.

Bacillus (L. *baculum*—stick): a rod-shaped bacterium.

Bactericide: any agent used to kill bacteria.

Bacteriostasis: prevention of the growth of bacteria.

Bark (Sw. *bark*—rind): in woody plants, the aggregation of tissues outside the cambium.

Basidiospores (Gr. *basis*—pedestal; *spora*—spore): the spores of basidiomycetes, produced in basidia.

Basidium (Gr. *basis*—pedestal): a club-shaped spore-producing structure of the basidiomycetes.

Berry (AS. *berige*—berry): a simple fruit, the entire pericarp of which is fleshy.

Biennial (L. *biennium*—a two-year period): a plant that produces seeds during the second year of its life, then dies.

Bilateral symmetry (L. *bis*—twice; *latus*—side; Gr. *syn*—together; *metron*—measure): the condition of having distinct and similar right and left sides, as in flowers of sweet pea or snapdragon.

Binomial system (L. *bi*—two; *nomen*—name): a system of naming organisms; a scientific name consists usually of two words, the first that of a genus, the second that of a species.

Biome (Gr. *bios*—life): a large, natural assemblage of associated plants and animals, extending over large regions of the earth's surface.

Bisexual (L. *bis*—twice; *sexus*—sex): describing an organism that produces both eggs and sperms, and a flower that bears both stamens and pistil(s).

Blade (AS. *blaed*—leaf): the expanded portion of a leaf.

Bract (L. *bractea*—a thin plate of precious metal): a modified leaf associated with a flower or inflorescence.

Branch gap: an interruption in the vascular tissue of a stem at the point where a branch trace arises.

Branch trace: vascular tissue that runs from a stem into a branch.

Bud (ME. *budde*—bud): on a stem, a terminal or axillary strucutre consisting of a small mass of meristematic tissue, covered wholly or in part by overlapping leaves.

Bud scale (ME. *budde*—bud; AS. *scale*—bowl): a specialized protective leaf of a bud.

Bud scar (ME. *budde*—bud; Gr. *eschara*—scab): a scar left on a twig by the falling away of a bud or a group of bud scales.

Budding (ME. *budde*—bud): a process of grafting in which the scion is a single bud; also, asexual reproduction of yeasts.

Bulb (Gr. *bolbos*—an enlarged root): a short, usually globose underground stem, bearing many fleshy, food-storing scale leaves; essentially a subterranean bud.

Bundle scars: scars left in leaf scars at the time of leaf fall by the breaking of vascular bundles passing from stem into a petiole.

Callus (L. *callus*—hard skin): a tissue of thin-walled cells developed on wound surfaces.

Calorie (L. *calor*—heat): a large Calorie (kilogram-calorie) is the amount of heat energy required to raise the temperature of 1 kilogram of water 1° Centigrade; a small calorie is the amount of heat energy required to raise the temperature of 1 gram of water 1°C.

Calyptra (Gr. *kalyptra*—veil): in the sporophyte of a moss, a sheath that covers the capsule and that consists of the upper portion of an archegonium.

Calyx (Gr. *kalyx*—cup): collective term for the sepals of a flower.

Cambium (L. *cambium*—exchange): layer of meristematic cells between xylem and phloem tissues; same as vascular cambium.

Capillary water (L. *capillus*—hair): water retained in the spaces among, and on the surfaces of, soil particles after drainage.

Capsule (L. *capsa*—box): a simple, dehiscent, dry fruit composed of two or more carpels; also, the spore case of a moss or liverwort; and a slimy outer wall layer of bacteria.

Carbohydrases (L. *carbo*—coal; Gr. *hydor*—water): enzymes that digest carbohydrates.

Carbohydrate (L. *carbo*—coal; Gr. *hydor*—water): a group of foods composed of carbon, hydrogen, and oxygen, with the hydrogen and oxygen in the ratio of 2 to 1.

Carboniferous period (L. *carbo*—coal; *ferre*—bear): a period of the Paleozoic era, characterized by the formation of great coal beds.

Carotenes (L. *carota*—carrot): reddish-orange pigments found in plant cells.

Carotenoids (L. *carota*—carrot): a class of chemical compounds that includes the carotenes and xanthophylls.

Carpel (Gr. *karpos*—fruit): a modified megasporophyll that bears and encloses ovules.

Carpogonium: female gametangium of a red alga.

Caruncle (L. *caruncula*—fleshy growth): a spongy structure at one end of a seed such as a castor bean.

Caryopsis (Gr. *karyon*—nut; *opsis*—appearance): a fruit characteristic of grasses; the fruit is dry, one-seeded, indehiscent, with the seed coat and pericarp completely united.

Catalyst (Gr. *kata*—down; *luo*—dissolve): a substance that regulates the speed of a chemical reaction without being used up in the reaction.

Cell (L. *cella*—small room): the unit of structure of plants and animals; the essential feature of a cell is its living protoplasm, surrounded in plant cells by a wall.

Cell division (L. *cella*—small room; *dividere*—divide): a process whereby cells reproduce.

Cell plate: a thin partition formed between daughter nuclei in a cell undergoing cytokinesis.

Cell sap (L. *cella*—small room): the liquid in the vacuoles of plant cells.

Cellulose (L. *cella*—small room): a complex carbohydrate forming the major part of the cell walls of most plants.

Centromere (Gr. *kentron*—center; *meros*—part): the constricted portion of a chromosome to which, in mitosis, the chromosomal fiber is attached.

Chemosynthesis (Gr. *chemeia*—chemistry; *syn*—together; *thesis*—setting): a process of food manufacture in certain bacteria, which utilizes energy derived from chemical reactions, such as the oxidation of sulfur, ammonia, etc.

Chemotropism (Gr. *chemeia*—chemistry; *trope*—turn): a growth movement induced by a chemical stimulus.

Chlorophyll (Gr. *chloros*—green; *phyllon*—leaf): a green pigment that occurs chiefly in chloroplasts and is involved in photosynthesis.

Chloroplast (Gr. *chloros*—green; *plastos*—formed): specialized cytoplasmic body containing chlorophyll.

Chlorosis (Gr. *chloros*—green; *osis*—diseased state): failure of chlorophyll development because of nutritional disturbance, such as lack of iron or magnesium, or because of disease.

Chromatid (Gr. *chroma*—color; *idios*—distinct): a chromosome half, formed by a longitudinal duplication of a chromosome.

Chromatin (Gr. *chroma*—color): deeply staining nuclear material of which hereditary determiners are composed.

Chromoplast (Gr. *chroma*—color; *plastos*—formed): yellowish or red cytoplasmic body containing carotene and xanthophyll.

Chromosomal fiber (Gr. *chroma*—color; *soma*—body): in mitosis, a minute strand that connects a chromosome with the spindle apparatus.

Chromosomes (Gr. *chroma*—color; *soma*—body): nuclear bodies of definite structure and number formed from chromatin and bearing hereditary determiners, or genes.

Cilium (L. *cilium*—eyelash): short, protoplasmic extrusion that propels certain types of unicellular organisms, gametes, and zoospores through water. See Flagellum.

Class (L. *classis*—collection): a taxonomic category made up of closely related orders.

Clay (AS. *claeg*—glue): complex, colloidal, inorganic fraction of soil, consisting largely of alumino-silicates; clay particles are usually negatively charged and adsorb positively charged ions.

Climax community: a relatively permanent community that maintains itself with little change in a given region so long as there are no major changes in environmental conditions.

Coccus (Gr. *kokkos*—berry): a spherical bacterium.

Coenocyte (Gr. *koinos*—shared; *kytos*—hollow place): a cell with several to many nuclei.

Coenzymes: the nonprotein portions of certain enzymes.

Colchicine (L. a plant with a poisonous root; named after Colchis, an ancient province in Asia east of the Black Sea): an alkaloid, which, when applied to plants, may cause polyploidy.

Collenchyma (Gr. *kolla*—glue; *en*—in; *chein*—pour): a strengthening tissue, composed of cells with walls usually thickened at the angles of the walls.

Colloid (Gr. *kolla*—glue; *eidos*—form, to pour): a state of subdivision or dispersion in which the particles of the dispersed substance are of super-molecular size and in which the particles do not diffuse (or diffuse with difficulty) through membranes. Colloidal systems are usually more stable than emulsions or suspensions, are usually electrically charged, and are usually turbid.

Colony (L. *colere*—cultivate, dwell): a group of similar organisms living together in close association; more specifically, a group of associated unicellular organisms among which there are no marked structural differences and little or no division of labor.

Companion cells (L. *cum*—together; *panis*—bread; *cella*—little room): elongated cells adjoining sieve tubes in phloem tissue of most plants.

Complete flower (L. *flos*—flower): a flower that bears 4 types of floral organs: sepals, petals, stamens, and carpels.

Compound fruit: see Multiple fruit.

Compound leaf: a leaf, the blade of which is subdivided into several distinct parts.

Compound middle lamella: a collective term for the middle lamella and the primary walls of two adjacent cells.

Compound pistil (L. *pistillum*—pestle): a pistil composed of two or more partially or wholly fused carpels.

Conceptacle (L. *concipere*—receive): in certain algae, a cavity within which antheridia or oogonia are produced.

Cone (Gr. *konos*—pine cone): a specialized branch bearing an aggregation of sporophylls or ovuliferous scales.

Conidiophore (Gr. *konis*—dust; *phoros*—bearer): a hypha that produces conidia.

Conidium (Gr. *konis*—dust): an asexual reproductive structure (regarded by some as a one-celled sporangium) in fungi; usually produced in chains by the terminal portions of hyphae of some fungi.

Coniferous (Gr. *konos*—cones; *phoros*—bearer): having cones.

Conjugation (L. *cum*—with; *jugum*—yoke): a type of isogamous sexual reproduction in which a gamete moves to another gamete through a specially developed connecting tube.

Contact movements (L. *contingere*—touch): turgor movements, chiefly of leaves and floral parts, that result from contact simuli.

Convergent evolution (L. *cum*—with; *vertere*—turn; Gr. *genea*—birth; L. *ex*—out; *volvere*—turn): evolution of unrelated or distantly related groups of organisms along similar lines, resulting in the development of similar traits or features in the unrelated groups.

Cork (L. *quercus*—oak): a suberized tissue formed on the stem and root surfaces (sometimes on other parts) chiefly of woody plants from the cork cambium.

Cork cambium (L. *quercus*—oak; *cambium*—exchange): a meristematic tissue that is formed in woody plants usually from certain cells of the cortex and that produces cork cells and phelloderm cells.

Corm (Gr. *kormos*—tree trunk): a short, often globose, upright, underground stem that stores food; differs from a bulb in that the latter consists chiefly of fleshy storage leaves growing from a small stem, whereas a corm is chiefly stem tissue.

Corolla (L. *corolla*—diminutive of *corona*—crown): collectively, the petals of a flower.

Correlation (L. *cum*—with; *relatus*—reported): the mutual interaction of plant parts and processes.

Cortex (L. *cortex*—bark): primary tissue lying between the epidermis and stele of a stem or root.

Cotyledon (Gr. *kotyle*—cup): a food-digesting and food-storing part of an embryo; also known as seed leaf.

Cristae: internal membrane extensions in mitochondria.

Cross-pollination (L. *pollen*—flour): the transfer of pollen from a stamen to the stigma of a flower on another plant.

Crossing over: the exchange of matching segments of two homologous chromatids.

Crustose (L. *crusta*—crust): closely appressed to the substratum and with a crusty appearance, as in crustose lichens.

Cuticle (L. *cutis*—skin): waxy layer formed on outer walls of epidermal cells.

Cutin (L. *cutis*—skin): waxy substance that is very impermeable to water; the cuticle is composed of cutin.

Cutting: a portion of a stem or leaf used in vegetative propagation as a result of formation of adventitious roots on the cutting.

Cytokinesis (Gr. *kytos*—hollow place; *kinesis*—movement): cytoplasmic division by cell plate formation, usually following mitosis or nuclear division.

Cytoplasm (Gr. *kytos*—hollow; *plasma*—form): all the protoplasm in a cell, except the nucleus.

Cytoplasmic membranes (see Cytoplasm; L. *membrana*—skin): membranes on the surface of cytoplasm and between cytoplasm and vacuoles.

Cytosine: one of the nitrogenous bases found in DNA and RNA.

Daughter cells: cells newly formed as a result of the division of a parent cell.

Deciduous (L. *deciduus*—falling): referring to plant parts that fall off within a year of the time of their production; refers also to plants that lose their leaves regularly each year, as opposed to evergreens, the leaves of which persist for more than one year.

Dedifferentiation: the process by which matured cells, chiefly parenchyma cells, revert to a meristematic condition.

Deficiency disease (L. *deficere*—be wanting): a disease resulting from lack of one or more essential elements.

Dehiscent (L. *dehiscere*—split open): splitting along definite seams at maturity.

Denitrification (L. *de*—off; Gr. *nitron*—saltpeter; L. *facere*—make): conversion of nitrogenous compounds in soil into gaseous nitrogen by denitrifying bacteria.

Deoxyribonucleic acid (DNA): the material that bears the genetic information of each cell; the principal constituent of chromatin.

Deoxyribose: a 5-carbon sugar that is one of the components of DNA.

Desert (L. *deserere*—forsake): a formation (or biome) characterized by scanty rainfall and usually sparse vegetation with ability to withstand drought and conserve moisture.

Diatomaceous earth (Gr. *dia*—through; *tome*—cut): a type of sedimentary deposit consisting of the dead, empty valves of diatoms.

Dichotomous (Gr. *dicha*—asunder; *tome*—cut): a type of branching in plants in which the main axis or stem forks repeatedly into two branches.

Dicotyledonous (Gr. *dis*—two; *kotyledon*—cup-shaped structure): having two cotyledons in an embryo.

Differentially permeable: referring to membranes that allow certain substances to pass through and that retard or prevent the passage of others.

Differentiation (L. *differe*—carry apart, be different): modification of cells, tissues, or organs for the performance of definite functions; maturation.

Diffuse-porous wood (L. *diffusus*—poured out, dispersed; Gr. *poros*—opening; AS. *wudu*—wood): a type of wood in which the vessels are more or less uniform in size and distribution throughout each growth ring.

Diffuse (fibrous) root system (L. *diffusus*—dispersed): a root system in which there is no single main root larger than other roots.

Diffusion (L. *diffusus*—dispersed): the spreading of a substance throughout available space from high to low concentrations of that substance, as a result of molecular motion.

Diffusion pressure: a pressure exerted by the molecules of a diffusing substance.

Digestion (L. *digerere*—separate, dissolve): the transformation of insoluble or complex foods into soluble or simpler substances, through the action of enzymes.

Dihybrid cross (Gr. *dis*—two; L. *hybrida*—mongrel): a cross between organisms differing in two characters.

Dioecious (Gr. *dis*—two; *oikos*—house): having the male and female gametangia, or staminate and pistillate flowers on separate plants.

Diploid (Gr. *diploos*—double): referring to the double chromosome number, characteristic of the sporophyte generation in plants.

Disbudding (L. *dis*—apart, ME. *budde*—bud): the removal of buds from a plant to control branching or to produce larger flowers from remaining buds.

Disinfectant (L. *dis*—apart; *in*—not; *facere*—make): a substance that kills bacteria and other microorganisms; same as germicide.

Division: a taxonomic category made up of closely related classes.

DNA: see Deoxyribonucleic acid.

Dominance (L. *dominor*—rule): a genetic principle, established by Mendel, that when two contrasting characters are brought together in a hybrid as the result of a cross, one character (dominant) may mask the other (recessive).

Dormancy (L. *dormire*—sleep): a period of reduced physiological activity occurring in seeds, buds, etc.; resting period.

Double fertilization (Gr. *diploos*—twofold; L. *ferre*—bear, produce): in flowering plants, the fusion of one sperm with an egg, of a second sperm with two polar nuclei, in an embryo sac.

Drupe (Gr. *druppa*—overripe olive): a simple fleshy fruit in which the endocarp (inner wall of ovary) becomes hard and stony, and encloses one or two seeds.

Ecosystem: the community and its environment treated as an interacting, functional unit.

Ecotone: the transition zone between two overlapping communities.

Ecotype: a genetically distinct population, physiologically adapted to a particular habitat.

Ectoplast: see Plasma membrane.

Ectotrophic (Gr. *ektos*—outside; *trophe*—food): feeding on the surface, as a fungus living on the surface of a host.

Edaphic (Gr. *edaphos*—ground): referring to the soil.

Egg (AS. *aeg*—egg): female gamete.

Elaters (Gr. *elater*—driver): hygroscopic structures that are produced in the sporophytes of liverworts and on the spores of horsetails and that aid in spore dispersal.

Embryo (Gr. *embryon*—embryo): a young sporophytic plant, before the beginning of its rapid growth; the "germ" of a seed.

Embryo sac (Gr. *embryon*—embryo; L. *saccus*—sac): the female gametophyte of an angiosperm—a structure within an angiosperm ovule in which the egg is fertilized; an embryo begins its development within an embryo sac.

Emulsion (L. *ex*—out of; *mulgeo*—milk): a dispersion system in which droplets of one liquid are suspended in another liquid, both liquids being immiscible; e.g., oil droplets in water.

Endocarp (Gr. *endon*—within; *karpos*—fruit): inner layer of fruit wall.

Endodermis (Gr. *endon*—within; *derma*—skin): the innermost layer of cortical cells; most conspicuous in roots.

Endoplasmic reticulum: an extensive system of cytoplasmic membranes within the protoplast.

Endosperm (Gr. *endon*—within; *sperma*—seed): a food storage tissue in angiosperm seeds; it results from the fusion of a sperm with two polar nuclei and is thus triploid.

Endotrophic (Gr. *endon*—within; *trophe*—food): feeding internally, as a fungus living inside the tissues of a host.

Enzyme (Gr. *en*—in; *zyme*—yeast): an organic proteinaceous catalyst, manufactured by living protoplasm, and controlling digestion and other physiological processes.

Epicotyl (Gr. *epi*—upon; *kotyle*—cup): the portion of an embryo axis above the attachment of the cotyledons; the growing apex of the epicotyl forms the young stem of a plant.

Epidermis (Gr. *epi*—upon; *derma*—skin): the surface layer of leaves and other soft plant parts.

Epigyny (Gr. *epi*—upon; *gyne*—female): a condition in which the ovary is embedded in the receptacle, so that the other floral parts seem to arise from the top of the ovary.

Epiphyte (Gr. *epi*—upon; *phyton*—plant): a plant that gains physical support from another plant, or from poles, wires, and other objects.

Ergastic substances: the nonprotoplasmic components of the protoplast; for example, crystals and oil droplets.

Essential elements (L. *essentia*, from *esse*—to be): chemical elements necessary for the normal growth and development of plants.

Essential oils (from L. *esse*—to be): widely distributed organic compounds in plants, having an oily texture and pronounced odors; thought to be metabolic wastes.

Etiolation (F. *etioler*—blanch): a condition involving abnormal stem elongation, failure of normal leaf development, and absence of chlorophyll, and characterizing plants grown in the absence of light.

Exocarp (Gr. *exo*—outside; *karpos*—fruit): outermost layer of a fruit wall.

Eyespot: a small, light-sensitive pigmented structure present in certain algae.

Facultative parasite: see Parasite.

Family: a taxonomic category ranking between genera and an order; a family is a group of related genera.

Fascicular cambium: cambium situated within a vascular bundle.

Fat (AS. *faett*—fatten): a kind of food, which is insoluble in water and is made up of carbon, hydrogen, and oxygen, with proportionately less oxygen than in carbohydrates.

Fermentation (L. *fermentum*—yeast): decomposition of organic substances by living organisms in the absence of free oxygen, or in the presence of limited amounts of oxygen. See Anaerobic respiration.

Fertilization (L. *fertilis*—producing, fertile): an essential feature of sexual reproduction, the fusion of one gamete with another.

Fiber (L. *fibra*—fiber): an elongated, tapering, thick-walled strengthening cell occurring in various plant parts.

Field capacity: the maximum amount of water the soil can hold against the force of gravity.

Filament (L. *filum*—thread): the stalk of a stamen, with an anther at its apex; also, a threadlike row of cells.

Fission (L. *fissus*—split): asexual reproduction in which a one-celled organism divides into two one-celled organisms.

Flagellum (L. *flagellum*—whip): a protoplasmic extrusion the movements of which propel unicellular organisms, zoospores, etc., through water; a flagellum is similar to a cilium (which see) but is longer.

Florigen (L. *flos*—flower; Gr. *genea*—birth): a name given to a hypothetical substance believed to be associated with flowering.

Flower (L. *flos*—flower): the characteristic reproductive structure of angiosperms, interpreted morphologically as a specialized branch system.

Flower bud (L. *flos*—flower; ME. *budde*—bud): a bud that grows into a flower.

Foliose (L. *folium*—leaf): leafy; referring, for example, to certain lichens.

Follicle (L. *follis*—bag): a simple, dry, dehiscent fruit, producing several to numerous seeds and composed of one carpel, which splits along one seam.

Food (ME. *fode*—food): an organic substance that furnishes energy for vital processes or is transformed into living protoplasm and cell walls.

Foot: in mosses, liverworts, ferns, and other plant groups, a portion of a young sporophyte that attaches the sporophyte to the gametophyte and often absorbs food from the latter.

Forest (L. *foris*—outside): a formation (or biome) in which the dominant plants are trees.

Formation: a large natural assemblage of plants, such as tundra or coniferous forest.

Fossil: (L. *fossus*—dug): the imprint or remains of an organism in the earth's crust.

Fragmentation (L. *fragere*—break): a type of asexual reproduction involving the separation of several- to many-celled pieces from a multicellular organism.

Frond (L. *frons*—leaf): a name applied to very large leaves, such as those of ferns.

Fruit (L. *fructus*—fruit): a matured ovary, or cluster of matured ovaries.

Fruit scar: the scar left on a twig after separation of the fruit.

Fruticose (L. *frutex*—shrub): shrublike, as in branching, shrublike lichens.

Fucoxanthin: a brown, xanthophyll pigment found in brown algae.

Funiculus (L. *funis*—cord): stalk that attaches an ovule to the inner portions of an ovary.

Gall (ME. *galle*—sore spot): an enlargement produced on leaves and other plant parts, usually as a result of insect or fungus attack.

Gametangium (Gr. *gametes*—spouse; *angos*—vessel): a structure bearing gametes.

Gamete (Gr. *gametes*—spouse): a cell that

fuses with another cell in sexual reproduction—usually an egg with a sperm.

Gametophyte (Gr. *gametes*—spouse; *phyton* —plant): the gamete-producing phase in alternation of generations, characterized by the haploid chromosome number. See Sporophyte.

Gel (L. *gelare*—freeze): jellylike colloidal system.

Gemma (L. *gemma*—bud): an asexual or vegetative outgrowth of a parent body, capable of growing into a new individual directly, as in liverworts.

Gene (Gr. *genea*—birth): a hereditary determiner, located on a chromosome.

Gene pool: all the genes of an interbreeding population.

Generative cell (Gr. *genesis*—origin; L. *cella*—small room): the cell that, upon division, forms sperms in a pollen tube.

Genotype (Gr. *genesis*—origin; *typos*— model): the genetic constitution of an organism.

Genus (L. *genus*—race, kind): a group of closely related species.

Geotropism (Gr. *ge*—earth; *trope*—turn): a growth movement induced by gravitational stimulus.

Germicide: see Disinfectant.

Germination (L. *germen*—sprig): the sprouting of a seed, spore, zygote, or other reproductive body.

Gibberellins: a class of growth-regulating compounds.

Gill (Gr. *chellos*—lip): flattened, spore-producing plates on underside of mushroom caps.

Girdling: the removal of a ring of bark from a portion of a stem.

Glucose (Gr. *glykos*—sweet): a 6-carbon sugar; also called grape sugar.

Glume (L. *gluma*—husk): a chaffy bract of a grass spikelet.

Glycogen (Gr. *glykos*—sweet): a starchlike carbohydrate found in some plants, especially certain algae and fungi.

Glycolysis (Gr. *glykos*—sweet; *lysis*— loosening): an early stage in respiration in which pyruvic acid is produced from a sugar.

Gonidia (Gr. *gonos*—reproduction; *idion*— small): minute, asexual reproductive structures produced by some bacteria.

Grafting (Gr. *graphion*—pencil): the joining of two plant parts, usually stems, so that their tissues grow together.

Grain (L. *granum*—grain): the fruit of a grass, chiefly of a cereal grass. See Caryopsis.

Grana: small, chlorophyll-bearing bodies found in chloroplasts.

Grassland (AS. *graes*—grass): a formation (or biome) in which the dominant plants are grasses.

Gravitational water (L. *gravis*—heavy): water that moves downward through soil as a result of the earth's gravitational force upon it.

Ground meristem (AS. *grund*—earth; Gr. *meristos*—divided): meristematic tissue that develops into pith and cortex.

Growth layer: a layer of secondary xylem or phloem produced (ordinarily) in a single growing season.

Growth ring: a growth layer seen in cross section.

Guanine: one of the nitrogenous bases found in DNA and RNA.

Guard cells: paired epidermal chlorophyllous cells that enclose stomata.

Gum (Gr. *kommi*—gum): colloidal, mucilaginous, water-soluble plant product, with numerous economic uses.

Guttation (L. *gutta*—drop): the exudation of liquid water from plants.

Halophyte (Gr. *hals*—salt; *phyton*—plant): a plant that grows in alkali soils or salt marshes.

Haploid (Gr. *haploos*—single): referring to the single chromosome number, characteristic of the gametophyte generation.

Hardening (ME. *hard*—strong): the treatment of plants in such a manner as to increase their hardiness.

Hardiness: the ability of plants to withstand low temperatures.

Hardwood: the wood of angiosperms.

Haustorium (L. *haurire*—draw up, drink): in parasitic plants, rootlike structure that penetrates host tissues and cells and absorbs food from them.

Head: a type of inflorescence in which numerous small flowers are densely crowded upon a usually disc-shaped common receptacle, as in a sunflower.

Heartwood: the inner growth layers that are nonconducting and contain no living cells;

heartwood is usually darker than sap-wood.

Herb (L. *herba*—grass) : a plant that does not develop much woody tissue and thus remains soft and succulent.

Herbaceous: describing an herb (which see).

Herbals (L. *herba*—grass) : medieval and Renaissance books picturing and describing plants.

Herbivorous (L. *herba*—grass; *vorare*—eat) : describing animals that eat plants.

Heredity (L. *heres*—heir) : the tendency of an organism to resemble its parents.

Heterocyst (Gr. *heteros*—different; *kystis*—pouch) : a cell in an algal filament that separates from other cells, causing the filament to separate into hormogonia (which see).

Heteroecism (Gr. *heteros*—different; *oikos*—house) : in rust fungi, the completion of the life cycle upon two kinds of host plants.

Heterogametes (Gr. *heteros*—different; *gametes*—spouse) : gametes that differ in size, structure, and behavior.

Heterogamy (Gr. *heteros*—different; *gamos*—marriage) : sexual reproduction by gametes differing in size, structure, and behavior.

Heterosis (Gr. *heteros*—different) : hybrid vigor; a type of increased vigor that often occurs in an organism that is the offspring of parents of different inbred lines, varieties, or species.

Heterosporous (Gr. *heteros*—different; *spore*—spore) : producing spores of two types.

Heterothallic (Gr. *heteros*—different; *thallos*—shoot) : describing a sexual condition in which an individual produces only one kind of gamete; used chiefly in reference to algae and fungi.

Heterotrophic (Gr. *heteros*—different; *trophe*—food) : referring to organisms that are unable to make their food and are thus parasites or saprophytes.

Heterozygous (Gr. *heteros*—different; *zygon*—yoke) : referring to a condition in which the members of a gene pair are dissimilar.

Hilum (L. *hilum*—trifle) : scar on a seed coat, marking the place of attachment of the seed stalk to the seed.

Holdfast: basal portion of a thallus that anchors it to a solid object in water.

Homologous chromosomes (Gr. *homo*—same; *logos*—discourse; *chroma*—color; *soma*—body) : the members of a chromosome pair.

Homosporous (Gr. *homos*—same; *spora*—spore) : producing spores of a single type.

Homothallic (Gr. *homos*—same; *thallos*—shoot) : describing a sexual condition in which an individual produces two kinds of gametes. See Heterothallic.

Homozygous (Gr. *homos*—same; *zygon*—yoke) : referring to a gene pair in which both genes are identical. See Heterozygous.

Hormogonia (Gr. *hormao*—set in motion; *gonos*—reproduction) : reproductive segments of algal filaments.

Hormones (Gr. *hormao*—set in motion) : organic substances that are produced by living organisms and that regulate various growth and developmental processes.

Host (L. *hospes*—guest) : a plant or animal that affords nourishment to a parasite.

Humus (L. *humus*—ground) : in soils, dark-colored organic matter resulting from the decomposition of plants and consisting chiefly of cellulose and lignin derivatives.

Hybrid (L. *hybrida*—mongrel) : a plant or animal that is the offspring of parents differing in one or more traits; also used for the offspring resulting from a cross between two species.

Hybrid vigor: see Heterosis.

Hybridization (L. *hybrida*—mongrel) : the production of hybrids by interbreeding parents of different types or species.

Hydathode (Gr. *hydor*—water; *hodus*—way) : epidermal glands, through which drops of water are exuded.

Hydrolysis (Gr. *hydor*—water; *luo*—dissolve) : transformation of a compound into a simpler compound, involving the uptake of water; digestion is a process of hydrolysis.

Hydrophyte (Gr. *hydor*—water; *phyton*—plant) : a plant that lives in water or exceedingly wet soils.

Hydroponics (Gr. *hydor*—water; L. *ponere*—put) : the growth of plants in aqueous solutions of nutrient chemicals.

Hypertrophy (Gr. *hyper*—over; *trophe*—

food): an abnormally large growth, resulting usually from a disease.

Hypha (Gr. *hyphe*—web): a fungous filament.

Hypocotyl (Gr. *hypo*—under; *kotyle*—cup): the portion of an embryo axis below the attachment of the cotyledons; the root meristem is situated at the tip of the hypocotyl.

Hypogyny (Gr. *hypo*—under; *gyne*—female): a condition in which the ovary of a flower surmounts a receptacle, and in which the sepals, petals, and stamens are attached below the ovary.

Imbibition (L. *imbibere*—drink in): the process by which solid (chiefly colloidal) particles absorb liquids and swell.

Imperfect flower (L. *imperfectus*—not perfect; *flos*—flower): a flower that bears stamens or carpels but not both.

Inbreeding: breeding of closely related individuals or races; used in plant breeding to obtain homozygous condition.

Incomplete dominance (L. *dominare*—dominate): in inheritance, a condition in which neither member of a pair of contrasting characters masks the other.

Incomplete flower: a flower that lacks one or more of the four kinds of floral organs. See Complete flower.

Indehiscent (L. *in*—not; *dehiscere*—split open): referring to a fruit that does not split open along regular seams.

Independent assortment: a genetic principle, established by Mendel, that the factors (genes) representing two or more contrasting pairs of characteristics are segregated to gametes independently of each other in meiosis, following which the gametes combine at random with each other.

Indeterminate inflorescence: in which the tip of the inflorescence continues to grow, forming new bracts and flowers in succession, with the oldest flowers at the base of the inflorescence, the youngest nearest the growing tip.

Indoleacetic acid: an organic compound belonging to the auxin class of growth-regulating substances.

Indusium (L. *indusium*—tunic): the membranous cover of a fern sorus.

Inferior ovary: see Epigyny.

Inflorescence (L. *inflorescere*—begin to flower): a flower cluster.

Insectivorous (L. *insecare*—cut in; *voro*—eating): insect-eating or insect-digesting.

Integument (L. *integumentum*—covering): the coat of an ovule.

Interfascicular cambium: cambium situated between vascular bundles.

Internode (L. *inter*—between; *nodus*—knot): the length of stem between two successive nodes.

Interphase (L. *inter*—between; Gr. *phasis*—appearance): the condition of a nucleus not undergoing mitosis.

Inulin (Gr. *helenion*—basket): a white, complex carbohydrate very similar to starch.

Invertase (L. *invertere*—turn over): the enzyme that hydrolyzes cane sugar into glucose and fructose.

Ion (Gr. *ienai*—to go): an electrified particle formed by the dissociation of molecules of certain substances called electrolytes.

Ion accumulation: absorption of ions against a concentration gradient as a result of expenditure of energy by living cells. See Active transport.

Irritability (L. *irritare*—excite): the ability of living protoplasm to receive stimuli and to react to them.

Isogametes (Gr. *isos*—equal; *gamos*—marriage): gametes that are alike in size, structure, and often in behavior.

Isogamy (Gr. *isos*—equal; *gamos*—marriage): sexual reproduction by isogametes.

Karyokinesis (Gr. *karyon*—nut; *kinesis*—movement): nuclear division; see Mitosis.

Knot (ME. *knot*—twist): the buried base of a branch in a larger branch or tree trunk.

Lamellae (L. diminutive of *lamina*—thin sheet): membranaceous, flattened vesicles or sacs, small stacks of which constitute grana.

Laminarin: the principal stored food in brown algae; a complex carbohydrate.

Lateral bud: an axillary bud.

Leaching (AS. *leccan*—moisten): the removal of solutes from soil by flowing or percolating water.

Leaf axil (L. *axilla*—armpit): the upper angle between a leaf petiole and the stem from which it grows.

Leaf bud: a bud that develops into a leafy shoot and does not produce flowers.

Leaf gap: a break in the vascular cylinder, caused by the branching of vascular tissue from the cylinder into a leaf.

Leaf primordium (L. *primordium*—beginning): an outgrowth that develops from the growing point of a bud and grows into a leaf.

Leaf scar: a scar left on a twig following the fall of a leaf.

Leaf trace: a branch of the vascular tissues of a stem, extending out into leaves.

Leaflet: one of the several blades of a compound leaf.

Legume (L. *legumen*, from L. *legere*—gather): a simple, dry, dehiscent, one-carpelled fruit splitting along two seams; also, a member of the legume family, the members of which have such fruits.

Lemma (Gr. *lemma*—something received): the lower of the two bracts enclosing a grass flower.

Lenticel (L. *lens*—lentil): in woody stems (and other plant parts), a pore through which exchange of gases occurs; in woody stems, lenticels occur in bark.

Leucoplast (Gr. *leukos*—white; *plastos*—formed): a colorless plastid involved in the formation of starch in many types of plant cells.

Leucosin: an albuminoid protein; the reserve food produced by some Chrysophyta.

Lignification (L. *lignum*—wood; *facere*—make): impregnation of cell walls with lignin.

Lignin (L. *lignum*—wood): an organic substance associated with cellulose in the cell walls, especially xylem, of many plants.

Linkage: the tendency for certain genes to remain together in inheritance because of their location on the same chromosome.

Lipase (Gr. *lipos*—fat): an enzyme that hydrolyzes fats to glycerol and fatty acids.

Lobed (Gr. *lobos*—lobe of ear): divided by clefts, as a maple leaf.

Locule (L. *locus*—place): one of the cavities of an ovary.

Macronutrients (Gr. *makros*—long; L. *nutrire*—nourish): those essential elements required in relatively large quantities by plants.

Maltase (AS. *mealt*—malt): an enzyme that hydrolyzes malt sugar (maltose) to grape sugar (glucose).

Maturation (L. *maturare*—ripen): process of becoming mature; see Differentiation.

Megagametophyte (Gr. *megas*—large; *gamos*—marriage; *phyton*—plant): a female gametophyte resulting from the growth of a megaspore and producing female gametes or eggs.

Megasporangium (Gr. *megas*—large; *spora*—spore; *angos*—vessel): a sporangium that produces megaspores.

Megaspores (Gr. *megas*—large; *spora*—spore): a spore, produced within a megasporangium, and forming a megagametophyte.

Megasporophyll (Gr. *megas*—large; *spora*—spore; *phyllon*—leaf): a leaf, or similar structure, which bears a megasporangium.

Meiosis (Gr. *meioun*—make smaller): reduction division; a process in the sexual cycle by means of which chromosome numbers are reduced one half.

Meristem (Gr. *meristos*—divided): a mass of growing cells, capable of frequent cell division.

Meristematic tissue: a tissue, the cells of which are capable of frequent division and which is thus responsible for the first phase of growth.

Mesocarp (Gr. *mesos*—middle; *karpos*—fruit): middle layer of a fruit wall.

Mesophyll (Gr. *mesos*—middle; *phyllon*—leaf): the chlorophyllous leaf tissues between the epidermal layers.

Mesophytes (Gr. *mesos*—middle; *phyton*—plant): plants that are intermediate between hydrophytes and xerophytes—that is, that grow in soils containing moderate amounts of available moisture.

Metabolism (Gr. *meta*—beyond, after; *ballein*—throw): the sum total of the chemical transformations occurring in the body of a living organism.

Metaphase (Gr. *meta*—after; *phasis*—appearance): the stage in mitosis at which the chromosomes lie at the equator of the spindle.

Micelles: the solid particles dispersed in a colloidal system.

Microfibrils: aggregations of chainlike cellulose molecules into ultramicroscopic fibrils.

Microgametophyte (Gr. *mikros*—small; *gamos*—marriage; *phyton*—plant): a male gametophyte resulting from the growth and development of a microspore.

Micronutrients (Gr. *mikros*—small; L. *nutrire*—nourish): those essential elements required in only minute amounts by plants.

Micropyle (Gr. *mikros*—small; *pyle*—gate): the minute opening in the integument of an ovule or seed, through which a pollen tube grows to reach the female gametophyte.

Microsporangium (Gr. *mikros*—small; *spora*—spore; *angos*—vessel): a sporangium that produces microspores.

Microspore (Gr. *mikros*—small; *spora*—spore): a spore that grows into a male gametophyte.

Microsporophyll (Gr. *mikros*—small; *spora*—spore; *phyllon*—leaf): a leaf, or similar structure, which bears microsporangia.

Middle lamella (L. *lamina*—plate): the thin layer of intercellular cementing substance, composed chiefly of calcium pectate.

Mitochondria (Gr. *mito*—thread; *chondros*—cartilage): granular or rod-shaped cytoplasmic bodies, functioning as centers of respiratory activity.

Mitosis (Gr. *mitos*—threads): a process of nuclear division involving the duplication of chromosomes, the formation of a spindle, and the separation of chromosome halves to two daughter nuclei. Mitosis is usually, but not always, followed by cytokinesis (which see).

Mixed bud: a bud that produces both flowers and vegetative shoots.

Monocotyledonous (Gr. *monos*—one; *cotyledon*—a cup-shaped structure): having one cotyledon in an embryo.

Monoecious (Gr. *monos*—one; *oikos*—house): having staminate and pistillate flowers, or male and female gametangia, on the same plant.

Monohybrid cross (Gr. *monos*—one; L. *hybrida*—mongrel): a cross between parents differing in a single character.

Mother cell: a cell that through cell division gives rise to new cells (daughter cells).

Mulch (ME. *molsh*—soft, rotten): material, such as straw, leaves, or paper, spread on a soil to retard water loss and weed growth, or to protect roots against cold, or to improve structure and fertility of the soil.

Multicellular (L. *multus*—much): many celled.

Multiple fruit (L. *multus*—much; *fructus*—fruit): a cluster of matured ovaries produced by separate flowers. Same as Compound fruit.

Mutation (L. *mutare*—change): a sudden, heritable change produced in the offspring of a parent organism as a result of an alteration in a gene or chromosome, or of an increase in chromosome number; also, the process by which such changes occur.

Mycelium (Gr. *mykes*—fungus): the mass of hyphae forming the body of a true fungus.

Mycorrhiza (Gr. *mykes*—fungus; *rhiza*—root): a symbiotic association of a fungus with the roots of higher plants.

Myxamoeba (Gr. *myxa*—slime; *amoibe*—change): a swarm cell of a slime fungus.

Naked bud: a bud that is not protected by bud scales.

Narcotic (Gr. *narkotikos*—benumb): a drug that produces stupor or coma, often accompanied by hallucinations and other nervous abnormalities.

Nastic movements (Gr. *nastos*—closed): growth movements of flattened organs, such as leaves and petals, as a result of differences in growth of cells on upper and lower surfaces of these organs.

Natural preservatives: preservative substances, such as tannins and resins, that occur naturally in woods and bark and that tend to reduce attacks by fungi and insects.

Natural (self) pruning: the natural abscission of branches and twigs of woody plants.

Natural selection: the process that tends to cause "survival of the fittest" (survival of the organisms with the most advantageous variations for a given environment); an important feature of Darwin's theory of the causes of evolution.

Neck: the tapering portion of an archegonium; a sperm enters an archegonium through a canal extending lengthwise through the neck.

Nectary (Gr. *nektar*—drink of the gods): a floral gland that secretes nectar, a sweetish liquid that insects obtain from flowers; rarely, nectaries occur on other parts.

Net venation (L. *vena*—vein): a scheme of vein arrangement in leaves, in which the veins branch frequently, forming a network.

Nitrification (L. *nitrum*—saltpeter; *facere*—make): the conversion of ammonia and ammonium compounds into nitrites and nitrates through bacterial action in soils.

Nitrogen fixation: the conversion of atmospheric, gaseous nitrogen into nitrogen compounds in soils or plant roots by certain bacteria and blue-green algae.

Node (L. *nodus*—knot): a point on a stem from which a leaf and bud arise.

Nodule (L. *nodus*—knot): on the roots of certain plants, an enlargement within which nitrogen-fixing bacteria live.

Nucellus (L. *nux*—nut): the megasporangium of an ovule, located inside the integument and enclosing the megagametophyte.

Nuclear membrane (L. *nucleus*—kernel of a nut; *membrana*—skin): a double membrane that surrounds the nuclear contents.

Nuclear sap: the liquid present within a living nucleus.

Nucleolus (diminutive of L. *nucleus*—kernel of a nut): a small, usually spherical body found within the nucleus of most kinds of cells.

Nucleotide: structural units of which nucleic acids are composed, each consisting of a sugar, a phosphate group, and a nitrogenous base.

Nucleus (L. *nucleus*—kernel of a nut): a usually spherical or ovoid protoplasmic body found in most cells and considered as a directive center of many protoplasmic activities, including the transmission of hereditary characteristics.

Nut (L. *nux*—nut): an indehiscent, dry, one-seeded, hard-walled fruit, produced from a compound ovary.

Obligate parasite: see Parasite.

Oil (L. *oleum*—oil): a fatty substance that is liquid at room temperatures.

Ontogeny (Gr. *on*—being; *genesis*—origin): the life history, or development, of an individual, as opposed to that (phylogeny) of the race.

Oogonium (Gr. *oon*—egg; *gonos*—offspring): the female gametangium in certain thallophytes; an oogonium is one celled and produces one or more eggs.

Operculum (L. *operculum*—lid): the lid covering a moss capsule.

Opposite: bearing two leaves or two buds at a node on opposite sides of a stem.

Order: a taxonomic category ranking between a family and a class. An order is composed of related families.

Organ: one of the major parts of a plant body—leaf, stem, root. An organ is composed of tissues.

Organic matter (in soils): materials derived from the decomposition of dead organisms and of their wastes.

Organism (Gr. *organon*—organ, tool): a living plant or animal.

Osmosis (Gr. *osmos*—push): the diffusion of water through a differentially permeable membrane from a region of high water concentration to a region of lower water concentration.

Osmotic concentration: the concentration of osmotically active particles in a solution.

Osmotic pressure: the maximum pressure that can be developed in a solution that is separated from pure water by a rigid membrane permeable only to water.

Ovary (L. *ovum*—egg): the basal, enlarged portion of a pistil, within which seeds develop.

Ovule (L. *ovum*—egg): a structure consisting of a female gametophyte, nucellus, and integuments, which develops after fertilization into a seed.

Palea (L. *palea*—chaff): the upper of the two enclosing bracts of a grass flower.

Palisade tissue (L. *palus*—pole): a leaf tissue composed of long, cylindrical chlorophyllous cells.

Palmately veined (L. *palma*—palm of the hand): a type of net venation in which the main veins of a leaf blade branch out from the apex of the petiole like the fingers of a hand.

Parallel evolution (Gr. *parallelos*—beside each other; L. *evolutio*—unrolling): evolution in a similar direction in different groups of organisms.

Parallel venation (Gr. *parallelos*—beside each other; L. *vena*—vein): a type of leaf venation, in which the principal veins are parallel with each other and to the longitudinal axis of the leaf.

Parasite (Gr. *para*—beside; *sitos*—food): a heterotrophic organism that derives its food from the living tissues of another organism; a facultative parasite is one that can obtain its food parasitically or saprophytically; an obligate parasite can obtain food only from the living tissues of a host.

Parenchyma (Gr. *parenchein*—pour in beside): a tissue composed of thin-walled, often isodiametric cells, which often store food or perform other functions and which usually retain meristematic potentialities.

Parthenocarpy (Gr. *partheno*—virgin; *karpos*—fruit): the development of a fruit without pollination.

Parthenogenesis (Gr. *partheno*—virgin; *genesis*—beginning): the development of an egg into a new individual without fertilization by a sperm.

Passive water absorption: the principal means of water uptake in a plant, initiated by the evaporation and subsequent loss of water from the plant's aerial parts.

Pasteurization (from Louis Pasteur, eminent French bacteriologist): treatment of substances with moderately high temperatures for brief periods to kill certain bacteria.

Pathogen (Gr. *pathos*—suffering, disease; *genesis*—origin): an organism that causes a disease in another organism.

Pathogenic (Gr. *pathos*—suffering; *genesis* —origin): producing disease.

Pectic substances (Gr. *pektos*—curdled): complex organic compounds found chiefly in the middle lamella.

Pedicel (L. *pediculus*—little foot): the stalk of an individual flower of an inflorescence.

Peduncle (L. *pedunculus*—form of *pediculus*—little foot): the stalk of a solitary flower, or the main stalk of an inflorescence.

Perennial (L. *per*—through; *annus*—year): a plant that lives for more than two years.

Perfect flower (L. *perfectus*—finished; *flos* —flower): a flower that bears both stamens and carpels.

Perianth (Gr. *peri*—around; *anthos*— flower): the floral envelope, i.e., calyx and corolla.

Pericarp (Gr. *peri*—around; *karpos*—fruit): the wall of a ripened ovary (fruit).

Pericycle (Gr. *peri*—around; *kyklos*—circle): in roots and some stems, a layer (or layers) of cells immediately outside the phloem and inside the endodermis.

Periderm (Gr. *peri*—around; *derma*— skin): a collective name for cork, cork cambium, and phelloderm, a tissue found on the inner surface of the cork cambium.

Perigyny (Gr. *peri*—around; *gyne*—female): a condition in flowers in which the petals and stamens are usually fused with the calyx and in which the pistil is seated in a concave receptacle.

Peristome (Gr. *peri*—around; *stoma*— mouth): a ring of teeth surrounding the opening of a moss capsule and by its hygroscopic movements scattering the spores.

Permanent wilting percentage: the amount of water in the soil at the time plants become permanently wilted.

Permeable (L. *permeare*—go, pass): capable of being passed through.

Petal (Gr. *petalon*—leaf): one of the structural units of a corolla.

Petiole (L. *petiolus*—little foot or stalk): a leaf stalk.

Phelloderm (Gr. *phellos*—cork; *derma*— skin): a secondary tissue produced by cork cambium and found on the inner surface of the cork cambium.

Phenotype (Gr. *phainein*—show; *typos*— model, type): the external, visible appearance of an organism.

Phloem (Gr. *phloos*—bark): a complex tissue that, in flowering plants, consists chiefly of sieve tube members, companion cells, parenchyma, and fibers; the chief function of phloem is food conduction.

Photolysis: a photochemical process that cleaves water molecules into [H] and [OH] fragments.

Photoperiod (Gr. *phos*—light; *peri*—around; *odos*—way): the relative duration of night and day to which plants are exposed.

Photoperiodism (Gr. *phos*—light; *peri*—around; *odos*—way); growth and developmental responses of plants to differing photoperiods.

Photosynthesis (Gr. *phos*—light; *syn*—together; *thesis*—setting): the fundamental process of food manufacture in nature.

Phototropism (Gr. *phos*—light; *trope*—turn): a growth movement induced by the stimulus of light.

Phycocyanin (Gr. *phykos*—seaweed; *kyanos*—dark-blue substance): a blue pigment found in blue-green and in red algae.

Phycoerythrin (Gr. *phykos*—seaweed; *erythros*—red): a red pigment found in red and in blue-green algae.

Phylogeny (Gr. *phylon*—tribe; *genesis*—beginning): the history of a plant or animal group in relation to other groups; the study of "family trees." See Ontogeny.

Phytochrome (Gr. *phyton*—plant; *chroma*—color): a photosensitive protein pigment that influences flowering, germination, and other physiological processes.

Pigment (L. *pigmentum*—dye): a colored compound, such as chlorophyll.

Pileus (L. *pileus*—cap): the umbrellalike cap of a mushroom.

Pinnately veined (L. *pinna*—feather; *vena*—vein): a type of net venation in which the secondary veins branch out in parallel fashion from the single midrib of a leaf blade.

Pistil (L. *pistillum*—pestle): the ovule-producing part of a flower, consisting of a carpel (simple pistil) or of two or more partly or wholly fused carpels (compound pistil).

Pistillate flower: a flower that bears a pistil but no stamens.

Pit (AS. *pytt*—hole): a thin place in a cell wall.

Pith (AS. *pitha*—pith): parenchyma tissue occupying the central portion of a stem inside the xylem.

Pith ray: a band of interfascicular parenchyma.

Placenta (L. *placenta*—cake): a small mass of ovary tissue to which a seed stalk is attached.

Placentation (L. *placenta*—cake): the arrangement of placentae within an ovary.

Plant formation: see Formation.

Plasma membrane (Gr. *plasma*—something molded; L. *membrana*—skin): the membrane delimiting the outer surface of the protoplast.

Plasmodesmata (Gr. *plasma*—something molded; *desma*—bond): fine protoplasmic connections between cells.

Plasmodium (Gr. *plasma*—something molded): the naked protoplasmic mass of a slime fungus.

Plasmolysis (Gr. *plasma*—something molded; *luo*—dissolve): shrinkage of protoplasm due to water loss.

Plastids (Gr. *plastos*—formed): cytoplasmic bodies involved in food synthesis, storage, etc.

Plumule (L. *pluma*—small feather): the bud, or shoot-forming meristem of an embryo. See Epicotyl.

Polar nuclei: the (two) nuclei that fuse with a sperm within the embryo sac to form a triploid endosperm nucleus.

Polarity (L. *polus*—pole): morphological and physiological direction in plants.

Poles (L. *polus*—pole): the opposite ends of a mitotic spindle.

Pollen grains (L. *pollen*—dust, flour): young male gametophytes of seed plants.

Pollen tube (L. *pollen*—dust, flour): a tube that is formed by a pollen grain and that transports sperms to the eggs in ovules. A pollen grain and it mature tube are a male (micro-) gametophyte.

Pollination (L. *pollen*—dust, flour): the transfer of pollen grains from a stamen or microsporophyll to a stigma or ovule.

Polyploid (Gr. *polys*—many; *haploos*—one fold): having more than two sets of chromosomes.

Pome (L. *pomum*—a kind of fruit): the apple type of fruit in which the true fruits (core sections) are surrounded by an enlarged fleshy, floral tube and receptacle.

Primary root (L. *primus*—first): the root that develops directly from the hypocotyl of an embryo.

Primary tissue (L. *primus*—first; F. *tisser*—weave): tissue developed by an apical meristem during growth in length.

Primary wall (L. *primus*—first): cell wall

layer lying next to middle lamella, or intercellular layer.

Primordium (L. *primordium*—beginning): the rudiment or beginning of a part.

Procambium (L. *pro*—before; *cambiare*—change): meristematic tissue from which primary phloem and primary xylem are derived.

Progressive evolution: evolution from simple toward more complex and more highly specialized structures.

Prophase (Gr. *pro*—before, in front; *phasis*—appearance): an early stage in mitosis in which the chromosomes become distinct and in which the nuclear membrane disappears.

Proteases (Gr. *proteios*—holding first place): enzymes that digest proteins.

Protective layer: a layer of suberized cells formed beneath the abscission layer.

Proteins (Gr. *proteios*—holding first place): complex, organic, nitrogenous substances, built up from amino acids and constituting the major portion of the organic materials in living protoplasm.

Proterandry (Gr. *proteros*—earlier; *andros*—man, male): a condition in flowers in which stamens mature and shed their pollen before the stigma of the same flower matures.

Proterogyny (Gr. *proteros*—earlier; *gyne*—female): a condition in flowers in which the stigma matures and is pollinated by foreign pollen before the stamens of the same flower shed their pollen.

Prothallus (prothallium) (Gr. *pro*—before; *thallos*—shoot): the gametophyte of ferns and similar plants.

Protoderm (Gr. *protos*—first; *dermo*—skin): meristematic tissue formed by a terminal meristem and developing into epidermis.

Protonema (Gr. *protos*—first; *nema*—thread): a branching filament forming an early stage in the gametophyte generation of a moss.

Protoplasm (Gr. *protos*—first; *plasma*—formed): the living substance in the cells of plants and animals.

Protoplast: the living component of a single cell.

Putrefaction (L. *putere*—be rotten; *facere*—make): the anaerobic decomposition of organic substances, especially proteins, by microorganisms.

Pycnia: flask-shaped spore-producing structures of certain rust fungi.

Pycniospores: small, haploid spores produced by pycnia.

Pyrenoid (Gr. *pyren*—fruit, stone; *eidos*—form): centers of starch formation on certain chloroplasts, especially of algae.

Quiescence (L. *quiescere*—become quiet): a rest period caused by external conditions unfavorable to germination or growth.

Radial section (L. *radius*—spoke, rod): a section of a stem or root cut longitudinally on a radius.

Radial symmetry (L. *radius*—spoke, rod; Gr. *syn*—together; *metron*—measure): a type of floral symmetry in which the flower may be separated into two approximately equal halves by a longitudinal cut in any plane passing through the center of the flower; that is, a flower built upon a wheel plan, rather than on a right-and-left plan. *Example:* rose.

Radicle (L. *radix*—root): the lower portion of the hypocotyl that grows into the primary root of a seedling; the root primordium of an embryo.

Raphe: the ridge formed by the fusion of the seed stalk with the seed coat.

Ray (L. *radius*—rod, spoke): the corolla of a marginal flower of a composite inflorescence; also, a vascular ray.

Receptacle (L. *recipere*—receive): the terminal portion of a pedicel (or peduncle) upon which the floral parts are borne; also, the inflated tips of certain brown algae within which gametangia are borne.

Recessive (L. *recedere*—go back, withdraw): one of a pair of contrasting characters that is masked, when both are present, by the other, or dominant, character; also refers to the genes determining such characters.

Regeneration (L. *re*—back; Gr. *genea*—birth): the replacement of lost parts by growth.

Reproduction (L. *re*—again; *producere*—bring forth): the formation of offspring.

Resins (Gr. *rhetine*—resin): sticky to brittle plant products derived from essential oils and often possessing marked odors; used in varnishes, incense, medicines, etc.

Respiration (L. *re*—again; *spiro*—breathe): chemical oxidative processes whereby living protoplasm breaks down certain organic substances with the release of energy that is used in growth, movements, etc.

Retrogressive evolution (L. *retrogradare*—go backward): evolution from a structurally complex or specialized condition toward a simpler, less specialized condition.

Rhizoid (Gr. *rhiza*—root; *eidos*—form): in some fungi, mosses, liverworts, etc., hairlike appendages that penetrate the soil or other substratum, anchoring the plant and absorbing water and other substances.

Rhizome (Gr. *rhiza*—root): a horizontal underground stem, often enlarged by food storage.

Ribonucleic acid (RNA): a nucleic acid found in the nucleus and cytoplasm; plays a major role in protein synthesis.

Ribose: a 5-carbon sugar; one of the components of RNA.

Ribosomes: minute cytoplasmic bodies that function as centers of synthesis of cytoplasmic proteins.

Ring-porous wood: wood in which the pores (vessels) of one part of a growth ring are distinctly different in size or number (or both) from those in the other part of the ring.

RNA: see Ribonucleic acid.

Root cap: a thimblelike mass of cells that fits over the apical meristem of a root and protects it.

Root pressure: a pressure developed in roots as a result of active water absorption.

Root system: the total mass of roots of a single plant.

Runner: a stem that grows horizontally over the surface of the soil, often developing new plants at its nodes.

Samara (L. *samara*—fruit of the elm): a dry, indehiscent, one-seeded, winged fruit, such as that of elm or maple.

Saprophyte (Gr. *sapros*—rotten; *phyton*—plant): a heterotrophic plant that derives its food from nonliving organic matter.

Sapwood (AS. *saep*—sap; *wudu*—tree.

wood): the young, physiologically active wood of a tree, consisting in part of living cells and comprising the usually light-colored, outermost growth layers.

Schizocarp (Gr. *schizo*—split; *karpos*—fruit): a simple, dry, indehiscent fruit, composed of two fused carpels, which split apart at maturity, each part usually with one seed.

Scion (F. *scion*—sprout): a detached shoot used in grafting; the shoot that receives a scion is called the stock.

Sclereid (Gr. *skleros*—hard): a thick-walled, often slightly elongated or irregularly shaped sclerenchyma cell.

Sclerenchyma (Gr. *skleros*—hard; *en*—in; *chein*—pour): a tissue composed of thick-walled, elongated cells (fibers) or shorter cells (sclereids).

Secondary root: a branch of a primary root.

Secondary tissues: tissues arising from a lateral or secondary meristem, such as the cambium or cork cambium, and increasing the diameter of a stem or root.

Secondary wall: the cell wall layer deposited by protoplasm upon the primary wall layer, after cell enlargement is completed.

Seed: the characteristic reproductive structure of seed plants, consisting of an embryo, enclosed by a seed coat, and a food storage tissue. In some species, the storage tissue is absorbed by the embryo before the seed reaches maturity.

Seed scarification: cutting or scratching a seed coat to facilitate the entry of water or oxygen.

Segregation (L. *se*—aside; *grex*—herd): a genetic principle, established by Mendel, that the factors (or genes) of a pair are separated from each other in reduction division.

Selection (L. *seligere*—select): the process of isolating and preserving certain individuals or characters from a group of individuals or characters.

Self-fertility (L. *ferre*—bear, produce): a condition in which sexual reproduction occurs as a result of the fusion of eggs and sperms produced by the same individual.

Self-pollination: the transfer of pollen from the stamen to the stigma of the same flower, or of another flower on the same plant.

Self-sterility: a condition in which sexual reproduction cannot be achieved by the fusion of eggs and sperms produced by the same individual.

Semipermeable: same as differentially permeable (which see).

Sepals (Gr. *skepe*—covering): the divisions of a calyx; the outermost floral organs.

Separation layer: see Abscission layer.

Sessile (L. *sessilis*—low, dwarf): lacking a stalk.

Seta (L. *seta*—bristle): in mosses and liverworts, the stalk that supports the capsule of the sporophyte.

Sex chromosome (L. *sexus*—sex): chromosomes that determine sex.

Sex linkage (L. *sexus*—sex; AS. *hlence*—link): the occurrence on sex chromosomes of genes that determine characters other than sex.

Sexual (L. *sexus*—sex): a type of reproduction in which both fertilization and meiosis are involved.

Shoot: a stem with its leaves.

Shrub: a woody plant with several stems arising from the root system.

Sieve cell: a phloem-conducting cell with perforations not restricted to end walls; does not occur in series or tubes.

Sieve plate: the perforated wall or wall portion of a sieve tube member.

Sieve tube: a series of sieve tube members arranged in end-to-end fashion.

Sieve tube member: one cell of a sieve tube; sieve tube members usually have their sieve areas on the end walls.

Silique (L. *siliqua*—pod): a simple, dry, dehiscent fruit; developed from two fused carpels that separate at maturity, leaving a persistent partition between.

Simple fruit: a fruit developed from the single ovary of a flower.

Sleep movements: turgor movements of plants initiated by changes in light intensity.

Softwood: the wood of gymnosperms; a wood lacking wood fibers.

Soil solution: the water, with dissolved substances, in the soil.

Sol: a liquid colloidal system.

Solute (L. *solvere*—melt): a dissolved substance.

Soredia: asexual reproductive structures of some lichens; each soredium consists of a small mass of fungal mycelium and a few associated algal cells.

Sorus (Gr. *soros*—heap): a cluster of sporangia on a fern sporophyte.

Species (L. *species*—form, kind): usually the smallest unit in the classification of organisms; a group of individuals of the same ancestry, of nearly identical structure and behavior, and of relative stability in nature; the individuals of a species ordinarily interbreed freely and maintain themselves and their characteristics in nature.

Sperm (Gr. *sperma*—seed): male gamete.

Spikelet (L. *spica*—ear of grain): a unit of a grass inflorescence, consisting of one or more flowers and their bracts.

Spindle: the ovoid mass of fine fibrils (spindle fibers) formed in a cell during mitosis.

Spirillum (L. *spira*—coil): a curved or spiral-shaped bacterium.

Spongy tissue (Gr. *spongos*—sponge): a leaf tissue composed of loosely packed, chlorophyllous cells of diverse form.

Sporangiophore (Gr. *spora*—seed; *angos*—vessel; *phoros*—bearer): a structure that bears one or more sporangia.

Sporangium (Gr. *spora*—seed; *angos*—vessel): a spore case.

Spore (Gr. *spora*—spore, seed): an asexual reproductive structure, commonly unicellular and usually produced in a sporangium.

Spore mother cell: a cell that, by cell divisions, produces typically four spores.

Sporophore (Gr. *spora*—spore; *phoros*—bearer): a spore-bearing structure, for example, a mushroom.

Sporophyll (Gr. *spora*—spore; *phyllon*—leaf): a spore-bearing leaf.

Sporophyte (Gr. *spora*—spore; *phyton*—plant): the spore-producing phase in alternation of generations, characterized by the diploid chromosome number.

Springwood: the xylem of a growth layer formed in the early part of a growing season and consisting typically of cells that are larger than those formed later in the season.

Stamen (L. *stamen*—thread): pollen-producing structure of a flower; a modified microsporophyll.

Staminate flower (L. *stamen*—thread; *flos*—

flower): a flower that bears stamens but no carpels.

Starch (Gr. *starke*—strength, starch): white, complex, water-insoluble carbohydrate that is a common storage food in plants.

Stele (Gr. *stele*—post, column): a collective name for the vascular and closely associated tissues in stems, roots, and other plant parts: xylem, phloem, and (when present) pith, pericycle, and interfascicular parenchyma.

Stem pressure: the positive pressure produced under certain conditions in the stems of some plants (for example, maple) and responsible for the exudation of sap from their stems.

Sterilization (L. *sterilis*—barren): the reduction or loss of sexual structures or processes in an individual or race; also, the destruction of bacteria, spores, etc. through the use of light, high temperature, etc.

Stigma (Gr. *stigma*—spot, mark): the part of a pistil, usually the apex, that receives pollen and upon which pollen grains germinate.

Stimulus (L. *stimulus*—goad, prick): an environmental factor or change that induces a reaction in a living organism.

Stipe (L. *stipes*—post, branch): a stalk, as the stalk of a mushroom, or a brown alga.

Stipule (L. *stipula*—stalk, stem): one of a pair of small appendages borne at the base of a leaf in many species of plants.

Stock: in a graft, the basal portion of a stem, upon which a scion is grafted; also, a stem, or a race or group of genetically similar organisms.

Stolon (L. *stolo*—shoot): a runner (which see).

Stoma (Gr. *stoma*—mouth): a pore, controlled by guard cells, in the epidermis of a leaf, or other plant parts.

Stone cells: thick-walled, isodiametric, sclerenchyma cells.

Strobilus (Gr. *strobilos*—a cone): a cone-like collection of sporophylls borne on a stem axis.

Stroma (Gr. *stroma*—bed): a mass of hyphae bearing reproductive structures.

Style (Gr. *stylos*—pillar): in flowers, a cylindrical structure that rises from the top of an ovary and through which pollen tubes grow.

Suberin (L. *suber*—cork): a fatty, waterproof substance deposited in the walls of certain types of cells, such as cork cells.

Succession (L. *succedere*—go under, follow): the orderly sequence of differing types of vegetation in a given region.

Sucrase (San. *sakkhara*—sugar): see Invertase.

Sucrose (San. *sakkhara*—sugar): cane sugar.

Summerwood: the xylem of a growth layer formed late in the growing season and consisting of cells smaller than those of springwood.

Superior ovary (L. *super*—above): an ovary borne above the points of origin of sepals and petals from a receptacle.

Suspension (L. *sub*—under; *pendere*—hang): a dispersion system in which particles of a solid are distributed in a liquid; e.g., soil particles in water.

Suspensor (L. *sub*—under; *pendere*—hang): a structure in the embryo sporophyte of higher plants, which attaches or forces the embryo into food storage tissue.

Symbiosis (Gr. *syn*—with; *bios*—life): an association of two or more kinds of living organisms, often resulting in mutual benefit.

Synapsis (Gr. *syn*—with; *apsis*—loop): the pairing of homologous chromosomes in meiosis.

Synergids (Gr. *synergos*—working together): two small cells lying near the egg at the micropylar end of the embryo sac in an ovule.

Tangential section (L. *tangere*—touch): a section of a cylindrical organ, such as a stem, cut lengthwise and at right angles to a radius of the organ.

Tannin: a bitter, astringent, organic substance found in certain plant tissues, such as bark, heartwood, and others.

Tap root system: a root system in which there is a primary root distinctly larger and more conspicuous than any of its branches. Contrast diffuse root system.

Taxon (pl. Taxa): any of the various taxonomic categories, such as a family, genus, or species.

Telia: rust fungus pustules containing teliospores.

Teliospores: dark-colored spores produced in telia; "winter spores."

Telophase (Gr. *telos*—end; *phasis*—appearance): the final stage in mitosis in which the two sets of chromosomes are organized into daughter nuclei, and processes leading to the formation of a cell plate separating the daughter nuclei are initiated.

Tendril (L. *tendere*—stretch out): a slender, coiling structure that aids in the support of plant stems; a tendril may be a modified stem, leaf, leaflet, or stipule.

Testa (L. *testa*—shell): seed coat, developed from the integument(s) of an ovule.

Tetrad (Gr. *tessares*—four): a group of four cells (usually spores) produced by two divisions of a mother cell.

Tetraploid (Gr. *tessares*—four; *haploos*—onefold): having four sets of chromosomes, that is, four times the haploid number.

Thallus (Gr. *thallos*—shoot): a simple plant body with relatively little cellular differentiation and lacking true roots, stems, and leaves; characteristic of algae, fungi, liverworts, etc.

Thymine: one of the nitrogenous bases found in DNA.

Tissue (F. *tisser*—weave): an aggregation of cells, usually of similar structure, that perform the same or related functions.

Tonoplast: vacuolar membrane.

Toxin (Gr. *toxikon*—arrow poison): poisonous secretion of a living organism.

Trace elements: see Micronutrients.

Tracheid (Gr. *tracheia*—windpipe): a type of nonperforate conducting and strengthening cell in xylem tissue, of elongated, tapering form and with pitted walls.

Translocation: the conduction of materials within a plant.

Transpiration (L. *trans*—across; *spirare*—breathe): the diffusion of water vapor from aerial parts of plants, chiefly through leaf stomata.

Transverse section (L. *trans*—across; *vertere*—turn): a section of a stem or other part cut at right angles to its longitudinal axis.

Travertine (L. *Tiber*—ancient Roman town): a type of calcium carbonate rock, some of which was formed by the secretion of carbonate by algae.

Tree: a woody, perennial plant with a single main stem (trunk) that rises some distance aboveground before it branches.

Trichogyne (Gr. *trichos*—hair; *gyne*—female): in a female gametangium, a slender outgrowth that receives sperms, as in red algae.

Triploid (Gr. *tria*—three; *haploos*—onefold): having three sets of chromosomes, that is, three times the haploid number.

Tropism (Gr. *trope*—turn): a blending movement of a cylindrical organ or other cylindrical structure, caused by differences in growth rate in different parts of the organ and induced by external stimuli.

Trunk (L. *truncus*—trunk): the single main stem of a tree.

Tube nucleus: one of the nuclei in a pollen tube, influencing the growth and behavior of the tube.

Tuber (L. *tuber*—lump): enlarged, fleshy, underground stem, commonly borne at the end of a rhizome.

Tundra: (of Russian origin): a plant formation (or biome) of subarctic regions, which has permanently frozen subsoil and a low vegetation of lichens, dwarf hardy herbs, and shrubs.

Turgidity (L. *turgere*—swell): state of being plump or swollen as a result of internal water pressure.

Turgor movements (L. *turgere*—swell): plant movements resulting from changes of water pressure in certain tissues.

Turgor pressure (L. *turgere*—swell): pressure developed by water present in plant cells.

Twig scar: a scar left by the falling away of a twig.

Twiner: a plant that climbs by the twining movements of its stems about a support.

Tylosis (Gr. *tyle*—lump): a growth from a parenchyma cell through a pit into the cavity of a xylem vessel or tracheid.

Unicellular (L. *unus*—one; *cella*—small room): one-celled, referring to an organism the entire body of which consists of a single cell.

Unisexual (L. *unus*—one; *sexus*—sex): describing an organism that produces eggs or sperms, but not both, or a flower that bears stamens or pistils, but not both.

Unit character (L. *unus*—one; Gr. *charakter*—engrave): a genetic principle, established by Mendel, that the various characters making up an individual are controlled in inheritance by independent determining factors.

Uracil: one of the nitrogenous bases found in RNA.

Uredia: rust fungus pustules containing urediospores.

Urediospores: reddish spores produced in uredia; "summer spores."

Vacuole (L. *vacuum*—vacuum): a cavity within the protoplasm containing a watery solution of sugars and other substances.

Variation (L. *varius*—various, different): in an organism, difference in structural or physiological characters from those typical or common in the species to which the organism belongs.

Vascular bundle (L. *vas*—vessel): a strand of conducting and strengthening tissues (xylem and phloem) in a plant organ.

Vascular ray (L. *vas*—vessel; *radius*—rod, spoke): a ribbonlike aggregate of cells extending radially in stems through the xylem and the phloem.

Vascular tissue (L. *vas*—vessel; Fr. *tisser*—weave): conducting tissue; xylem and phloem.

Vegetative activities (L. *vegere*—be active): activities most directly concerned with growth and the maintenance of the individual, rather than with reproduction.

Vegetative reproduction: asexual reproduction by a root, stem, leaf, or some other primarily vegetative part of a plant body.

Vein (L. *vena*—vein): one of the vascular bundles of a leaf, petal, or other plant part.

Venation (L. *vena*—vein): the arrangement of the vascular bundles in a leaf.

Venter (L. *venter*—belly): the enlarged base of an archegonium within which an egg develops.

Vernalization: the brief exposure to low temperatures required by some plants in order to induce flower formation.

Vessel (L. *vas*—vessel): a conducting tube in xylem tissue.

Vessel member: at maturity, a perforate, nonliving xylem cell; one segment of a vessel.

Viability (L. *vita*—life): the ability to live and grow; applied usually to seeds and spores.

Vitamin (L. *vita*—life; *amine*—a type of compound derived from ammonia): organic substances synthesized by plants and necessary in minute quantities for certain respiratory and developmental processes.

Whorl: a circle of parts, such as leaves.

Whorled: having several parts arranged in a circle at the same level; commonly applied to the condition in which three or more leaves occur at a node.

Wood: technically, xylem; popularly, the xylem of trees and shrubs.

Woody plant: a plant with a large development of xylem.

Xanthophylls (Gr. *xanthos*—yellow; *phyllon*—leaf): yellowish-orange pigments of plants, occurring usually in plastids.

Xerophyte (Gr. *xeros*—dry; *phyton*—plant): a plant that grows in soils with scanty water supply, or in soils in which water is absorbed only with difficulty.

Xylem (Gr. *xylon*—wood): a complex plant vascular tissue, composed of such cells as tracheids, vessel members, wood fibers, ray cells, and parenchyma cells; wood.

Zoogloea (Gr. *zoon*—animal; *gloia*—glue): a gelatinous mass produced by certain bacteria.

Zoospores (Gr. *zoon*—animal; *spora*—seed): spores that are enabled to swim by movements of cilia or flagella.

Zygote (Gr. *zygon*—yoke): a fertilized egg; a cell arising from the fusion of gametes.

Zymase (Gr. *zyme*—yeast): an enzyme system that acts upon simple sugars, breaking them down to alcohol and carbon dioxide.

Index